Chemistry and Properties of Crosslinked Polymers

ACADEMIC PRESS RAPID MANUSCRIPT PRODUCTION

Proceedings of the ACS Symposium on "Chemistry and Properties of Crosslinked Polymers" held in San Francisco, August 31—September 2, 1976

Chemistry and Properties of Crosslinked Polymers

edited by

SANTOKH S. LABANA

Engineering and Research Staff
Ford Motor Company
Dearborn, Michigan

ACADEMIC PRESS, INC. New York San Francisco London 1977
A Subsidiary of Harcourt Brace Jovanovich, Publishers

ACADEMIC PRESS, INC.
111 Fifth Avenue, New York, New York 10003

United Kingdom Edition published by
ACADEMIC PRESS, INC. (LONDON) LTD.
24/28 Oval Road, London NW1

Library of Congress Cataloging in Publication Data

ACS Symposium on Chemistry and Properties of Crosslinked Polymers, San Francisco, 1976.
Chemistry and properties of crosslinked polymers.

Sponsored by the Division of Organic Coatings and Plastics Chemistry, American Chemical Society.
Includes index.
1. Polymers and polymerization—Congresses.
I. Labana, Santokh S., Date II. American Chemical Society. Division of Organic Coatings and Plastics Chemistry. III. Title.
QD380.A14 1976 574'.84 77-1098
ISBN 0-12-432250-3

PRINTED IN THE UNITED STATES OF AMERICA

Contents

List of Contributors

J.J. AKLONIS,Department of Chemistry, University of Southern California, Los Angeles, California 90007

M. ANAND, Department of Materials Science and Engineering, Washington State University, Pullman, WA 99163

FRED E. ARNOLD, Nonmetallic Materials Division, Air Force Materials Laboratory, Wright-Patterson Air Force Base, Ohio 45433

G.K. BAKER, The Bendix Corporation, Kansas City Division, Kansas City, Missouri

F.P. BALDWIN, 2094W-320N, Coupeville, Washington 98239

A.W. BEDWIN, Union Carbide Corporation, Research and Development Corporation, Bound Brook, New Jersey

R. BLOCK, Department of Chemical Engineering, California Institute of Technology, Pasadena, CA 91125

G.L. BRODE, Union Carbide Corporation, Research and Development Corporation, Bound Brook, New Jersey

W.V. CHANG, Department of Chemical Engineering, University of Southern California, Los Angeles, CA 90007

A.J. CHOMPFF, University of Southern California, Department of Chemical Engineering, Lost Angeles, Cal. 90007

S.Y. CHUNG, Jet Propulsion Laboratory, 4800 Oak Grove Drive, Pasadena, CA 91103

A. CONDE, Universidad Industrial de Santander, Department of Chemical Engineering, Bucaramanga, Colombia

PETER DELVIGS, National Aeronautics and Space Administration, Lewis Research Center, Cleveland, Ohio 44135

C.R. DYBOWSKI, Division of Chemistry and Chemical Engineering, California Institute of Technology, Pasadena, CA 91125

ROBERT EBEWELE, University of Wisconsin, Department of Chemical Engineering, Madison, Wis. 53706

GERHARD F.L. EHLERS, Nonmetallic Materials Division, Air Force Materials Laboratory, Wright-Patterson Air Force Base, Ohio 45433

M. JEAN FARRALL, Department of Chemistry, University of Ottawa, Ottawa, Ontario KIN 6N5, Canada

JOHN D. FERRY, University of Wisconsin, Department of Chemistry, Madison, Wis 53706

JEAN M.J. FRÉCHET, Department of Chemistry, University of Ottawa, Ottawa, Ontario K1N 6N5, Canada

H.L. FRISCH, State University of New York at Albany, Department of Chemistry, Albany, New York 12222

K.C. FRISCH, University of Detroit, Chemical Engineering Department, Detroit, MI 48221

I.J. GARDNER, Exxon Chemical Company, P.O. Box 45, Linden, New Jersey 07036

RICHARD J. GAYLORD, Department of Metallurgy and Mining Engineering, University of Illinois at Urbana-Champaign, Urbana, Illinois 61801

J.K. GILLHAM, Polymer Materials Program Department of Chemical Engineering, Princeton University, Princeton, New Jersey 08540

C.A. GLANDT, Polymer Materials Program, Department of Chemical Engineering, Princeton University, Princeton, New Jersey 08540

P.M. HERGENROTHER, NASA Langley Research Center, Hampton, VA 23665

G.C. HSU, Jet Propulsion Laboratory, 4800 Oak Grove Drive, Pasadena, CA 91103

WU-NAN HUANG, Department of Chemistry, University of Southern California, Los Angeles, California 90007

J. JANACEK, Nonmetallic Materials Division, Air Force Materials Laboratory, Wright-Patterson Air Force Base, Ohio 45433

ROBERT A. JEWELL, NASA Langley Research Center, Hampton, Virginia 23665

JAMES F. KINSTLE, Departmet of Chemistry, The University of Tennessee, Knoxville, TN 37916

D. KLEMPNER, Chemical Engineering Department, University of Detroit, Detroit, MI 48221

J. KOLARIK, Istituto di Principi di Ingegneria Chimica, University of Naples, Italy

JAMES A. KOUTSKY, University of Wisconsin, Department of Chemical Engineering, Madison, Wis. 53706

ROBERT F. KOVAR, University of Dayton Research Institute, Dayton, Ohio 45409

OLE KRAMER, Department of Chemistry, University of Copenhagen, Universitetsparken 5, DK-2100 Copenhagen, Denmark

G.T. KWIATKOWSKI, Union Carbide Corporation, Research and Development Corporation, Bound Brook, New Jersey

C.W. MACOSKO, Department of Chemical Engineering and Materials Science, University of Minnesota, Minneapolis, Minnesota 55455

C.A. MCPHERSON, Western Electric Company, Engineering & Research Center, Carter Road, Princeton, N.J. 08525

J.A. MANSON, Lehigh University, Materials Research Center, Coxe Laboratory, #32, Bethlehem, Pa. 18015

MARK MARKOVITZ, General Electric Company, Steam Turbine-Generator Products Division, Materials and Processes Laboratory, Schenectady, New York 12345

H.E. MARSH, JR., Jet Propulsion Laboratory, 4800 Oak Grove Drive, Pasadena, CA 91103

JAMES E. MOORE, General Electric Company, Corporate Research and Development, Schenectady, New York 12301

ROGER J. MORGAN, McDonnell Douglas Research Laboratories, McDonnell Douglas Corporation, St. Louis, Missouri 63166

L. NICOLAIS, Istituto di Principi di Ingegneria Chimica, University of Naples, Italy

JAMES E. O'NEAL, McDonnell Douglas Research Laboratories, McDonnell Douglas Corporation, St. Louis, Missouri 63166

NIKOLAOS A. PEPPAS, School of Chemical Engineering, Purdue University, West Lafayette, Indiana 47907

T.F. PROTZMAN, A.D. Staley Mfg. Co., P.O. Box 151, Decatur, Illinois 62525

JAMES L. RACICH, University of Wisconsin, Department of Chemical Engineering, Madison, Wis. 53706

L.M. ROBESON, Union Carbide Corporation, Research and Development Corporation, Bound Brook, New Jersey

L. ERIC SEPULVEDA, Department of Chemistry, The University of Tennessee, Knoxville, Tennessee 37916

C.H. SMITH, The Bendix Corporation, Kansas City Division, Kansas City, Missouri

R.M. SMITH, The Bendix Corporation, Kansas City Division, Kansas City, Missouri

L.H. SPERLING, Materials Research Center, Lehigh University, Bethlehem, Pa. 18015

R.V. SUBRAMANIAN, Department of Materials Science and Engineering, Washington State University, Pullman, WA 99163

GEORGE F. SYKES, NASA Langley Research Center, Hampton, Virginia 23665

N.W. TSCHOEGL, Department of Chemical Engineering, California Institute of Technology, Pasadena, CA 91125

E.M. VALLES, Universidad del Sur, Bahia Blanca, Argentina

P. VAN RIPER, Union Carbide Corporation, Research and Development Corporation, Bound Brook, New Jersey

R.W. VAUGHAN, Division of Chemistry and Chemical Engineering, California Institute of Technology, Pasadena, California 91125

F. VERBANAC, A.E. Staley Mfg. Company, P.O. Box 151, Decatur, Illinois 62525

C.J. WALLACE, Jet Propulsion Laboratory, 4800 Oak Grove Drive, Pasadena, CA 91103

STANLEY E. WENTWORTH, U.S. Army Materials and Mechanics Research Center, Watertown, MA 02172

K.L. WUN, Department of Physiology, California College of Medicine, University of California, Irvine, California 92717

G.M. YENWO, Lehigh University, Materials Research Center, Coxe Laboratory, #32, Bethlehem, Pa. 18015

H.K. YOON, Polymer Institute, University of Detroit, Detroit, Michigan 48221

A.H. YOUNG, A.E. Staley Mfg. Company, P.O. Box 151, Decatur, Illinois 62525

Preface

This book describes chemistry, structure property relationship, and methods of characterization of crosslinked polymers. It should be of interest to scientists engaged in research or graduate studies in polymer science.

Crosslinked polymers are an important class of materials used in fiber reinforced plastics, thermosetting molding compounds, elastomers, coatings, adhesives, ion exchange resins, and many other applications. Although the use of these materials has grown rapidly, the understanding of the relationship of structure or chemical nature and properties has not progressed very well, mostly because of the difficulties in the characterization of the network structure and morphology. It is difficult to measure accurately such features as crosslink density, entanglement points, dangling chains, and unattached chains. Hypotheses about the formation of morphological structure during crosslinking remain unproven. This volume contains several papers that attempt to deduce information on network structure from theoretical considerations and several more that describe experimental techniques to study network structure.

Interpenetrating polymer networks have been receiving considerable attention in recent years because of the versatility available in their syntheses and the range of morphological and mechanical properties obtainable. A review on the subject, suggestions for nomenclature, and details on a number of interpenetrating polymer networks are included.

Other papers describe crosslinked polymers for high temperature applications, a novel class of polyurethanes, new crosslinking agents, and the influence of crosslinking agents on thermal and mechanical properties.

I take pleasure in acknowledging Ford Motor Company and Dr. S. Gratch for their support of and interest in this project. I also wish to express my appreciation to Anne Oslanci for her secretarial assistance. My sincere thanks to the authors who put in a great deal of effort to make this book possible. Finally, I thank the Division of Organic Coatings and Plastics Chemistry, American Chemical Society for sponsoring the symposium.

PROPERTIES OF ORGANOTIN POLYESTERS CROSSLINKED BY CYCLOALIPHATIC EPOXIDES

R.V. Subramanian and M. Anand
Washington State University

A new synthesis of thermoset antifouling polymer systems was achieved by the crosslinking reaction of cycloaliphatic epoxides with the free carboxyl groups present on a base polymer partially esterified with tributyltin oxide. The network structure was varied, and the average separation, length and type of epoxy crosslinks were altered by changing the degree of esterification of the base polymer, the structure and proportion of epoxy monomer, and the type of catalyst. Concurrent changes in measured strength, fracture toughness and dynamic mechanical behavior of the polymer systems have been correlated with the structural variables employed. Results presented here pertain mainly to systems based on styrene-maleic anhydride copolymer crosslinked by cycloaliphatic epoxides. Toughening by carboxyl terminated liquid elastomers has also been studied and the improvement in fracture toughness related to the average particle size of the dispersed elastomer phase which was in turn controlled by elastomer content, A:E ratio, and tributyltin content. The formation of domains in the matrix with independent glass transitions was followed by observing variations in loss moduli which also reflected the structural effects of bulky tributyltin groups and different epoxy monomers. The highest degrees of crosslinking were found with uranyl nitrate catalyst.

I. INTRODUCTION

Tributyltin compounds are known to be toxic to marine organisms and have been incorporated as toxic additives in marine biocidal paints (1-3). The polymerization and copolymerization with other vinyl monomers of tributyltin and tripropyltin acrylates to form antifouling polymers has been reported (4,5). Recent research in our laboratories has involved chemical anchoring of toxic trialkyltin groups to thermoset polymers in a new approach to the synthesis of polymer compositions that might be suitable for application as antifouling coatings (6,7). The objective of the investigation reported here was to study the structure-property relationships in antifouling organotin epoxy polymers.

A. Synthesis of Crosslinked Organotin Epoxy Polymers

The synthetic scheme adopted for the preparation of the polymers involves the partial esterification, with tributyltin oxide, of polymers containing carboxylic acid or anhydride groups as the first step. The free carboxyl function of the partial tin ester is then reacted with epoxy monomers to form crosslinked polymer systems as shown below for the simplest crosslinking reaction.

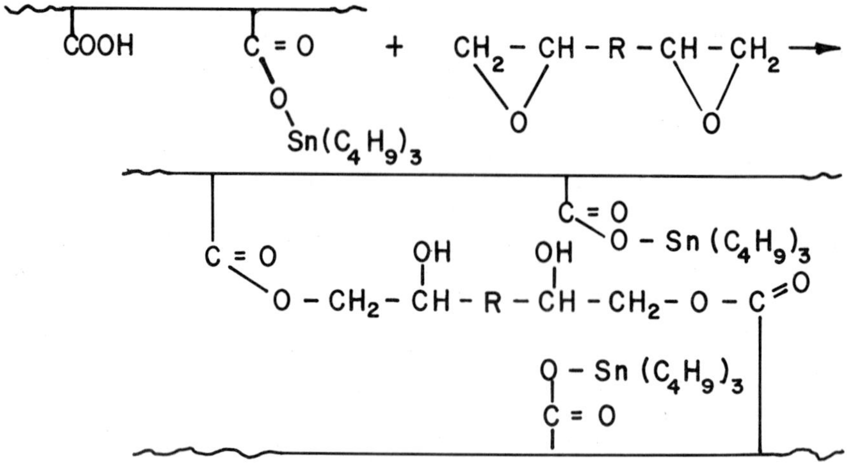

The properties of the network structure obtained thus can be varied over a wide range by changing the chemical structure of the base polymer as well as that of the crosslinking epoxy monomer. The tin content of the polymer is altered by controlling the degree of esterification of the base polymer, which also varies the crosslink density obtained in the second step. Greater esterification with tributyltin oxide will lead to fewer available carboxyl groups for crosslinking, and, consequently, to larger separation between points of crosslinking on the base polymer. Promotion of homopolymerization at high epoxy to anhydride ratios will have the general effect of extending the lengths of epoxy crosslinks. This can be achieved by appropriate choice of catalysts for the curing reaction.

Results are reported here mainly for thermoset systems obtained by the reaction of tributyltin esters of a 1:1 styrene-maleic anhydride copolymer (SMA-1000A) with three cycloaliphatic epoxides, namely bis(3,4-epoxy-6-methylcyclohexylmethyl) adipate (ERL 4289), 3,4-epoxycyclohexylmethyl-(3,4-epoxy) cyclohexane carboxylate (ERL 4221) and [2-(3,4-epoxy) cyclohexyl-5,5-spiro (3,4 epoxy)-cyclohexane-*m*-dioxane] (ERL 4234).

II. EXPERIMENTAL

The molecular weight of poly(styrene-*co*-maleic anhydride), SMA 1000A of ARCO Chemical Co., was in the range 1600-1800. Other 1:1 copolymers used as base polymer were poly(methyl vinyl ether-*co*-maleic anhydride), AN 139, poly(methyl vinyl ether-*co*-maleic acid), AT 795 (both of General Aniline and Film Corporation) and Gulf polyanhydrides PA-6 and PA-10 which are copolymers of maleic anhydride respectively with hexene-1 and decene-1. Epoxy monomers ERL 4289, ERL 4221, ERL 4234, whose structures are indicated below, and ERL 4206 (vinylcyclohexene dioxide) were obtained from Union Carbide.

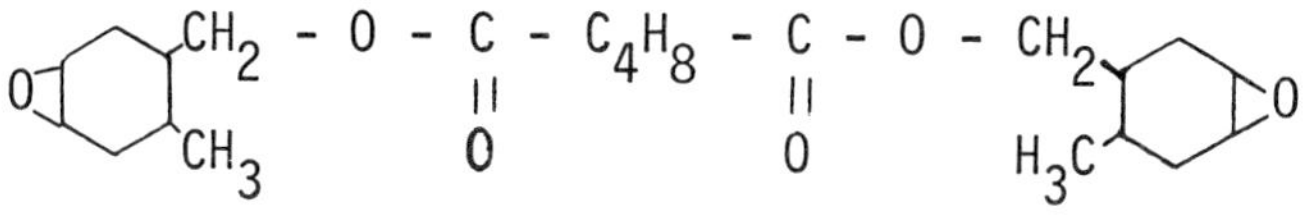

ERL 4289

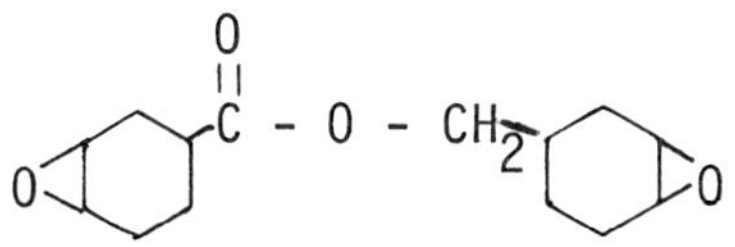

ERL 4221

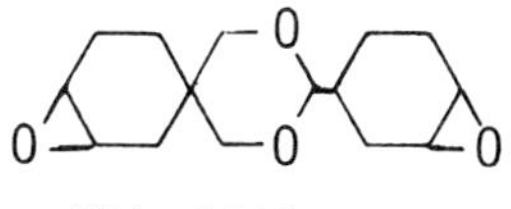

ERL 4234

The tributyltin esters were prepared by refluxing the base polymer with the stoichiometric amount of tributyltin oxide (M&T Chemicals) in benzene for 12 hours (8), recovered from solution by vacuum evaporation of the solvent benzene, and dried *in vacuo* at 80-90°C for 24 hours. The tin content was estimated by acid oxidation and incineration to tin oxide (9); the values confirmed the degree of esterification achieved. The esters of SMA 1000A were soluble in the liquid epoxy monomers; in other cases a small amount of solvent, xylene, was used to prepare the prepolymer-epoxide mixture which was cured, after the addition of a suitable catalyst, in silicone molds at 140°C for 24 hours to prepare impact and tensile test specimens. Benzyl dimethyl amine (BDMA), dimethylaniline (DMA), stannous octoate and uranyl nitrate were the various catalysts employed. A Tinius-Olsen Plastic Impact Tester was used for measuring Izod impact strengths of notched specimens (2.50"x0.50"x0.25", notch radius 0.25 mm). Dog-bone specimens with a gauge length of 2.25" were tested at 0.02 cm/min in an Instron tensile testing machine. Thin pieces were sawed off from impact-tested specimens and thinned down further on emery paper, solvent extracted and dried for use in dynamic mechanical tests in a Rheovibron DDV IIC viscoelastometer.

The effect of added liquid elastomer, carboxyl-terminated butadiene-nitrile copolymer (CTBN), on the strength and fracture properties of the network polymers was studied using HYCAR 1300X8 of B.F. Goodrich Chemical Company, having a molecular weight of 3,200 and an acrylonitrile content of 18%. Thin (≃1000Å) films were microtomed from the bottom remnant of impact test pieces, stained in 4% osmium tetroxide solution and examined by transmission electron microscopy.

III. RESULTS AND DISCUSSION

As was indicated earlier, the variety of prepolymers that could be utilized is an essential merit of the synthetic scheme adopted here. Accordingly a number of maleic anhydride copolymers detailed in the experimental section were screened in preliminary tests and found to produce thermoset systems readily. However, the styrene-maleic anhydride copolymer systems were chosen first for detailed study as the most tractable for arriving at structure-property relationships.

A. Catalyst Efficiency and Structure of Cured Polymer

The curing of 40 TBTE-SMA 1000A and ERL 4206 was carried out at various temperatures using different catalysts, and percent extractables were evaluated at various time intervals of the curing cycle. The efficiency of the various catalysts and curing conditions in producing crosslinked structures was evaluated mainly by such solvent extraction using methyl ethyl ketone to determine the soluble fractions. The extractable portion was a minimum at an epoxy to anhydride ratio of 2 using the basic catalyst BDMA which indicated that the carboxyl-epoxide esterification reaction was the main crosslinking reaction under these conditions. This is illustrated in Figure I with results obtained when the curing reaction was conducted at 95°C for 24 hours.

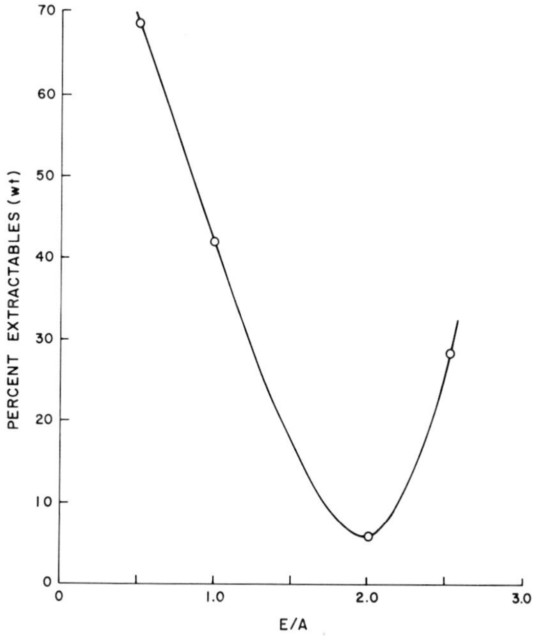

Fig. 1. The variation of percent extractables as a function of E:A ratio for 40 TBTE-SMA 1000A-ERL 4206 using 0.5% (wt) BDMA.

On the other hand, using stannous octoate catalyst, the extractable fraction progressively decreased with epoxide to anhydride ratios up to 4, as shown in Figure 2. It was found in later experiments that even larger amounts of epoxide monomer could be incorporated in the polymerizing systems.

Thus the best thermosetting systems with cycloaliphatic epoxides were obtained by using acid catalysts. In these systems with acid catalysts, it is apparent that considerable homopolymerization of the diepoxide leading to the formation of polyether links must be occurring in addition to crosslinking by ester formation. The initial reaction under acid con-

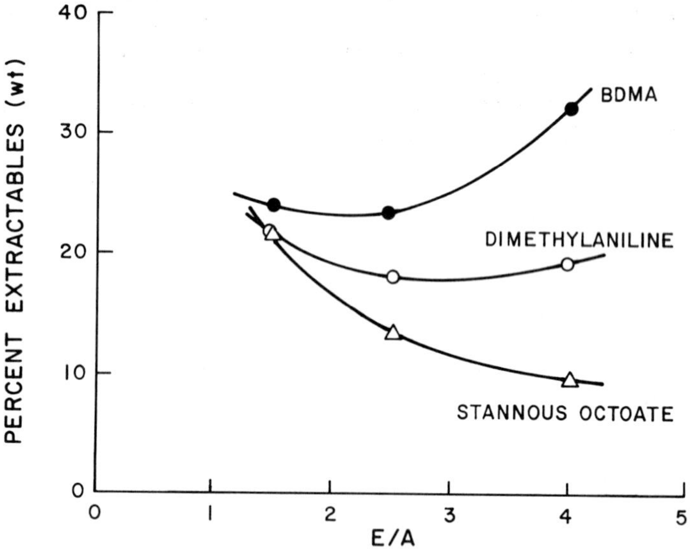

Fig. 2. The variation of percent extractables as a function of E:A for 40 TBTE-SMA 1000A-ERL 4206 cured at 110°C for 20 hours using BDMA, dimethyl aniline, and stannous octoate as catalysts at one weight percent.

ditions is one of esterification by the epoxy of the carboxylic acid groups formed from the anhydride on the base polymer. As a result of this reaction, a hydroxyl group is formed which is capable of further reaction with epoxide monomer in the presence of the acid catalyst. The hydroxyl group which is thus regenerated can initiate the addition of more epoxide monomers to form a homopolymer chain; and, since the soluble fraction is very low, 10% or less, the homopolymerization is probably initiated *on* the crosslinks to form multiple and branched epoxide crosslinks. This deduction is confirmed by the fact that the neat diepoxide monomer, ERL 4289, in the absence of any carboxyl containing base polymer, could be homopolymerized with stannous octoate catalyst to yield crosslinked polymers with less than 15% extractable fraction. A much more striking observation was that, with uranyl nitrate catalyst, a crosslinked homopolymer was obtained with no extractable fraction. Using stannous octoate or uranyl nitrate, therefore, long sequences of epoxy monomer are efficiently incorporated in the crosslinks of the network structure. Except where otherwise indicated, all results reported below were obtained with stannous octoate catalyst (0.5%). The curing temperature was held in the range 135-140°C which was found to be optimum.

B. Tensile Strength

It is pertinent to note here that in polycarboxyl-epoxy thermoset polymers based on terpolymers of methacrylic acid, methacrylonitrile and methyl methacrylate using N,N-dimethyl benzylamine as catalyst, optimum values of mechanical properties were recorded by Fellers and Golovoy at carboxyl to epoxy ratios close to one, the stoichiometry required for crosslinking by carboxyl-epoxy esterification (10). In contrast, in the stannous octoate catalysed systems based on the 40% tin ester of styrene-maleic anhydride copolymer (SMA) and ERL 4289, the tensile strength and elongation to break increased progressively with the epoxide:anhydride ratio (Fig. 3).

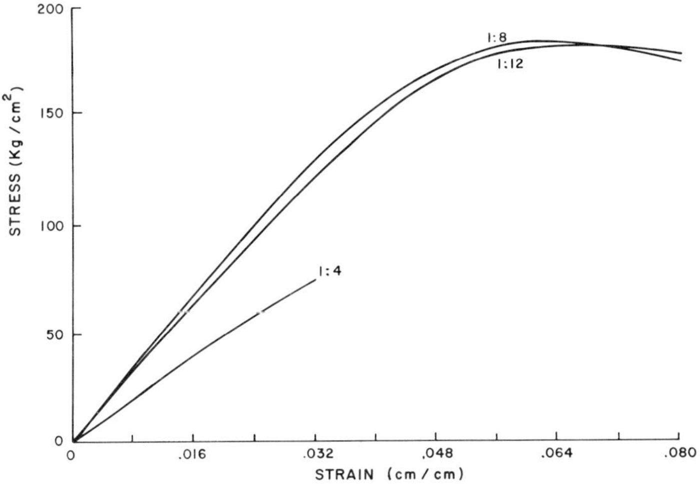

Fig. 3. Stress-strain curves for SMA 40% ester/ERL 4289 polymers formed at indicated A:E ratios.

Similar observations were made in polymers prepared from the 60% ester of SMA and ERL 4289. The position at which the ultimate tensile strength was obtained shifted to a higher E/A ratio with increased esterification of the polymer. This result should be expected because a greater epoxy content is required to compensate for increased distance between crosslinks. However, the increase in tin esterification of the prepolymer from 40% to 60% decreased the strength of the cured polymer considerably. In the case of ERL 4221, the strength showed a slight initial decrease with increasing E/A ratio. The results are summarized in Table I.

TABLE I
Tensile Strengths and Moduli of Cured Products of SMA 1000A

SMA Ester	*Epoxide*	*A:E Ratio*	*Strength MPa*	*Modulus MPa*
40%	ERL 4289	1:4	7.38	276
		1:8	18.6	441
		1:12	17.8	400
60%	ERL 4289	1:8	1.76	53.8
		1:12	5.58	103
		1:16	5.93	89.6
40%	ERL 4221	1:4	15.4	538
		1:8	11.3	634
		1:12	11.9	689

It can be seen that modulus values show trends similar to those of strength with 40% and 60% esters of SMA and ERL 4289. The initial increase in modulus can be explained on the basis of greater stiffness of the epoxy polymer as compared to the base polymer. As the E/A ratio is increased, the network probably becomes less constrained because of the longer homopolymer chains. In the case of ERL 4221, which is a more rigid and shorter epoxy monomer than ERL 4289, a steady though smaller increase in modulus was observed in the range of E/A ratios studied. These results are also shown in Table I.

C. Impact Strength

Impact strengths were also determined as a function of the amount and type of epoxy polymer which controlled the chemical structure and length of crosslinks, the extent of esterification of the prepolymer which changed the distance between crosslink points, and the content of liquid elastomer CTBN in the polymerizing system.

The three epoxy monomers in order of decreasing flexibility are ERL 4289, ERL 4221 and ERL 4234. As expected from this, cured products with ERL 4289 showed higher impact strengths than those with ERL 4221 which in turn showed higher impact strengths as compared to compositions with ERL 4234.

With ERL 4289, increasing the content and length of epoxide crosslinks by increasing the E/A ratio gave increasingly higher values of impact strengths in the case of 40%, 60% and 80% esters (Table 2). Increased esterification of the base

TABLE 2
Impact Strengths of Thermoset Polymers

SMA Ester	*Epoxide*	*A:E*	*Impact Strength* J/cm^2
40%	ERL 4289	1:4	0.057
		1:8	0.088
		1:12	0.108
60%	ERL 4289	1:4	0.050
		1:12	0.063
80%	ERL 4289	1:30	0.104
		1:50	0.168
40%	ERL 4221	1:4	0.025
		1:8	0.030
		1:12	0.033

prepolymer showed a tendency to decrease strength values. These observations are consistent with the higher strength of the epoxy polymer compared to the base polyester.

In comparison with ERL 4289 systems, cured products with ERL 4221 showed much lower impact strengths because of the rigidity of their structure. Further, an increase in E/A ratio caused no significant change in impact strength. These results are also included in Table 2. With ERL 4234, an extremely rigid epoxy monomer, impact strength values were even lower. This reduced the reliability of measurements considerably. As in the case of ERL 4221, increase in E/A ratio did not change impact strengths.

The toughness of the polymer systems was also evident in the appearance of the fracture surfaces of the specimens under the scanning electron microscope, as shown in Figure 4(a) for a thermoset incorporating ERL 4289 at A:E of 1:12 and in 4(b) for one incorporating ERL 4221, also at the same A:E ratio. Considerable deformation of the matrix surface is seen in the former while the latter reveals a brittle fracture surface.

The effect of increasing E/A ratios in increasing impact strength is maintained in the presence of added liquid elastomer (CTBN), as illustrated in Figure 5. Toughening of the matrix was achieved by the addition of CTBN which was found to separate out as particles 1-20 μ in diameter (Figure 6) and caused increases of the order of 300% in regions of high E/A ratios and CTBN contents with ERL 4289. Much less improvement was observed with ERL 4221.

TABLE 3
Variation of Elastomer Particle Size and Impact Strength with CTBN Content at Constant A:E ratios

SMA Ester	*Epoxide*	*A:E*	*CTBN Content*	*Particle Size μ*	*Impact Strength J/cm^2*
40%	ERL 4289	1:4	4	2.7	0.059
		1:4	8	3.3	0.107
		1:12	4	0.3	0.130
		1:12	8	1.2	0.241
60%	ERL 4289	1:12	4	5.5	0.170
		1:12	8	10.0	0.180
40%	ERL 4221	1:12	4	0.2	0.030
		1:12	8	2.0	0.107

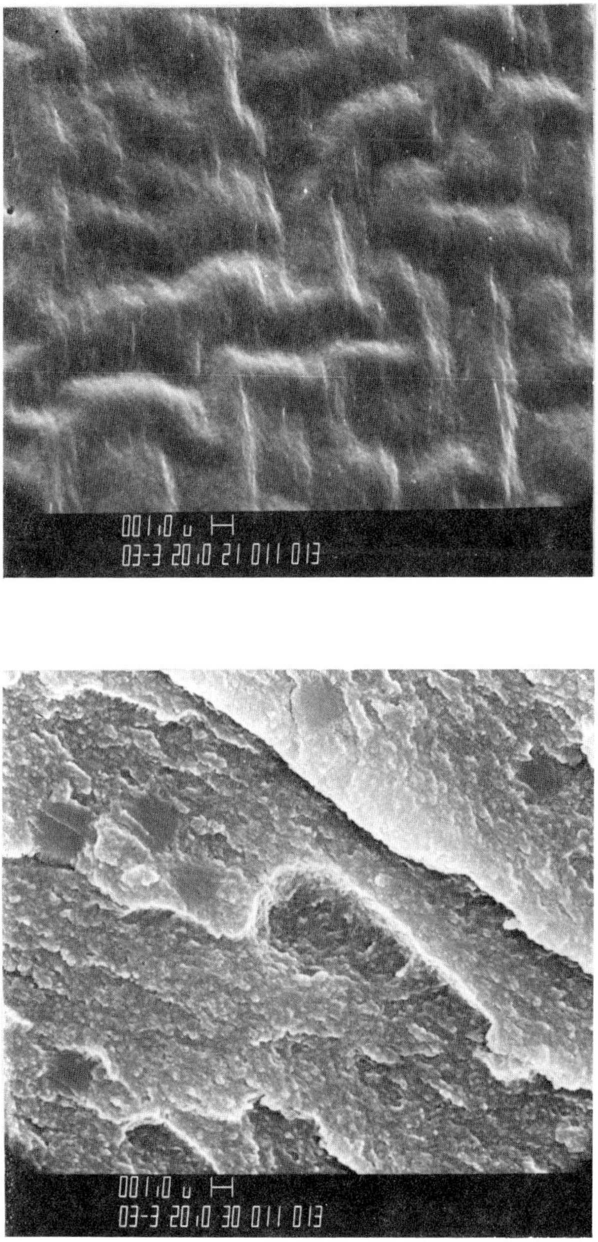

(a)

(b)

Fig. 4. Fracture surface of crosslinked polymers of (a) ERL 4289 and (b) ERL 4221 at A:E = 1:12, both using SMA 40% tin ester as prepolymer (3000X).

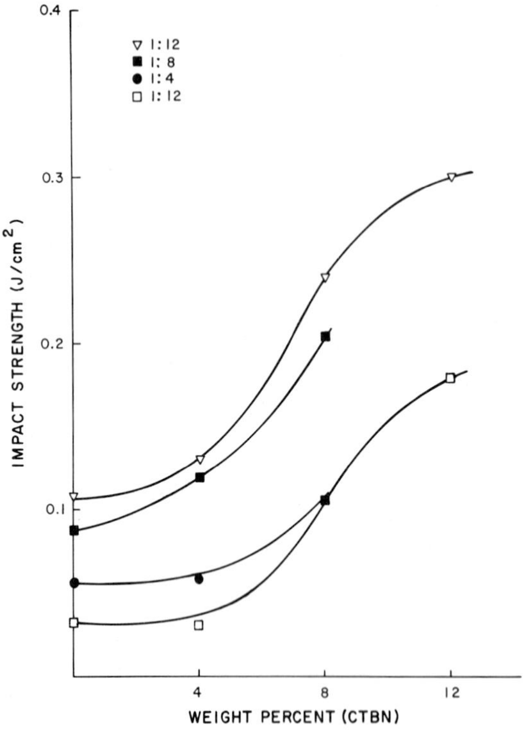

Fig. 5. Increase in impact strength with CTBN content at various A:E ratios for SMA 40% tin ester crosslinked by ERL 4289 (▽, ■, ●) and by ERL 4221 (□).

The improvements in impact strength seem to be associated with an increase in size of the rubber particles with increasing CTBN content at the same A:E ratio, as revealed in electron micrographs of microtomed sections (Table 3). The average particle size was also increased considerably for polymers with higher degree of esterification by tributyltin as is shown in the same table.

D. Dynamic Mechanical Measurements

The dynamic mechanical responses of the organotin-epoxy polymer systems were measured in the Rheovibron at 110 Hz from room temperature to about 240°C. Both $T<T_g$ and T_g transitions were observed for the crosslinked polymers as shown in the plots of loss moduli in Figure 7 for 40% ester-ERL 4289 sys-

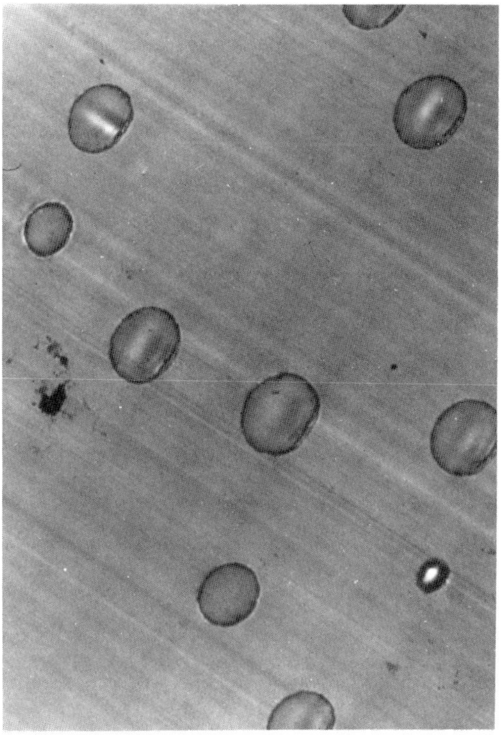

Fig. 6. 40 TBTE - SMA 1000 A - ERL 4289 with 8% CTBN (A:E = 1:4); average size of particles = 3.3 μ (≃3000 X).

tems at various A:E ratios. Since the $T<T_g$ transition involves only a small group of 4 or 5 atoms (11) it is seen to be relatively insensitive to the crosslink density of the network structure and is unchanged by A:E ratios in the range 1:4 to 1:12. On the other hand, the main glass transition which occurs as closely spaced double peaks for this system, is increased progressively from 75 to 90°C by increasing epoxy content; the shift seems to be caused both by the increasing proportion of the epoxy polymer which is stiffer than the base polyester and also by the concurrent formation of multiple crosslinks. The evidence for the formation of such multiple crosslinks under acidic catalysts was discussed earlier. The observation of the double glass transition would indicate the presence of two separate domains each with a characteristic T_g of its own.

The closely spaced double transitions are not discern-

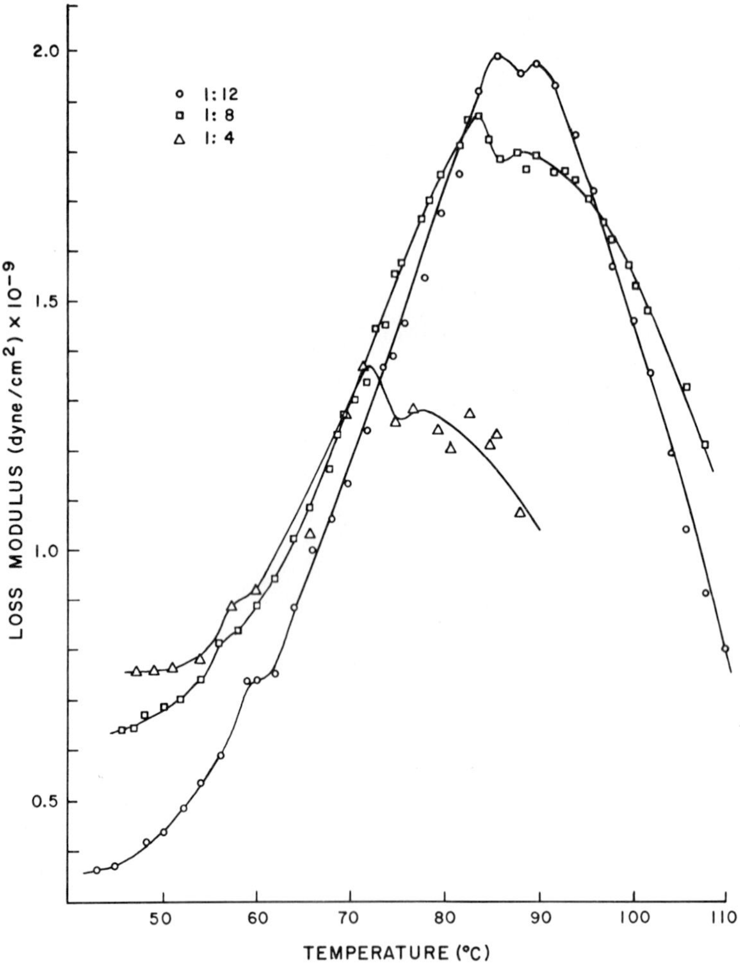

Fig. 7. Loss modulus versus temperature plots for SMA 40% tin ester/ERL 4289 at the indicated ratios of A:E.

ible and seem to have merged in systems based on 60 TBTE - SMA 1000 A - ERL 4289 (Figure 8); but they did tend to become discernible with the 80% ester where the peaks were much broader. The stiffening effect of the bulky tributyltin groups would seem to be the cause of the increase in T_g observed for ERL 4289 systems based on the 60% ester (Table 4). The same phenomenon is observed in systems incorporating ERL 4221; a higher degree of esterification in the base polymer

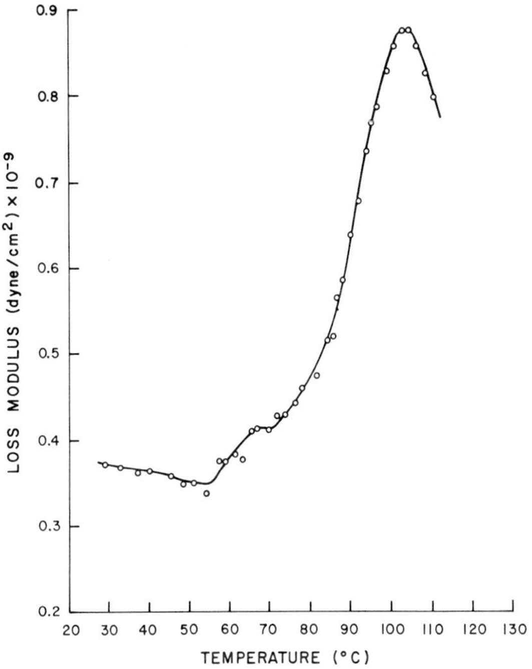

Fig. 8. Loss modulus versus temperature plots for SMA 60% tin ester/ERL 4289 at A:E = 1:4.

has resulted in higher T_g for the cured network. The observed glass transition for the crosslinked polymers incorporating ERL 4234, viz., >250°C, is the highest for all systems studied here. The clear indication from the progressive increase in T_g with increasing stiffness of the epoxy monomer is that the properties of the crosslinked network are dominated by the epoxy network. The base polymer however, does modify the properties with contribution from the bulky tributyltin groups.

E. Catalysis by Uranyl Nitrate

Uranyl nitrate was employed as catalyst (0.2%) for curing the 40% ester of SMA 1000 A and maleic anhydride with ERL 4289 and ERL 4221 in separate experiments. The same epoxy monomers were also homopolymerized in the presence of uranyl nitrate without any other hardener. In all cases, T_g observed was

TABLE 4
T_g of Organotin Epoxy Polymers Determined from Dynamic Mechanical Measurements

SMA Ester	*Epoxide*	*A:E*	*T_g °C*
40%	ERL 4289	1:4	77
		1:8	88
		1:12	90
60%	ERL 4289	1:4	104
		1:12	108
40%	ERL 4221	1:8	194
60%	ERL 4221	1:8	200
40%	ERL 4234	1:4	>240

higher than the corresponding one in stannous octoate. Some of the T_g values are reported in Table 5. Further, it was observed that reaction rates were much faster with uranyl nitrate as compared to those with stannous octoate.

Some mechanical tests were performed with cured products of 40% ester of SMA 1000 A and ERL 4289 in uranyl nitrate, and the results compared with the corresponding values of polymers prepared using stannous octoate catalyst (Table 6). It was observed that there was an almost 200% increase in tensile strength and about 25% increase in modulus using uranyl nitrate as catalyst. Since T_g is also higher, 125°C compared to 77°C, these observations indicate that uranyl nitrate imparts higher crosslink density to the cured products than stannous octoate.

Epoxy monomers were cured at 140°C using uranyl nitrate and stannous octoate, and the crosslinked homopolymers were solvent-extracted in methyl ethyl ketone. ERL 4221 and ERL 4289 cured with uranyl nitrate showed no extractables (Table 5) while with stannous octoate, ERL 4289 showed 15% and ERL 4221, 3% extractables. The cured products were hard,

TABLE 5
Comparison of T_g Values of Polymers Cured with Stannous Octoate and Uranyl Nitrate as Catalysts

Base Polymer/ Curing Agent	*Epoxy*	*Extractables, Percent*	T_g °C	*Catalyst*
40 TBTE SMA 1000 A	ERL 4289[a]	5.6	125	Uranyl Nitrate
40 TBTE - SMA 1000 A	ERL 4289[a]	17.9	77	Stannous Octoate
Maleic Anhydride	ERL 4289[a]	2.9	80	Uranyl Nitrate
Maleic Anhydride	ERL 4289[a]	5.2	76	Stannous Octoate
none	ERL 4289	0.0	60	Uranyl Nitrate
none	ERL 4289	14.8	<20	Stannous Octoate

a. A:E = 1:4

TABLE 6
Mechanical Properties of SMA 40% Tin Ester/ERL 4289 (A:E = 1:4 Cured with Stannous Octoate and Uranyl Nitrate as Catalysts

Catalyst	*Impact Strength* J/cm^2	*Strength MPa*	*Modulus MPa*
Uranyl Nitrate	0.046	20.0	338
Stannous Octoate	0.048	7.38	275

strong, tough and clear. It was observed that reactions with uranyl nitrate were considerably faster than those in stannous octoate. The diglycidyl ether of bisphenol-A, EPON 828 was also polymerized by uranyl nitrate but the reaction, as expected with an acid catalyst, was much slower than that of the cycloaliphatic epoxides.

Homopolymerization of cycloaliphatic epoxy monomers was followed by reaction on KCl crystals directly. The epoxy band at 815 cm^{-1} disappeared rapidly and completely at the end of the reaction.

Further, it was observed that with ERL 4289, products cured in uranyl nitrate and stannous octoate showed significantly different T_g's. The homopolymer formed with uranyl nitrate showed T_g at 60°C while with stannous octoate, T_g was below 20°C (Table 5).

The difference in percent extractables and crosslink density explain the variation in T_g's as was also observed for 40 TBTE - SMA 1000 A and ERL 4289 (A:E = 1:4) cured with uranyl nitrate compared to that with stannous octoate. These results confirm the advantages of uranyl nitrate as catalyst for obtaining highly crosslinked products and recommend its increasing application in further experiments with similar epoxy systems. It should be interesting to study, in more detail, the properties of the individual polymers prepared with uranyl nitrate catalyst.

F. Conclusions

A novel class of thermoset organotin epoxy polymers can be prepared by crosslinking prepolymers containing tributyltin and free carboxyl groups with cycloaliphatic epoxides. The properties of the network structure are predominantly controlled by the epoxy monomer structure, by the A:E ratio and by appropriate choice of catalysts. Toughening by liquid elastomers can be achieved as in conventional epoxy systems. Uranyl nitrate catalyst confers enhanced strength and toughness to the cured polymers. It should be interesting to study the mechanical properties of the homopolymers obtained from cycloaliphatic and other epoxy monomers using this catalyst.

The scheme of reactions discussed here can be extended to other styrene-maleic anhydride copolymers which have different ratios of styrene to maleic anhydride. Copolymers of maleic anhydride with α-olefins, hexene, decene, etc., can also be employed. Other base polymers containing acid groups like the copolymer of maleic acid with methylvinylether require more careful and detailed experimentation for further study. The spectrum of available base polymers provides considerable scope to change and control the properties of the network structure obtained by the synthetic route employed here.

Chemical binding of the toxic group, trialkyltin oxide, to the polymer matrix as adopted here, can lead to controlled rates of hydrolysis and leaching and consequently to long range protection against marine fouling.

IV. ACKNOWLEDGEMENTS

This study was supported in part by the Ocean Environment and Fouling Branch of David W. Taylor Naval Ship Research and Development Center, Annapolis, Maryland. The paper is based on the thesis submitted to WSU by M. Anand for the M.S. degree in Materials Science.

V. REFERENCES

1. J.M. Barnes and H.B. Stoner, Brit. J. Ind. Med. 15,14 (1958).
2. F.H. De La Court and H.J. De Vries, Prog. Org. Coatings, 1,375(1973).
3. A.T. Phillip, Prog. Org. Coatings, 2,159(1973/74).
4. J.C. Montermoso, T.M. Andrews and L.P. Marinelli, J. Polymer Sci., 32,523 (1958).
5. J.A. Montemarano and E.J. Dyckman, J. Paint Technol., 47(600),59(1975).
6. R.V. Subramanian, B.K. Garg, J. Jakubowski, J. Corredor, J.A. Montemarano and E.C. Fischer, Am. Chem. Soc., Div. Org. Coatings Plast. Chem., 36(2),660,(1976).
7. M. Anand, M.S. Thesis, Washington State University (1976).
8. S. Migdal, D. Gestner and A. Zilkha, Israel J. Chem.,5, 1963(1967).
9. H. Gilman and D. Rosenberg, J. Amer. Chem. Soc. 75,3592 (1953).
10. J. Fellers and A. Golovoy, J. Appl. Polym. Sci., 15,731 (1971).
11. R.F. Boyer, J. Polymer Sci., Symposium No. 50, 189(1975).

SYNTHESIS AND CHARACTERIZATION OF LINEAR AND CROSSLINKED AB-TYPE POLYURETHANES

James F. Kinstle and L. Eric Sepulveda
Department of Chemistry
The University of Tennessee

Novel AB-type polyurethanes have been prepared. Six of these contain in-chain aromatic units and have generic formula I, including ortho-substituted structures with m, n combinations of (1,0), (0,1), (1,1), (0,2) and para-substituted structures with m, n combinations of (0,0) and (0,2).

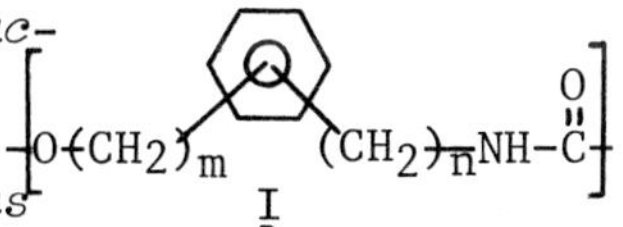

I

The aliphatic $-\!\!\{O(CH_2)_5NHCO\}\!\!-$ *was prepared for comparison. Ortho (0,0) could not be prepared by either the decomposition-intermolecular reaction of the hydroxy acylazide (cyclic benzoxazolinone was formed) or by thermal ring-opening of the benzo-substituted cyclic carbamate. Ortho (1,0) and (0,1) could be prepared by either route, though ring formation was favored in the Curtius reaction. Thermal polymerization of the cyclic benzoxazinones under mild conditions formed the amorphous linear polyurethanes; upon polymerization at high temperature or upon heating of the linear polymers, crosslinked materials were obtained, with urea, isocyanurate, and diarylmethane and polymerized carbodiimide moieties, respectively, being favored as the temperature was increased. Crystalline ortho (1,1), amorphous ortho (0,2), and crystalline para (0,0) and (0,2) could be prepared in good yield by the Curtius route; again the crosslinked structures progressively increased with post-polymerization heating. Infrared spectroscopy in the "near IR" range was found to be a valuable supplement in characterization of these polymeric materials.*

I. INTRODUCTION

The most familiar polyurethanes are prepared by reaction of diisocyanates with polyols.[1] Formation of linear polyurethanes by such a reaction can be illustrated schematically as

$$\text{n HO-R-OH} + \text{n OCN-R'-NCO} \rightarrow \left[\text{O-R-O}\overset{\text{O}}{\overset{\|}{\text{C}}}\text{NH-R'-NH}\overset{\text{O}}{\overset{\|}{\text{C}}}\right]_n \quad (1)$$

and, in terms of the sequence of functional group incorporation, can be designated AABB-type polymers. Much less investigated are the so-called AB-type polyurethanes. The formation of a linear AB-type polyurethane can be illustrated schematically as

$$\text{n HO-R''-NCO} \rightarrow \left[\text{O-R''-NH}\overset{\text{O}}{\overset{\|}{\text{C}}}\right]_n \quad (2)$$

Since hydroxyl and isocyanate groups react with each other very readily, such polymers are generally prepared directly upon generation of the free alcohol and/or isocyanate moieties. Preparative routes to AB-type polyurethanes (with one example referenced for each) include interfacial poly-condensation of ω-aminochloroformates,[2] metathetical reaction of ω-chlorohydrins with metal cyanates,[3] Curtius reaction of hydroxy acylhydrazides,[4] melt polycondensation of ω-hydroxyamines with ethylene carbonate,[6] thermal ring-opening of cyclic carbamates,[7] and, for the special case of poly(ethylene urethane), copolymerization of CO_2 and ethylene imine.[8]

II. OBJECTIVES, PERSPECTIVES

In principle, the AB-type polyurethanes (like the AABB-type) may be prepared with a wide range of chemical structures, ranging from highly aromatic to wholly aliphatic. The AB-type may be quite different from the AABB-type in their thermal and photolytic stability, flammability, and other physical and chemical properties. These considerations, along with the elimination of the stoichiometry requirement during their preparation, have prompted us to initiate studies on the formation and characterization of novel linear and crosslinked polyurethanes of the AB-type.

Specifically, our studies have centered on synthesis and characterization of the following AB-type polyurethanes (structures and Chemical Abstracts names correspond to idealized linear repeat units):

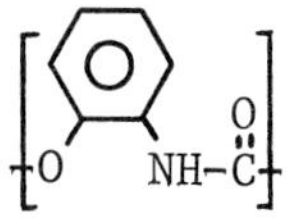

I poly(oxycarbonylimino-1,2-phenylene)

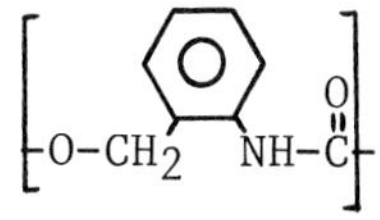

II poly(oxycarbonylimino-1,2-phenylenemethylene)

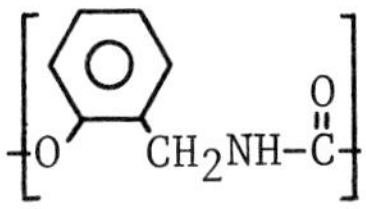

III poly(oxycarbonyliminomethylene-1,2-phenylene)

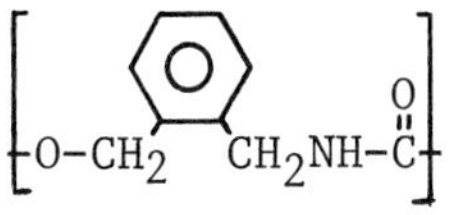

IV poly(oxycarbonyliminomethylene-1,2-phenylenemethylene)

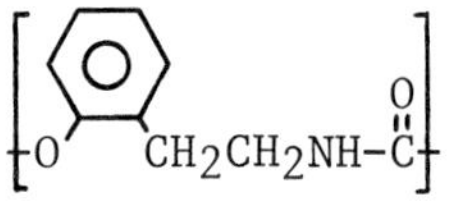

V poly(oxycarbonylimino-1,2-ethanediyl-1,2-phenylene)

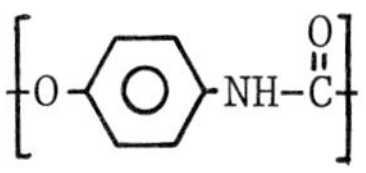

VI poly(oxycarbonylimino-1,4-phenylene)

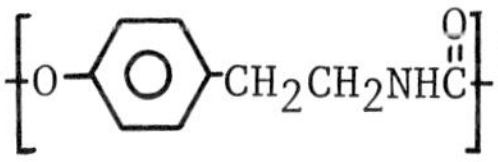

VII poly(oxycarbonylimino-1,2-ethanediyl-1,4-phenylene)

In addition to the above phenylene-linked polymers, of which only VI has been previously reported,[4] the wholly aliphatic poly(pentamethylene urethane) (VIII) was prepared for comparison. Polymer VIII has been made by several reported routes.[3,5,9]

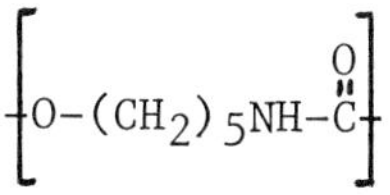

VIII poly(oxycarbonylimino-1,5-pentanediyl)

The Curtius reaction route is expected to be the most generally applicable for polyurethanes I through VIII. The generalized Curtius route can be shown as:

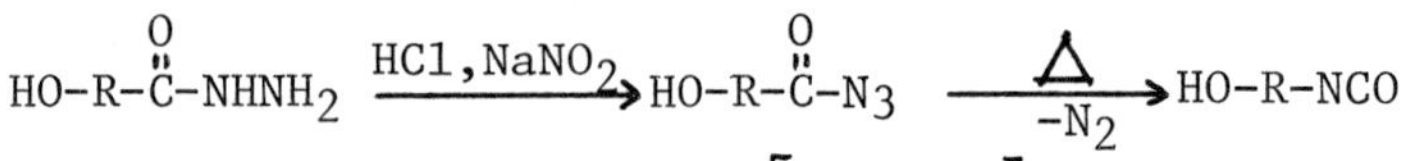

(3)

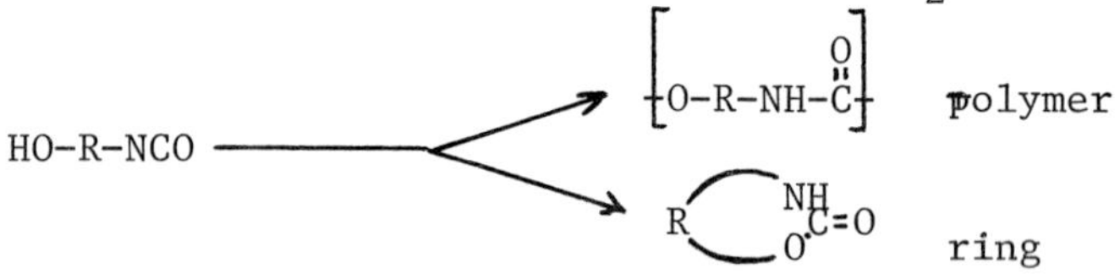

(4a)

(4b)

The intermediate ω-hydroxyisocyanate formed in reaction 3 can react intermolecularly to form polymer (4a). But if a 5,6 or even 7 membered aliphatic or o-benzosubstituted ring can be formed, it may react intramolecularly to form cyclic carbamate (4b). Two other side reactions may occur during the Curtius sequence; vis., loss of hydrazine from the acylhydrazide (5a) and/or loss of hydrazoic acid from the acylazide (5b). Both result in formation of linear and/or cyclic ester linkages.

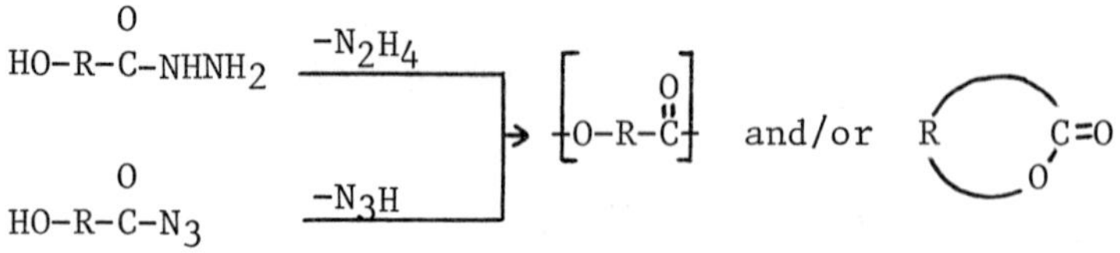

(5a)

(5b)

An alternative preparative route to ortho-phenylene linked polymers I through V is the thermal ring-opening polymerization of the corresponding cyclic carbamates. In the absence of a catalyst, this route also most likely proceeds via an ω-hydroxyisocyanate, which again may reform the ring or react intermolecularly to form polymer.

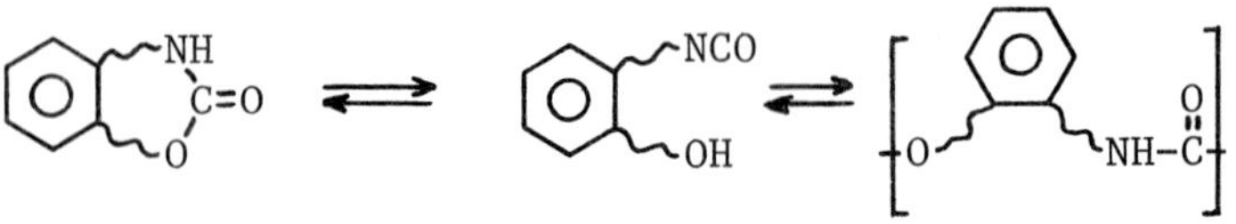

(6)

Two side reactions that are possible for either route, even at relatively low temperatures, are formation of isocyanurate (7) or urea (8) functions:

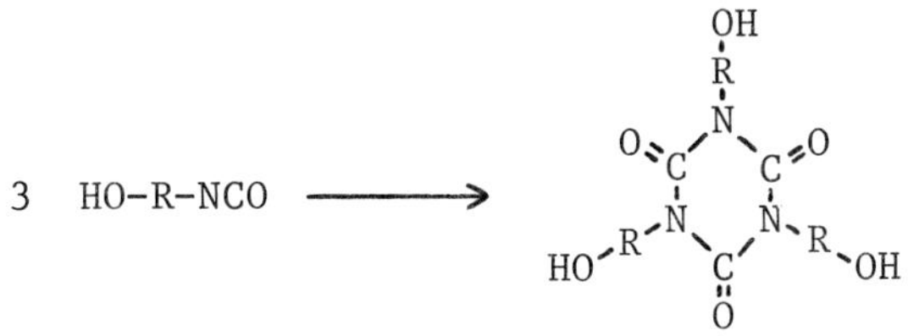

(7)

$$HO\text{-}RNCO \xrightarrow{H_2O} HO\text{-}R\text{-}NH_2 \xrightarrow{HO\text{-}R\text{-}NCO} HO\text{-}R\text{-}NH\text{-}\overset{O}{\overset{\|}{C}}\text{-}NH\text{-}R\text{-}OH \qquad (8)$$

Isocyanurate formation is catalyzed by a wide variety of substances, including amines. Ureas can be formed by reaction of an amine, however introduced, with an isocyanate group or by direct amine attack on an existing urethane link.[10]

Other "side reactions," several of which lead to crosslink formation, will be discussed later as appropriate.

III. EXPERIMENTAL RESULTS AND DISCUSSION

A. Polymer I

The Curtius route (reactions 3 and 4) that might lead to this polymer, starting with the hydrazide of salicylic acid, yielded the ring 2-benzoxazolinone as the nearly exclusive product.[4,11] Less than 1% yield of a nonvolatile product was obtained, whose main infrared absorptions occurred at 3.0-3 3.25μ, 5.8μ, 7.7-7.9μ, and 13.5μ. The carbonyl absorption matches that of the linear model phenyl carbanilate rather than that of 2-benzoxazolinone, suggesting the structure of Polymer I. However the pattern of absorptions between 7.0 and 10μ is very dissimilar to that of three carbamate models: 2-benzoxazolinone, phenyl carbanilate, and poly-p-phenylene urethane (Polymer VI discussed later).

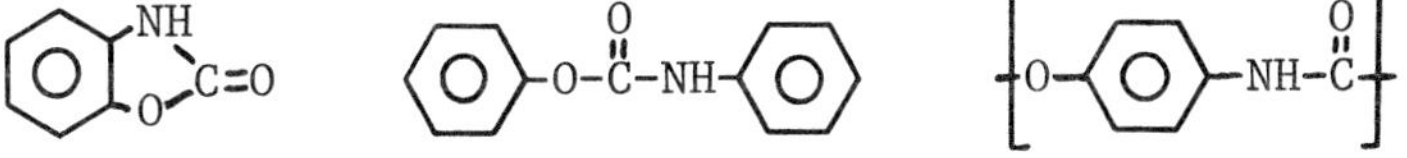

Because the Amide III band and the C-O and C-N stretching bands do not lie in the expected positions, the residue is not likely to consist appreciably of Polymer I. Because of extremely low yield, this residue was not studied further.

The ring 2-benzoxazolinone has high thermal stability (reversible bp 360°).[12] An unsuccessful attempt to polymerize 2-benzoxazolinone by heat has been reported,[13] but conditions were not specified. The possibility of forming Polymer I by reaction 6 was reinvestigated. Heating the pure ring (anhydrous form, mp 140-141°) at temperatures up to 222° for 3 days failed to produce any polymer. Heating the ring at 240° for 6 days in an evacuated sealed tube gave less than 5% nonvolatile product. Heating for 24 hrs at temperatures from 260° to 290° produced similar yields of nonvolatile product (up to 7% at 290°). The silica tubes always ruptured above 300° due to gas evolution.

The midrange infrared spectra of the various products were quite similar, suggesting similar linkages in similar amounts. The presence of open-chain carbamate linkages (Polymer I) is definitely ruled out. Diarylurea and oxazolinone structures predominated, the latter undoubtedly due to substitution of the parent compound on the benzene ring. The substituent is likely to be benzoxazole-2, as the water thus eliminated would give rise to the diarylurea structures. The mechanism proposed is the initial autoionization of 2-benzoxazolinone followed by attack of the protonated compound on an aromatic substrate (another 2-benzoxazolinone at the start).

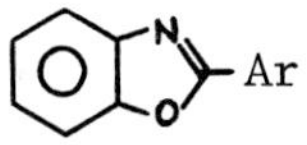

Another method of heating 2-benzoxazolinone was devised to circumvent the pressure buildup. The ring was dissolved in refluxing paraffin, heated by a bath of molten solder (Sn-Pb, 50/50), the temperature rising gradually from 260° to 370° over a 5-day period (as the lower paraffin fractions were removed). The nonvolatile product (obtained in 16% yield) was black and insoluble in THF. It appeared to consist of polymerized carbodiimide, a substance which contains N-aryl guanidine moieties.

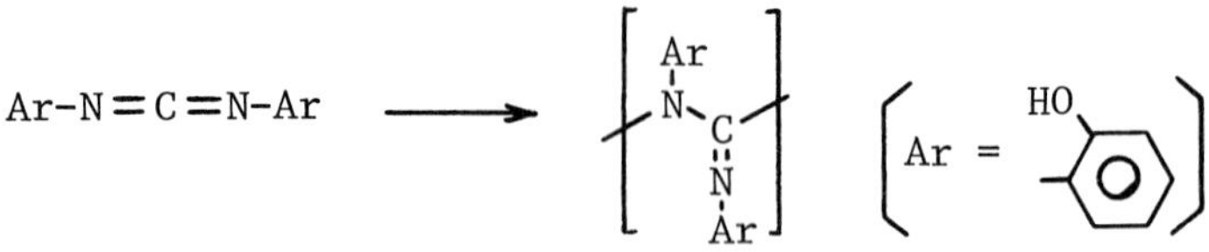

The diaryl carbodiimide would arise via the hydroxyisocyanate, with loss of CO_2:

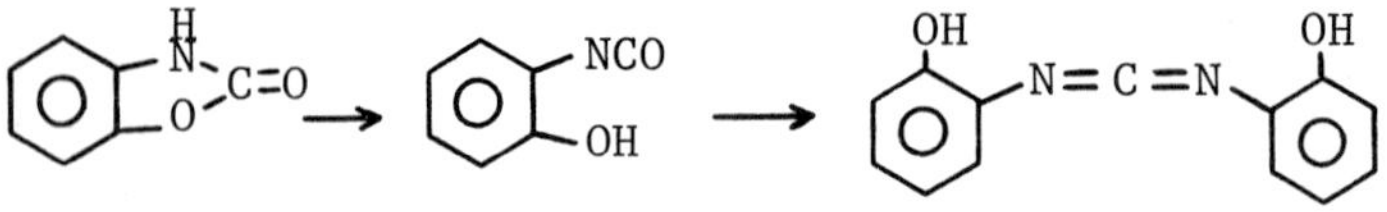

The evolution of CO_2 would account for the buildup of high pressure above 300°. The structure of the product was suggested strongly by the infrared spectrum of polymerized diphenylcarbodiimide, obtained by the same technique at 370°:

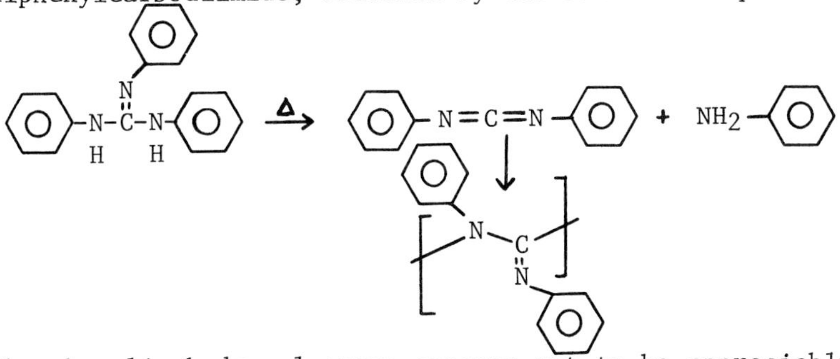

The phenolic hydroxyl group appears not to be appreciably ionized (strong infrared peak closer to 8.2μ than to 7.9μ), so that the guanidinium ion is probably not formed to a large extent. Because of the weakness of the 5.9μ peak in the product, the cyclic carbodiimide trimer shown below is in much lower concentration than the linear polymer.

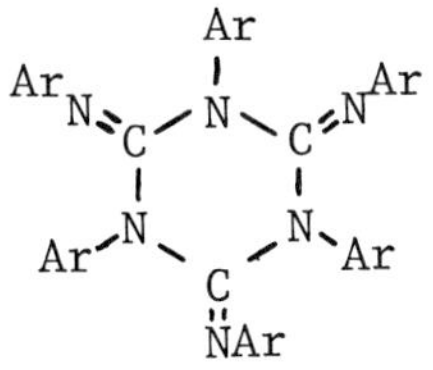

The isopiestic method of Barger[14] was used to determine approximate number-average molecular weights in this study (with a mixed solvent of tetrahydrofuran/5% water). A nonvolatile residue obtained at 260-265° had an $\overline{M}_n$ of 515, while one obtained at 290-295° had an $\overline{M}_n$ of 585. These materials are thus polymeric by the criterion of nonvolatility but only tetramers or pentamers by the criterion of molecular weight.

Thermogravimetric analyses of 2-benzoxazolinone and its thermally derived polymer are given in Table 1.

Examination by x-ray diffraction showed these materials to be completely amorphous.

B. Polymer II

The Curtius route, starting with phthalyl hydrazide, was carried out with various modifications. Decomposition of the intermediate azide at low temperature (80°) gave low yield (5-10%) of nearly pure polymer II. At the higher azide decomposition temperatures (120°), a greater percentage of nonvolatile product was formed, but it contained no carbamate link-

TABLE 1.

*Thermogravimetric Analyses of 2-Benzoxazolinone and Its Polymers***

Sample	Atm.	Temp. at wt. loss 10%	25%	50%	Residue at 400°(%)	Residue at 500°(%)	First Inflection %wt. loss	Temp.	Second Inflection %wt. loss	Temp.
Monomer	N_2	180	200	215	0	0	90	230	--	--
Monomer	Air	185	205	220	0	0	90	235	--	--
Polymer	N_2	263	310	380	46	30	32	330	64	460

**Heating rate of 10° per minute*

ages. Instead mostly urea, with some isocyanurate and diaryl methane linkages, was shown by IR. This Curtius reaction is, however, a good synthetic route to the cyclic monomer 3,1-benzoxazin-2-one, as shown by Lindemann and Schultheis.[15]

Thermal ring opening of the cyclic carbamate affords a clearly better route to polyurethane II. The data in Table 2 were obtained by heating the cyclic carbamate in evacuated closed tubes for 2 days in an oil bath at the specified temperature.

TABLE 2.
Polymers From Heating 3,1-Benzoxazin-2-one in Bulk

	Yield,%*			Predominate Linkages		
Temp, °C	*sol*	*insol*	*II*	*iso-cyanurate*	*urea*	*diaryl-methane*
154	5	0	√			
	7		√			
160-165		5	little	√	√	
	8		√			
165-170		11	little	√	√	
	10		little	√	√	
176-185		40		√	√	√
193-198	0	60		√	√	√
207-211	0	81		√		√
216**	0	83		√		√

**yield is % nonvolatile based on initial weight*
***216° sample was heated 48 hr in tube furnace*

The trends in Table 2 are apparent; as the temperature is increased, the percentage of linear polymer II decreases and urea, isocyanurate, and diarylmethane structures increase. At temperatures over 200°, 3,1-benzoxazin-2-one is almost quantitatively converted to insoluble polymer containing predominately isocyanurate and diarylmethane structures. Polymers formed at lower temperature could be converted to resemble those formed at higher temperature. For example, the predominately carbamate-linked soluble fraction formed at 165-170°, after heating at 210°, contained predominately isocyanurate and diarylmethane groups. All these data clearly reflect the degree of reversibility and thermal stability of individual groups. Thermal degradation of carbamates (linear or cyclic) or of ureas leads to isocyanurate groups plus alcohols and amines, respectively. Amines catalyze the essentially irreversible formation of the trimeric isocyanurates. The alcohol group in this case is an hydroxymethylaryl moiety,

TABLE 3.
Polymers From Heating 3,1-Benzoxazin-2-one in Refluxing Solvents

		Yield %*		Linkages in Soluble Fraction				
Solvent	*bp*	*sol*	*insol*	*Solvent***	*II*	*iso-cyanurate*	*urea*	*diaryl-methane*
C_6H_5Cl	132	10	–		√	little		
C_6H_5Et	136	32	–	√	√	little	√	
$(n\text{-}bu)_2O$	142	21	–		√	√	√	√
o-oxylene	144	40	–		√	√		√
$Cl_2CHCHCl_2$	146	91	25	√	√	√		√
cumene	152	150	–	√	√	little		
anisole	154	10	–		√	√	√	
cyclohexanone	156	95	–	√	√	√		
C_6H_5Br	156	63	–		√	√		
$(pr)_3N$	156	72	10		little		√	√
mesitylene	164	43	–		√	√	√	√
phenetole	170	63	–		√	√	√	√
m-dichlorobenzene	173	82	–		√	√	√	√
s-butylbenzene	173	78	–	√	√	√	√	√

p-cymene	177	70	–	√	little		√		
tetramethylurea	177	45	8		little		√	√	√
o-dichlorobenzene	181	72	–		√	√	√	√	
n-butylbenzene	183	95	–	√	√	√	√	√	
pentyl ether	187	88	–		√	√	√	√	
durene	190	93	–		little		√	√	√
dimethylaniline	193	123	–	√	none	√	little	√	
veratrole	206	76	–	√	none	√	√	√	
tetralin	207	89	–	√	none	√	√	√	
$(bu)_3N$	216	84	–		none	√	√	√	
quinoline	237	82	–		none	√		√	

* *yield is % nonvolatile based on initial weight*
** *solvent designation signifies chemical incorporation of solvent into product.*

reminiscent of the intermediates in phenol-formaldehyde polymerization. Upon capture of a proton, the methylol group loses water, forming a benzylic carbonium ion. The water can hydrolyze an isocyanate, a urethane, or a urea, each of which reacts further. The carbonium ion can alkylate another aromatic ring, forming diarylmethane structures.

Additional data on polymerization of 3,1-benzoxazin-2-one were obtained by mixing 1.0g monomer with 30ml of "inert" solvent and heating at reflux for one week. Reaction variables such as reflux time and monomer concentration have not yet been studied. Table 3 shows the results from the wide range of solvents investigated.

Obviously, the solvent approach leads to a much higher conversion to soluble polymers. Also striking is the high degree of solvent incorporation into the polymeric products, readily explainable for amines and alkyl halides and rationalizable for solvents with benzylic H atoms (interchange, nucleophilic substitution, and radical reactions including oxidation products, respectively). It is very likely that these polymers are highly branched.

For several polymers, the peak heights (absorbances) at 9.4μ (carbamate) and at 7.1μ (isocyanurate) were utilized in an attempt to determine molar concentrations of these linkages. For those polymers prepared below 170° that contained relatively low concentration of urea groups, the amount of isocyanurate varied between 10 and 30%. This range was found to be true for nearly all those polymers formed by either bulk thermal or by refluxing solvent techniques, irrespective of the relative concentrations of urea and diarylmethane structures. The concentration of isocyanurate groups was lower in those polymers formed by the Curtius reaction.

Seven products of refluxing solvent polymerizations were examined by near infrared spectroscopy (this technique required at least 0.3g of material). These materials showed the presence of unreacted hydroxymethyl groups, with strong absorptions in the region from 2270 to 2410 nm, and noticeable absorption at 1410nm (free OH). The intensity of the carbonyl second overtone between 1950 and 2100nm showed a high isocyanurate composition in the samples made in o-xylene, cyclohexanone, mesitylene, s-butylbenzene, and n-butylbenzene (weak absorptions). The strong absorption of the sample prepared in bromobenzene in this region suggests a high urea composition. The sample prepared in phenetole has a high carbamate composition.

Wide-angle x-ray diffraction of various powdered samples showed these materials to be non-crystalline. Differential scanning calorimetry (DSC) did not show a glass transition temperature.

Inherent viscosities of some samples of II are given in Table 4.

TABLE 4.
*Inherent Viscosities of Polymers From 3,1-Benzoxazin-2-one**

Polymerization Conditions		η_{inh}
Curtius Reaction Product		0.16
	160-165°	0.22
Bulk Thermal	165-170°	0.19
	176-185°	0.20
	chlorobenzene	0.28, 0.35
	ethylbenzene	0.37
Refluxing Solvent	o-xylene	0.24
	bromobenzene	0.21

**1.0g II per 100ml meta-cresol at 30°*

The isopiestic number average molecular weights were determined for three samples of II; the results are given in Table 5.

TABLE 5.
*Number Average Molecular Weights of Polymers from 3,1-Benzoxazin-2-one**

Polymerization Conditions		$\overline{M}_n$
	ethylbenzene	1460
Refluxing Solvent	chlorobenzene	1215
	chlorobenzene	1435

**isopiestic method,[14] using 95% THF/5% H_2O*

Again, these are fairly low molecular weight materials (number average degree of polymerization ~10).

Since most of the polymers from 3,1-benzoxazin-2-one are formed by thermally induced ring opening polymerization, the fate of the polymers when heated is of interest. Especially intriguing is the possibility of forming new cross-linked polymers upon thermal modification of soluble samples of polymer II.

Thermolyses were accomplished by heating various samples for 1 hour in the chamber of a DSC under nitrogen atmosphere. At 200° most carbamate was converted to urea, isocyanurate, and diarylmethane. At 250° no carbamate or urea remained, with isocyanurate and diarylmethane linkages dominant in the residue. At temperatures from 300° to 500°, the diarylmethane structures remained, but the isocyanurate content steadily decreased while polymerized carbodiimide steadily increased.

Thermolyses were also accomplished on larger samples of II by heating at a specified temperature for 24 hours under continuously applied vacuum. A bath of molten solder (50% Sn/50% Pb) was used for heating. Thermolysis at 180° was sufficient to remove all carbamate linkages, but only about 25% were converted to the cyclic carbamate, the rest being converted to isocyanurate and urea. At 200° much more isocyanurate than urea was produced. At 280°, guanidine was more prominent than isocyanurate, with a small amount of polymerized carbodiimide. At 370° isocyanurate and guanidine were negligible relative to polymerized carbodimide.

Thermogravimetric analysis (TGA) was also carried out on the cyclic precursor to II, and on several samples of II that had been formed under different conditions. The TGA results, obtained under N_2 or air, are given in Table 6.

These data illustrate that the polymers lose less weight at a given temperature or, equivalently, take more heat before losing a given percentage of weight, when heated in air as opposed to nitrogen. This indicates that oxygen is inhibiting the degradation to volatile products, and is likely being incorporated into the residue. A likely pathway for oxygen incorporation is:

a) $$\text{Ar-CH}_2\text{-Ar} \longrightarrow \text{Ar-}\dot{\text{C}}\text{H-Ar} + \text{H}^{\bullet}$$

b) $$\text{Ar-}\dot{\text{C}}\text{H-Ar} + \text{O}_2 \longrightarrow \text{Ar-}\overset{\text{OO}^{\bullet}}{\text{CH}}\text{-Ar}$$

c) $$\text{Ar-}\overset{\text{OO}^{\bullet}}{\text{CH}}\text{-Ar} + \text{Ar-CH}_2\text{-Ar} \longrightarrow \text{Ar-}\overset{\text{OOH}}{\text{CH}}\text{-Ar} + \text{Ar-}\dot{\text{C}}\text{H-Ar}$$

d) $$\text{Ar-}\overset{\text{OOH}}{\text{CH}}\text{-Ar} \longrightarrow \text{Ar-}\overset{\text{O}^{\bullet}}{\text{CH}}\text{-Ar} + \dot{\text{O}}\text{H}$$

e) $$2\ \text{Ar-CH-}\overset{\text{O}^{\bullet}}{\text{CH}}\text{-Ar} \longrightarrow \text{Ar-}\overset{\text{OH}}{\text{CH}}\text{-Ar} + \text{Ar-}\overset{\text{O}}{\overset{\|}{\text{C}}}\text{-Ar}$$

Here b, c and (at least in part d) are propagation steps in the chain reaction, and the disproportionation-type reaction e leads without polymer scission to two oxygen-containing residues, one of which is susceptible to further oxidation.

B. Polymer III

Again, the Curtius route formed predominately cyclic carbamate - in this case 1,3-benzoxazin-2-one. Only 6% of soluble polymer III was formed upon decomposition of the azide at 80°. Polymer III prepared in this way contained some isocyanurate, but no urea linkages. Because of overlapping absorptions, isocyanurate cannot be quantitated and diarylmethane cannot be detected in the presence of carbamate linkages of the N-benzyl-O-phenyl type.

TABLE 6.
*Thermogravimetric Analyses of 3,1-Benzoxazin-2-one and Its Polymers**

		Temp. at wt. loss			Residue	Residue	First Inflection		Second Inflection	
Sample	*Atm.*	*10%*	*25%*	*50%*	*at 400°(%)*	*at 500°(%)*	*%wt. loss*	*Temp.*	*%wt. loss*	*Temp.*
Monomer	N_2	185	210	228	1	0	65	242	--	--
Monomer	Air	196	220	238	6	?	70	248	--	--
II,bulk 160-165°	N_2	210	330	465	66	30	16	238	61	477
	Air	219	427	525	77	55	13	235	37	474
II,bulk 176-185°	N_2	246	360	485	70	43	11	250	50	485
II,reflux quinoline (237°)	N_2	260	312	378	45	34	37	340	>66	>500
	Air	275	323	490	55	49	25	323	>51	>500

**Heating rate of 10° per minute*

The 1,3-benzoxazin-2-one was also heated in bulk, in the same manner as given for the 3,1-benzoxazin-2-one. The results are shown in Table 7.

TABLE 7.
Polymers From Heating 1,3-Benzoxazin-2-one in Bulk

	Yield, %			Predominate Linkages			
Temp, °C	*sol*	*insol*	*III*	*iso-cyanurate*	*urea*	*iso-urea*	*diaryl-methane*
170-176	20		√	little			
180-185	30		√	√	little		
190-194	47		√	√	√		
		*		√		√	
206-209	16		√				
		52		√		√	little
227-230	<1		√		√		
		∿70		√		√	little

**undetermined*

Thus, the percentage of soluble III obtained from the cyclic carbamate at a given temperature was higher than that observed in the formation of polymer II. Again, polymer formed at the lower temperatures could be modified by heating, but the correspondence (polymer formed at 160° and then heated at 210° vs. polymer initially formed at 210°) was less quantitative than in similar studies of polymer II.

Polymers have also been prepared from 1,3-benzoxazin-2-one in refluxing solvents. The general trend was formation of lesser amounts of III than of II under equivalent conditions. The results are given in Table 8.

Again, an appreciable amount of solvent was incorporated into the polymeric product in several cases, most notably for cyclohexanone and for aromatic hydrocarbons with benzylic hydrogens.

A large proportion of the urea linkages formed in the thermal polymerizations, detected by infrared spectroscopy, may in fact be isoureas. In the presence of both urea and carbamate linkages, isourea linkages would be difficult to detect. The N,N'-dialkyl-O-aryl isoureas are characterized by absorptions at 6.0-6.1μ, 7.1μ, 7.75μ, 8.1-835μ, and 8.95-9.25μ.[16] In the presence of phenolic hydroxyl groups, a large proportion of these isoureas would be converted to isouronium phenolate salts, which would shift the above infrared absorptions to lower wavelengths. What is observed is a broadening of the above wavelengths to the left.

Several other direct syntheses of 1,3-benzoxazin-2-one and/or its polymers were attempted, using o-hydroxyl-benzyl-

TABLE 8.
Polymers From Heating 1,3-Benzoxazin-2-one in Refluxing Solvents

Solvent	*bp*	*Yield, %* *sol*	*insol*	*Linkages in Soluble Fraction* *solvent*	*III*	*iso-cyanurate*	*urea*	*iso-urea*	*diaryl-methane*
C_6H_5Cl	131	5	--		√	little			
C_6H_5Et	136	20	--		√	little			
$(n\text{-}bu)_2O$	142	5	--		√	little			
o-xylene	144	15	--		√		√		
cumene	152	110	--	√	√	√	√		
anisole	153	6	--		√		√		
cyclohexanone	156	132	--	√	√		√		
C_6H_5Br	156	5	--		√	little			
mesitylene	164	7	--		√	little			
phenetole	170	18	--		√		little		
s-butylbenzene	173	32	--	√	√		little		
p-cymene	177	81	--	√	√	√	little		
tetramethylurea	177	29	--			√	√		
o-dichlorobenzene	180	6	--		√		little		
n-butylbenzene	183	82	--	√		√	√		
pentyl ether	187	54	--			√	√		
dimethylaniline	193	116	--	√	little	√		√	
veratrole	206	71	12	√	little	√		√	
tetralin	207	110	--	√	little	√		√	
$(bu)_3N$	216	94	--					√	√
quinoline	237	21	40					√	√

amine with various reagents that supply the carbonyl moiety. The o-hydroxylbenzylamine was synthesized in 16% yield by the electrolytic reduction of salicylamide, using the procedure of Coleman and Johnson[17] with slight modifications. The carbonyl contributors included phosgene,[18] dimethyl carbonate, diethyl carbonate, ethyl chloroformate, and ethylene carbonate. Each reaction yielded some (usually little) of the cyclic monomeric carbamate. Use of the last three listed carbonyl sources also yielded fractions that could not be volatilized, all of which showed the presence of substantial amounts of dibenzyl urea linkages. The only nonvolatile sample that showed substantial amount of carbamate linkage was that prepared in ethylene carbonate, and this sample exhibited the rather low inherent viscosity of 0.065 (m-cresol, 30°, 1g/100ml).

Several polymer III samples prepared in refluxing solvents were examined by near infrared spectroscopy. Absorptions in the region 2400 to 2270nm indicated that carbamate and isocyanurate structures predominated over the urea structure. The presence of substantial amounts of isocyanurate is also shown by the weakness of the absorptions in the regions 2050 to 1950nm and around 1480nm.

Several samples of III, which were highest in carbamate composition and hence most likely to be crystalline, were examined by x-ray diffraction and found to be noncrystalline.

Selected viscometry data are given in Table 9, in which it is seen that the inherent viscosities of bulk-polymerized III are significantly higher than those noted for II.

TABLE 9.
*Inherent Viscosities of Polymers From 1,3-Benzoxazin-2-one**

Polymerization Conditions		η_{inh}
Curtius Reaction		0.49
Bulk Thermal	170-176°	0.61
	180-185°	0.58
Refluxing Ethylbenzene		0.23
Refluxing Dibutylether		0.41

**1.0g III per 100ml meta-cresol at 30°*

Isopiestic molecular weights are given in Table 10, again showing higher molecular weights than for II (still, $\bar{M}_n$ of 2080 ≈degree of polymerization 14).

TABLE 10.
*Number Average Molecular Weights of Polymers From 1,3-Benzoxazin-2-one**

Polymerization Conditions		$\overline{M}_n$
Bulk Thermal	170-176°	2080
Refluxing Dibutylether		1630

**isopiestic method,[14] using 95% THF/5% H_2O*

Upon heating of III for 1 hour under isothermal conditions under N_2 in the DSC, almost no change was noted at 200°. Carbamate and urea linkages disappeared at 250°, with concomitant appearance of isocyanurate and isouronium phenolate linkages. At 300°, isocyanurate, isouronium phenolate, and polymerized carbodiimide were formed.

Heating of a larger sample in a continuously evacuated tube at 200° caused little change except for a slight increase of isocyanurate linkages. The residue after heating III at 280° showed mostly isouronium phenolate, with some isocyanurate and polymerized carbodiimide. That from heating at 370° contained mostly polymerized carbodiimide, with some isocyanurate.

TGA data for 1,3-benzoxazin-2-one and its derived polymers are given in Table 11.

C. Polymer IV

As we have reported,[19] polymer IV is obtainable in good yield (>70%) via the Curtius reaction. The benzoxazepinone cyclic carbamate precursor to IV was not isolable from the Curtius reaction products. Neither could the benzoxazepinone be prepared by a previously reported phosgenation route,[20] due to difficulties in isolation of the pure aminoalcohol. Therefore, all product characterization, modification, and degradation studies have been carried out on polymer IV prepared by the Curtius route.

Polymer IV samples very closely resemble the idealized linear polyurethane structure shown earlier. The midrange IR data were substantiated by the near IR, the absence of appreciable isocyanurate and urea linkages being shown by minimal absorption at 2020-2045nm and 2295-2405nm, respectively. The purity of IV is consistent with the temperature of its formation being too low to favor isocyanurate formation and with the removal of any urea structures by their lack of solubility in the azide-decomposition medium.

The polymer exhibits limited solubility in tetrahydrofuran, and is soluble in hot (80°) dimethylformamide and

TABLE 11.
Thermogravimetric Analyses of 1,3-Benzoxazin-2-one and Its Polymers[*]

Sample	Atm.	Temp. at wt. loss(°C) 10%	25%	50%	Residue at 400°(%)	Residue at 500°(%)	First Inflection %wt. loss	First Inflection Temp.	Second Inflection %wt. loss	Second Inflection Temp.
Monomer	N_2	195	220	235	--	--	75	245	--	--
Monomer	Air	200	220	240	--	--	90	255	--	--
III, bulk 180-185°	N_2	220	245	275	37	34	34	250	>70	>580
	Air	215	240	270	42	33	31	250	84	540
III, soluble 206-209°	N_2	267	307	362	45	38	44	350	>62	>500
III, reflux quinoline (237°)	N_2	240	375	--	72	60	7	200	>40	>500
	Air	217	428	--	78	57	13	250	>43	>500

[*] *Heating rate of 10° per minute.*

in m-cresol. The inherent viscosity of a typical sample (1.0g IV in 100ml m-cresol at 30°) was 0.46. The polymers were highly crystalline, as shown by wide angle x-ray diffraction. The following d-spacings were found: 6.11, 4.44, 4.17, and 4.0 Å. The DSC trace did not reveal a melting endotherm up to decomposition temperature.

Isothermal treatment of IV in a continuously evacuated tube at 150° caused formation of some isocyanurate and diarylmethane in the residue, with no unreacted hydroxymethyl groups detectable. At 200° some polymerized carbodiimide also appeared, but the overall IR spectrum was still quite similar to that of IV. At 280°, the dominant linkages in the residue were diarylmethane, isocyanurate, and polymerized carbodiimide. At 370°, the polymer was completely converted to volatile products, most likely by cleavage of the benzylheteroatom bond.

Thermogravimetric analyses of IV are detailed in Table 12, along with the TGA data from Polymers V through VIII.

D. Polymer V

Polymer V is also obtained in good yield (>75%) via the Curtius route. The polymer closely resembles the idealized linear structure shown earlier. Urea and isocyanurate are very minor components according to the midrange IR data. The weakness of the phenolic absorption in the near IR (∿1417nm) substantiates that urea and/or isocyanurate groups are in very low concentration. About 8% of the previously reported[21] bis[2(2-hydroxyphenyl)ethyl]urea could be isolated from the Curtius products.

The benzoxazepinone cyclic carbamate analog of V could not be isolated as a product of the Curtius reaction, nor is it likely to be prepared by phosgenation of the precursor aminophenol, since the latter is zwitterionic. Hence, as for IV, formation of V by thermal ring opening of the cyclic carbamate has not been accomplished.

Polymer V is soluble in a range of organic solvents. It is noncrystalline, as shown by x-ray diffraction. The inherent viscosities of two samples of V (1.0g per 100ml m-cresol at 30°) was 0.31 and 0.26, with isopiestic molecular weights of ∿1320 and ∿1190.

Heating under nitrogen in the DSC for an hour at 200° caused an increase in the amount of isourea and isouronium phenolate. At 250° the isocyanurate composition appeared unchanged, the polymerized carbodiimide linkages became noticeable, and the isouronium phenolate structures increased greatly. The carbamate and urea structures vanished. At 300° the isocyanurate composition fell to nearly zero, the

TABLE 12.
*Thermogravimetric Analyses of Polymers IV through VIII**

Sample	Atm.	Temp. at wt. loss (°C) 10%	25%	50%	Residue at 400°(%)	Residue at 500°(%)	First Inflection %wt.loss	Temp.	Second Inflection %wt.loss	Temp.
IV, Curtius	N_2	137	167	280	2.5	2	25	167	67	300
IV, Curtius	Air	137	167	280	7.0	6	30	175	74	305
IV, heated at 130°	N_2	273	287	297	2.5	2	40	292	--	--
V, Curtius	N_2	257	283	312	10	8	40	300	--	--
V, Curtius	Air	253	278	308	17	14	40	295	--	--
VI, Curtius	N_2	197	248	285	17	15	47	280	--	--
VI, Curtius	Air	200	258	297	22	19	52	300	--	--
VII, Curtius	N_2	247	283	317	17	14	48	314	--	--
VII, Curtius	Air	247	283	323	27	21	45	315	--	--
VIII,Curtius	N_2	323	343	355	2	>1	60	359	--	--
VIII,Curtius	Air	313	338	356	6	3	60	360	--	--

**Heating rate of 10° per minute*

polymerized carbodiimide structures increased, and the isouronium phenolate structure was dominant.

Heating was also accomplished under continuously applied vacuum. At 200°, the residue contained a little carbamate, but mostly isocyanurate and isouronium phenolate. At 280°, some isocyanurate remained, but the residue contained mostly isouronium phenolate and polymerized carbodiimide linkages. At 370° the residue consisted almost entirely of polymerized carbodiimide. This residue was very hard and extremely tough, more so than any other thermolysis product in this study.

TGA data from a typical polymer V in N_2 and in air are given in Table 12. Volatilization is nearly complete at ∿500°, but the hard, tough residue is stable up to much higher temperature.

E. Polymer VI

This polymer has been studied by several authors,[22] including by Stoermer who used the Curtius route from p-hydroxy benzoylhydrazide.[4] A typical yield in our preparations is ∿85%. The polymer could be fractionated according to limited solubility vs. insolubility in THF. The soluble fraction contained ∿12% isocyanurate, and the insoluble fraction around 20%. The rather large near IR absorption in the 1400-1440nm range is due to phenolic OH groups in the isocyanurate component.

Wide angle x-ray showed VI to be highly crystalline, the diffracted rings corresponding to d-spacings of 4.29, 3.95, 3.87, 3.25, and 2.25 Å.

The inherent viscosity of VI was determined at the very low concentration of 0.2g per 100ml m-cresol at 30° due to limited solubility, and was 0.050.

Our principal interest in Polymer VI was its thermal behavior, since it is clearly an extreme case (N-aryl, O-aryl). Its behavior when heated is somewhat unusual among polymers, at least among "condensation" polymers. Like the N-aryl, O-aryl urethane model compounds, the carbamate links in VI undergo facile dissociation into isocyanate and hydroxyl components. The polymer volatilizes by loss of monomer. The monomer is too reactive to exist in the monomeric state in the condensed phase, so it repolymerizes on the nearest cooler surface. The rather small residue when VI was heated under nitrogen in DSC at 200° showed little change from the original polymer. The small changes were due to incorporation of isourea and polymerized carbodiimide structures. At 250°, the relative amount of carbamate was further decreased, and by 300° polymerized carbodiimide and isourea accounted for all of the residue. Heating under continuously applied vacuum at 200° for

24 hours left a minute residue that consisted mainly of isocyanurate and isourea, with some polymerized carbodiimide. At 280° the residue consisted of isocyanurate and polymerized carbodiimide, while at 370° only polymerized carbodiimide remained. These residues were similar to those from V, i.e. very hard and tough.

TGA data for VI in N_2 and in air are given in Table 12. As expected, the rather singular dissociation-to-monomer degradation mechanism leads to only one region of rapid weight loss (deflection) in the thermogram.

F. Polymer VII

Polymer VII was prepared primarily as a sort of model compound, both for assistance in midrange and near IR spectral studies and for comparison of thermolysis behaviors. This polymer does not appear to have been reported previously, though it is easily obtained by the Curtius route from the commercially available p-hydroxyphenyl propionylhydrazide. Yields from the hydrazide were always over 70%.

Both midrange and near IR spectra showed the product to be a quite pure polyurethane. It was soluble in hot (80°) dimethylformamide, but had low solubility in THF and in m-cresol. Due to its limited solubility, inherent viscosities were obtained on solutions of 0.5g per 100ml of m-cresol at 30°, and were 0.175 and 0.158. Polymer VII is highly crystalline, with d-spacings of 4.44, 4.10, 3.49, and 3.13 Å.

Heating of VII in the DSC under nitrogen for 1 hour at 200° caused a slight increase in the isocyanurate content and a more significant formation of isouronium phenolate. At 250° all carbamate linkages were converted to isocyanurate, polymerized carbodiimide, and, predominantly, isouronium phenolate. Heating for 24 hours under continuously applied vacuum at 200° caused loss of nearly all carbamate linkages. The residue consisted mainly of isouronium phenolate, with some isocyanurate and polymerized carbodiimide. At 280°, isocyanurate and isouronium phenolate were minor components, and polymerized carbodiimide predominated. At 370°, polymerized carbodiimide was the only apparent component of the residue.

Like the residues of V and VI, the thermolysis products of VII were extremely hard and tough. These materials could not be removed from a pyrex or silica vessel without removing glass fragments. Adhesion was also extreme on aluminum surfaces.

The TGA scans of VII in N_2 and in air are detailed in Table 12.

G. Polymer VIII

Polymer VIII is by far the most studied of the AB-type polyurethanes. It was prepared primarily as a model for comparison, it being an extreme or limiting case (N-alkyl, O-alkyl). The polymer was prepared as previously reported,[9,23] using the hydrazide prepared from ε-caprolactone.[24]

As in the other polyurethanes studied, isocyanurate linkages were present to a small extent. Their presence was substantiated by the near IR absorption of the pendant hydroxyl groups.

Heating of VIII in the DSC at 200° caused little change in the polymer, though some isocyanurate, isourea, and polymerized carbodiimide appeared. Some carbamate remained even at 250°, but isocyanurate predominated. This residue was a viscous liquid. Heating of VIII under continuous vacuum for 24 hours at 200° showed similar results to the 200° DSC heat treatment. At 280°, the residue contained mostly isocyanurate, with some isourea and polymerized carbodiimide. At 370° the residue consisted entirely of isocyanurate and polymerized carbodiimide. The residues after heating at 280° and at 370° were viscous liquids.

The TGA data in Table 12 show the relatively high stability of the carbamate linkage in this N-alkyl, O-alkyl polyurethane, yet VIII was almost completely volatilized below 400°. The minute thermolysis residues were liquids.

IV. SUMMARY

A series of novel AB-type polyurethanes, each containing an in-chain phenylene unit, have been prepared by the intermolecular reaction of the intermediate hydroxy isocyanates generated from the Curtius reaction. When a 5-membered ring (benzoxazolinone) could be formed, intramolecular reaction occurred exclusively. When 6-membered rings (benzoxazinones) could be formed, both intramolecular and intermolecular reactions occurred, with the former predominating. If only 7-membered rings (benzoxazepinones) could be formed, or if ring formation was precluded by using p-phenylene substituted precursors, intermolecular reaction occurred exclusively.

The ortho-phenylene substituted linear polyurethanes in which either the O or N of the carbamate was attached directly to the aromatic ring were amorphous. The ortho-phenylene polymer in which O and N were separated from the aromatic ring by a methylene unit, and the para-phenylene substituted polymers, were crystalline. Each of these AB-type polyurethanes could be heated, and in those cases that the cyclic carbamate precursors were available could be directly formed, to yield crosslinked polymers. The crosslinked polymers contained isocyanurate moieties. On further heating (or upon formation at higher temperature), carbamate functions tended to disappear and isocyanurate, polymerized carbodiimide and, depending on the aromatic substitution pattern either diarylmethane or isouronium phenolate, structures became dominant. At yet higher temperatures, polymerized carbodiimide and diarylmethane/isouronium phenolate structures predominated.

V. ACKNOWLEDGEMENTS

The authors express their gratitude for an Eastman Kodak Research Fellowship (LES), for support from contributors to the University of Tennessee Polymer Consortium, and for support of a portion of the work from a Biomedical Sciences Support Grant through the General Research Support Branch of the National Institutes of Health. We also thank Union Carbide Corporation for certain of the thermal analyses.

VI. REFERENCES

1. J. H. Saunders and K. C. Frisch, "Polyurethanes, Chemistry and Technology," Vol. 1, Wiley-Interscience, New York, N. Y., 1962.

2. Fr. 961,754 to BASF, May 1950; CA 46, 6148i (1952).

3. B. L. Phillips and P. A. Argabright, J. Hetero. Chem. 3, 84 (1966).

4. R. Stoermer, Ber., 43, 3133 (1909).

5. M. Matzner, R. P. Kurkjy, and R. J. Cotter, Chem. Rev., 1964, 675.

6. E. Dyer and H. Scott, J. Amer. Chem. Soc., 79, 672 (1957).

7. E. K. Drechsel, U. S. 2,744,897 May, 1956; CA 51, 498 (1957).

8. K. Soga, S. Hosada, and S. Ikeda, Makromol. Chem., 175, 3309 (1974).

9. Y. Iwakura, K. Hayashi, and K. Iwata, Makromol. Chem., 89, 214 (1965).

10. Reference 1, Chapters 4 and 5.

11. H. Lindemann and W. Schultheis, Ann., 451, 241 (1926).

12. W. G. Bywater, W. R. Coleman, O. Kamm, and H. H. Merrit, J. Amer. Chem. Soc., 67, 905 (1945).

13. H. K. Hall and A. K. Schneider, J. Amer. Chem. Soc., 80, 6409 (1958).

14. G. Barger, J. Chem. Soc., 85, 286 (1904).

15. H. Lindemann and W. Schultheis, Ann., 464, 237 (1928).

16. S. E. Forman, C. A. Erickson, H. Adelman, J. Org. Chem., 28, 2653 (1963); E. Vowinkel and C. Wolff, Chem. Ber., 107, 907 (1974); Prism IR Spectrum 33178, Sadtler Standard Spectra, Sadtler Research Laboratories, Philadelphia, Pennsylvania.

17. G. H. Coleman and H. L. Johnson, "Organic Syntheses," Coll. Vol. III, pp. 60-62. Wiley-Interscience, New York, N. Y., 1953.

18. Fr. M 2933 to E. Merck A. G., Dec. 1964.

19. J. F. Kinstle and L. E. Sepulveda, ACS Polym. Prepr., 16 (1), 628 (1975).

20. G. Pifferi, L. Fontanella, E. Ocelli, R. Monguzzi, J. Hetero. Chem., 9, 1209 (1972).

21. R. Pschorr and H. Einbeck, Ber., 38, 2067 (1905).

22. H. Ulrich, Brit. 1,153,261, May 1969; U. S. 3,488,376; Fr. 1,554,979 to Upjohn Co.

23. Y. Iwakura, Chem. High Polym (Japan), 2, 305 (1945); CA 44, 5103 (1950).

24. C. F. H. Allen and E. W. Magder, J. Hetero. Chem., 6, 349 (1969).

CONTROLLABLE REACTIVITY EPOXY RESIN HARDENERS

Mark Markovitz
General Electric Company

Epoxy resin hardeners having a wide reactivity range were prepared from organometallic compounds plus a phenolic compound or a phenolic resin. It is possible to formulate epoxy resins with these hardeners having a working life stability of months at room temperature to resins which gel instantly by varying the phenolic compound or its content. The organometallic compounds used were organic titanates, metal acetylacetonates and bis(trialkyltin) oxides. While many epoxy resins are only reactive toward certain classes of hardeners, every epoxy resin tested was cured by these controllable reactivity hardeners. The cured resins were hard solids with excellent electrical properties at 25 to at least 170°C. High heat distortion temperatures were also obtained with many of these compositions.

I. INTRODUCTION

There are many epoxy resin hardeners currently in use (1). The most common types are the aromatic polyamines, aliphatic polyamines and their adducts, carboxylic acid anhydrides, polyamides and catalytic curing agents. Examples of the catalytic curing agents are tertiary amines, imidazoles, boron trifluoride-amine complexes, and dicyandiamide. These hardeners have many useful properties but each type has its limitations. The polyamines and polyamides are most reactive toward glycidyl ether epoxy resins, most amines can cause dermatitis and many are toxic; the cured products have poor electrical properties. Epoxy resins crosslinked with carboxylic acid anhydrided have good electrical and heat aging properties, but very long cure times and high cure temperatures are required to obtain these properties. The working life stability of epoxy-anhydride resins is usually less than one month at room temperature. Many anhydrides are difficult to work with because of their insolubility, volatility and odor. Anhydride cured epoxy resins are also susceptible to reversion under high humidity due to the hydrolyzable ester linkages. The catalytic curing agents are limited by their very high reactivity at the cure temperature and the poor high temperature electrical properties of the cured resins. The catalytic curing agents can only be used with certain epoxy resins, for example, BF_3-amine complexes cannot usually be used with cycloaliphatic epoxy resins because of uncontrollable exotherms even with small samples. There are many other hardeners available but each type can be used with only certain epoxy resins and the reactivity can be controlled over a narrow range only. For example, it is common to use less than the optimum stoichiometric quantity of an aliphatic polyamine in order to reduce the exotherm and increase the working life.

One advantage of unsaturated polyester resins over epoxy resins has been the ability to control reactivity by use of a mixture of peroxides, accelerators and inhibitors. This versatility is now possible with epoxy resins by using as hardener a combination of an organometallic compound plus a phenolic accelerator. Organic titanates, metal acetylacetonates and bis(trialkyltin) oxides can be used as the organometallic compound and a phenolic compound or a phenolic resin can be used as the accelerator.

The organometallic-phenolic hardeners have in addition to their controllable reactivity many other desirable properties. The electrical properties at ambient and elevated temperatures of the cured resins are excellent. Many of the resins have high heat distortion temperatures even after short cure schedules. The polyether structure of the cured resins is also expected to make these resins resist hydrolysis under high humidity.

II. RESULTS AND DISCUSSION

The properties of many combinations of epoxy resins and organometallic-phenolic hardeners were investigated. Reactivity, dissipation factor and heat distortion temperature of some of these resins will be discussed to demonstrate the versatility of these hardeners.

A. Reactivity

The organometallic compounds used were organic titanates, bis(tri-n-butyltin) oxide, and metal acetylacetonates because of their stability and ease of handling. With the quantity of phenolic used in the compositions that will be discussed, gelation and cure occurred only with the organometallic compound. The quantity or the functionality of the phenolic was not high enough to result in any significant crosslinking of the epoxy resin.

The reactivity of the epoxy-organometallic-phenolic compositions was related to the acidity of the phenolic, e.g., p-nitrophenol was much more effective than either phenol or p-cresol. Phenolic compounds capable of complexing (for example, catechol and o-hydroxybenzyl alcohol) were also very strong accelerators.

The gel times of the cycloaliphatic epoxy resin ERL 4221 containing 1.0 phr of tetraoctylene glycol titanate (TOGT) and 1.0 phr of different phenolic compounds were determined (TABLE 1).

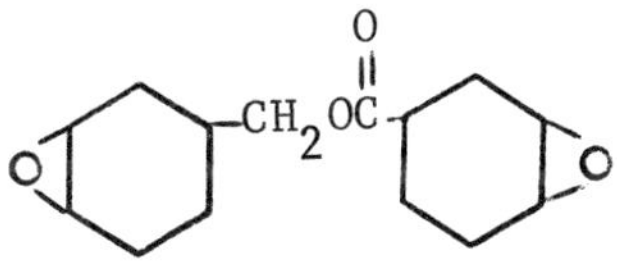

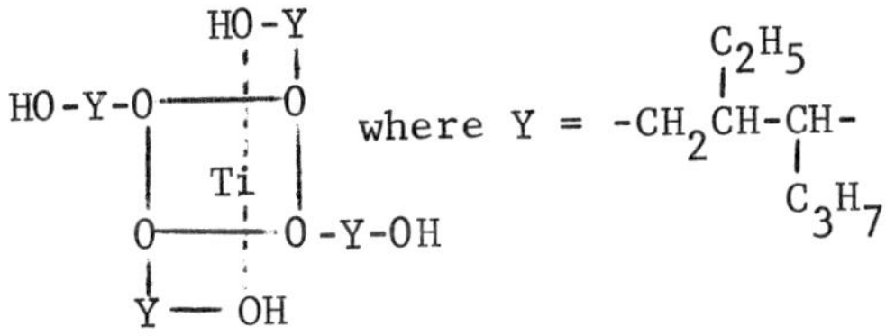

ERL 4221
Epoxide equiv. wt. 126-140
Union Carbide Corporation

Tetraoctylene glycol titanate (TOGT)

A control sample containing no phenolic compound had a gel time of > 3 hours @ 150°C. Addition of 1.0 phr of bisphenol A decreased the gel time to 60 minutes at 150°C while 1.0 phr of catechol caused the resin to exotherm and gel within 5 minutes at room temperature. Use of 1.0 phr of hydroquinone, resorcinol, salicylaldehyde and a phenol-formaldehyde resin BRRE 5833 reduced the gel time of the ERL 4221-TOGT resin to 35, 20, 15 and 10 min. @ 150°C, respectively.

TABLE 1

Reactivity of ERL 4221-TOGT Resins

ERL 4221	100	100	100	100	100	100	100
TOGT	1.0	1.0	1.0	1.0	1.0	1.0	1.0
Bisphenol A		1.0					
Hydroquinone			1.0				
Resorcinol				1.0			
Salicylaldehyde					1.0		
BRRE 5833						1.0	
Catechol							1.0
Gel time @ 150°C, min.	> 180	60	35	20	15	10	< 5 min. @ RT

The bisphenol A-diglycidyl ether epoxy resin Epon 828 (epoxide equivalent wt. 185-192) and 5.0 phr of TOGT did not gel even after 420 minutes at 160°C. Solutions of catechol in TOGT caused the resin to gel and cure with increasing reactivity as the catechol content was increased (TABLE 2). The resin containing 5.0 phr of a 50:50 catechol:TOGT solution exothermed and gelled after 40-45 minutes at room temperature.

TABLE 2

Reactivity of Epon 828-TOGT Resins

Epon 828	100	100	100	100	100
TOGT	5.0				
TOGT-Catechol (85:15)		5.0			
TOGT-Catechol (80:20)			5.0		
TOGT-Catechol (75:25)				5.0	
TOGT-Catechol (50:50)					5.0
Gel time @ 160°C, min.	> 420	60	30	10	< 5 (40-45 min @ RT)

Bis(tri-n-butyltin) oxide was also used as a hardener. When 1.0 phr of bis(tri-n-butyltin) oxide (TBTO) was used as a hardener for ERL 4221, no gelation occurred after 3 hours at 150°C.

$$(C_4H_9)_3Sn\text{-}O\text{-}Sn(C_4H_9)_3$$

Bis(tri-n-butyltin) oxide (TBTO)

b.p. 254°C @ 50 mm

Addition of only 1.0 phr of various phenolic compounds caused the resin to gel in < 5 min. to 50 min. @ 150°C depending on the phenolic compound used (TABLE 3).

TABLE 3

Reactivity of ERL 4221-TBTO Resins

ERL 4221	100	100	100	100	100
TBTO	1.0	1.0	1.0	1.0	1.0
Bisphenol A		1.0			
BRZ 7541 (1)			1.0		
BRRE 5833 (1)				1.0	
Catechol					1.0
Gel time @ 150°C, min.	> 180	50	35	20	< 5 (15 min. @ 100°C)

(1) BRZ 7541-phenol-formaldehyde resin, softening point 50°C
(2) BRRE 5833-phenol-formaldehyde resin, softening point 95-115°C

ERL 4221 containing 1.0 phr of aluminum acetylacetonate (AlAA) gelled after 4 hours at 160°C.

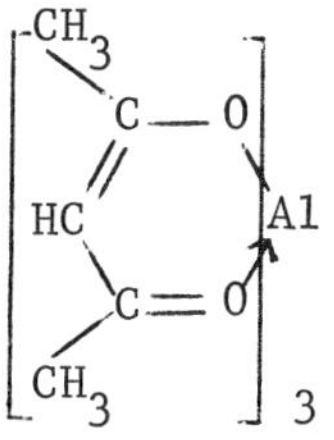

Aluminum acetylacetonate (AlAA)

Addition of 1.0 phr of bisphenol A decreased the gel time to 45 min. @ 160°C while 2.0 phr of bisphenol A decreased it to 20 minutes (TABLE 4). A violent exotherm occurred after 7 minutes at 160°C when 3.0 phr of the phenol-formaldehyde resin BRRE 5555 was used as an accelerator; the resin gelled to a clear hard solid after 15 minutes at 120°C. The gel time was only 5 minutes when 1.0 phr of catechol was added.

TABLE 4

Reactivity of ERL 4221-AlAA Resins

ERL 4221	100	100	100	100	100
AlAA	1.0	1.0	1.0	1.0	1.0
Bisphenol A		1.0	2.0		
BRRE 5555				3.0	
Catechol					1.0
Gel time @ 160 C, min.	240	45	20	7 (15 min. @ 120°C)	5

A resin made from 100 pbw of Epon 828 and 2.0 pbw of titanium acetylacetonate (TiAA) did not gel after more than 2 hours at 160°C.

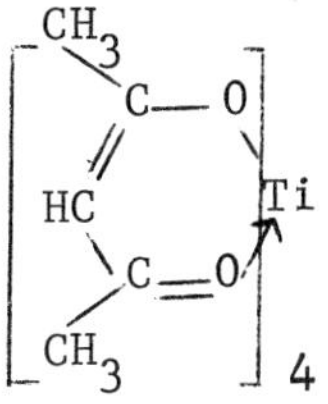

Titanium acetylacetonate (TiAA)

However, a resin made from 100 pbw of Epon 828, 2.0 pbw of TiAA and 1.0 pbw of catechol gelled after 7 minutes at 160°C.

B. Dissipation Factor (Tan Delta)

Dissipation factor (tan delta) is a measure of energy dissipated in an insulating material. Properties of dissipation factor versus temperature were determined for various epoxy resins crosslinked by TOGT-phenolic hardeners. The dissipation factor values were low at room temperature to at least 170°C for ERL 4221-TOGT-hydroquinone resins even after a relatively short cure of 5 hours at 150°C (TABLE 5).

TABLE 5

Dissipation Factor vs. Temperature

ERL 4221	100	100	100
TOGT	1.0	1.0	1.0
Hydroquinone	1.0	2.0	3.0

Cure: 5 hours @ 150°C

Temperature, °C	Dissipation Factor (60 Hz., 10 VPM)		
25	0.0036	0.0041	0.0053
75	0.0086	0.0097	0.0158
100	0.0118	0.0159	0.0199
125	0.0141	0.0152	0.0161
155	0.0167	0.0176	0.0188
170	0.0168	0.0175	0.0189

Dissipation factor at room temperature, 100, 155 and 170°C were determined for the bisphenol A-diglycidyl ether resin Epon 828 crosslinked by 10.0 phr of various hardeners. The hardeners were solutions of the phenol-formaldehyde resin BRZ 7541 in TOGT. The dissipation factor values were not affected by the TOGT:BRZ 7541 ratio used as the hardener (TABLE 6).

TABLE 6

Dissipation Factor vs. Temperature

Epon 828	100	100	100
TOGT-BRZ 7541(30:70)	10.0		
TOGT-BRZ 7541(40:60)		10.0	
TOGT-BRZ 7541(50:50)			10.0

Cure: 10 hours @ 150°C

Temperature, °C	Dissipation Factor (60 Hz., 10 VPM)		
25	0.0017	0.0026	0.0016
100	0.0062	0.0114	0.0211
155	0.0167	0.0129	0.0121
170	0.0133	0.0102	0.0117

The cycloaliphatic epoxy resin ERL 4221 was crosslinked using aluminum acetylacetonate plus catechol as the hardener. The samples were cured 2 hours at 160°C. Low dissipation factor values resulted at room temperature to 160°C (TABLE 7). The dissipation factor values were not significantly affected by either the AlAA or the catechol content.

TABLE 7

Dissipation Factor vs. Temperature

ERL 4221	100	100	100	100	100	100
AlAA	1.0	1.0	1.0	2.0	2.0	2.0
Catechol	0.5	1.0	2.0	0.5	1.0	2.0
Cure: 2 hours @ 160°C						
Temperature, °C	Dissipation Factor (60 Hz., 10 VPM)					
25	0.0050	0.0052	0.0052	0.0058	0.0055	0.0059
100	0.0163	0.0167	0.0165	0.0134	0.0131	0.0137
150	0.0294	0.0309	0.0305	0.0256	0.0262	0.0266
160	0.0293	0.0304	0.0299	0.0276	0.0280	0.0280

Dissipation factor at 25 to 160°C was determined for ERL 4221 containing 3.0 phr of the phenol-formaldehyde resin BRRE 5555 and 0.5 to 3.0 phr of bis(tri-n-butyltin) oxide. The samples were cured 45 minutes @ 140°C + 4 hours @ 160°C. The dissipation factor values were $\leq$ 0.02 @ 25-160°C (TABLE 8). The dissipation factor values were similar although the TBTO content was varied by a factor as high as 6.

TABLE 8

Dissipation Factor vs. Temperature

ERL 4221	100	100	100	100
TBTO	0.5	1.0	2.0	3.0
BRRE 5555	3.0	3.0	3.0	3.0
Cure: 45 min. @ 140°C + 4 hrs. @ 160°C				
Temperature, °C	Dissipation Factor (60 Hz., 10 VPM)			
25	0.0050	0.0050	0.0050	0.0050
100	0.0116	0.0108	0.0108	0.0106
150	0.0189	0.0179	0.0172	0.0174
160	0.0190	0.0188	0.0183	0.0178

C. Heat Distortion Temperature

Heat deflection temperatures were determined using 5" x ½" x ½" samples that were subjected to a 264 psi stress at the center of their span. ASTM test method D648 was used. This test measures the temperature at which the loaded beam sample deflects 10 mils when immersed in an oil bath thermostatically regulated to provide a temperature rise of 2°C per minute.

ERL 4221 was crosslinked by a 1:1 solution of tetraoctyleneglycol titanate and the phenol-formaldehyde resin BRZ 7541. The samples were cured 5 hours at 150°C. The heat distortion temperatures were similar for resins containing 1.0 to 10.0 phr of the hardener (TABLE 9).

TABLE 9

Heat Distortion Temperature @ 264 psi

ERL 4221	100	100	100	100	100
TOGT-BRZ 7541(50:50)	1.0	2.5	5.0	7.5	10.0

Cure: 5 hours @ 150°C

Mils Deflection	Temperature, °C				
1	131	125	137	136	126
5	152	121	158	156	152
10 (HDT)	164	162	167	166	164

A solution was made from 20 pbw of TOGT and 80 pbw of BRZ 7541 by heating and stirring at 50-80°C. The heat distortion temperatures of resins made from DEN 438 catalyzed with 12.5 to 17.5 pbw of this hardener were 170-172°C (TABLE 10). DEN 438 is an epoxy novolac with an epoxide functionality of 3.6 and an epoxide equivalent weight of 175-182.

TABLE 10

Heat Distortion Temperature @ 264 psi

DEN 438	100	100	100
TOGT-BRZ 7541(20:80)	12.5	15.0	17.5

Cure: 15 hrs. @ 160°C

Mils Deflection	Temperature, °C		
1	136	142	137
5	159	162	160
10 (HDT)	170	172	171

Aluminum acetylacetonate and catechol were used to cure ERL 4221. High heat distortion temperatures resulted after only a 2 hours at 160°C cure. The heat distortion temperatures were 5 to 10 degrees higher when the AlAA content was increased from 1.0 to 2.0 phr (TABLE 11).

TABLE 11

Heat Distortion Temperature @ 264 psi

ERL 4221	100	100	100	100	100	100
AlAA	1.0	1.0	1.0	2.0	2.0	2.0
Catechol	0.5	1.0	2.0	0.5	1.0	2.0

Cure: 2 hours @ 160°C

Mils Deflection	Temperature, °C					
1	122	118	112	124	128	115
5	139	134	135	146	144	139
10 (HDT)	148	145	145	158	153	150

Heat distortion temperatures were also determined for ERL 4221 cured with bis(tri-n-butyltin) oxide and catechol. The catechol content was kept constant at 1.0 phr, while the TBTO content was varied from 0.10 to 2.0 phr. The heat distortion temperatures were within the 171-179°C range (TABLE 12).

TABLE 12

Heat Distortion Temperature @ 264 psi

ERL 4221	100	100	100	100	100	100	100
TBTO	1.0	1.0	1.0	1.0	1.0	1.0	1.0
Catechol	0.10	0.20	0.30	0.40	0.50	1.0	2.0

Cure: 1 hr. @ 100°C + 1 hr. @ 140°C + 4 hrs. @ 160°C

Mils Deflection	Temperature, °C						
1	135	123	139	123	132	145	141
5	162	155	168	163	168	169	162
10 (HDT)	173	171	176	178	179	179	173

III. CONCLUSIONS

Epoxy resins can be cured using a combination of an organometallic catalyst (organic titanates, metal acetylacetonates, bis-trialkyltin oxides) and a phenolic accelerator. The reactivity of these resins can be controlled over a wide range by varying the phenolic compound or the phenolic compound content. While many epoxy resins are only reactive toward certain types of hardeners, every epoxy resin tested was cured by some combination of an organometallic catalyst and a phenolic accelerator.

The cured resins had excellent electrical properties at 25°C to at least 170°C. High heat distortion temperatures resulted after relatively short cure schedules.

The polyether structure of the cured resins is expected to make these resins more stable to hydrolysis under high humidity than acid anhydride cured epoxy resins.

IV. REFERENCES

1. H. Lee and K. Neville, "Handbook of Epoxy Resins", McGraw-Hill, New York, 1967.

FUNCTIONALIZATION OF CROSSLINKED POLYSTYRENE RESINS BY CHEMICAL MODIFICATION: A REVIEW

Jean M.J. Fréchet and M. Jean Farrall
University of Ottawa

Functionalized crosslinked polystyrene resins have received much attention recently due to their numerous possible applications in chemistry and biochemistry. Three types of insoluble polymers with various degrees of crosslinking and different physical properties are used frequently as starting materials in the functionalization reactions; these are popcorn polymers, solvent swellable beads and macroreticular beads. The reactions used in the chemical modification of these polymers are reviewed with emphasis on those reactions which introduce versatile, easily transformed functional groups which may serve to anchor the more specific functionalities of many special use resins. The following reactions of crosslinked polystyrene resins are reviewed: halogenation, chloromethylation, metalation, formylation, acylation, carboxylation, phosphination, nitration, amination and the introduction of hydroxyl, anhydride and sulfur containing functional groups. Finally, the analytical problems encountered in the characterization of the functionalized resins are reviewed.

A number of novel applications of functionalized polystyrene resins have been reported since the first polymeric reagents, ion exchange resins, were prepared some thirty years ago. Thus, functionalized polystyrene resins, in addition to their use as ion exchangers, are now used extensively as supports in solid phase synthesis(1-3); reagents(4) or protecting groups(5) in organic synthesis, supports for chromatography or catalysis(2,6,7), complexing agents for hydrometallurgy, etc.

Although functionalized polystyrene resins can also be prepared by direct copolymerization of appropriate monomers, this review will only concern itself with some reactions which are useful for the introduction of functional groups on pre-formed crosslinked polystyrene resins. These reactions are generally similar to those which are used in the functionalization of soluble polystyrene but they are often more difficult to carry out due to the insolubility of the resin, the presence of surface impurities which remain from the suspending and stabilizing agents used in the emulsion polymerization process; and the difficult characterization of the insoluble products.

I. PHYSICAL NATURE OF THE CROSSLINKED POLYMERS

The physical nature of the copolymers has a great importance both for the introduction of the functional groups and for the eventual application of the functionalized polymer. In general, the degree of crosslinking determines the solubility, extent of swelling, pore size, and mechanical stability of the polymer. The polystyrene resins which are used most often in the applications listed above are spherical beads which are obtained by emulsion polymerization of styrene divinylbenzene mixtures. The degree of crosslinking of these polymers is generally expressed as the initial percentage of DVB in the mixture of monomers.

A. Solvent Swellable Resin Beads

Solvent swellable resin beads usually contain 1 to 5% of crosslinks. Their degree of swelling is inversely proportional to their degree of crosslinking. Typically, 1g of a 1% crosslinked polymer will swell to occupy a volume of 10ml in benzene while in the same solvent 1g of a 5% crosslinked polymer will only swell to occupy 4ml. Good swelling solvents include halogenated hydrocarbons such as dichloromethane, chloroform and carbon tetrachloride; aromatics such as benzene, toluene or pyridine; and cyclic ethers such as tetrahydrofuran or dioxane. Swelling of the resin beads is very important as it brings the polymer to a state of complete solvation and thus allows easy penetration of the network by the molecules of reagent. The degree of swelling of the polymer determines the effective pore size and the molecular weight exclusion limit for penetration of the reagents. It is possible to cause a reaction to occur at a fraction of the available sites by control of the swelling of the polymers. However, such reactions on partially swollen resins give functional polymers in which the reactive sites are not distributed evenly throughout the bead but concentrated in the more accessible sites only.

Reactions in swollen 1 or 2% crosslinked polymer beads resemble those in dilute gels since the rates of reaction are of the same order of magnitude as those of reactions in solution(8). More highly crosslinked beads suffer from less complete and slower reactions probably due to hindered diffusion of the reagents through the polymer beads.

B. Rigid Macroporous or Macroreticular Beads

An alternative to swelling the polymer beads to make reactive sites available is to increase the surface to volume ratio of the dry bead to decrease the importance of diffusion into the gel matrix. Thus, macroporous or macroreticular resins are rigid highly crosslinked copolymers containing large pores. These polymers have an effective surface area several hundred times larger than that of suspension polymers. Their use is facilitated by a wider choice of solvents since no swelling is required. In addition the macroporous or macroreticular beads are ideally suited for applications involving stationery resin beds or columns since usually no large change in volume is observed during their use. However, these resins usually react slower or to a lesser extent than their swellable counterparts and difficulties may arise due to the easy fragmentation of the resin beads during handling (5,9).

C. Popcorn Polymers

Low density popcorn polymers, which typically contain only 0.1 - 0.5% of crosslinks, do not swell in any solvent and are easily penetrated by small molecules. Best results with popcorn polymers are obtained when the polymers are finely divided. Popcorn polymers have a reactivity comparable to that of solvent swellable beads but are often more difficult to handle.

II. FUNCTIONALIZATION BY CHEMICAL MODIFICATION

A. Removal of Surface Impurities From the Polymer Beads

The use of styrene-divinylbenzene beads in chemical reactions is often complicated by the presence of surface impurities which remain from the emulsion polymerization process. These impurities are usually traces of suspending or stabilizing agents such as hydrated colloidal alumina. Removal of most of these impurities is necessary if the functionalization of the polymer is to succeed since the surface contaminants can prevent the penetration of reagents into the swollen beads. This is particularly true with organometallic reagents which might form an ionic layer at the surface of the bead(10,11). In other cases, reaction is possible but more drastic reaction conditions are needed than would be required for a pure polymer; a classical example is that of the sulfonation of crosslinked polystyrene for which a high "penetration temperature" is required. Typical washing procedures(3,10,11) include steam distillation to remove excess monomers and aromatic impurities, repeated washing with acidic and basic solutions followed by extractions with various organic solvents. Macroreticular resins having a much larger surface area are often less affected by surface impurities and react somewhat better than unwashed solvent swellable resins.

B. Halogenation

I. Bromination

Several methods have been developed for the bromination of crosslinked polystyrene. In most cases the reactions used were catalytic brominations using bromine and ferric chloride (11,12), iodine(3), iron powder(13), pyridine(14), mercuric acetate(14), or thallium III salts(11). Other recents preparations used stoichiometric amounts of thallium III acetate (15) or boron trifluoride(10) for the bromination.

a. *With ferric chloride as catalyst.* The catalytic bromination with ferric chloride in carbon tetrachloride was developed by Heitz and Michels(12) who obtained polymers containing from 2.2 to 3.9 mequiv of bromine per gram of polymer. This reaction has been used by a number of other workers some of whom reported unreproducible results or highly colored products lacking homogeneity. Our experience (11) with the ferric chloride catalyzed reaction confirmed these reports but also indicated that the reaction can be carried out satisfactorily to give an homogeneous product by refluxing briefly in the dark a suspension of the polymer in carbon tetrachloride containing the desired amount of bromine. The degree of functionalization can be controlled easily[1] by adjusting the molar ratio bromine/polymer, although an excess of bromine is usually required to obtain a degree of

1. However, results of duplicate experiments were only reproducible within 10-20%.

functionalization[2] in the range 0.9 to 1.

b. With thallium III salts in stoichiometric amount. The bromination of crosslinked polystyrene in the presence of a stoichiometric amount of thallium III acetate was introduced by Camps and Coworkers(15,16) who prepared polymers containing approximately 1 mequiv. of bromine per gram. This procedure which yield a very homogeneous polymer, visually cleaner than that obtained by the ferric chloride catalyzed reaction, was also used by Crosby, Weinshenker, Uh and Wong (17,18) to prepare polymers with a higher degree of functionalization. The reaction itself is patterned after the aromatic thallation-halogeneration method developed by Taylor and McKillop(19); it is believed to be a two-step reaction involving the formation of an arylthallium derivative which, by reaction with bromine, gives exclusively the para substituted bromide. A major drawback of this otherwise excellent procedure is that an elaborate washing of the brominated resin is required to remove the large amount of highly toxic and sparingly soluble thallium salts which are produced in the reaction. Another obvious disadvantage is the high cost of the thallic acetate which is needed for the bromination.

c. With thallium III salts in catalytic amount. We have recently reinvestigated the bromination with bromine and thallium salts and found that only a catalytic amount of thallium acetate was required(11). The degree of functionalization which was independent of the amount of thallic acetate used, could be controlled easily by regulating the amount of bromine used. Washing of the brominated resin after reaction did not present any difficulty since only a small amount of thallium salt was present in the reaction mixture. Another useful catalyst for this reaction was thallic chloride which gave results comparable to those obtained for thallic acetate.

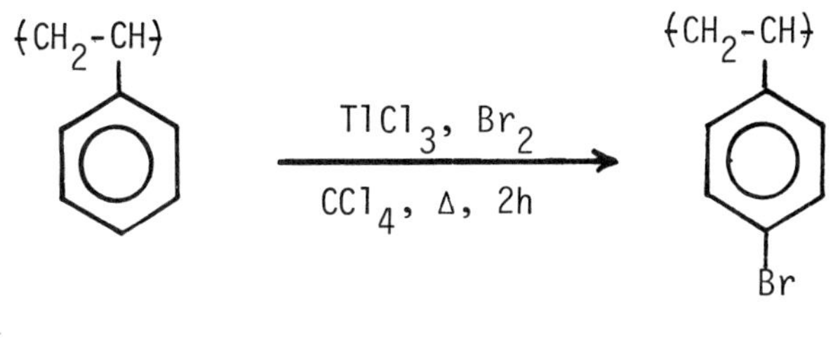

---

2. The degree of functionalization represents the fraction of styrene residues which carry the desired functional group.

In every case the brominated polymers obtained were homogeneous and almost colorless.

d. Other methods. A brominated resin with a degree of functionalization of 0.9 has been prepared recently by Relles & Schluenz(10) using polystyrene beads, boron trifluoride and bromine in molar ratio of 1:1:2 in nitrobenzene. This method has not been tested in the preparation of resins with lower degrees of functionalization. Another bromination procedure developped by Pittman and Hanes(13) involved the reaction of polystyrene beads with bromine in carbon disulfide in the presence of iron powder. Brominated polymers with degrees of functionalization of 0.05 to 0.3 were obtained by this procedure. We have also tested the bromination of crosslinked polystyrene using zinc chloride in tetrahydrofuran or stannic chloride in carbon tetrachloride as catalysts(11). These catalytic brominations only produce brominated polymers with a low degree of functionalization and the results of the bromination were not as predictable as those obtained in the thallium salt catalyzed reactions.

2. Iodination

Few methods are available for the iodination of crosslinked polystyrene. Unlike the bromination, the iodination in the presence of thallium III salts is not a catalytic process. We have observed(11) that a stoichiometric amount of thallium trifluoroacetate is required for the reaction and thus the degree of functionalization is dependent on the amount of thallium salt and not the amount of iodine. This method is not satisfactory for large scale preparations due to the high cost of the thallium trifluoracetate and the extensive washing which is required to remove the thallium iodide after reaction. Another procedure developped by Yamada and Okawara (20) for the preparation of polymeric iodonium salts involves the reaction of the polystyrene resin swollen in nitrobenzene with a mixture of iodine, iodine pentoxide and sulfuric acid at 90° for 50 hours. This procedure affords a polymer with a degree of functionalization of 0.33. However, control of the degree of functionalization is probably difficult to achieve using this method.

C. Chloromethylation

1. Procedures for the preparation of chloromethylated crosslinked polystyrene. The chloromethylation of crosslinked polystyrene, a key reaction in the synthesis of anion exchange resins, has been studied extensively. Two main routes have been explored and are the object of a number of patents. The chloromethylation can be accomplished by reaction of the styrene-divinylbenzene copolymer with paraformaldehyde and hydrogen chloride(21) or by reaction of the copolymer with chloromethyl methyl ether in the presence of a catalyst such as $AlCl_3$ or $ZnCl_2$(21,22). An extensive study of the chloromethylation of crosslinked polystyrene was published in 1953 by Pepper, Paisley, and Young who used the Friedel-Crafts alkylation with chloromethyl methyl ether in the presence of stannic chloride(23). The reaction is accompanied by methylene bridging which usually increases the degree of crosslinking of the polymer. Thus, methylene bridging can account for up to 80% of the nominal crosslinking of numerous commercial anion exchange resins prepared from chloromethylated polymers. In general a very pure grade of chloromethyl methyl ether and of Friedel-Crafts catalyst should be used if extensive methylene bridging is not desired. Our experience with this reaction (J.M.J. Fréchet, unpublished results) indicates that the reaction is easier to control and methylene bridging is reduced when the reaction is carried out in a mixture of chloroform or carbon tetrachloride and chloromethyl methyl ether. These solvents mixtures allow for maximum swelling of the polymer and thus reduce bridging since a fully swollen matrix reacts faster with chloromethyl methyl ether and is less prone to intramolecular reactions. The degree of functionalization is a function of the catalyst concentration, reaction time and temperature.

A new procedure for the chloromethylation was described recently by Merrifield(24). The procedure which uses chloromethyl methyl ether with zinc chloride in tetrahydrofuran affords a polymer with a very low degree of functionalization which is particularly well suited for use in the solid phase synthesis of some peptides. Another recent procedure developed by Sparrow(25) affords a good control of the degree of functionalization through the use of varying amount of boron trifluoride etherate and is useful in applications where capacities of less than 1 mequiv. per gram are required.

2. *Selected applications of the chloromethylated crosslinked polystyrene resins.* Chloromethylated polystyrene resins have been used extensively in the preparation of resins carrying various functionalities. One of the most important application, the preparation of anion exchange resins is discussed briefly in paragraph J of this review. Another very important application of chloromethylated crosslinked polystyrene was conceived by Merrifield(3,29) who used this polymer as solid support in the solid phase synthesis of polypeptides. This method has been used extensively and has led to the rapid synthesis of molecules as complex as ribonuclease(28). Other applications in the field of polymer supported catalysts have

followed two routes. The first one consisted of the phosphination of the chloromethylated resin followed by attachment of a catalyst such as the Wilkinson hydrogenation catalyst(26).

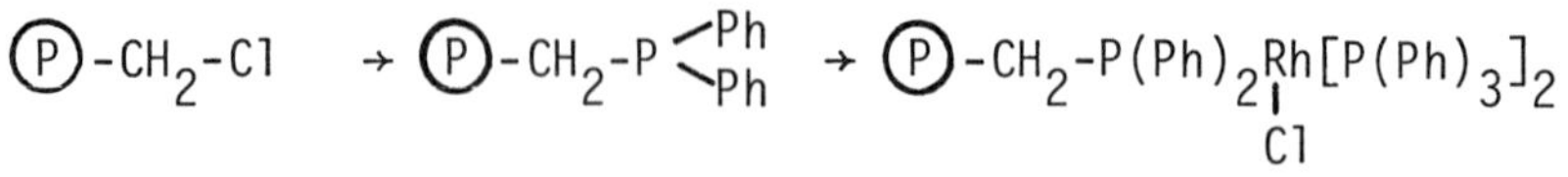

This catalyst which could be reused repeatedly was used in the selective hydrogenation of small alkenes. Numerous other polymer supported catalysts have been prepared using a similar route by Pittman and coworkers(13). The second route, in the field of polymer supported catalysts, was also explored by Grubbs and coworkers(27) and is shown below.

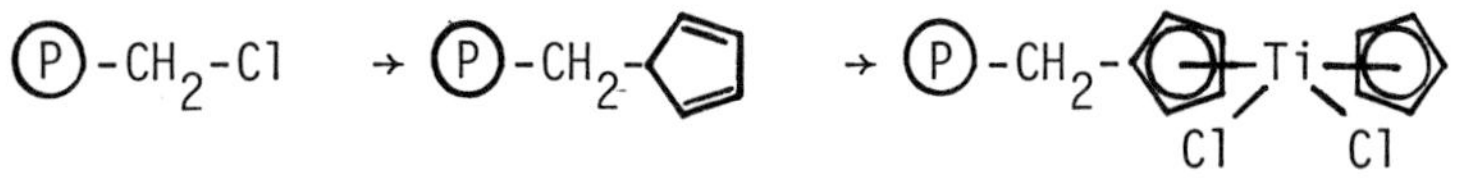

The polymer bound titanocene dichloride was used in the catalytic hydrogenation of alkenes and alkynes.

Numerous other applications of chloromethylated crosslinked polystyrene are found in the journal and patent literature; a number of these are shown in Table 1.

D. Lithiation

The methods used in the lithiation of crosslinked polystyrene resins are usually adapted from those which were developed for the preparation of soluble polystyryllithium. The lithiation of soluble polystyrene has been studied extensively by Braun(30-32) who used the reaction of a soluble ring-halogenated polystyrene with an excess of n-butyllithium. A second method developed by Chalk(33) involved the direct lithiation of soluble polystyrene by reaction with a 1:1 mixture of n-butyllithium and N,N,N',N'-tetramethylethylenediamine. This second procedure yielded polymers in which both para and meta lithiation had occured in a ratio of 1:2 (34).

A number of workers have used the procedure of Braun to prepare crosslinked polystyryllithium from the corresponding brominated or iodinated polymer(11,14-18,35). We have completed recently a thorough study of this reaction(11) and found that the results obtained varied considerably depending on the type of polymer used, its bromine content and the

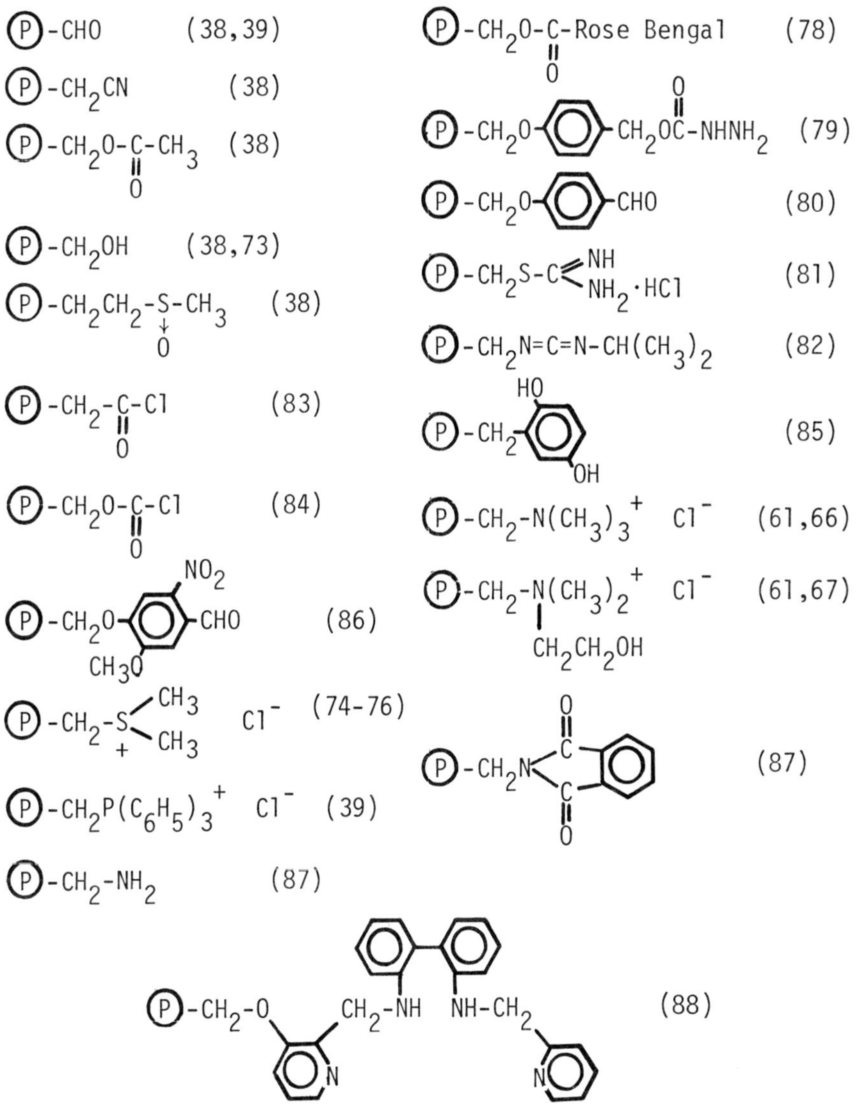

TABLE I. Selected functionalized crosslinked polystyrene resins prepared from chloromethylated polystyrene; reference to the original literature is given in parenthesis.

Ⓟ-COOH	(11,36)	Ⓟ-CHO	(11)
Ⓟ-SH	(11)	Ⓟ-$P(C_6H_5)_2$	(10,11,13, 16,46-49)
Ⓟ-SCH_3	(11,17)	Ⓟ-$Si(CH_3)_2$-Cl	(11)
Ⓟ-CH_2CH_2Br	(11)	Ⓟ-$C(C_6H_5)_2$-OH	(11,36)
Ⓟ-CH_2CH_2OH	(11)	Ⓟ-$C(C_6H_5)(Cl)$-C_6H_4-OCH_3	(35)
Ⓟ-C(=O)-NH-C_6H_5	(11)	Ⓟ-$B(OH)_2$	(11,14,89)
Ⓟ-$Sn(Bu)_2$-Cl	(37)		
Ⓟ-SnH_2-Bu	(18)		
Ⓟ-MgBr	(17)		

TABLE II. Selected functionalized crosslinked polystyrene resins prepared from polystyryllithium; reference to the original literature is given in parenthesis.

solvent used for the lithiation. Thus, while a solvent-swellable resin with a high bromine content could be lithiated completely by a single treatment with an excess of n-butyllithium in benzene or toluene, only a fraction of the functional groups were lithiated when the reaction was carried out in tetrahydrofuran, and several successive reactions with intermediate quenching were required to effect complete removal of the bromine. Presumably this difference in behavior was due to ionic replusions which, in the more polar solvent, limit the accessibility and cause the reaction to stop once a certain number of the functional groups have reacted with n-butyllithium. In contrast complete removal of the bromine from a brominated macroreticular resin could be done in tetrahydrofuran without intermediate quenching of the partially lithiated resin. It should be noted however that the lithiation of a macroreticular resin was also easier to accomplish in a non-polar solvent such as benzene or cyclohexane.

The direct metalation of crosslinked polystyrene by reaction with a complex of n-butyllithium and N,N,N',N'-tetramethylethylenediamine has been reported by Leznoff(36). This procedure which required a reaction time of 1-2 days at 60° gave lithiated resins which, after quenching with carbon dioxide, contained up to 0.9 mequiv. of functional group per gram (this corresponds to a degree of functionalization of 0.1) in the case of solvent swellable 2% crosslinked polystyrene, and up to 1.5 mequiv. per gram in the case of a macroreticular resin. We have also investigated the direct lithiation of a 1% crosslinked solvent swellable resin with the aim of improving the degree of functionalization(11). Our results showed that the degree of functionalization was independent of the molar ratio TMEDA/n-Buli and that resins containing at least 2 mequiv. of functional group per gram could be obtained easily. This functionalization which was measured after quenching with carbon dioxide corresponds to the introduction of carboxyl groups on 23% of the aromatic rings of the resin. Presumably the limiting factor in the functionalization was the swelling of the polymer matrix; thus, cyclohexane is unable to swell the resin and only the most accessible sites can react with the bulky TMEDA-n-Buli complex. We have also tested(11) the direct lithiation of solvent swellable crosslinked polystyrene with a mixture of triethylenediamine and n-butyllithium and found that the reaction was more sluggish than that with TMEDA but could be used to prepare lithiated resins containing more than 1 mequiv. of functional group per gram.[3]

A comparison of the bromination-lithiation vs direct lithiation, shows that the direct lithiation is advantageous for its rapidity and is best suited for applications in which the position of substitution on the aromatic ring is unimportant (meta substitution is favored). The two step bromination-lithiation procedure affords a better control of the position of substitution and the degree of functionalization since both of these are controlled by the bromination step. In addition, a higher degree of functionalization and a more even distribution of the functional groups on the polymer matrix can be achieved with the bromination lithiation procedure.

---

3. Presumably the reaction with triethylene diamine-n-BuLi also gave resins which were lithiated in both meta and para positions.

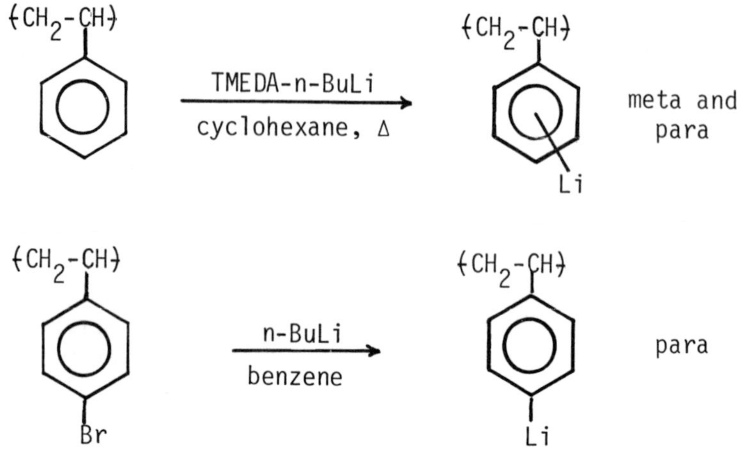

Two other procedures can be used for the metalation of crosslinked polystyrene; one is the reaction of a brominated resin with sodium or lithium naphtalide (J.M.J. Fréchet and M.J. Farrall unpublished results) and the other is a mercuration of the resin with mercuric trifluoroacetate followed by conversion to the corresponding polymer bound mercuric chloride, and finally, reaction with n-butyllithium(37).

The lithiated crosslinked polystyrene resins are important intermediates in the preparation of various functional resins. Selected applications are shown in Table II.

E. Formylation

The procedure which is most commonly used for the formylation of crosslinked polystyrene involves the oxydation of a chloromethylated resin with dimethylsulfoxide in the presence of an acid acceptor at 155°(38-40).

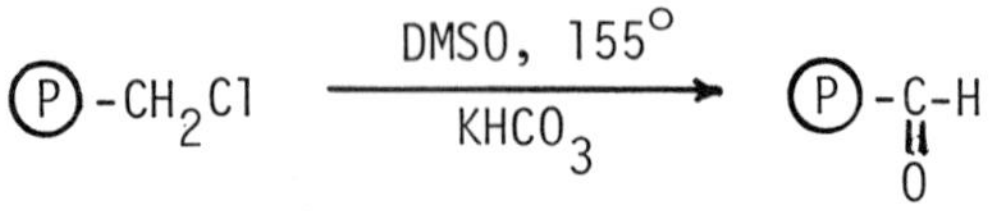

The reaction is carried out in pure DMSO which also acts as swelling agent. With 1-2% crosslinked solvent swellable resins the reaction is complete in 3-4 hours while longer reaction times are required with macroreticular polymers(9). Estimation of the degree of functionalization is possible through the preparation of an oxime derivative or by infrared spectroscopy using a polystyrene blank in the reference beam of the infrared spectrometer, these methods are described in more detail in part 3 of this chapter.

Another useful method for the formylation of crosslinked polystyrene involves the reaction of a lithiated resin with an excess of dimethylformamide(11). This method has been used successfully both with solvent swellable and macroreticular resins and it has the advantage of avoiding the chloromethylation step which usually requires the use of highly carcinogenic reagents.

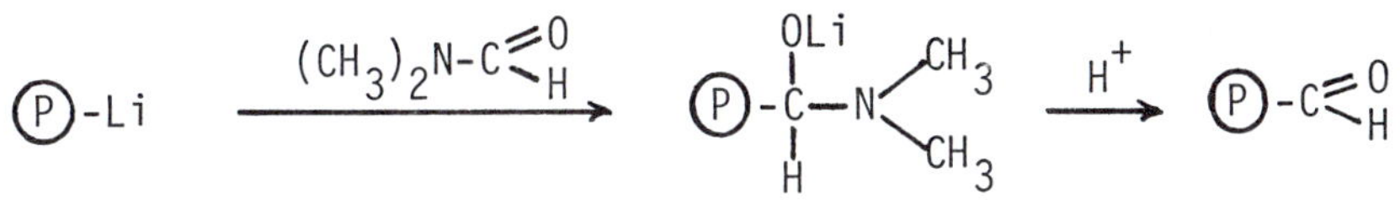

F. Acylation and Carboxylation

The Friedel-Crafts acylation of crosslinked polystyrene is usually carried out in nitrobenzene(40-41) or in carbon disulfide(9,40) with aluminium chloride catalyst. In the case of popcorn polymers, the reaction in carbon disulfide has been reported to yield a partially soluble glassy polymer (40) while nitrobenzene afforded better results. However, with more highly crosslinked polymers the reaction in carbon disulfide was preferred(9) as it led to a product which was visually cleaner and required a less extensive work up than that obtained in nitrobenzene. Acetylated resins prepared by Friedel-Crafts reactions have been used in the preparation of resins carring carboxylic acid(9,40,41), peracid(9), acid chloride(9,41) and other functional groups. A resin prepared by benzoylation of crosslinked polystyrene was used in the preparation of a polymeric reagent containing trityl chloride functional groups(42).

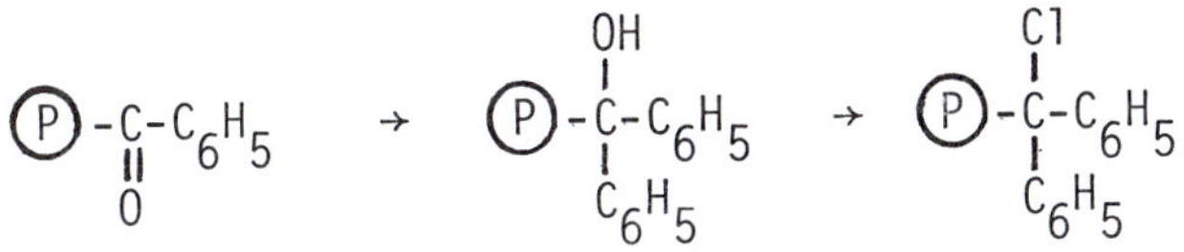

Another useful procedure for the acylation of crosslinked polystyrene (J.M.J. Fréchet, unpublished results) involves the reaction of a lithiated resin with an excess of an acyl halide. Best results are obtained by adding the resin suspended in dry THF to the acid halide.

Several methods are available for the carboxylation of crosslinked polystyrene resins. Letsinger and coworkers prepared a popcorn polymer containing 0.33 mequiv. of carboxylic acid per gram by hydrolysis of a carboxamido resin obtained by Friedel-Crafts reaction of diphenylcarbamyl chloride with a popcorn polystyrene(40).

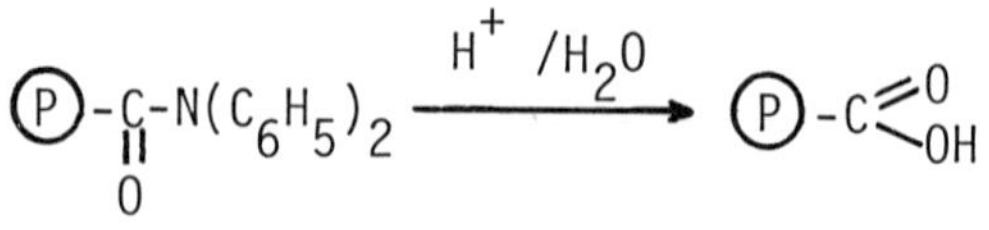

The same group also prepared carboxylated popcorn(40) and solvent swellable resins(41) via a Friedel-Crafts acetylation followed by oxidation with hypobromite. The popcorn polymer prepared by this method contained 0.74 mequiv. COOH per gram while the solvent swellable beads contained 1.5 mequiv. COOH per gram. A macroreticular resin has also been carboxylated by this method(9).

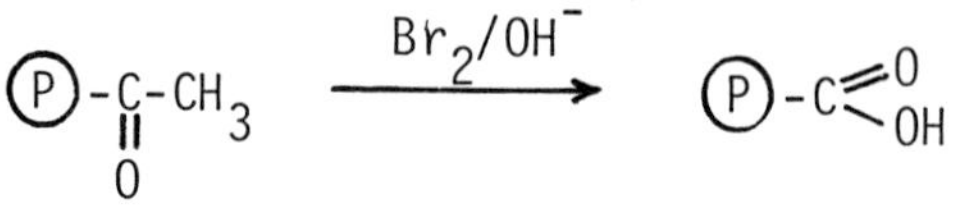

Carboxylated polystyrene can also be obtained by oxydation of a formylated resin using sodium or potassium dichromate in acetic acid(9,38)

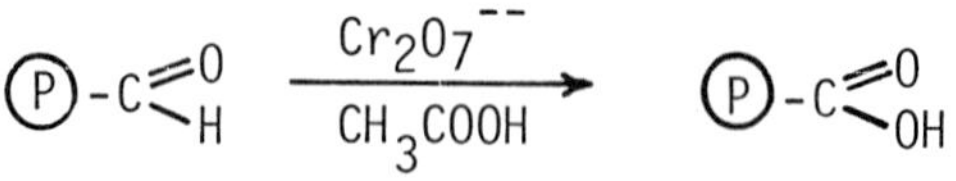

The reaction of organolithium compounds with carbon dioxide is a valuable general method for the preparation of carboxylic acids. It has been determined(43) that a large excess of carbon dioxide must be present throughout the reaction to avoid the formation of side products such as ketones or tertiary alcohols. This is particularly true in the case of the reaction with a solid lithiated resin since the reaction is controlled by the diffusion of carbon dioxide through the pores of the resin. Yields of 90% and over can be obtained by reaction of the lithiated resin with a slurry of dry ice in THF(11) while lower yields are obtained when gaseous carbon dioxide is bubbled through a suspension ot the lithiated resin (see for example ref. 36).

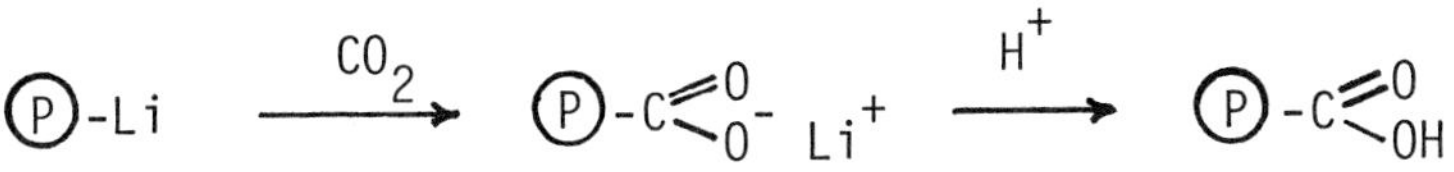

In a related area, the following reactions have been used to introduce side chains containing a carboxylic acid group on crosslinked polystyrene resins (38,39,65)

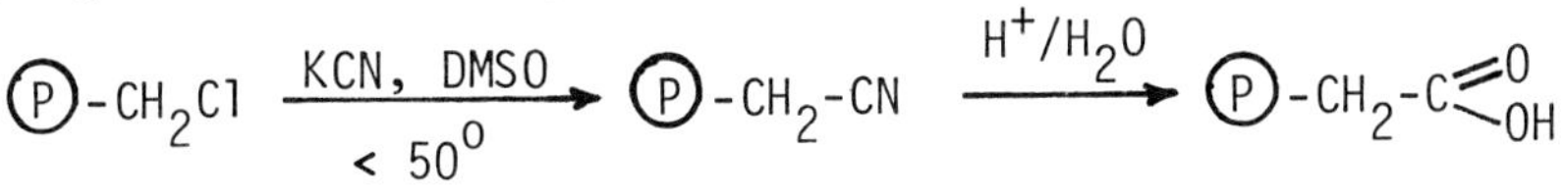

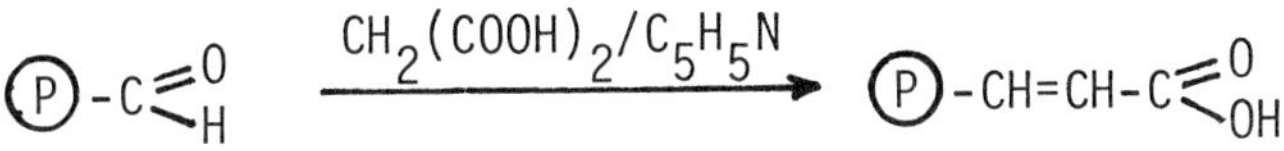

G. Phosphination

The introduction of phosphine groups on crosslinked polystyrene resins or on their chloromethylated derivatives has received much attention since Haag and Whitehurst (44) prepared the first polymer bound catalysts using resins containing phosphine groups (45). Phosphine groups can be introduced on crosslinked polystyrene resins by reaction of a brominated resin with lithium or sodium diphenylphosphonide (10,13,46,47)

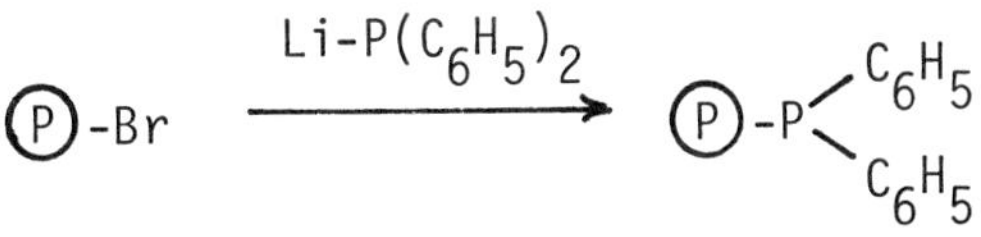

or by reaction of a lithiated resin with chlorodiphenylphosphine (11,16,48,49).

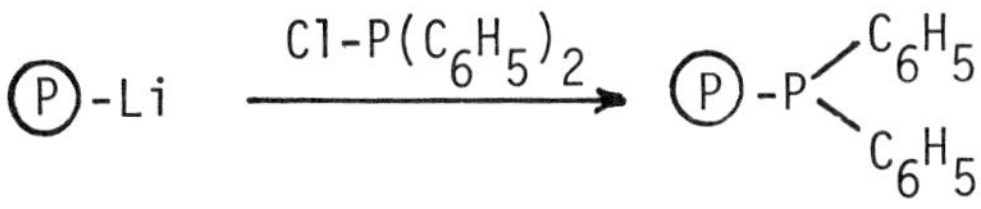

Similarly, phosphine groups can be introduced onto chloromethylated resins by reaction with lithium or sodium diphenylphosphonide (10,26,50,54)

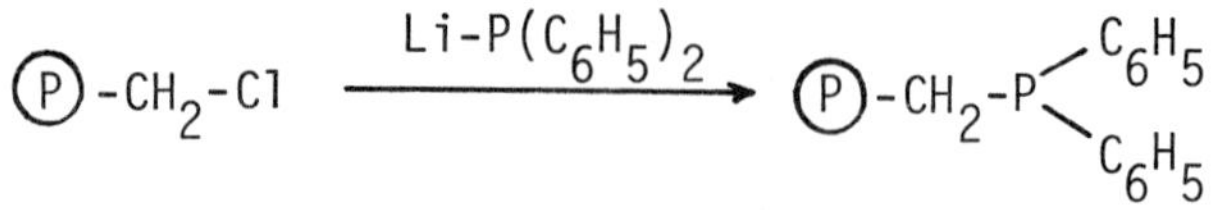

Phosphinated resins have found applications in organic synthesis in Wittig reactions(46,49,55-57) or chlorination reactions(10,47), and in the field of polymer supported catalysis(1,2,7,13,16,26,27,44,45,48,50,54,58-60).

H. Sulfonation

The sulfonation of crosslinked polystyrene was used extensively in the preparation of cation exchange resins. A recent review(61) discusses three methods of sulfonation which can be used in laboratory preparations: sulfonation with sulfuric acid alone, sulfuric acid and perchloroethylene, and chlorosulfonic acid in methylene chloride. All three methods yield a polymer substituted mainly in the para position. A vast body of articles and patents describing the sulfonation of crosslinked polystyrene can be found in the literature. Unlike most other functional resins described above, sulfonated polystyrene resins are widely available commercially.

I. Nitration and Amination

The nitration of crosslinked polystyrene is an important functionalization since it is the first step in the preparation of resins containing amino groups and their derivatives. The nitration which, typically, is carried out in mixtures of nitric and sulfuric acids(62), is usually accompanied by some oxidative degradation of the polymer which liberates some linear nitrated polymer. The soluble material should be removed from the insoluble resin prior to final drying or use to avoid agglomeration of the resin beads.

Amination of the nitrated resin is carried out by reduction with stannous chloride in acidic medium (63,64)

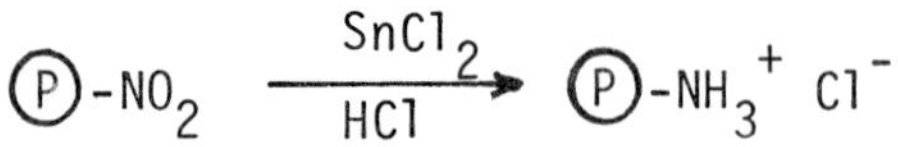

The amino resin, which is unstable, should be used immediately since it decomposes readily in air and light. Typical applications include the preparation of polymeric isocyanates or isothiocyanates.(65)

$$\text{Ⓟ}-NH_2 \xrightarrow[\text{pyridine}]{CS_2/ClCOOC_2H_5} \text{Ⓟ}-N=C=S$$

J. <u>Amination of chloromethylated Polystyrene</u>

This reaction is of prime importance in the preparation of anion exchange resins. In typical reactions the chloromethylated resin is allowed to react with trimethylamine to produce a strong anion exchange resin or with dimethylethanolamine to produce an intermediate anion exchange resin (61,66,67)

$$\text{Ⓟ}-CH_2-Cl + (CH_3)_3N \rightarrow \text{Ⓟ}-CH_2-N(CH_3)_3^+\ Cl^-$$

$$\text{Ⓟ}-CH_2-Cl + (CH_3)_2NCH_2CH_2OH \rightarrow \text{Ⓟ}-CH_2-\overset{+}{N}(CH_3)_2CH_2CH_2OH\ \ Cl^-$$

These reactions have also been reviewed recently(61) and a large number of resins are available commercially.

K. <u>Introduction of Selected Miscellaneous Functional Groups</u>

a) Alcohol functional groups.
Polymers containing hydroxymethyl functional groups have been prepared by reduction of the corresponding carboxylic acids (40) or by reaction of a chloromethylated resin with acetate ion followed by base hydrolysis of the product(38)

$$\text{Ⓟ}-CH_2-Cl \xrightarrow[\text{DMSO}]{CH_3COOK} \text{Ⓟ}-CH_2-O-\underset{\underset{O}{\|}}{C}-CH_3 \xrightarrow{OH^-} \text{Ⓟ}-CH_2-OH$$

A resin containing phenylethanol type side chains has been prepared recently by reaction of a crosslinked polystyryllithium with ethylene oxide followed by acidification of the resulting alkoxide(11)

$$\text{Ⓟ}-Li + (CH_2CH_2)O \rightarrow \text{Ⓟ}-CH_2CH_2OLi \rightarrow \text{Ⓟ}-CH_2CH_2-OH$$

A resin containing a three carbon hydroxylated side chain was prepared by condensation of formylated solvent swellable polystyrene with malonic acid followed by reduction of the resulting unsaturated acid(39). Reduction with lithium aluminium hydride led to the saturated alcohol while reduction with aluminium hydride led to the unsaturated alcohol.

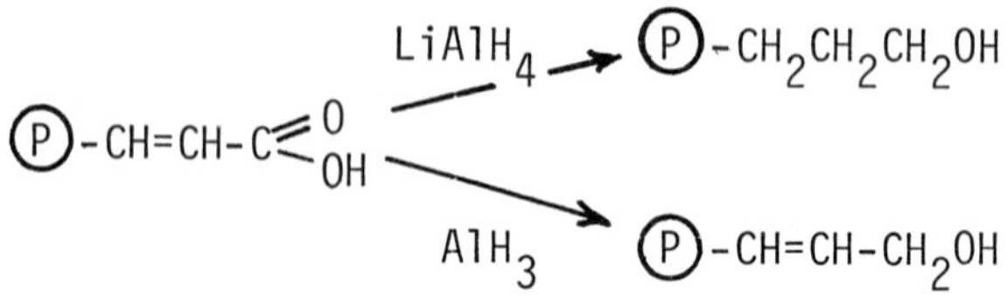

The unsaturated polymeric alcohol has been used in the solid phase synthesis of oligosaccharides(39,68,69).

b) Anhydride

A resins containing mixed sulfonic-acetic anhydride units has been prepared by reaction of a sulfonated cross-linked polystyrene with acetyl chloride(70).

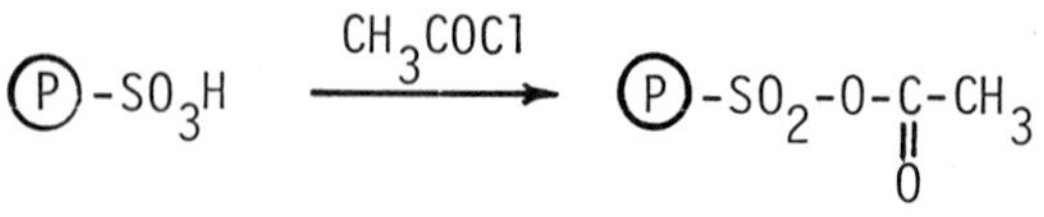

Similarly, a carboxylated popcorn polystyrene was used to prepare the polymeric analogue of benzoic anhydride(71), and a succinylated popcorn polystyrene was also used to prepare a polymeric mixed anhydride(71)

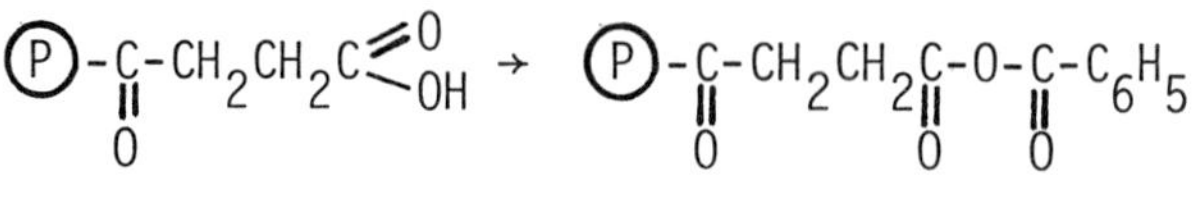

Finally, a popcorn resin containing mixed carbonic-benzoic anhydride functional groups was prepared from a chloromethylated resin(73)

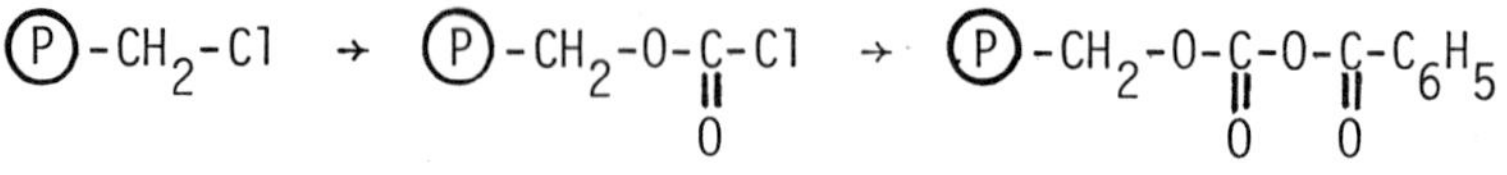

These resins have been used to acylate alcohols, amines, or carboxylic acids.

c) Thiol, Sulfide, and Sulfonium salt.

The introduction of thiol or sulfide functional groups onto polystyrene is easily carried out by reaction of crosslinked polystyryllithium with sulfur(11) or with disulfides (11,17). The reaction of polystyryllithium with sulfur in tetrahydrofuran yields a polymer which contains S-S bonds from which the thiol can be obtained by reduction with lithium aluminium hydride. To control the degree of functionalization it is preferable to use a brominated polystyrene resin as the starting material from which the lithiated resin is readily obtained. Using the sequence resin bromide→lithiated resin→ resin thiol, functional yields of 90% and over are easily obtained.

$$\text{(P)-Br} \xrightarrow{\text{n-BuLi}} \text{(P)-Li} \xrightarrow[\text{2) LiAlH}_4]{\text{1) S}_8} \text{(P)-SH}$$

To control the degree of functionalization in the preparation of crosslinked polystyrene resins containing sulfide functional groups, it is also convenient to use a brominated resin as starting material. Thus the polymeric analogue of thioanisole can be prepared as follows(11,17):

$$\text{(P)-Br} \xrightarrow{\text{n-BuLi}} \text{(P)-Li} \xrightarrow{CH_3S\text{-}SCH_3} \text{(P)-SCH}_3$$

This reaction has also been used to prepare a number of other polymeric sulfides. Thus, in our laboratory the following sulfides have been prepared on a crosslinked polystyrene matrix (M.J. Farrall and J.M.J. Fréchet, manuscript in preparation)

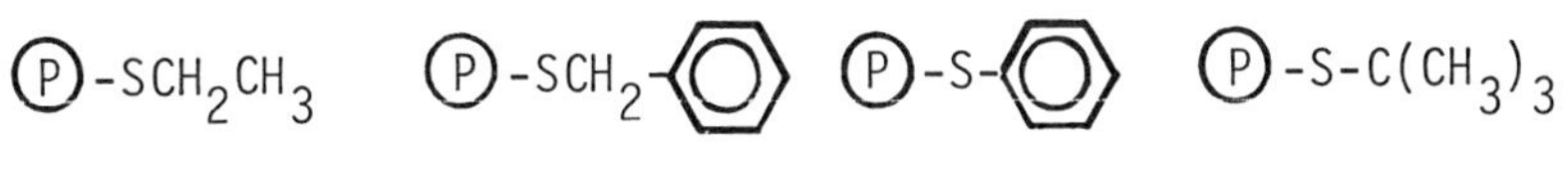

Polystyrene resins containing sulfonium salt functional groups have been obtained by reaction of the sulfides described above with alkylating agents such as dialkylsulfates or alkyl fluorosulfonates (M.J. Farrall and J.M.J. Fréchet, manuscript in preparation)

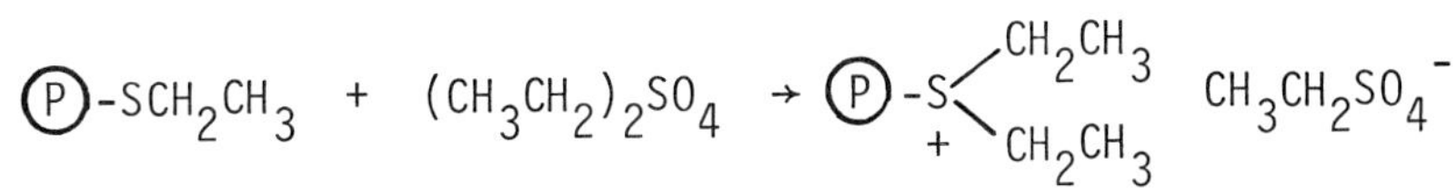

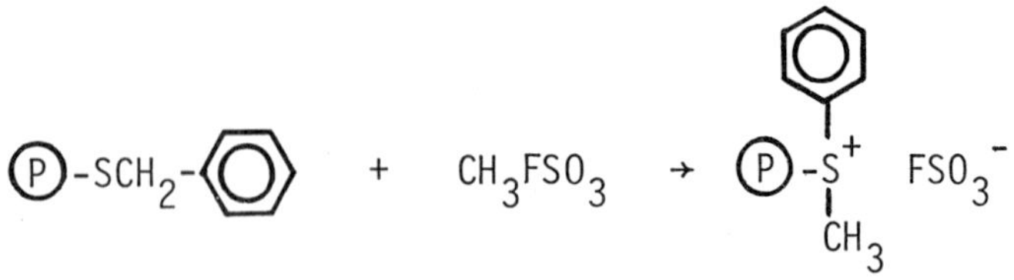

The preparation of another polystyrene-bound sulfonium salt according to the scheme below has been reported(74)

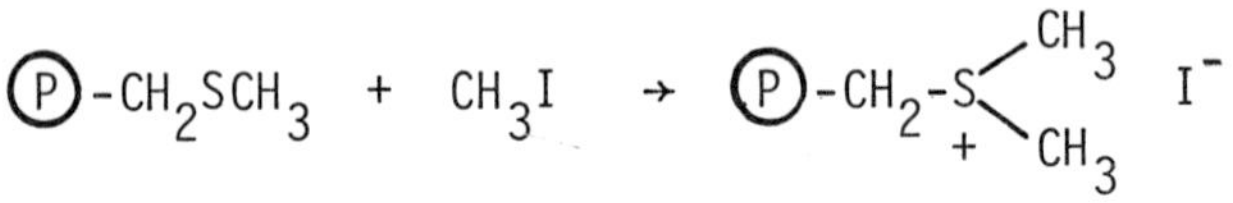

Other Japanese workers have reported the preparation of a similar resin by reaction of a chloromethylated polystyrene resin with dimethylsulfide(75,76)

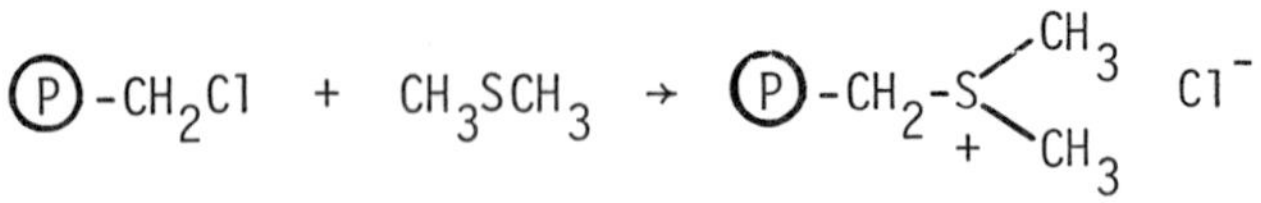

3. ANALYTICAL PROBLEMS

The analysis of functionalized crosslinked polystyrene resins is severely restricted by their insolubility. Infrared spectroscopy is perhaps the single most useful method to follow the various steps in the chemical modification of polystyrene. A classical example of such application of infrared spectroscopy is found in the work of Letsinger and coworkers(40) who followed the chemical transformation of a popcorn polystyrene into its hydroxymethyl, chloroformyl, hydrazide and anilide derivatives. Other interesting examples are found in the preparation of a support for peptide synthesis(77) and in the preparation of a support for the solid phase synthesis of oligosaccharides(39). While infared spectroscopy is well suited to follow the appearance or disappearance of functional groups with a strong absorption, such as carbonyl or hydroxyl groups, it is less suitable to observe weak absorptions which may also be obscured by the absorption bands of the polymer itself. In such instances it is possible to record the bands which are due to the new functional group only by using a pellet of the starting unfunctionalized resin in the reference beam of the instrument (J.M.J. Fréchet and L.J. Nuyens, unpublished results).

Although infrared spectroscopy provides excellent qualitative informations on the chemical transformations of the resins, it can only be used for quantitative studies in cases where the spectra of a number of "standard" polymers carrying varying percentages of the same functional groups are available. Thus, the degree of functionalization of carboxylated polystyrene resins could be estimated from their infrared spectra by comparison with the spectra of other carboxylated resins of known degree of functionalization (M.J. Farrall and J.M.J. Fréchet, unpublished results).

In some cases the functionalized resins can be titrated directly. Thus, in general, acid-base titrations can be used to estimate the degree of functionalization of resins containing acidic or basic substituents. However, the results of such titrations will only be meaningful if the reagent used in the titration can penetrate fully the pores of the functional polymer. Thus, while a macroreticular resin containing carboxylic acid groups can be titrated easily with ethanolic sodium hydroxide, a carboxylated solvent swellable resin can only be titrated while fully swollen using a very strong base such as an alkyllithium in benzene or tetrahydrofuran(9,11,39).

Many functionalization reactions can be quantified by elemental analysis of the product after isolation and drying. Thus, halogen, nitrogen, sulfur and other analyses can provide valuable information on the degree of functionalization of the polymers. Phosphorus and oxygen analyses have often been found to yield erratic results.

The analysis of some functional groups can be carried out by preparation of derivatives which can, in turn, be subjected to elemental analysis. Thus a double bond can be transformed into its dibromide, or an aldehyde into an oxime(39). Elemental analysis for bromine or nitrogen respectively will give a measure of the minimum degree of functionalization(11).

A number of special procedures which have been developed to monitor the solid phase synthesis of peptides have been reviewed by Marshall and Merrifield(29). Significant advances in the analysis of functional derivatives of crosslinked polystyrene may result from the application of ^{13}C NMR spectroscopy.

REFERENCES

1. A volume containing reprints of 62 important papers in this field has been published recently. E.C. Blossey and D.C. Neckers, Editors. "Solid Phase Synthesis", Halsted Press (1975).
2. D.C. Neckers, J. Chem. Educ., 52, 695 (1975).
3. R.B. Merrifield, J. Am. Chem. Soc., 85, 2149 (1963).
4. C.C. Leznoff, Chem. Soc. Rev., 3, 65 (1974).
5. J.M.J. Fréchet and L.J. Nuyens, Can. J. Chem. 54, 926 (1976).
6. P. Cuatrecasas in "Biochemical Aspects of Reactions on Solid Supports" (G.R. Stork, Ed.), Academic Press (1971).
7. C.U. Pittman Jr. and G.O. Evans, Chem. Tech., 560 (1973).
8. R.L. Letsinger and D.M. Jerina, J. Poly. Sci. A-1, 5, 1977 (1967).
9. J.M.J. Fréchet and K.E. Haque, Macromolecules, 8, 130 (1975).
10. H.M. Relles and R.W. Schluenz, J. Am. Chem. Soc., 96, 6469 (1974).
11. M.J. Farrall and J.M.J. Fréchet, J. Org. Chem., in press (1976).
12. W. Heitz and R. Michels, Makromol. Chem., 148, 9, (1971).
13. C.U. Pittman and R.M. Hanes, Ann. N.Y. Acad. Sci., 239, 76 (1974).
14. E. Seymour and J.M.J. Fréchet, Tetrahedron Lett., 1149 (1976).
15. F. Camps, J. Castells, M. Ferrando, and J. Font, Tetrahedron Lett., 1713 (1971).
16. J. Moreto, J. Albaiges, and F. Camps, Ann. Quim., 70, 638 (1974).
17. G.A. Crosby, N.M. Weinshenker, and H. Uh, J.Am. Chem. Soc., 97, 2232 (1975).
18. N.M. Weinshenker, G.A. Crosby, and J. Wong, J. Org. Chem., 40, 1966 (1975).
19. A. McKillop, D. Bromley, and E.C. Taylor, J. Org. Chem., 37, 88 (1972).
20. Y. Yamada and M. Okawara, Makromol. Chem., 152, 153 (1972).
21. See for example: C. McBurney (Rohm & Haas Co.) U.S. Patent 2,591,573 (1952).
22. See for example: E.L. McMaster (Dow Chemical Co.) U.S. Patent 2,616,877 (1952).
23. K.W. Pepper, H.M. Paisley, and M.A. Young, J. Chem. Soc., 4097 (1953).

24. R.S. Feinberg and R.B. Merrifield, Tetrahedron, 30, 3209 (1974).
25. J.T. Sparrow, Tetrahedron Lett., 4637 (1975).
26. R.H. Grubbs and L.C. Kroll, J. Am. Chem. Soc., 93, 3062 (1971).
27. R.H. Grubbs, C. Gibbons, L.C. Kroll, W.D. Bond, and C.H. Brubaker, J. Am. Chem. Soc., 95, 2373 (1973).
28. B. Gutte and R.B. Merrifield, J. Am. Chem. Soc., 91, 501 (1969).
29. G.R. Marshall and R.B. Merrifield in "Biochemical Aspects of Reactions on Solid Supports" (G.R. Stark, Ed.) Academic Press, New York (1971).
30. D. Braun, Makromol. Chem. 30, 85 (1959).
31. D. Braun, Makromol. Chem., 33, 181 (1959).
32. D. Braun, Makromol. Chem., 44, 269 (1961).
33. A.J. Chalk, J. Polym. Sci., B 6, 649 (1968).
34. D.C. Evans, M.H. George, and J.A. Barrie, J. Polym. Sci. Polym. Chem. Ed., 12, 247 (1974).
35. L.R. Melby and D.R. Strobach, J. Am. Chem. Soc., 89, 450 (1967).
36. T.M. Fyles and C.C. Leznoff, Can. J. Chem., 54, 935 (1976).
37. J.M. Burlitch and R.C. Winterton, J. Am. Chem. Soc., 97, 5605 (1975).
38. J.T. Ayres and C.K. Mann, Polym. Lett., 3, 505, (1965).
39. J.M.J. Fréchet and C. Schuerch, J. Am. Chem. Soc., 93, 492 (1971).
40. R.L. Letsinger, M.J. Kornet, V. Mahadevan, and D.M. Jerina, J. Am. Chem. Soc., 86, 5163 (1964).
41. R.L. Letsinger and D.M. Jerina, J. Poly. Sci., A1, 1977 (1967).
42. J.M.J. Fréchet and K.E. Haque, Tetrahedron Lett., 3055 (1975).
43. H. Gilman, J. Am. Chem. Soc., 55, 1258 (1933).
44. W.O. Haag and D.D. Whitehurst, Bel. Pat. 721,686 (1968).
45. Numerous examples of resin bound catalysts can be found in the patent literature. See for example P.L. Ragg, Ger. Pat. 1,937,225 (1970); Mobil oil Co. U.S. Pat. 1,800,371 (1969); British Petroleum Co., Belg. Pat. 739,607 and 739,609 (1969). S.V. McKinley and J.W. Rackshays, U.S. Pat. 3,708,462 (1973).
46. W. Heitz and R. Michels, Angew. Chem. International Ed., 11, 298 (1972).
47. S.L. Regen and D.P. Lee, J. Org. Chem., 40, 1669 (1975).
48. J.P. Collman, L.S. Hegedus, M.P. Cooke, J.R. Norton G. Dolcetti, D.N. Marquardt, J. Am. Chem. Soc., 94, 1789 (1972).

49. S.V. McKinley and J.W. Rakshys, J. Chem. Soc. Chem. Comm., 134 (1972).
50. R.H. Grubbs and L.C. Kroll, Polymer Preprints, 12, 423 (1971).
51. R.H. Grubbs, L.C. Kroll, and E.M. Sweet, J. Macromol. Sci. A7, 1047 (1973).
52. M.S. Jarrel and B.C. Gates, J. Catalysis, 40, 255 (1975).
53. M. Čapka, P. Svoboda, M. Černý, and J. Hetflegě, Tetrahedron Lett. 4784 (1971).
54. G.O. Evans, C.V. Pittman, R. McMillan, R.T. Beach, and R. Jones, J. Organomet. Chem., 67, 295 (1974).
55. F. Camps, J. Castells, J. Font, and F. Vela, Tetrahedron Lett.; 1715 (1971).
56. F. Camps. J. Castells and F. Vela, Ann. Quim., 70, 374 (1974).
57. W. Heitz and R. Michels, Liebigs Ann. Chem., 227 (1973).
58. C.U. Pittman, L.R. Smith and R.M. Hanes, J. Am. Chem. Soc., 97, 1742 (1975).
59. C.U. Pittman and L.R. Smith, J. Am. Chem. Soc., 97, 1749 (1975).
60. G. Dolcetti, M. Ghedini, and O. Gandolfi, La Chimica E L'Industria, 57, 336 (1975).
61. J.A. Patterson in "Biochemical Aspects of Reactions on Solid Supports" (G.R. Stark, Ed.) p. 183, Academic Press, New York 1971.
62. H. Zenftman and A. McLean, British Patent 616,453 (1949).
63. C.H. Chen, Ph.D. Thesis, Polytechnic Institute of Brooklyn, New York 1955.
64. G.R. Stark in "Biochemical Aspects of Reactions on Solid Supports" (G.R. Stark, Ed.) p. 171, Academic Press, New York 1971.
65. D.L. Garmaise, R. Schwartz, and A.F. McKay, J. Am. Chem. Soc., 80, 3332 (1958).
66. R. Kunin in "Ion Exchange Resins". John Wiley and Sons, New York (1958).
67. E.B. Tooper and L.L. Wirth in "Ion Exchange Technology" (F. Nachad, Ed.) p7, Academic Press, New York (1956).
68. J.M.J. Fréchet and C. Schuerch, J. Am. Chem. Soc., 94, 604 (1972).
69. J.M.J. Fréchet and C. Schuerch, Carbohyd. Res., 22, 399 (1972).
70. T.L. Ang and H.J. Harwood, J. Macromol. Sci. Chem., A7, 1079 (1973).
71. M.B. Shambhu and G.A. Digenis, Tetrahedron Lett, 1627 (1973).
72. K.F. Yip and K.C. Tsou, J. Am. Chem. Soc., 93, 3272 (1971).

73. M.B. Shambhu and G.A. Digenis, J. Chem. Soc. Chem. Comm., 619 (1974).
74. S. Tanimoto, J. Horikawa, and R. Oda, Kogyo Kagaku Zasshi, 70, 1269 (1967).
75. H. Kawabe and M. Yanagita, J. Sci. Res. Inst. (Tokyo), 51, 182 (1957), Chem. Abstracts, 52, 40651 (1958).
76. H. Kawabe and H. Yanagita, Kogyo Kagaku Zasshi, 61, 137, (1958).
77. S.S. Wang and R.B. Merrifield, J. Am. Chem. Soc., 91, 6488 (1969).
78. A.P. Schaap, A.L. Thayer, E.C. Blossey, and D.C. Neckers, J. Am. Chem. Soc., 97, 3741 (1975). See also J. Am. Chem. Soc., 95, 5820 (1973).
79. S.S. Wang, J. Am. Chem. Soc., 95, 1328 (1973).
80. H.W. Gibson, Macromolecules, 8, 89, (1975).
81. J. Cerny and M. Wichterle, Ger. Patent 1,043,633 (1958). Chem. Abstr., 55, 1969 (1961).
82. N.M. Weinshenker and C.M. Shen, Tetrahedron Lett., 3281 (1972).
83. T. Kusama and H. Hayatsu, Chem. Pharm. Bull., 18, 319 (1970).
84. A.M. Felix and R.B. Merrifield, J. Am. Chem. Soc., 92, 1385 (1970).
85. K.A. Kun, J. Poly. Sci., A3, 1833 (1965).
86. U. Zehavi and A. Patchornik, J. Am. Chem. Soc., 95, 5673 (1973).
87. J.T. Sparrow, J. Org. Chem., 41, 1350 (1976).
88. L.R. Melby, J. Am. Chem. Soc., 97, 4044 (1975).
89. E. Seymour and J.M.J. Fréchet, Tetrahedron Lett., in press (1976).

EFFECTS OF TETRAAMINE CROSSLINKING AGENTS ON THE THERMOMECHANICAL PROPERTIES OF PMR POLYIMIDE COMPOSITES

Peter Delvigs

NASA-LEWIS RESEARCH CENTER

Studies were performed to investigate the effects of partial substitution of tetraamine crosslinking agents for diamine reactants on the thermomechanical properties of PMR polyimide resins and graphite fiber-reinforced composites. The effect of tetraamine content on isothermal weight loss, glass transition, and softening temperatures of neat resin samples is discussed. Composites were fabricated using PMR methodology. Monomeric solution of various stoichiometric ratios were used to impregnate Hercules HTS graphite fiber. The mechanical property retention characteristics of the composites at 316°C (600°F) are described.

I. INTRODUCTION

One of the potential applications of high temperature resistant polymers is their use as matrix resins in fiber-reinforced composites for turbofan engine components. Prior studies in our laboratory (1-3) have demonstrated the effectiveness of the PMR (in situ polymerization of monomer reactants on the surface of the reinforcing fibers) approach for preparing high temperature resistant fiber-reinforced polyimide matrix composites. The PMR polyimide resins are beginning to achieve acceptance by fabricators because of their facile processability characteristics. Currently available PMR polyimide resins are based on the monomers 5-norbornene-2,3-dicarboxylic acid monomethyl ester (NE), 3,3',4,4'-benzophenonetetracarboxylic acid dimethyl ester (BTDE), and 4,4'-methylenedianiline (MDA). The final cure of these resins proceeds by a complex set of reactions involving chain extension and some degree of crosslinking by the norbornene end-caps. However, these PMR resins must be subjected to a postcure at 316° C (600° F) to eliminate thermoplastic yielding under load at elevated temperatures. Recent studies (4) have shown that substitution of 4,4'-(hexafluoroisopropylidene)-bis(phthalic acid) dimethyl ester (HFDE) for BTDE significantly increases the thermooxidative stability of the PMR polyimide composites. However, because of their lower glass transition temperatures (T_g), the HFDE/MDA/NE resin composites exhibit considerably lower mechanical properties at 316° C (600° F) than the BTDE/MDA/NE composites.

The purpose of this investigation was to reduce thermoplastic behavior of graphite fiber-reinforced PMR polyimide composites by partial substitution of the diamine monomer MDA with tetraamine crosslinking agents. Recent studies with condensation type polyimide films (5) have shown that partial substitution of tri- and tetrafunctional amines for the diamine component significantly increases the polymer T_g and softening temperature (T_s).

This paper describes the effect of tetraamine content on isothermal weight loss, T_g, and softening temperatures of molded neat PMR polyimide samples prepared from NE, MDA, BTDE, and NE, MDA, HFDE. Composites were fabricated from HTS graphite fiber using PMR methodology. The effect of crosslink density on the mechanical properties of composites at room temperature and 316° C (600° F) is discussed.

II. EXPERIMENTAL

A. Monomers

The monomers and crosslinking agents used in this study are shown in figure 1. The monomethyl ester of 5-norbornene-2,3-dicarboxylic acid (NE), 4,4'-methylenedianiline (MDA), and 3,3',4,4'-benzophenonetetracarboxylic dianhydride (BTDA) were obtained from commercial sources. The 4,4'-(hexafluoroisopropylidene)-bis(phthalic anhydride) (HFDA), the corresponding dimethyl ester (HFDE), and the dimethyl ester of 3,3',4,4'-benzophenonetetracarboxylic acid (BTDE) were prepared according to reference 4. The 6,6'-bis[2,3-di(p-aminophenyl) quinoxalyl] ketone (TABK) was synthesized according to reference 5. The 3,3',5,5'-tetraaminobenzophenone (TEAB) was synthesized by the following method: a solution of 3,3',5-trinitrobenzophenone (5) (9.51 g, 3.00×10^{-2} mole) in conc. H_2SO_4 (90 ml) and 90% fuming HNO_3 (45 ml) was stirred at 100° to 110° for 4 hours, cooled to room temperature and poured on crushed ice. The product was filtered, washed with H_2O until free of acid, and dried. The crude product (8.72 g) was crystallized from 1:1 EtOH/DMF to yield 6.29 g (58%) of 3,3',5,5'-tetranitrobenzophenone, m.p. 251° to 252° C (literature (6) m.p. 250°). The tetranitro compound (3.62 g, 1.00×10^{-2} mole) was added to a solution of $SnCl_2 \cdot 2H_2O$ (27.1 g, 1.20×10^{-1} mole) in conc. HCl (36 ml). The mixture was stirred at room temperature for 0.5 hour, then at 100° C for 2 hours. After filtration, the solution was poured slowly into 40% aq. KOH(162 ml) while adding ice chips. The product was filtered, washed with H_2O and dried. Crystallization of the crude product from H_2O, then EtOH yielded 1.78 g (74%) of 3,3',5,5'-tetraaminobenzophenone, m.p. 210° to 211° C dec. Anal. - Calcd. for $C_{13}H_{14}N_4O$: C, 64.44%; H, 5.82%; N, 23.13%. Found: C, 65.01%; H, 5.84%; N, 23.00%.

B. Molding Powders and PMR Polyimide Plugs

Monomers in the desired stoichiometric ratios were dissolved in 1-methyl-2-pyrrolidinone (NMP) at a solids loading of 50 wt %, and the solution heated in vacuum at 150° C for 4 hours, then at 200° C for 2 hours. The dry solid was ground into a fine powder. The molding powder (approx. 5 g) was placed into a circular matched metal die (diameter 5.05 cm) preheated to 260° C (500° F). Following a dwell time of 5 to 30 minutes, 2000 psi pressure was applied, and the temperature raised to 321° C (610° F). Pressure and temperature were maintained for 1 hour.

The stoichiometry of the monomeric reactants used was $n/(1 - m)(n + 1)/\frac{m}{2}(n + 1)/2$, where n = moles of BTDE or HFDE, $(1 - m)(n + 1)$ = moles of MDA, $\frac{m}{2}(n + 1)$ = moles of TABK or TEAB, 2 = moles of NE, and where m = mole fraction of MDA replaced with TABK or TEAB.

The glass transition temperatures (T_g) and softening temperatures (T_s) of the polymers were determined with a thermomechanical analyzer (TMA) using a penetration probe at a heating rate of 10° C/min with a 5 g load. The weight loss of the polymers was determined by isothermal exposure at 316° C (600° F) in a forced draft oven with an air change rate of 100 cm^3/min.

C. Composite Fabrication and Testing

Composites were fabricated essentially according to the method described in reference 4. Prepreg tapes were made by drum-winding and impregnating Hercules HTS graphite fiber with the PMR monomer solutions to yield prepregs containing 45.5 wt % monomers and 54.5 wt % fiber. The solutions were prepared by dissolving the monomers in the desired stoichiometric ratios in anhydrous methanol to give a solids content of 40 wt %. It should be noted that a 2:1 mixture of MeOH/NMP was employed for formulations containing the tetraamine TABK, due to the extremely limited solubility of TABK in MeOH. The prepreg tapes were dried on the drum at room temperature for 1 hour, then at 50° C for 1 hour. The tapes were cut into 3 in by 8 in plies and stacked 8 plies thick unidirectionally. The prepreg stack was placed into a preforming mold and staged at 120° C for 3 hours under a pressure of 0.1 psi. Prepreg impregnated with solutions containing NMP was staged at 200° C for 3 hours. Composites were molded by placing the staged prepreg into a matched metal die preheated to 232° C (450° F). Following a dwell time of 5 to 10 minutes (depending on tetraamine content), 500 psi pressure was applied, and the temperature was increased to 316° C (600° F) at a rate of 5.5° C (10° F)/minute. Pressure and temperature were maintained for 1 hour. After curing, all composites were postcured for 16 hours at 316° C (600° F). All laminates were inspected using an ultrasonic C scan technique. Flexural strength tests were performed using a three point loading fixture with a fixed span of 2 inches. The rate of center loading was 0.05 in/min. The thickness of the laminates ranged from 0.070 in to 0.085 in, resulting in a span/depth ratio of 24 to 29. Interlaminar shear strength tests were conducted at a constant span/depth ratio of 5. All mechanical property values are averages of 3 tests. Fiber content was determined for all laminates and ranged from 60.0 to 62.1 volume percent. For flexural tests all results were normalized to 60 volume percent fiber.

III. RESULTS AND DISCUSSION

A. Properties of PMR Polyimide Plugs

Table 1 lists isothermal weight loss and glass transition temperature (T_g) of the BTDE-PMR control sample, as well as three other resin samples where the tetraamine crosslinking agent TABK is partially substituted for the diamine MDA. It can be seen that the T_g shows a significant increase as the tetraamine content is increased, from 352° C in control sample 1 to 390° C for sample 2. Samples 3 and 4 did not exhibit a T_g value below 400° C, at which temperature the polymers began to decompose.

While the isothermal weight loss of samples 1 and 2 on exposure in air at 316° C (600° F) for 1000 hours was not significantly different, there is nevertheless a trend toward a higher weight loss as the tetraamine content of the polymer is increased. This could be attributed to decreased thermooxidative stability of the bisquinoxaline nucleus of the tetraamine TABK, or to the possible higher concentration of unreacted amino groups.

Table 2 summarizes the T_g values and isothermal weight loss of PMR polyimide plugs prepared from the monomer HFDE. The weight loss of all three samples after exposure to 316° C (600° F) for 1000 hours shows no significant difference, indicating a comparable thermoxidative stability. The T_g values of the polymers again show a significant increase with increasing tetraamine content. However, due to the more flexible hexafluoroisopropylidene connecting group of HFDE compared to the more rigid carbonyl group of BTDE, the T_g of all three polymers was found to be below 316° C (600° F). In addition, samples 1 and 2 exhibited a softening temperature (T_s), which was not shown by the BTDE-PMR polyimides. After the polymer samples were subjected to a 16 hour postcure at 316° C (600° F), their T_g values were increased by approximately 40° C, and all polymers failed to exhibit softening behavior below 450° C, at which temperature significant decomposition began to occur. The TMA curves for control sample 1 before and after postcure are shown in figure 2.

The results obtained in this phase of the investigation indicate that incorporation of tetraamine crosslinking agents in the PMR polyimide matrix would significantly decrease the thermoplastic behavior of graphite fiber-reinforced PMR composites and increase their mechanical properties.

B. Composite Properties

Table 3 summarizes T_g values and mechanical properties of BTDE-PMR/HTS graphite fiber composites containing the tetraamine TABK. The T_g values of the composites correspond closely with those of the corresponding neat resin T_g values shown in table I. It can be seen that the 316° C interlaminar shear strength (ILSS) of control sample 1 is considerably lower than its room temperature value. This seems to be a phenomenon associated with intermediate modulus graphite fibers derived from polyacrylonitrile fibers (7). The control sample also exhibits a large difference between the room temperature and elevated temperature flexural strength and modulus. Comparison of control sample 1 with samples 2 and 3 shows no increase in the elevated temperature mechanical properties with increasing crosslink density. The control sample of course already contains a certain amount of crosslinks due to the nature of the PMR curing mechanism involving the norbornene end-caps. It appears that no increase in elevated temperature mechanical properties can be achieved by using additional inchain crosslinking agents in BTDE-PMR composites. The mechanical properties of composite sample 4 are signficantly lower than those of samples 1 to 3. This can be explained by the presence of voids in sample 4, as determined by ultrasonic inspection. It should be noted that the resin flow during cure decreased with increasing tetraamine content. Sample 4, having the highest TABK content, exhibited a very severely restricted resin flow, which apparently prevented the fabrication of a void-free composite.

Table 4 shows the T_g values and mechanical properties of HEDE-PMR composites using the tetraamine crosslinking agent TEAB. Tetraamine TABK was not used in this composite series because of its extremely low solubility in methanol. The room temperature mechanical properties of all composites are closely comparable. The 316° C ILSS of control sample 1 exhibits a substantial dropoff from its room temperature value. This can be explained by the fact that the Tg of the composite (314° C) is slightly below the test temperature (316° C). Composite samples 2 to 4, using increasing amounts of tetraamine TEAB, show a gradual increase in 316° C ILSS. Composite sample 2 exhibits a 40% increase of 316° C flexural strength over that of the control sample 1, from 87 000 to 122 000 psi. Similarly, composite 2 exhibits a flexural modulus of 15.3×10^6 psi, compared to 9.4×10^6 psi for composite 1, an increase of 63%. It should also be noted that at 316° C, composite 2 retains 89% of its room temperature flexural modulus. However, the flexural strength and modulus values of composites 3 and 4, having progressively higher resin crosslink density, did not show an increase over the flexural strength and modulus of composite 2. It may be noted that composites 2, 3, and 4 exhibit almost identical T_g values (342° to 347° C). It is possible that the use of in-chain crosslinking agents above the level used in composite 2 would not lead to a further increase of flexural properties.

Figure 3 shows the weight loss characteristics of HFDE-PMR composites after exposure in air at 316° C (600° F). All of the composites exhibited excellent thermooxidative stability. Although the control sample had a slightly higher weight loss after 1000 hours than the composites prepared with tetraamine TEAB, the difference in weight loss was not pronounced.

The ILSS values of the HFDE-PMR composites during extended exposure at 316° C are compared in figure 4. It can be seen that composites 2 to 4 show excellent retention of their initial 316° C ILSS values throughout the exposure period, ranging from 87 to 89 percent after 1000 hours at 316° C. In contrast, the ILSS values of control sample 1 are consistently lower during the first 500 hours of exposure. On further exposure the ILSS shows a gradual increase, apparently due to a postcure effect. After 1000 hours of exposure the ILSS of composite 1 has increased to the same level as the ILSS of composites 2 to 4.

The effect of isothermal exposure at 316° C on the flexural strength of the HFDE-PMR composites is shown in figure 5.

Most of the comments made about the ILSS retention on isothermal exposure apply to the flexural strength retention as well. Composites 2 to 4 exhibited excellent flexural strength retention after 1000 hours exposure in air, ranging from 95 to 100 percent of their initial 316° C values. The flexural strength of the control sample again remained significantly lower during 600 hours of exposure, then showed a gradual increase during the next 400 hours.

Figure 6 shows the flexural modulus of the HFDE-PMR composites during extended exposure at 316° C. The flexural modulus values of composites 2 to 4 exhibited a decrease during the initial 400 hours of exposure at 316° C, but then remained at nearly the same levels during further exposure. After 1000 hours of exposure, composites 2 to 4 retained 67 to 75 percent of their initial 316° C modulus. The flexural modulus values of control sample 1 were signficantly lower during the entire exposure period.

It can be seen in figures 4 to 6 that the 316° C mechanical properties of composite samples 2 to 4 are closely comparable at any given exposure time. There appears to be an overall trend toward higher mechanical properties with increasing tetraamine content. However, since only three measurements were taken to obtain each data point, no firm conclusion can be drawn about the relation of improved mechanical properties to the amount of the tetraamine crosslinking agent.

IV. CONCLUSIONS

The results of this investigation show that the use of tetraamines for introducing in-chain crosslinks into the PMR polyimide structure significantly increased the polymer glass transition temperature. The substitution of tetraamines had no significant effect on the thermooxidative stability of HFDE-PMR resins, but slightly decreased the thermooxidative stability of BTDE-PMR polyimides. The incorporation of tetraamine TABK into the polymer matrix of BTDE-PMR/HTS graphite fiber composites did not have a significant effect on composite mechanical properties. In contrast, substitution of tetraamine TEAB into the matrix of HFDE-PMR/HTS composites provided a substantial increase of elevated temperature flexural strength, flexural modulus, and interlaminar shear strength. The HFDE-PMR/HTS composites exhibited excellent thermooxidative stability and retention of elevated temperature mechanical properties after long-term isothermal exposure in air at 316° C (600° F).

V. REFERENCES

1. T. T. Serafini, P. Delvigs, and G. R. Lightsey, J. Appl. Polym. Sci. 16, 905 (1972).
2. P. Delvigs, T. T. Serafini, and G. R. Lightsey, "Addition-Type Polyimides from Solutions of Monomeric Reactants," NASA TN D-6877, 1972.
3. T. T. Serafini and R. D. Vannucci, "Tailor Making High Performance Graphite Fiber Reinforced PMR Polyimides," NASA TM X-71616, 1975.
4. R. D. Vannucci and W. B. Alston, "PMR Polyimides with Improved High Temperature Performance," NASA TM X-71816, 1976.
5. P. Delvigs, Polym. Engr. Sci. 16, 323 (1976).
6. F. Bardone, Compt. Rend. Hebd. Acad. Sci. 236, 828 (1953).
7. M. P. Hanson and T. T. Serafini, "Effects of Thermal and Environmental Exposure on the Mechanical Properties of Graphite/Polyimide Composites," NASA TN D-6604, 1972.

TABLE 1. - THERMOMECHANICAL PROPERTIES OF BTDE-PMR POLYIMIDES[a]

Sample	m[b]	T_g, °C	Percent weight loss[c]
1	0	352	6.6
2	.08	390	7.7
3	.16	>400	10.2
4	.32	>400	14.2

[a]Prepared from BTDE/MDA/TABK/NE, n = 1.672.
[b]Mole fraction of MDA replaced by TABK.
[c]After 1000 hours in air at 316° C.

TABLE 2. - THERMOMECHANICAL PROPERTIES OF HFDE-PMR POLYIMIDES[a]

Sample	m[b]	T_g, °C		T_s, °C		
		Before postcure	After postcure[c]	Before postcure	After postcure	Percent weight loss[d]
1	0	269	309	420	>450	8.7
2	.08	297	335	440	>450	8.9
3	.16	306	346	>450	>450	9.5

[a]Prepared from HFDE/MDA/TEAB/NE, n = 1.50.
[b]Mole fraction of MDA replaced by TEAB.
[c]16 hours in air at 316° C.
[d]After 1000 hours in air at 316° C.

TABLE 3. - MECHANICAL PROPERTIES OF BTDE-PMR/HTS GRAPHITE FIBER COMPOSITES[a]

Sample	m[b]	T_g, °C	Interlaminar shear strength, psix10^{-3}		Flexural strength, psix10^{-3}		Flexural modulus, psix10^{-6}	
			25° C	316° C	25° C	316° C	25° C	316° C
1	0	358	16.3	6.6	251	111	15.6	11.0
2	.08	392	12.5	6.1	205	106	14.7	10.8
3	.16	>400	----	6.2	---	93	----	11.7
4	.32	>400	----	4.8	---	56	----	8.6

[a]Prepared from BTDE/MDA/TABK/NE, n = 1.672.
[b]Mole fraction of MDA replaced by TABK.

TABLE 4. - MECHANICAL PROPERTIES OF HFDE-PMR/HTS GRAPHITE FIBER COMPOSITES[a]

Sample	m[b]	T_g, °C	Interlaminar shear strength, psix10^{-3}		Flexural strength, psix10^{-3}		Flexural modulus, psix10^{-6}	
			25° C	316° C	25° C	316° C	25° C	316° C
1	0	314	13.5	4.4	240	87	16.6	9.4
2	.02	342	15.0	5.9	230	122	16.8	15.3
3	.04	343	15.7	6.3	228	131	16.6	15.5
4	.08	347	16.1	6.7	233	124	17.1	15.2

[a]Prepared from HFDE/MDA/TEAB/NE, n = 1.50.
[b]Mole fraction of MDA replaced by TEAB.

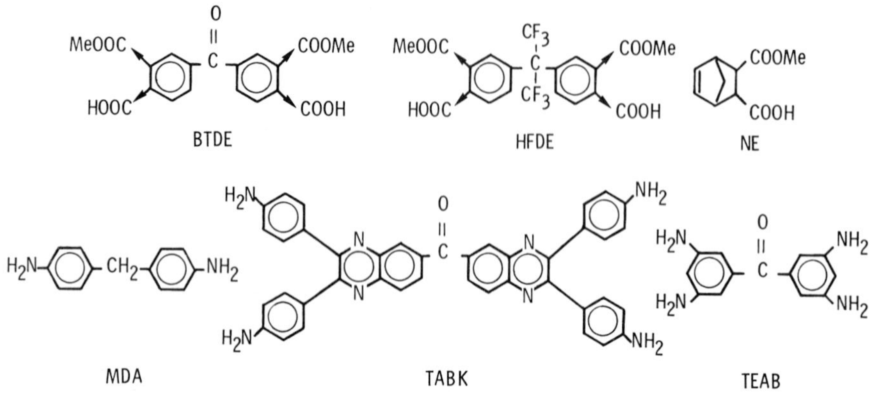

Fig. 1. Monomers used for PMR polyimide synthesis.

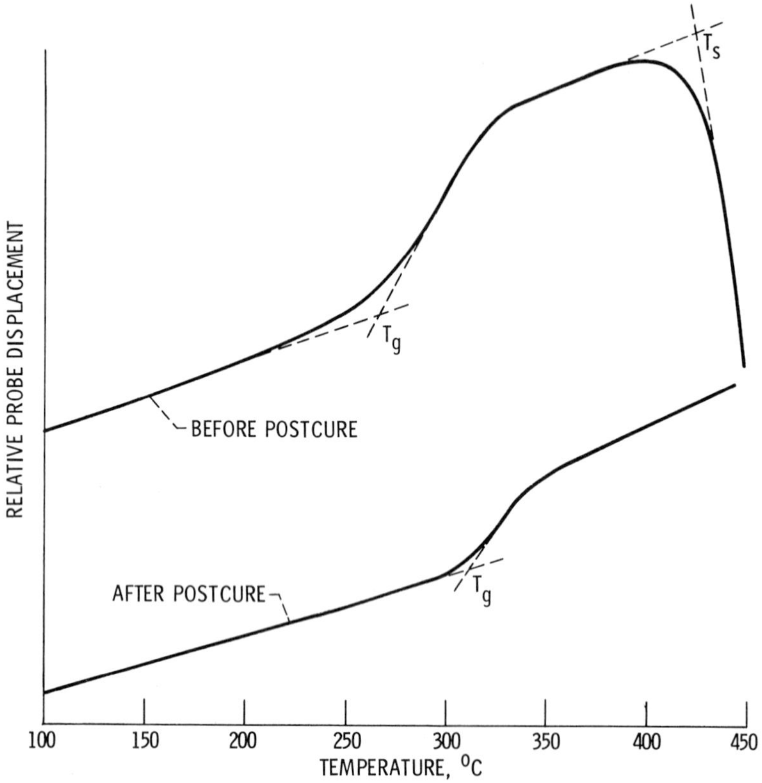

Fig. 2. TMA analysis of PMR polyimide from HFDE/MDA/NE, n = 1.50. Penetration probe; 5 g load, heating rate, 10^0 C/min.

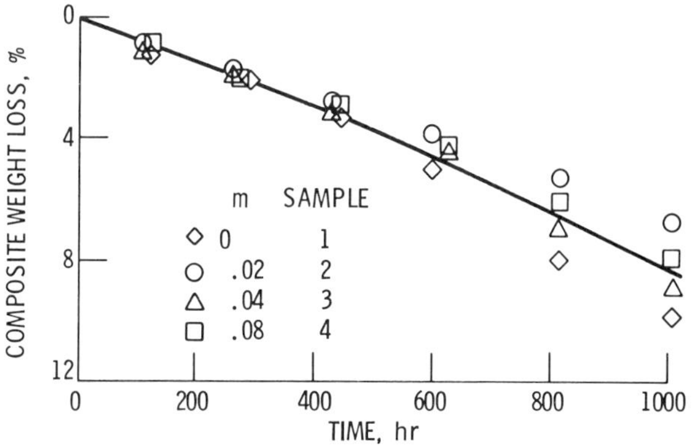

Fig. 3. Weight loss of PMR polyimide/HTS graphite fiber composites from HFDE/MDA/TEAB/NE, n = 1.50, exposed in air at 316 °C

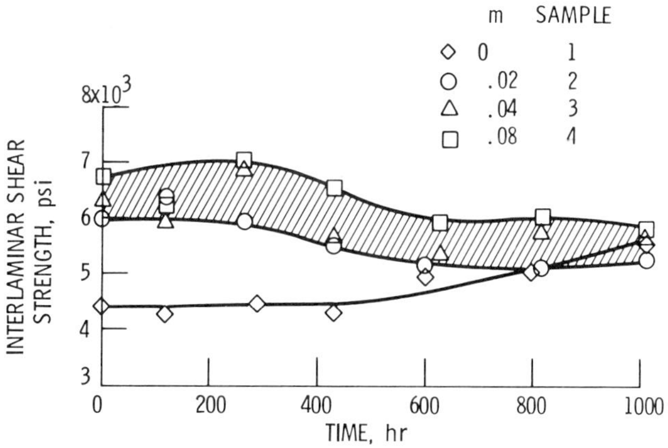

Fig. 4. Interlaminar shear strength of PMR polyimide/HTS graphite fiber composites from HFDE/MDA/TEAB/NE, n = 1.50, exposed and tested at 316 °C.

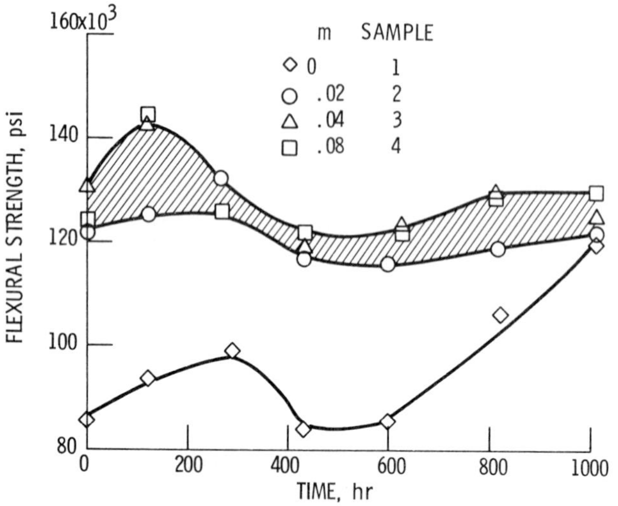

Fig. 5. Flexural strength of PMR polyimide/HTS graphite fiber composites from HFDE/MDA/TEAB/NE, n = 1.50, exposed and tested at 316 °C.

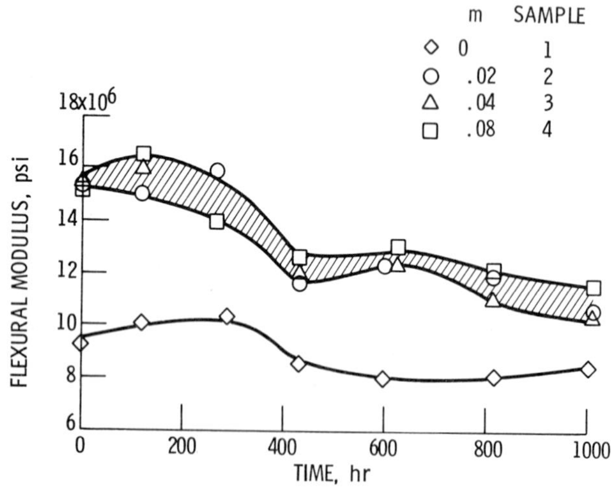

Fig. 6. Flexural modulus of PMR polyimide/HTS graphite fiber composites from HFDE/MDA/TEAB/NE, n = 1.50, exposed and tested at 316 °C.

THERMOOXIDATION OF METHYLENE BRIDGING GROUPS IN POLYIMIDES

Robert A. Jewell and George F. Sykes
NASA Langley Research Center

ABSTRACT

The methylene compound 4,4'-diaminodiphenyl-methane (MDA) is used extensively in the synthesis of aromatic polyimides. Investigators have proposed that, on prolonged heating in air, the methylene group in such polyimides and other thermally stable polymers, oxidizes and provides readily available cross-linking sites. In this study, polyimide films prepared by the reaction of three dianhydrides with MDA were cured in air and in vacuo at temperature/time ratios that closely relate to their processing and use capability. They were then characterized by thermogravimetric, torsional braid, and infrared techniques to determine the fate of the $-CH_2-$ moiety. Infrared spectra of films heated in air to $300^{o}C$ suggest heavy carbonyl formation with incomplete conversion to a benzophenone structure. By both dynamic and isothermal heating in air, films of two compositions displayed weight gains of 1.5 to 2.0 percent, indicating severe oxidation. Glass transition temperatures (T_g) of the thermally oxidized methylene-containing polyimides increased well beyond the T_g's noted for companion, 4,4'-diaminobenzophenone polyimides, suggesting that crosslinking also occurred.

I. INTRODUCTION

Polyimides occupy a dominant position among the thermally stable aromatic polymers. They are produced commercially as films, molding compounds, laminating varnishes, adhesives, coatings, foams, and fibers. Diamines containing a methylene bridge between phenyl rings are widely used in the synthesis of polyimides since such monomers provide a flexibilizing group in the imide structure and are relatively inexpensive.

Investigations made on the thermal oxidation of $-CH_2-$ main chain groups generally indicate carbonyl formation accompanied by crosslinking. J. Lady *et al.*,[1] noted that the $-CH_2-$ groups of polybenzyl oxidized initially to hydroxyl groups which were subsequently converted to esters, anhydrides, and approximately 12 percent by weight benzophenone. Nishizaki and Fukami[2] used differential thermal analysis to show that oxidation of methylene linkages in several polyimides occurred in the 200° to 300°C region. Dine-Hart and Wright,[3] in a thermal stability study at 400°C, noted unexpectedly good weight retention for those polyimides containing a methylene bridge. They also gave evidence for carbonyl formation.

This study deals with polyimides formed from 4,4'-diaminodiphenylmethane (MDA) monomer and their oxidation in the region of 300°C, a temperature well within polyimide processing requirements and utility. The polymerization of MDA with three aromatic dianhydrides containing different flexibilizing linkages provided polymer films with varying thermophysical properties. To follow the oxidation of the MDA-type polyimides, companion polymers were made with 4,4'-diaminobenzophenone (DABP). Complementing thermogravimetric, torsional braid, and infrared techniques were used to determine the effects of thermooxidation.

II. EXPERIMENTAL PROCEDURES

The theoretical polymer repeat units and the abbreviations used in this study are:

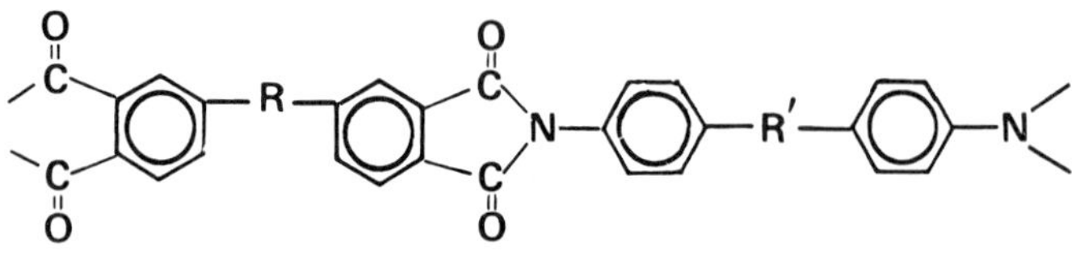

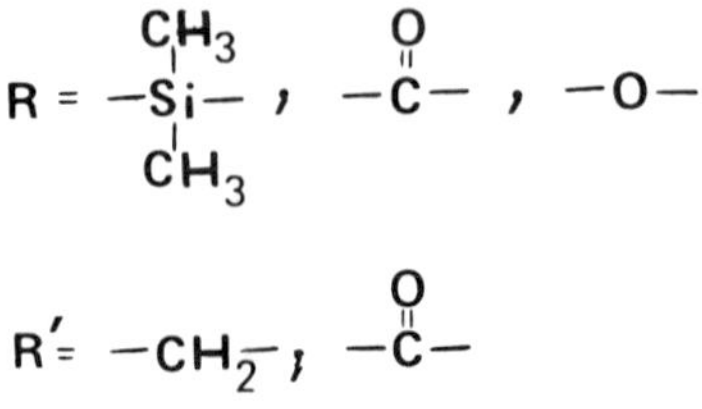

The dianhydrides, bis (3,4-dicarboxyphenyl) dimethylsilane dianhydride[4] (SIDA), 3,3',4,4'-benzophenone tetracarboxylic dianhydride (BTDA), and bis (3,4-dicarboxyphenyl) ether dianhydride[5] (ODPA), were polymerized with 4,4'-diaminodiphenylmethane (MDA), and with 4,4'-diaminobenzophenone (DABP).

All test samples were formed from 10 percent solutions of polyamic acids in dimethylacetamide. Each specimen was air dried at ambient temperature, then progressively heated for 1 hour at 100°C, 1 hour at 200°C, and 1 hour at 300°C, in air, nitrogen, or vacuum. Infrared spectra of films nominally 0.15 mil thick were obtained on a Perkin-Elmer Model 421 grating spectrophotometer. Isothermal and dynamic (2° C/min) weight loss data of films nominally 1 mil thick were obtained from thermogravimetric apparatus described previously.[6] Torsional braid analyses (TBA)[7] were performed at 3° C/min in a constant nitrogen flow of 40 cc/min.

III. RESULTS AND DISCUSSION

A. Thermogravimetric Analysis

Thermal and thermooxidative degradation curves, Figures 1 through 6, provided evidence of both oxidation and crosslinking. Under dynamic and isothermal heating in air, Figures 1, 5, and 6, the MDA-type films gain between 1 percent and 2 percent in weight prior to onset of weight loss. Since the films had been precured in air at 300°C, the degree of oxidation would seem considerable. However, isothermal data in Figures 3 and 4 show that oxidized MDA polymer was lower in overall stability than its DABP counterpart, indicating that a methylene-bridged polymer had not completely converted to benzophenone structure.

Others[3] have suggested that crosslinking activity accompanies oxidation of the $-CH_2-$ linkage, with crosslinking beneficially altering the rate of degradation above 400°C. At these rather high temperatures, the effects of degradation might be represented by dynamic heating results, as shown in Figures 1 and 2. In both air and vacuum the order of relative stability was SIDA > ODPA > BTDA. At the more conservative isothermal temperature of 300°C, Figure 3, the order of stability was ODPA > BTDA > SIDA. Thus, the silyl-containing polymer appeared the most stable under dynamic heating and the least stable under isothermal heating. Isothermal experiments between 250°C and 350°C showed a different temperature at which each MDA-film exhibited a weight increase.

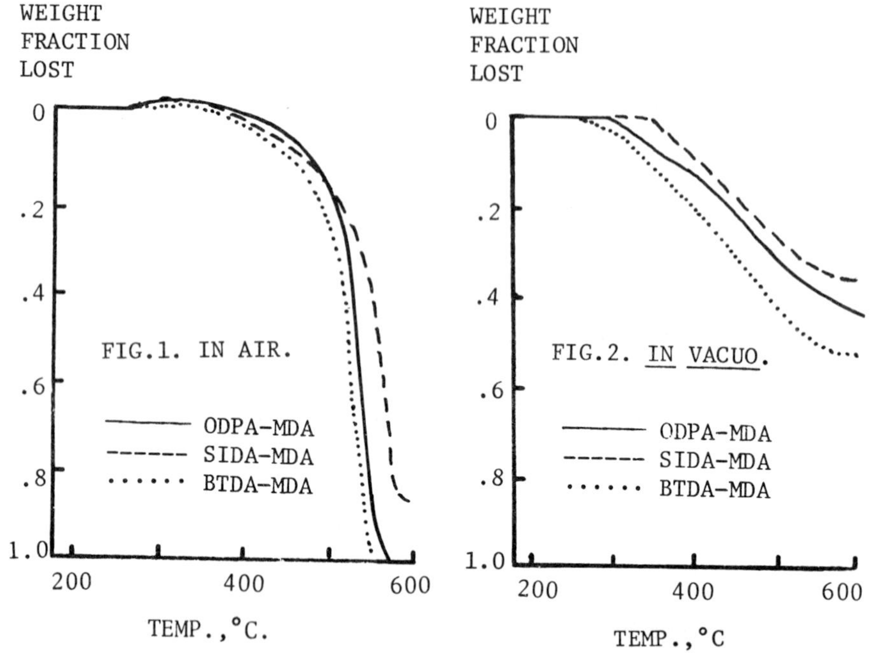

Figs. 1 and 2. Thermograms of polyimides with diphenylmethane moieties.

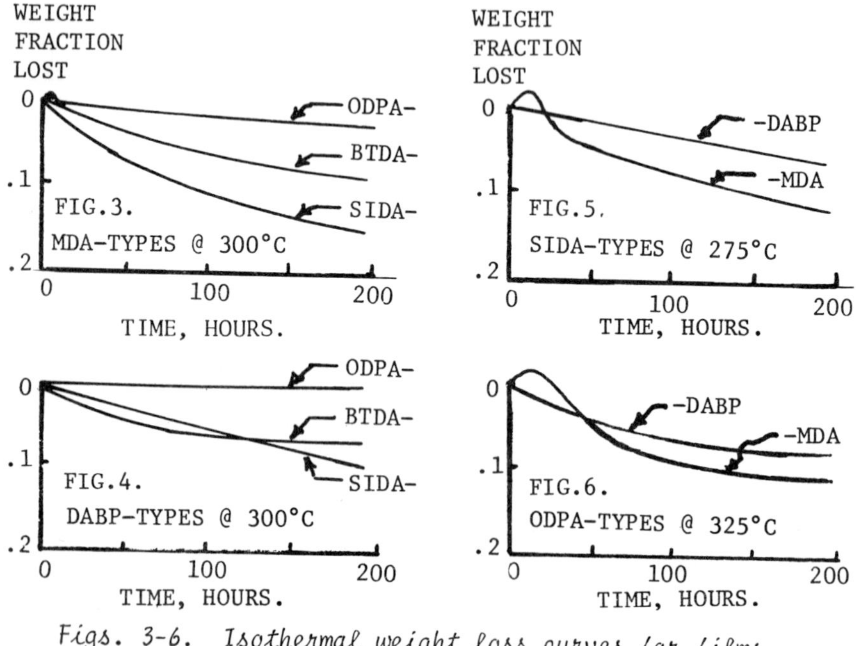

Figs. 3-6. Isothermal weight loss curves for films heated in air.

At 275°C, SIDA-MDA (Fig. 5) showed a weight gain of approximately 2 percent, whereas ODPA-MDA (Fig. 6) required 325°C for a similar gain. The BTDA-MDA gained slightly more than 1 percent at 300°C. Possibly the more readily oxidizable the polyimide, the more readily and more completely it might crosslink. The result would be a transient improvement in oxidative resistance, with degree of enhancement dependent upon polymer chemistry and exposure conditions.

B. Infrared Spectral Analysis

Figures 7a, 7b and 7c show the infrared spectral differences between films cured in vacuum and in air at 300°C. For each of the three MDA-type films these differences emerged only after curing above 200°C in air, and these spectral changes were similar for each type. However, the ether and carbonyl groups in the ODPA- and BTDA-imides, respectively, contributed characteristic vibrational frequencies which made certain band assignments somewhat difficult. Therefore, this analysis concentrated upon changes in the SIDA-MDA spectrum. The relatively early oxidation of SIDA-MDA film, as noted by thermogravimetric data, also tended to simplify identification of these structural changes.

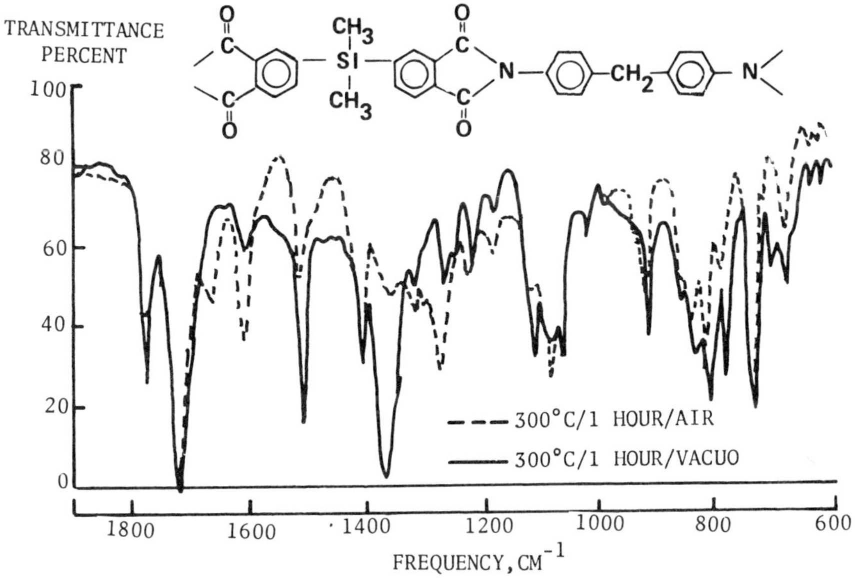

Fig. 7a. IR spectral changes from thermal oxidation of SIDA-4,4'MDA film.

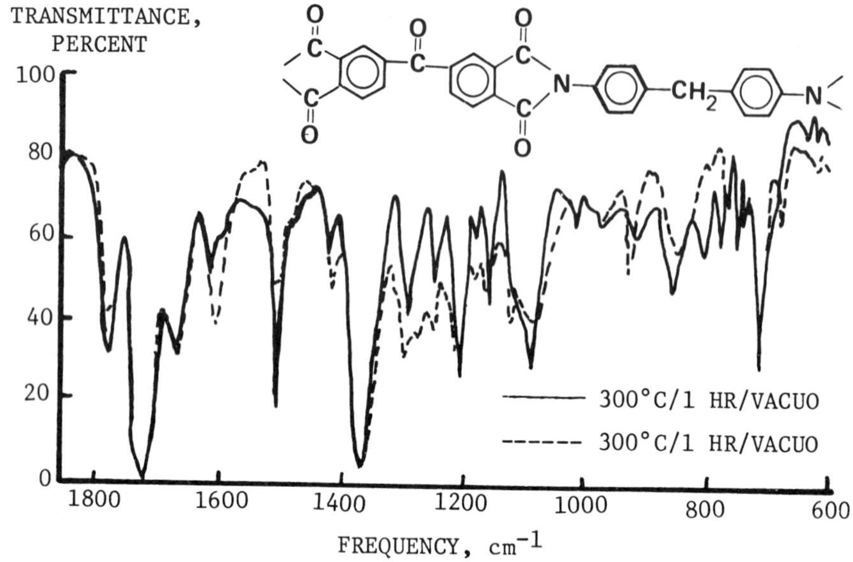

Fig. 7b. IR spectral changes from thermal oxidation of BTDA-4,4'MDA film.

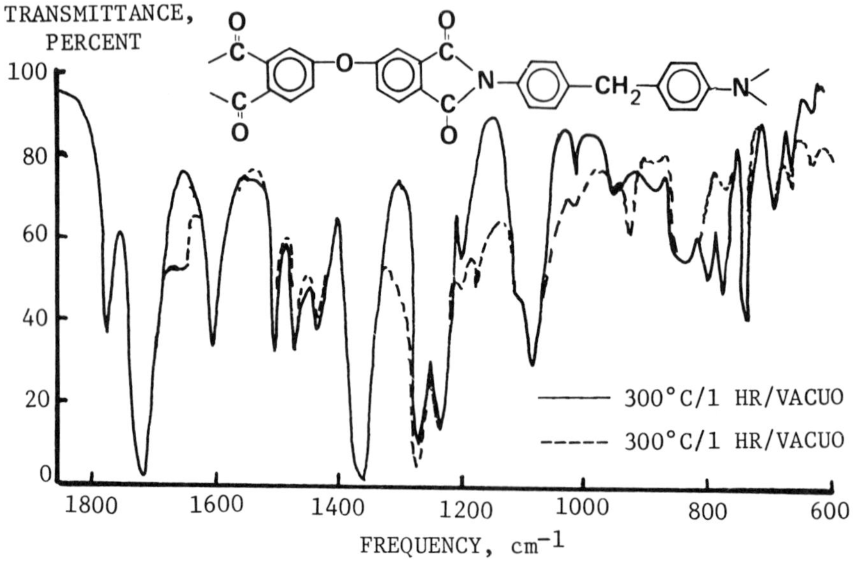

Fig. 7c. IR spectra changes thermal oxidation of ODPA-4,4'MDA film.

Previous investigators[3] noted that oxidized methylene-bridged polymers developed bands at 1660 cm^{-1} and 930 cm^{-1} and associated these bands with ketone stretching and aromatic C=0 rocking frequencies. We have noted other major differences between these spectra, and our tentative assignments[8] are listed in Table I. These assignments, actually evincive arguments, depict the distinct loss of CH_2 character accompanied by strong C=0 formation.

TABLE I
Changes in IR Spectra with Thermooxidation of SIDA-MDA Polyimide Film

Frequency, cm^{-1}	Intensity	Change	Tentative assignment
1660	Medium	Increase	Ketone stretch
1605	Strong	Increase	Quadrant stretch for substituted benzene, sensitive to C=0 conjunction
1510	Medium	Decrease	Semicircular stretch for substituted benzene, sensitive to electron donor group activity
1410	Medium	None	Component of 1510 cm^{-1} band, but relatively independent of substituent
1270	Strong	Increase	Asymmetric stretch for substituted benzene, more sensitive generally to C=0, C=N conjugation
1120 1080 1055	Medium	Decrease	CH_2 wag
930	Medium	Increase	Aromatic C=0 wag, particularly with all-para geometry
855 805	Weak Medium	Decrease	CH_3 rocking doublet
695	Weak	Decrease	CH_2 rock
670	Medium	Increase	C=0 bend

This strong C=0 formation is particularly noticeable when comparing spectra for the oxidized SIDA-MDA and the SIDA-DABP films (Fig. 8). The spectrum of oxidized SIDA-MDA (a repeat of the dashed-line spectrum in Fig. 7a) clearly bears a close resemblance to the SIDA-DABP spectrum with two small exceptions noted by arrows. The weaker absorption at 1660 cm^{-1} in the SIDA-MDA scan could reflect incomplete oxidation after only 1 hour at 300°C. However, the lack of absorption at 1150 cm^{-1}, a band found in all three of the DABP-type films but in none of the oxidized MDA-type, suggests that oxidation of the methylene bridge did not result in simple conversion to benzophenone structure.

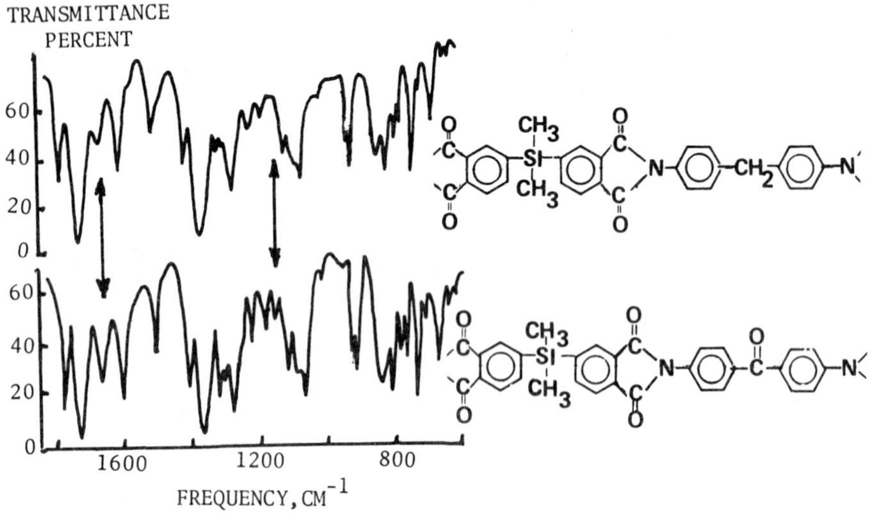

Fig. 8. IR spectra for two dimethylsilyl-containing polyimides cured in air at 300°C.

Thermooxidation of the dimethylsilyl group is difficult to detect. Any change in the 1255 cm^{-1} methyl band is probably hidden by the large increase in the 1270 cm^{-1} band (Fig. 7a). However, the decrease in absorption at 855 cm^{-1} and 805 cm^{-1}, frequencies tentatively attributed to a methyl rocking doublet, might indirectly suggest that some degradation of the dimethylsilyl group also occurred.

C. Torsional Braid Analysis

Figure 9 shows thermomechanical data obtained by torsional braid analysis (TBA) for the two silyl-containing polymers. For the SIDA-MDA imide, both rigidity and damping index curves obtained in an air environment differed significantly from those obtained under nitrogen. In air, a general stiffening occurred above 300°C, indicative of crosslinking. Taken in conjunction with the continued decrease in damping above 320°C, thermooxidative degradation and crosslinking appeared to occur simultaneously.

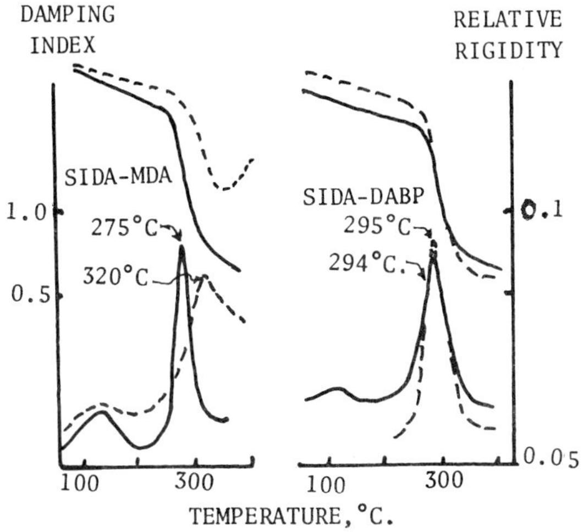

Fig. 9. TBA curves for two dimethylsilyl-containing polyimides cured in air (---) and in N_2 (——).

The major damping peak for SIDA-MDA, which represents the polymer glass transition temperature, shifted from 275°C in nitrogen to 320°C in air. This rather large increase in T_g, coupled with the weight gain noted in Figure 5, indicates that crosslinking had commenced well before exposure to 300°C in air. This argument was supported by changes in the beta transition region at 100° to 150°C, which might relate to segmental and/or intermolecular motions.

TABLE II
Effects of Environment on T_g by TBA

Polymer	N_2	Air	ΔT_g
SIDA-MDA	275°C	320°C	45°C
SIDA-DABP	294	295	1
ODPA-MDA	277	310	33
ODPA-DABP	271	281	10
BTDA-MDA	288	311	23
BTDA-DABP	287	293	6

Figure 9 also shows the TBA results for the SIDA-DABP polymer. Not only were the effects of thermooxidation minor for this polymer, but the T_g of 294° to 295°C did not agree with the T_g's of 275°C or 320°C noted for SIDA-MDA polymer. Table II tabulates T_g values for all six polyimides obtained by TBA in nitrogen and in air. Differences between the T_g's for the DABP-type polyimides and the MDA-types indicate that the thermooxidation of polymers containing the $-CH_2-$ linkage did not proceed cleanly to the benzophenone moiety.

IV. CONCLUSIONS

An investigation of polyimides prepared by reacting 4,4'-diaminodiphenylmethane and each of three different aromatic dianhydrides disclosed a complex mechanism of thermooxidative degradation. Thermogravimetric, infrared, and torsional braid analytical techniques showed oxidation of the methylenedianiline moiety to benzophenone carbonyl groups. However, comparisons with three similar polyimides prepared from 4,4'-diaminobenzophenone established that oxidation of the methylene group was by no means an exclusive conversion to the carbonyl function but probably was accompanied by an indeterminate amount of crosslinking.

V. REFERENCES

1. J. Lady, R. E. Adams, and I. Kesse, J. Appl. Polymer Sci., 3 (7), 65 (1960).

2. S. Nishizaki and A. Fukami, Kogyo Kagaku Zasshi, 67, (3), 474 (1964).

3. R. A. Dine-Hart and W. W. Wright, Die Makromolekulare Chemie, 153, 237 (1972).

4. J. R. Pratt and S. F. Thames, J. Org. Chem., 38, 4271 (1973).

5. G. S. Kolesnikov, O. Ya. Fedotova, E. I. Hofbaver, and V. G. Shelgayera, Polymer Sci., U.S.S.R., 9:3, 685 (1967).

6. R. A. Jewell, J. Appl. Polym. Sci., 12, 1137 (1968).

7. S. K. Dalal, G. L. Carl, A. T. Inge, and N. J. Johnston, ACS Polymer Preprints, 15, (1), 576 (1974).

8. N. B. Colthrop, L. H. Daly, and S. E. Wiberley, "Introduction to Infrared and Raman Spectroscopy," Academic Press, Inc., New York, N.Y. (1964).

ACETYLENE TERMINATED PHENYLQUINOXALINE OLIGOMERS

P. M. Hergenrother*
NASA Langley Research Center
Hampton, VA 23665

Acetylene terminated phenylquinoxaline oligomers were prepared by the condensation of 4-ethynylphenoxybenzil with o-diamino end-capped phenylquinoxaline oligomers and also by the reaction of 4-acetylphenoxybenzil with an o-diamino end-capped phenyquinoxaline oligomer, followed by treating the acetyl end-capped oligomer with the Vilsmeier reagent and subsequent cleavage of the β-chlorocinnamaldehyde with base. The acetylene terminated phenylquinoxaline oligomers were thermally polymerized and characterized. In addition, a model compound, 2-[4-(4-ethynylphenoxy)phenylene]-3-phenylquinoxaline, was prepared and studies were conducted to determine the minimum temperature for reaction of the acetylene group, the effect of higher temperature upon the product, and the identity of the major component in the thermally induced reaction product.

I. INTRODUCTION

High temperature structural resins require high dimensional stability at elevated temperatures to perform successfully as adhesives, foams, or composite matrices. The dimensional stability is achieved primarily as a result of the high heat distortion temperature (HDT) and high thermo-oxidative stability of the resin. The principal way to obtain a high HDT is through crosslinking (induced order can be viewed as crosslinking). Crosslinking can be affected by joining high molecular weight linear molecules together to form a network structure and also by chain extending low molecular weight molecules in such a manner as to form a

*NASA Grant NSG-1124 with Virginia Polytechnic Institute and State University, Blacksburg, VA 24061.

network structure. Both approaches have been used in high temperature polymers but with only moderate success.

Various methods such as high temperature exposure (thermal and thermooxidative crosslinking), high energy radiation, addition of free radical generators, induced order (crystallinity), and synthetic crosslinking through latent groups incorporated within the polymer or end-capped on oligomers have been studied as a means of obtaining dimensional stability in high temperature polymers. The two methods most commonly employed to alleviate the thermoplasticity in high temperature polymers are high temperature exposure (postcure) and synthetic crosslinking. High temperature postcure generally results in improved high temperature structural performance but at the sacrifice of lowering the use life at elevated temperatures. Synthetic crosslinking appears to offer the most attractive route to obtain a polymer with long term high temperature structural properties. Several different groups such as those in Table I have been used to effect crosslinking in a variety of high temperature polymers. For the most part, crosslinking is obtained by compromising the processability, certain mechanical properties, and thermooxidative stability of the resin.

One of the main problems in achieving crosslinking through latent groups is that as crosslinking occurs, the mobility of the molecules decrease and the latent groups can no longer come into contact with one another as readily. As a result, high temperature postcures are employed to effect additional crosslinking which occurs not only through further reaction of the latent groups but also through thermal and/or thermooxidative mechanisms. The effect of the residual latent groups upon long term high temperature performance must be given attention. In addition, several other factors must be considered in crosslinking high temperature polymers such as processability (e.g. adequate flow and preferably no volatiles), retention of desired mechanical properties (e.g. toughness, impact resistance), high thermal and thermooxidative stability, resistance to moisture (e.g. hydrolytic and plasticization) and solvents, cost, and safety.

As indicated in Table I, the acetylene group has undergone evaluation in several polymers as a means of chain extension and crosslinking. The use of acetylene groups to chain extend a high temperature polymer was first reported (12) in 1974. Acetylene terminated imide oligomers were thermally polymerized with the mechanism of cure proposed as aromatization or acetylenic trimerization (12). Further studies reported (21) in 1975 using nmr lended support to substantiate the trimerization mechanism.

Table 1

Representative Synthetic Crosslinking Groups For High Temperature Polymers

Crosslinking Group or monomer	Proposed Crosslink	Polymer Type	Reference
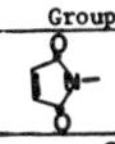	Addition through double bond	Endcapped oligomeric polyimides (PI)	1
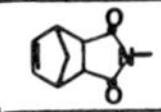	Diels-Alder type reaction, evolves cyclopentadiene	Endcapped oligomeric PI	2
CH_2=CH-	Addition	On pendant phenyl group on polyphenylquinoxalines (PPQ)	3
Active $-CH_3$	Addition through tautomeric form	(1) On linear poly-as-triazine (2) On pendant phenyl group on PPQ	4 5
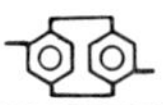	Thermal formation of free radicals	(1) Within backbone of polybenzimidazole (2) Within backbone of polyketone	6 7
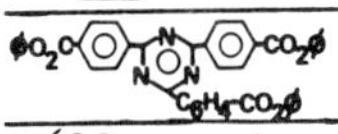	As a trifunctional monomer	Polybenzimidazoquinazolines	8, 9
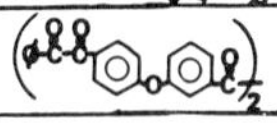	As a trifunctional monomer	PPQ	10
HC≡C-	Addition	(1) Oligomeric polyphenylenes (2) Endcapped oligomeric PI (3) Endcapped oligomeric PPQ (4) Within backbone of PPQ (5) Within backbone of polysulfone	11 12 13 14 15
N≡C-	(1) Addition with nitrile oxide (2) Trimerization to sym-triazine	(1) Endcapped oligomeric PI (chain extension and crosslinking) (2) On pendant phenyl group on PPQ	16 17
N≡C-O-	Trimerization to cyanurate	(1) On pendant phenyl group on PPQ (2) On polyphenyl-as-triazine	17 4
Active $-CH_2-$	Aldol type reaction with carbonyl to form >C=C<	Within backbone of PI	18
	Reaction with a divinyl or bismaleimide compound	(1) Pendant group on polyquinoxalines (2) Endcapped oligomeric PI	19 20

The preparation of acetylene terminated phenylquinoxaline oligomers (ATPQ) from the reaction of 3-(3,4-diaminophenoxy) phenyl acetylene with phenylquinoxaline oligomers end-capped with 1,2-dicarbonyl groups was recently reported (13). An ATPQ of the following idealized structure reportedly (13) exhibited good solubility (20 to 30%) in low boiling organic solvents (e.g. chloroform, tetrahydrofuran) and an apparent

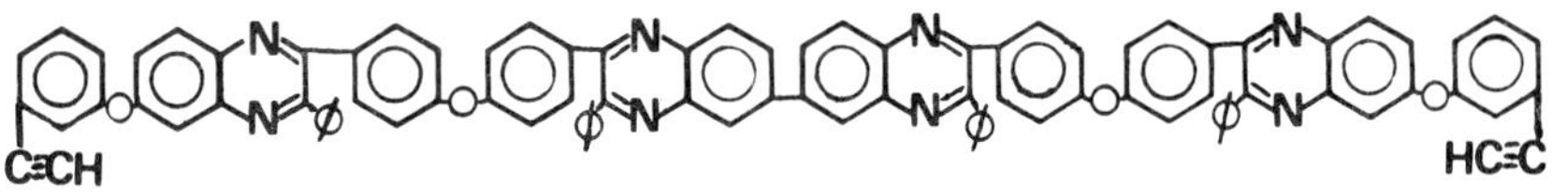

Tg of 318°C after 2 hours at 280°C in nitrogen. Similar to the acetylene terminated polyimides (12), the ATPQ cure by an addition mechanism (no volatiles) at moderate temperatures which is an attractive feature for processing as adhesives and composite matrices.

The work reported herein was performed to evaluate two new synthetic routes to ATPQ and resins therefrom. In addition, model compound work was performed to determine the minimum temperature for reaction of the acetylene group, the effect of higher temperature upon the product, and the identity of the major component in the product.

II. EXPERIMENTAL

A. Monomers

4-Ethynylphenoxybenzil was prepared according to the reaction scheme in Eq. 1.

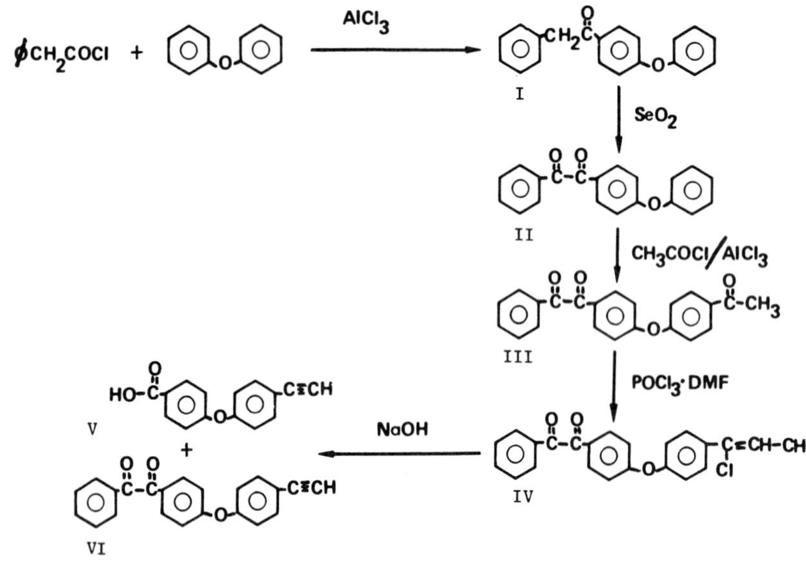

(1)

4-Phenoxybenzil (II) - A solution of diphenyl ether (340 g, 2.0 mole) and phenylacetyl chloride (140 g, 0.91 mole) in methylene chloride (150 ml) was added dropwise during 2 hours to a stirred slurry of anhydrous aluminum chloride (140 g, 1.1 mole) in methylene chloride (450 ml) at ambient temperature. After stirring overnight, the dark red reaction mixture was poured into a stirred mixture of ice and hydrochloric acid. The organic phase was separated, washed thoroughly with water and saturated sodium chloride, dried over calcium sulfate, and concentrated to dryness. The white residue was thoroughly washed with two 400 ml portions of cold cyclohexane to yield 4-phenylacetylphenoxybenzene (I) as a white solid (223 g, 85% yield), m.p. 83-85.5°C. Recrystallization from cyclohexane (2 l.) provided white crystals (191 g, 86% recovery), m.p. 87-88°C. Compound I (191 g, 0.66 mole) and selenium dioxide (73.5 g, 0.66 mole) in glacial acetic acid (800 ml) were refluxed overnight. The black reaction mixture was filtered hot and the cooled yellow filtrate poured into cold water (2 l.) to precipitate a yellow gum. The gum was washed thoroughly with hot water and taken up in methylene chloride. After drying over calcium sulfate, the solution was concentrated to dryness to provide 4-phenoxybenzil (II) as a yellow solid (192 g, 96% yield), m.p. 43-44°C. Recrystallization from ethanol provided yellow crystals, m.p. 45-46°C [lit. (22) m.p. 65.0-65.7°C]

Anal. Calcd. for $C_{20}H_{14}O_3$: C,79.45;H,4.67

Found: C,79.38;H,4.61

<u>4-Acetylphenoxybenzil (III)</u> - A solution of II (60.4 g, 0.2 mole) and acetyl chloride (16.4 g, 0.21 mole) in methylene chloride (250 ml) was added dropwise during 2.5 hours to a stirred slurry of anhydrous aluminum chloride (93.1 g, 0.7 mole) in methylene chloride (200 ml) at ambient temperature. The dark purple reaction mixture was stirred overnight and poured into a stirred mixture of ice and hydrochloric acid. The organic phase was separated, washed thoroughly with water and saturated sodium chloride, dried over calcium sulfate, and concentrated to dryness. The residual yellow solid (67.4 g, 98% yield), m.p. 55-59°C, was dissolved in methanol (700 ml) and the hot methanol solution placed in an ice bath. Yellow crystals (53 g) formed which melted at 59-61°C, resolidified, and remelted at 93-94°C. When the methanol solution was cooled slowly, near-white crystals of 4-acetylphenoxybenzil (III) formed, m.p. 93-94°C.

Anal. Calcd. for $C_{22}H_{16}O_4$: C,76.73;H,4.68

Found: C,76.82;H,4.73

<u>4-Phenylglyoxalylphenoxy-β-chlorocinnamaldehyde (IV)</u> - Compound III (10.3 g, 0.03 mole) in dry DMF (45 ml) was added dropwise during 0.5 hour at ambient temperature to a stirred solution of the Vilsmeier reagent [prepared by the dropwise

addition of redistilled phosphorus oxychloride (8.3 ml, 0.09 mole) to dry DMF (35 ml) at 5°C followed by stirring at ambient temperature for 2 hours]. The reaction mixture was stirred overnight and the orange solution poured into cold aqueous sodium acetate (30 g in 200 ml of water) to yield a yellow gum. The yellow gum was extracted with methylene chloride, washed thoroughly with water followed by saturated sodium chloride, dried over calcium sulfate, and concentrated to dryness to yield an orange gum (10.3 g, 88% yield). Extraction twice with boiling cyclohexane (250 ml) yielded an insoluble orange gum (6.7 g) and clear yellow solution. Upon cooling, the yellow solution provided pale yellow crystals (3.0 g, 29% yield), m.p. 82-84°C, of 4-phenylglyoxalylphenoxy-β-chlorocinnamaldehyde (IV).

Anal. Calcd. for $C_{23}H_{15}O_4$ Cl: C,70.68;H,3.87;Cl,9.07

Found: C,70.53;H,3.85;Cl,8.88

4-Ethynylphenoxybenzil (VI) - A solution of the yellow crystals of IV (3.0 g, 0.0077 mole) in dioxane (30 ml) was added to a solution of sodium hydroxide (3.0 g, 0.075 mole) in water (30 ml). The brown reaction mixture was stirred at 55-60°C for 2 hours followed by pouring into cold water (200 ml). The orange aqueous solution was extracted twice with methylene chloride (150 ml) and the methylene chloride solution washed with water, dried over calcium sulfate, and concentrated to dryness to yield 4-ethynylphenoxybenzil (VI) as a yellow oil (0.5 g, 20% yield).

Anal. Calcd. for $C_{22}H_{14}O_3$: C,80.97;H,4.32

Found: C,80.69;H,4.44

The aqueous phase was acidified with dilute hydrochloric acid to provide a yellow solid (1.4 g) which was extracted with benzene (100 ml). The benzene solution was concentrated to dryness to yield 4-ethynylphenoxybenzoic acid (V) as a yellow solid (1.0 g), m.p. 161-163° (introduced into preheated bath at 150°C) Mass spectrum: M^+ at 238.

3,3',4,4'-Tetraaminobiphenyl(VII) - This tetraamine was obtained commercially and recrystallized from water (20 g/l) containing a pinch of sodium dithionite under nitrogen. Near white crystals, mp 177-178°C [lit. (23) mp 179-180°C] were obtained in 70% recovery.

4,4'-Oxydibenzil (VIII) - The dibenzil was prepared following a known procedure (24) and obtained in 66% overall yield after recrystallization from ethanol as yellow crystals, mp 106-

107°C [lit. (25) mp 106.4-107.4°C].
1,3-Bis(phenylglyoxalyl)benzene (IX) - Following a known procedure (26), 1,3-bis(phenylglyoxalyl)benzene was obtained in 61% overall yield after recrystallization from ethanol as yellow crystals, mp 98-99°C [lit. (27) mp 98-99.5°C].

B. Model Compound

A model compound, 2-[4-(4-ethynylphenoxy)phenylene]-3-phenylquinoxaline (X), was prepared by two routes as shown in Eq. 2.

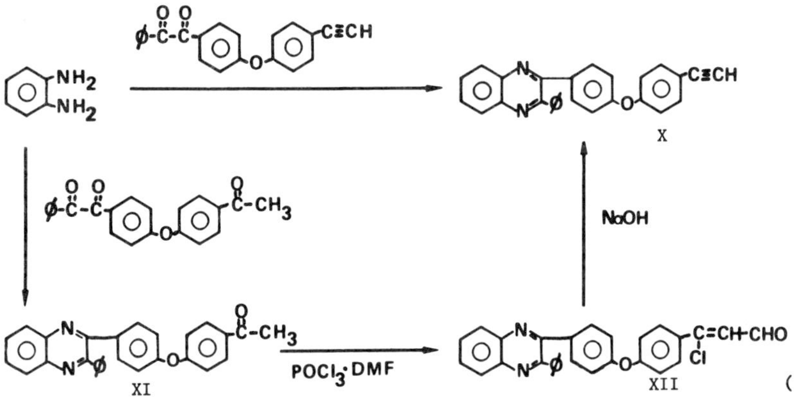

(2)

2-[4-(4-Ethynylphenoxy)phenylene]-3-phenylquinoxaline (X) - A solution of VI (0.8636 g, 0.0027 mole) and 1,2-diaminobenzene (0.2866 g, 0.0027 mole) in ethanol (100 ml) was refluxed for 0.5 hour. The yellow solution was poured into cold water (100 ml) and extracted with methylene chloride. The methylene chloride was evaporated to leave X as a glassy yellow solid (1.00 g, 94% yield) which melted at 61-65°C, resolidified, and remelted at 132-134°C. After standing for several days, the yellow solid sintered at 126 and melted at 132-134°C. Recrystallization from cyclohexane provided a yellow solid, m.p. 132-134°C.

Anal. Calcd. for $C_{28}H_{18}N_2O$: C,84.40;H,4.55;N,7.03

Found: C,84.24;H,4.65;N,6.97

2-[4-(4-Acetylphenoxy) phenylene]-3-phenylquinoxaline (XI) - A solution of III (5.16 g, 0.015 mole) and 1,2-diaminobenzene (1.62 g, 0.015 mole) in ethanol (100 ml) was refluxed for 1 hour. The resulting hot yellow solution was treated with charcoal, filtered, and concentrated to dryness to provide a glassy yellow solid (6.0 g, 97% yield), m.p. 62-64°C. A 1.0 gram portion was recrystallized from cyclohexane (50 ml) to yield XI as pale yellow crystals, m.p. 146.5-147.5°C.

Anal. Calcd. for $C_{28}H_{20}N_2O_2$: C,80.75;H,4.84;N,6.73

Found: C,80.67;H,4.90;N,6.66

4-(3-Phenylquinoxalinyl)phenoxy-β-chlorocinnamaldehyde (XII) - A solution of XI (4.3 g, 0.010 mole) in dry DMF (40 ml) was added to a solution of the Vilsmeier reagent (9.0 ml phosphorus oxychloride and 30 ml DMF) and stirred overnight at ambient temperature under nitrogen. The orange solution was poured into aqueous sodium acetate (30 g in 250 ml of water) to precipitate a yellow solid which was thoroughly washed with water and dried over phosphorus pentoxide *in vacuo*. The resulting yellow solid (4.5 g), m.p. 71-75°C (DMF still present), was extracted twice with boiling cyclohexane (150 ml) to provide an insoluble yellow solid (2.8 g), m.p. 146-148°C, and yellow solution. The solution was concentrated to 50 ml. and cooled to provided XII as pale yellow crystals (1.4 g, 30% yield) m.p. 171-173°C.

Anal. Calcd. for $C_{29}H_{19}N_2O_2Cl$: C,75.24;H,4.14;N,6.05;Cl,7.66

Found: C,75.30;H,4.27;N,5.93;Cl,7.58

2-[4-(4-Ethynylphenoxy)phenylene]-3-phenylquinoxaline (X) - A solution of XII (0.93 g, 0.002 mole) in dioxane (10 ml) was added to a stirred solution of sodium hydroxide (2.0 g, 0.05 mole) in water (15 ml) and the reaction mixture stirred at 55-63°C for 2 hours. The dark orange solution was poured into cold water (100 ml) and extracted with methylene chloride. The methylene chloride solution was washed thoroughly with water, dried over calcium sulfate, and concentrated to dryness to provide a glassy orange solid (0.53 g, 68% yield) which melted at 62-65°C, resolidified, and remelted at 131-133°C. An analytically pure sample, m.p. 132-134°C, was obtained by recrystallizing from cyclohexane.

Thermal Reaction of X - Small portions (~20 mg) of X were heated in the DSC at a rate of 20°C/minute in a nitrogen atmosphere and held for 0.5 hour at 195°, 247°, 298°, and 350°C. Each sample was then analyzed by high pressure liquid chromatography and the major component in the $350^{\circ}C$ product isolated and analyzed by infrared and mass spectroscopy.

C. Polymers

As shown in Eq. 3, ATPQ was prepared by two routes. 3,3',4,4'-Tetraaminobiphenyl (0.010 mole) was reacted with 4,4'-oxydibenzil (0.0050 mole) or 1,3-bis(phenylglyoxalyl)-benzene (0.0050 mole) in _m_-cresol (35 ml) for 1 hour at $90^{\circ}C$. A solution of 4-ethynylphenoxybenzil (0.010 mole) in _m_-cresol (5 ml) was added to the _o_-diamino end-capped phenyl-quinoxaline oligomer solution and stirred at RT for 2 hr

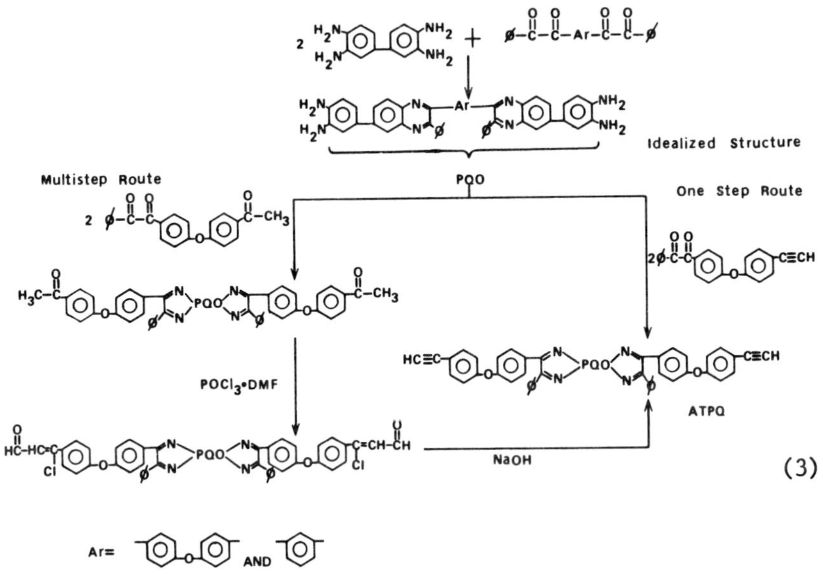

(3)

followed by heating for 1 hr at $90^{\circ}C$. The resulting ATPQ (quantitative yield) was isolated as a yellow powder by precipitation in methanol, washed in boiling methanol, and dried at $100^{\circ}C$ for 18 hr.

The alternate but less preferred route to ATPQ involved reaction of the o-diamino end-capped phenylquinoxaline oligomer with 4-acetylphenoxybenzil in _m_-cresol followed by treating the isolated acetyl end-capped oligomer in chloroform with the Vilsmeier reagent (DMF solution) and subsequently cleaving the β-chlorocinnamaldehyde end-capped oligomer in dioxane with aqueous sodium hydroxide at 60-70°C. The resulting ATPQ exhibited an infrared spectrum and other properties similar to those obtained for the ATPQ prepared by the first route. Polymer characterization is presented in Table 2.

TABLE 2

Polymer Characterization

Polymer	oxy-ATPQ[1]	oxy-ATPQ[1]	m-ATPQ[2]
Synthetic Route (see Eq. 3)	one step	multistep	one step
Solubility (20% solids @RT, w/v)	dioxane, tetrahydrofuran, methylene chloride, chloroform, *m*-cresol		
Polymer Melt Temperature, °C	197-213	190-218	234-247
Exotherm of Chain Extension R_x[3], °C	~200 to ~350, peaks@268 (see Fig. 1)	~190 to ~350, peaks@270	~205 to ~280, peaks@246
Apparent Tg by DSC[3], °C			
after heating to 350°C, N_2	326	318	270
after 0.5 hr @350°C, N_2	333	325	275
after 0.5 hr @375°C, N_2	335	327	279
after 0.5 hr @400°C, N_2	342	330	299
after 2.0 hr @400°C, N_2	349	332	313
Apparent Tg by TBA[4], °C			
after heating to 400°C, N_2	348 (see Fig. 2)	—	311
after 0.5 hr @268°C, N_2	332	—	305
Apparent Tg by TMA[5,6], °C	320	—	268
Polymer Decomposition Temperature[6,7], °C	525, air; 530, N_2 (see Fig. 3)	490, air; 510, N_2	530, air; 532, N_2
Weight Loss (%) after 200 hr @316°C ±3 in air[6,8]	12	25	15

1. See Eq. 3, *o*-amino end-capped phenylquinoxaline oligomer prepared from 4,4'-oxydibenzil
2. See Eq. 3, *o*-amino end-capped phenylquinoxaline oligomer prepared from 1,3-bis(phenylglyoxalyl)benzene
3. Heating rate of 20°C/min.
4. Heating rate of 3°C/min.
5. Heating rate of 5°C/min. (penetration)
6. Cured 0.5 hr @350°C, N_2
7. Heating rate of 2°C/min.
8. Powder, <40 mesh particle size, circulating air

III. RESULTS AND DISCUSSION

A. Synthesis

1,2-Dicarbonyl compounds (α-diketones) are known to rearrange (28) or cleave in the presence of strong base. Therefore, prior to the preparation of 4-ethynylphenoxybenzil, a brief study was conducted on the reaction of 4-phenoxybenzil in dioxane with aqueous sodium hydroxide at 26°, 55-60°, and 93°C. Under these conditions, unreacted 4-phenoxybenzil was isolated in ~50% recovery and 4-phenoxybenzoic acid was obtained in ~50% yield. Thus, it was demonstrated that α-diketones could survive the conditions required to cleave the β-chlorocinnamaldehyde to the acetylene. 4-Ethynylphenoxybenzil was prepared is low yield according to the reaction scheme in Eq. 1. The nmr and mass spectra and detailed synthetic discussion involving the various compounds are presented elsewhere (29). A new and improved synthetic route to 4-ethynylphenoxybenzil involving the displacement of a nitro group from 4-nitrobenzil with 4-ethynylphenolate anion is under study and will be reported later.

Thermal polymerization of an acetylene terminated oligomer yields a material whose properties are obviously governed by the moieties formed during the thermal reaction. Since the thermally induced reaction of an acetylene group is very complex and can yield different structures such as $-C{\equiv}C{-}\overset{\overset{\displaystyle CH_2}{\|}}{C}{-}$, $-C{\equiv}C{-}CH{=}CH{-}$, benzene, and cyclooctatetrene, it was of interest to determine the identity of the major component. Dimerization would provide linearity to the polymer whereas addition reactions to form aromatic rings would result in a network structure. Therefore, a model compound, 2-[4-(4-ethynylphenoxy)phenylene]-3-phenylquinoxaline (X), was prepared and exposed in nitrogen for 0.5 hour at 195°, 247°, 298°, and 350°C. The reaction product from each temperature exposure was soluble is chloroform and thus permitted characterization by high pressure liquid chromatography (HPLC). At 195°C, compound X failed to undergo any substantial reaction. One major and four minor components plus about 50% of unreacted compound X were present in the 247°C reaction product. The chromatogram of the 298°C product showed a small amount (~10%) of compound X, one major, and five minor components. No unreacted X, one major and four minor components were present in the 350°C product. The major component formed at 247°, 298°, and 350°C exhibited the same retention time. A preparative separation on the 350°C product by HPLC was performed and this component was analyzed by infrared and mass spectroscopy. The fragmentation pattern and infrared spectrum were consistent with that expected for the proposed dimer (XIII) from addition of one acetylene to another. Detailed discussion of this work is presented elsewhere (29).

Acetylene terminated phenylquinoxaline oligomers (ATPQ) were prepared by two routes as shown in Eq. 3. One involved the reaction of stoichiometric quantities of 4-ethynylphenoxybenzil with the o-diamino end-capped phenylquinoxaline oligomer in m-cresol. The alternate and less preferred route concerned the reaction of stoichiometric quantities of 4-acetylphenoxybenzil with the o-diamino end-capped phenylquinoxaline oligomer to yield an acetyl terminated phenylquinoxaline oligomer. This was treated with the Vilsmeier reagent and the resulting β-chlorocinnamaldehyde terminated phenylquinoxaline oligomer treated with sodium hydroxide to yield ATPQ. Although the thermal properties of the ATPQ prepared by this multistep route are similar to those of the ATPQ prepared by the one step route, differences were observed in their infrared spectra, rate of thermal chain extension, and thermooxidative stability due to structural impurities introduced during the multistep synthesis.

B. Polymer Characterization

Polymer characterization is presented in Table 2. The ATPQ exhibited good solubility in a variety of low boiling solvents at RT with is highly attractive for the preparation of prepreg and adhesive tape. The processability of the oxy-ATPQ should be excellent since the polymer melt temperature (197-213°C) is sufficiently low to permit good flow and melting prior to thermal chain extension. In addition, the exotherm of the chain extending reaction (Fig. 1) is broad (~200 to ~350°C) which is indicative of a wide processing stage. The processability of the m-ATPQ would not be expected to be as good as the oxy-ATPQ since the polymer melt temperature (234-247°C) is higher (closer to the exothermic peak) and the exotherm of the chain extending reaction more narrow (~205 to ~285°C, Table 2).

As shown in the differential scanning calorimetry (DSC) curve in Fig. 1, the exotherm of the chain extending reaction of the oxy-ATPQ occurred at ~200 to ~350°C, peaking at 268°C. This compared favorably with that obtained for the model compound. After heating the ATPQ to 400°C is nitrogen, cooling, and rerunning, no exotherm was observed. As shown in Table 2, several samples of the ATPQ were heated at various temperature in nitrogen. As the exposure temperature increased, the apparent Tg also increased. It was surprising to observe that the Tg of the oxy-ATPQ was higher than that of the m-ATPQ after the same exposure conditions. This may

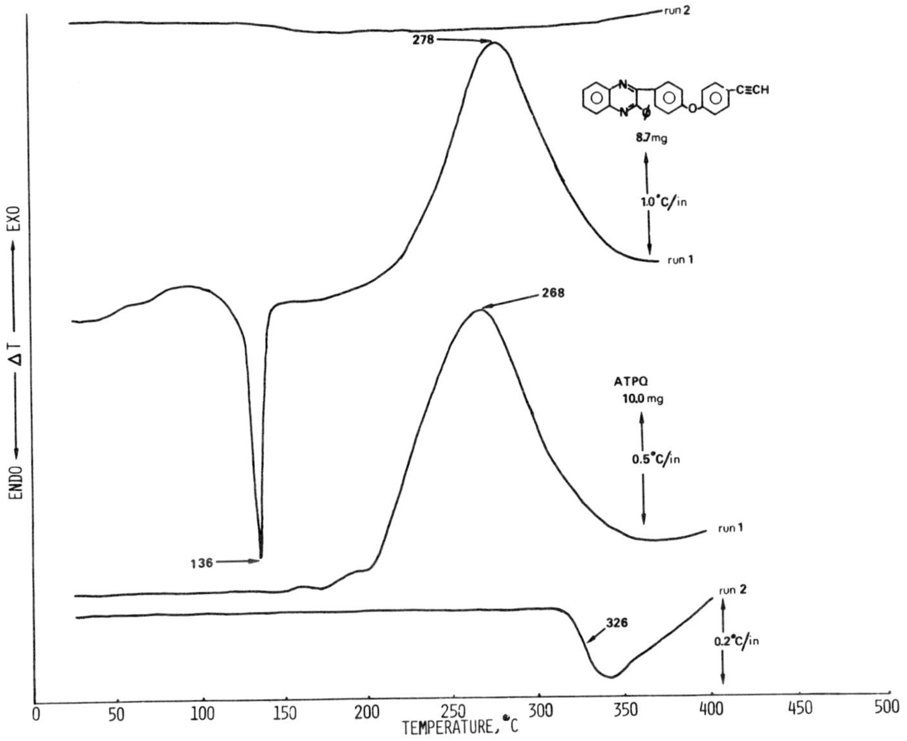

Fig. 1 - Differential Scanning Calorimetry Curves of Compound X and ATPQ

be due to the ability of the oxy-ATPQ to undergo a more effective cure due to better molecular mobility. As previously mentioned, the broad exotherm of the oxy-ATPQ in the DSC curves is indicative of a broad curing stage. The apparent Tg was also determined by torsional braid analysis (TBA) and thermal mechanical analysis (TMA, penetration). The TBA curve in Fig. 2 shows an intense damping peak in the 200°C range accompanied by a decrease in relative rigidity, due to melting of the oligomer. The damping index then decreases and the relative rigidity increases as the oligomer undergoes cure with the reverse effect occurring for the cured polymer in the Tg range. After cooling the sample and rerunning, the Tg taken at the maximum damping

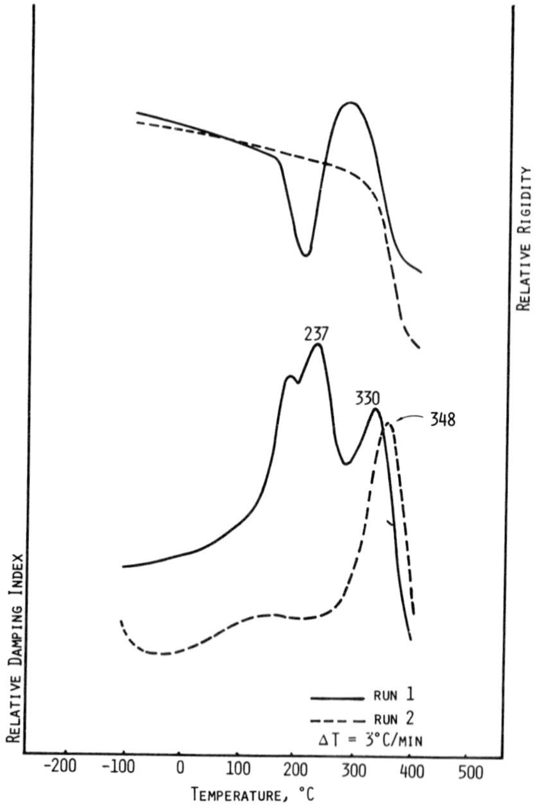

Fig. 2 - Torsional Braid Analysis of ATPQ

peak was 348°C. The apparent Tg by TMA of pressed polymer discs compared favorably with that obtained by DSC.

The polymer decomposition temperature was obtained by thermogravimetric analysis as shown in Fig. 3 at a heating rate of 2°C/min. The initial weight loss for the oxy-ATPQ and m-ATPQ prepared by the one step synthesis commenced at ~460°C with ~10% weight loss observed at ~525°C. The oxy-ATPQ prepared by the multistep route exhibited poorer thermal stability than the oxy-ATPQ prepared by the one step route with the initial weight loss commencing at ~440°C and ~20% weight loss recorded at ~500°C. The thermooxidative stability of each polymer was evaluated by aging powder samples in a circulating air oven at 316°±3°C for 200 hr and their weight loss recorded. As reported in Table 2, the

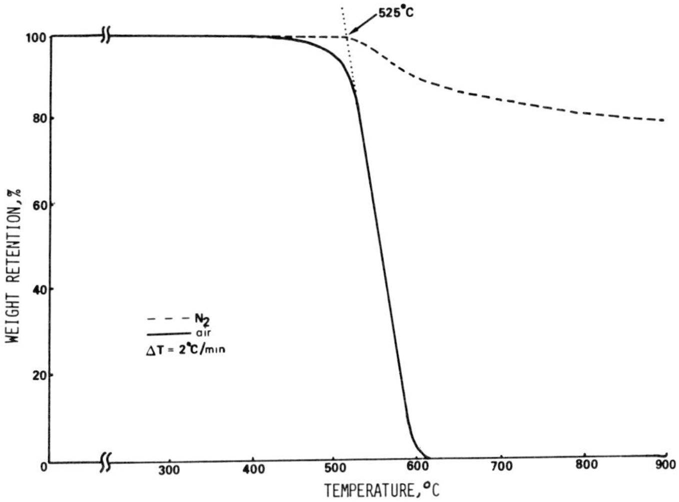

Fig. 3 - Thermal Gravimetric Analysis of 350°C cured (0.5hr) ATPQ

oxy-ATPQ and the m-ATPQ prepared by the single step route exhibited weight losses of 12 and 15% respectively whereas the oxy-ATPQ prepared by the multistep route exhibited significantly high weight loss.

IV. CONCLUSIONS

The reaction of 4-ethynylphenoxybenzil with o-diamino end-capped phenylquinoxaline oligomers provided soluble acetylene terminated phenylquinoxaline oligomers which were thermally polymerized to yield resinous materials with Tg>300°C. Model compound work demonstrated that the principal component formed at 350°C in nitrogen was a dimer from addition of one acetylene with another.

The assistance of Mr. George Sykes for the TBA and TGA work and Dr. Phil Young for the high pressure liquid chromatography work is gratefully acknowledged.

V. REFERENCES

1. M. A. J. Mallet and F. P. Darmory, Am. Chem. Soc. Div. Org. Coatings and Plastics Chem. Prepr., 43(1), 173 (1974).
2. H. R. Lubowitz, Am. Chem. Soc. Div. Polym. Chem. Prepr., 12(1), 329 (1971) and reference therein.
3. S. E. Wentworth, J. Polym. Sci., Polym. Chem. Ed. (in press).
4. P. M. Hergenrother, J. Macromol. Sci-Revs. Macromol. Chem. C13(2), 189 (1975).
5. S. E. Wentworth and G. D. Mulligan, Am. Chem. Soc. Div. Polym. Chem. Prepr. 15(1), 697 (1974).
6. R. A. Meyers, J. W. Hamersma, and H. E. Green, J. Polym. Sci., B, 10, 685 (1972).
7. D. M. Chang and C. S. Marvel, J. Polym. Sci., Polym. Chem. Ed., 13, 2507 (1975).
8. T. J. Aponyi and C. B. Delano, Sci. Adv. Mat'r and Process Eng. Series 19, 178 (1974).
9. R. Milligan, C. B. Delano, and T. J. Aponyi, J. Macromol. Sci.-Chem. (in press).
10. R. T. Rafter and E. S. Harrison, Am. Chem. Soc. Div. Coatings and Plastics Chem. Prepr. 35 (2), 204 (1975).
11. J. E. French, Am. Chem. Soc. Div. Coatings and Plastics Chem. Prepr. 35 (2), 72 (1975).
12. A. L. Landis, N. Bilow, R. H. Boschan, R. E. Lawrence and T. J. Aponyi, Am. Chem. Soc. Div. Polym. Chem. Prepr. 15 (2), 537 (1974).
13. R. F. Kovar, G. F. L. Ehlers, and F. E. Arnold, Am. Chem. Soc. Div. Polym. Chem. Prepr. 16 (2), 247 (1975).
14. F. L. Hedberg and F. E. Arnold, Am. Chem. Soc. Div. of Polym. Chem. Prepr. 16 (1), 677 (1975).
15. C. Samyn and C. S. Marvel, J. Polym. Sci., Polym. Chem. Ed, 13, 1095 (1975).
16. N. Bilow, A. L. Landis, L. J. Miller, R. E. Lawrence, and T. J. Aponyi, Am. Chem. Soc. Div. Polym. Chem. Prepr. 15 (2), 542 (1974).
17. P. M. Hergenrother, Macromolecules 7, 575 (1974).
18. O. Y. Fedotova, Y. I. Nesterova, V. V. Korshak, and M. A. Il'yenko, Polymer Science USSR 15 (7), 1683 (1973).
19. R. J. Jones, U. S. Patent 3,905,941 (1975) to TRW Inc.
20. R. J. Jones, M. K. O'Rell, R. W. Vaughan, and C. H. Sheppard, to be presented at 8th Nat'l SAMPE Symposium and Technical Conference, Seattle, WA, Oct. 1976.
21. N. Bilow, A. L. Landis, and T. J. Aponyi Sci. Adv. Mat'r and Process Eng. Series 20, 618 (1975).

22. V. F. D'Agostino, M. J. Dunn, A. E. Ehrlich, and E. I. Becker J. Org. Chem. 23, 1539 (1958).
23. H. Vogel and C. S. Marvel J. Polymer Sci. 50, 511 (1961).
24. P. M. Hergenrother J. Polymer Sci. A-1, 7, 945 (1969).
25. M. A. Ogliaruso, L. A. Shadoff, and E. I. Becker, J. Org. Chem. 28, 2725 (1963).
26. P. M. Hergenrother and D. E. Kiyohara J. Macromol. Sci.-Chem. A5 (2), 365 (1971).
27. W. Wrasidlo and J. M. Augl J. Polymer Sci. A-1, 7, 3393 (1969).
28. D. Selman and J. F. Eastham Quart. Reviews 14, 221 (1960).
29. P. M. Hergenrother, G. F. Sykes, and P. R. Young J. Heterocyclic Chem. (in press).

SYNTHESIS AND THERMAL CROSSLINKING OF p-TOLYL CONTAINING POLYQUINOXALINES

Stanley E. Wentworth
U. S. Army Materials and Mechanics Research Center

p-Tolyl containing polyquinoxalines have been synthesized and subjected to a series of experiments designed to demonstrate their enhanced thermal crosslinkability relative to polyphenylquinoxalines. Poly-p-tolylquinoxaline itself is shown to be much superior in this regard though significantly inferior in terms of thermooxidative stability. A series of phenylquinoxaline/p-tolyquinoxaline copolymers was then prepared in an effort to find an optimum composition incorporating the crosslinkability of the latter and the thermooxidative stability of the former. It is shown that, in fact, no such optimum composition exists with this system. Thermooxidative stability decreases with increasing p-tolyl content much more rapidly than crosslinkability increases. It is concluded that a system utilizing a more efficient crosslinking reaction is necessary in order for an optimum copolymer composition to be attained.

I. INTRODUCTION

Polyphenylquinoxalines are amongst the best of the currently available high temperature resistant resins, both in terms of thermal and thermooxidative stability. In addition, they possess inherent ease of processing as a consequence of their good solubility in solvents such as m-cresol and even chloroform (1,2). However, their use for structural applications at elevated temperatures, whether as adhesives or resin matrices for advanced composites, is severely limited by thermoplasticity and attendant loss of mechanical properties (3). It has been our objective to reduce or eliminate this deficiancy by means of the controlled introduction of crosslinks. Our particular approach has been to synthetically modify the polymer so as to enhance the low degree of thermal crosslinkability demonstrated by the conventional polyphenylquinoxalines. Such modification is achieved by an appropriate modification of the tetraketone monomer rather than of the polymer itself. Ideally, the modified polymer should crosslink by means of a reaction independent of that which forms the polymer so that solubility (and hence processability) is not impaired. In addition, it should not produce volatiles which can lead to void formation with its detrimental effect on mechanical properties. In practice, this approach should result in a resin system in which the fully formed but uncrosslinked polymer is used for fabrication and crosslinking is thermally induced by means of a post-cure operation on the fabricated item. Several variants of this approach have been described for polyquinoxalines (4-6) and other polyheteroaromatics (7-9). In all of these cases, the crosslinking involves an addition and/or cycloaddition reaction. In the variant to be described here, the p-tolyl containing polyquinoxalines, use is made of an apparent facilitation of the thermal crosslinking process undergone by the parent polyphenylquinoxalines.

II. RESULTS AND DISCUSSION

A. Poly-p-Tolylquinoxaline

1. Synthesis

Poly-p-tolylquinoxaline is readily prepared from equimolar solutions of 1,4-bis(p-tolylglyoxaloyl)benzene (TGB) and 3,3'-diaminobenzidine (DAB) in m-cresol (Fig. 1). Warming to 100°C for 24 hours gives a polymer with an intrinsic visocity of 1.2.

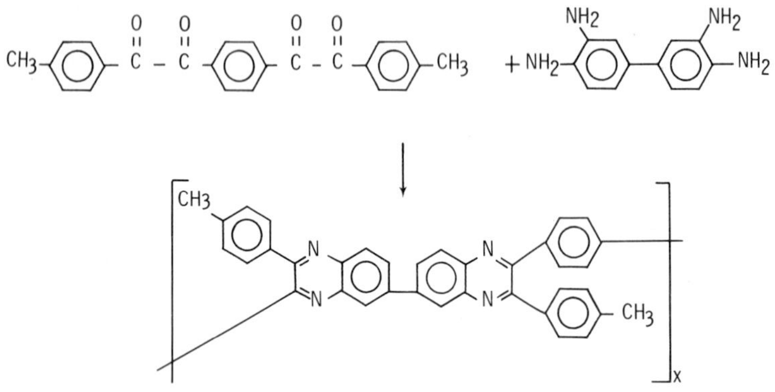

Fig. 1. Synthesis of poly-p-tolylquinoxaline

The previously unreported TGB is prepared by a route exactly analogous to one we have developed for 1,4-bis(phenylglyoxaloyl)benzene (PGB), a monomer for conventional polyphenylquinoxalines (10) (Fig. 2.). It consists of three steps starting with p-tolylacetylene which is converted to its cuprous acetylide in good yield. Reaction of the acetylide with p-diiodobenzene in hexamethylphosphoramide affords 1,4-bis(p-tolylethynyl)benzene which is oxidized to the tetraketone using N-bromosuccinimide in dimethylsulfoxide according to the method of Wolfe *et al* (11).

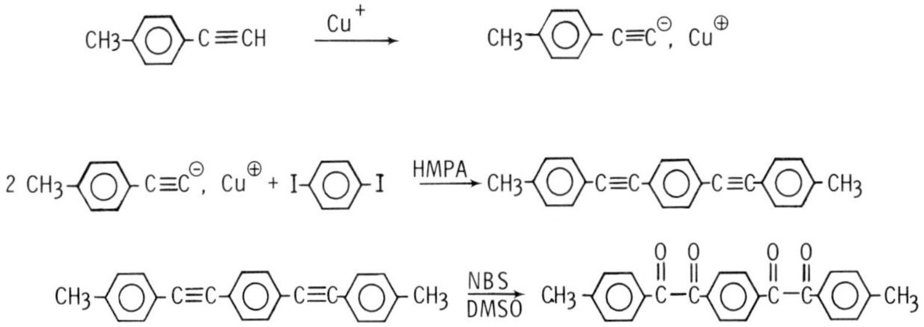

Fig. 2. Synthesis of 1,4-bis(p-tolylglyoxaloyl)benzene

2. *Thermal Analysis and Crosslinking*

These initial investigations were conducted with a poly-p-tolyquinoxaline of 0.46 inherent viscosity. Conventional thermogravimetric analysis (Fig. 3.) indicates poly-p-tolylquinoxaline to be roughly comparable in thermal stability to that reported for the analogous polyphenylquinoxaline (12).

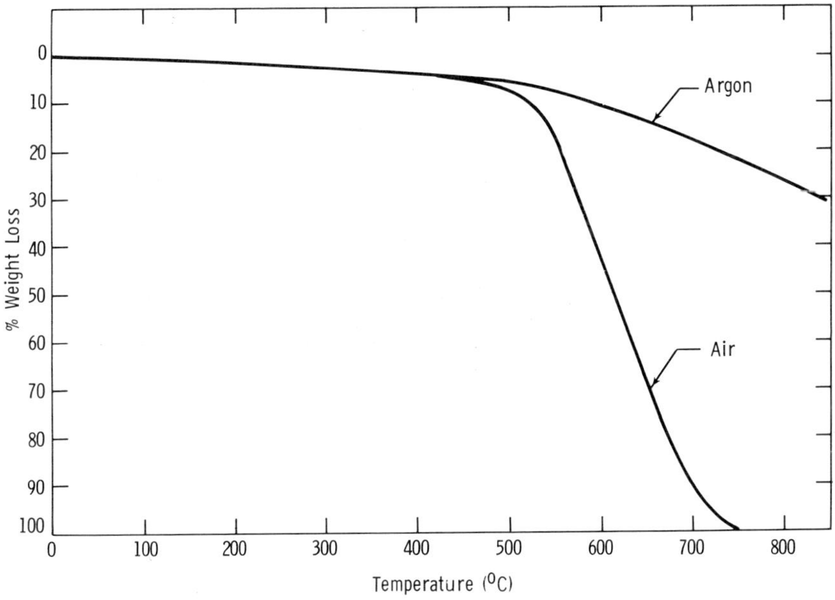

Fig. 3. Thermogravimetric analysis of poly-p-tolylquinoxaline in air and argon. Heating rate 10°C/minute.

However, when subjected to isothermal aging in air at 400°C, a condition much more sensitive to thermooxidative instability, poly-p-tolylquinoxaline is shown to be distinctly inferior. Whereas Augl (12) reports nearly 50% weight retention after 60 hours under these conditions by the analogous polyphenylquinoxaline, poly-p-tolylquinoxaline is virtually gone after only 13 hours (Fig. 4., broken curve). If, on the other hand,

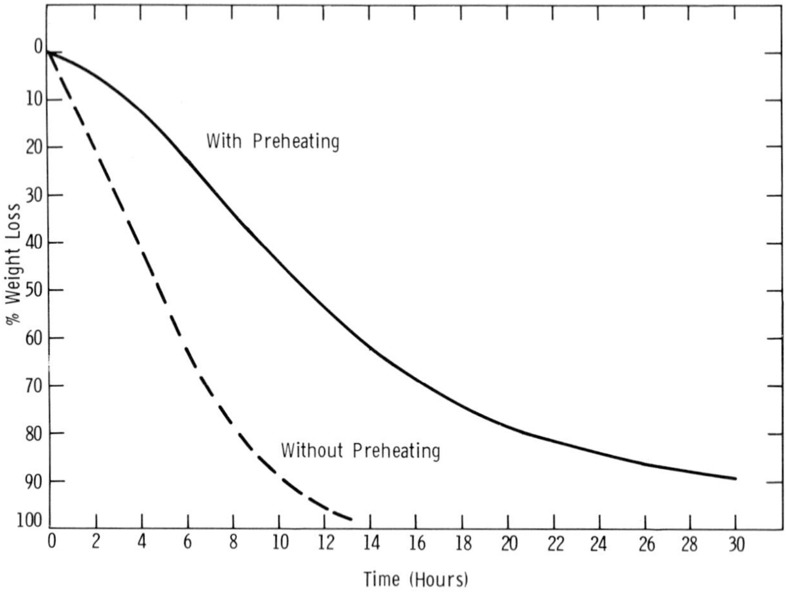

Fig. 4. Isothermal aging of poly-p-tolylquinoxaline in static air at 400°C with (——) and without (---) 16 hours preconditioning in argon at 400°C.

the sample is first held at 400°C in argon for 16 hours (during which time no significant weight loss is observed) and then subjected to isothermal aging in air, the weight retention is dramatically improved, complete burn-off now requiring more than 30 hours (Fig. 4, solid curve). This improved performance is attributed to thermally induced crosslinking.

Much more compelling evidence for crosslinking was obtained in an experiment using torsional braid analysis in a manner we have previously employed as a probe for crosslinkability (4). In this case a much higher molecular weight poly-p-tolylquinoxaline with an intrinsic viscosity of 1.22 was used. Comparison was made with a polyphenylquinoxaline prepared under identical conditions. The technique is based on the assumption that an increase in glass transition temperature (T_g) is a valid indicator of increased crosslink density. The T_g of the unconditioned polymer (T_go) is compared to that of the polymer after conditioning for 2 hours under nitrogen at various temperatures (T_gT). The results are reported as ΔT_g which is defined as T_gT-T_go. It is emphasized that a fresh sample is used for each temperature and that a cumulative effect is not being observed. The results of this experiment are given in Fig. 5.

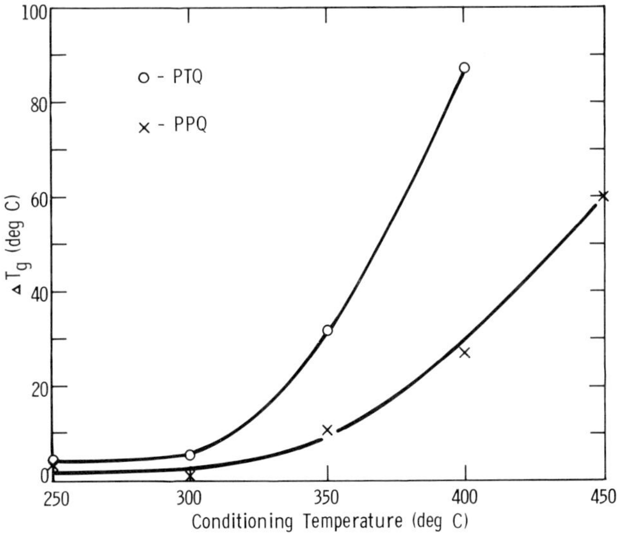

Fig. 5. Variation of glass transition temperature with conditioning temperature, 2 hours under nitrogen for poly-p-tolylquinoxaline (PTQ; 0-0) and polyphenylquinoxaline (PPQ; X-X).

These results clearly indicate poly-p-tolylquinoxaline to be significantly more thermally crosslinkable than the analogous polyphenylquinoxaline. However this enhancement has been achieved only with a considerable loss in thermo-oxidative stability. Naturally enough, we then began to speculate that an appropriately constituted copolymer of the two might possess an optimum combination of crosslinkability and thermooxidative stability.

B. Phenylquinoxaline/p-Tolyquinoxaline Copolymers

1. Polymer Synthesis and Characterization

The polymers and copolymers synthesized for this phase of the study together with their intrinsic viscosities, decomposition temperatures, glass transition temperatures and yields are given in Table 1. As can be seen, a high yield of high molecular weight polymer was obtained in all cases.

TABLE 1
Variation of Selected Polymer Properties with Composition

EXPT#	Composition (%PTQ)	Yield (%)	Intrinsic Viscosity dl/g	PDT[a] (°C)	T_g[b] (°C)
1001-57	0	96.2	1.22	598	356
1001-58	5	92.6	1.02	605	355
1001-59	10	96.4	1.24	582	361
1001-61	20	98.8	1.53	569	364
1001-63	100	92.2	0.57	540	353

a In static air
b Determined by torsional braid analysis

The synthesis, as described in the experimental section, is straightforward with no complications other than a tendency of the finely divided polymer to clog the fritted glass funnel during isolation. All of the polymers were readily soluble in chloroform, thus facilitating the preparation of samples for torsional braid analysis. The glass transition temperature is apparently independent of polymer composition but does seem to show a small dependence on molecular weight as indicated by the parallel between T_g and intrinsic viscosity. As might be expected, the polymer decomposition temperature decreases with increasing p-tolyl content. Finally, it is presumed that the copolymers are random based on the method of synthesis, i.e., addition of a solution of both tetraketones to a solution of the tetraamine. The production of a non-random copolymer from such a procedure requires greatly different reactivities for the competing monomers. This is not expected to be the case in the present system.

2. *Isothermal Aging*

Isothermal aging in static air at 400°C was used to determine the relative thermooxidative stabilities of the various polymers and copolymers. In view of the earlier observation that preconditioning in an inert atmosphere at 400°C significantly enhanced the isothermal aging performance of poly-p-tolylquinoxaline, the following experiment was conducted on each of the polymers. Approximately 8 mg of the powdered polymer was placed in the balance pan of the thermogravimetric analyzer, the quartz furnace tube affixed and a slow flow of nitrogen established through the system. The sample was then inserted into the furnace which had equilibrated to 400°C. After 18 hours, the sample was removed from the furnace and allowed to come to ambient temperature. Virtually no weight loss was observed during this procedure. At this point, the nitrogen flow was interrupted, the furnace tube was removed and flushed with air and then replaced and the sample reinserted into the 400°C furnace. This point is taken as 0 hours. Fig. 6 shows the results of this experiment. Each curve is the average of 2 runs. The half-lives reported in Table 2, are taken from this figure.

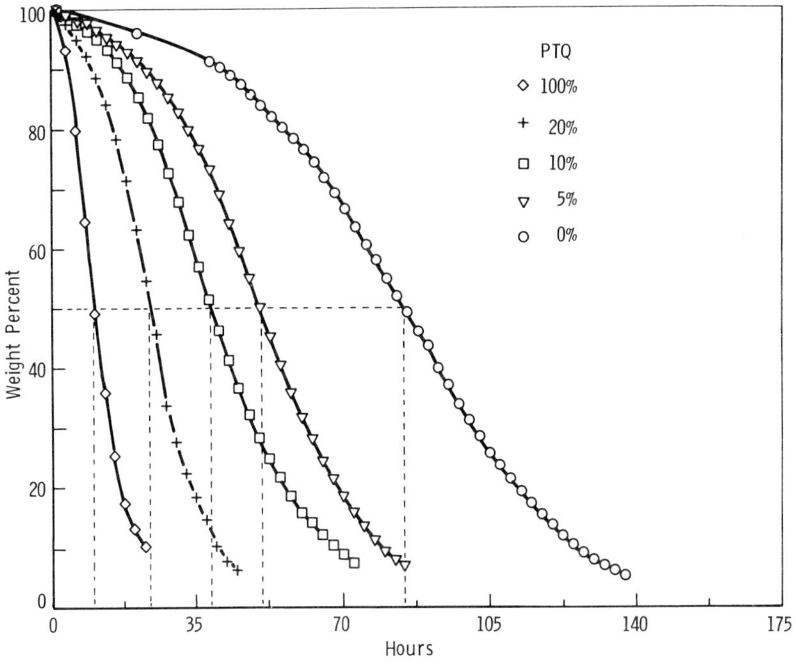

Fig. 6. Isothermal aging of polyquinoxalines containing varying amounts of p-tolyl at 400°C in static air.

TABLE 2
Variation of Half-Life at 400°C in Static Air with Composition

EXPT#	Composition (% PTQ)	Half-Life (Hrs)
1001-57	0	84
1001-58	5	51
1001-59	10	38
1001-61	20	24
1001-63	100	10

The data show very clearly the progressive loss of thermooxidative stability with increasing p-tolyl content. At 20% p-tolyl content, half-life has diminished by over 70%. Even the introduction of only 5% p-tolyl content causes an almost 40% loss in thermooxidative stability. Thus, contrary to our initial speculation, it is obvious that any copolymer with significant p-tolyl content will have markedly reduced stability in air at elevated temperatures.

3. *Thermal Crosslinking*

The thermal crosslinkability of these same polymers was evaluated by means of torsional braid analysis using precisely the same technique described above. The results are presented in Table 3 and graphically in Fig. 7.

TABLE 3
Effect of Conditioning Temperature on Glass Transition Temperature

Polymer	Conditioning Temperature (°C)											
	Ambient		250		300		350		400		450	
	T_g	ΔT_g	T_g	ΔT_g	T_g	ΔT_g	T_g	ΔT_g	T_g	ΔT_g	T_g	ΔT_g
1001-57 0% PTQ	360	-	359	3	357	1	367	11	383	27	416	60
1001-58 5% PTQ	355	-	352	-	354	-	365	10	382	27	427	72
1001-59 10% PTQ	361	-	360	-	360	-	365	5	391	31	440	79
1001-61 20% PTQ	364	-	362	-	363	-	369	5	390	26	440	76
1001-63 100% PTQ	353	-	357	4	358	5	385	32	440	87	-	-

As can be seen, the only polymer to exhibit a significant enhancement in crosslinkability relative to polyphenylquinoxaline is the 100% poly-p-tolylquinoxaline. In fact, to a first approximation, the curves for the three copolymers coincide with that of polyphenylquinoxaline. This stands in marked constrast to the isothermal aging results where thermal stability varies systematically with p-tolyl content.

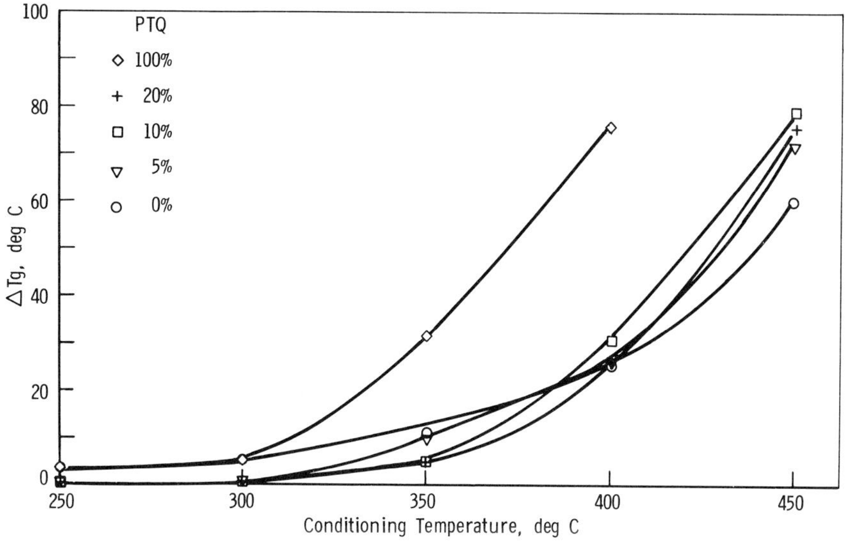

Fig. 7. Variation of glass transition temperature with conditioning temperature, 2 hours under nitrogen.

III CONCLUSIONS

It is obvious that the hoped for optimum copolymer composition in which crosslinkability is maximized while thermo-oxidative instability is minimized does not exist for this system. Apparently the crosslinking reaction is not very efficient such that only high concentrations of the cross-linkable species can lead to a significant elevation of T_g. Conversly, the thermal oxidation reaction appears to be quite efficient, very modest levels of p-tolyl content leading to serious loss in stability. These results do not invalidate the copolymer concept however. To be successful, a system must be found in which the crosslinking reaction is more efficient than the thermal oxidation reaction. We are currently searching for such a system.

It is also possible that the thermooxidative instability revealed in the laboratory on small finely divided polymer samples will be much less important with large, low surface-to-volume composite specimens. This possibility is soon to be investigated.

Finally, even if the above possibility is not borne out, p-tolyl containing polyquinoxalines should be useful in applications where retention of mechanical properties for a short time is more important than long service life at elevated temperatures.

IV EXPERIMENTAL

A. Materials

p-Tolylacetylene was obtained from Farchan Research Laboratories and used as received. PGB and DAB were obtained from Whittaker R&D and recrystallized once from ethanol and water respectively. m-Cresol was vacuum distilled. All other reagents and solvents were obtained from standard sources and used as received except as noted.

B. Monomer Synthesis

1. *Cuprous p-Tolylacetylide*

This compound was prepared according to the procedure of Castro *et al* (13). [Caution; reported to detonate on heating (14) though we have experienced no such difficulty.]

2. *1,4-bis(p-tolylethynyl)benzene*

In a 1 liter three-neck flask fitted with a mechanical stirrer, a gas inlet and an air condenser connected to a mercury valve (to maintain a positive argon pressure) was placed 28.4g (0.143 mole) of cuprous p-tolylacetylide, 26.4g (0.080 mole) of p-diiodobenzene and 450 ml hexamethylphosphoramide (stored over 4A molecular sieves). The mixture was heated with stirring under an argon sweep to a bath temperature of 120°C. After cooling, the mixture was poured into 3 liters of water. The resulting precipitate was removed by filtration and air dried for several days. Soxhlet extraction with 3 portions of acetone and 1 of chloroform gave crops of crystals on cooling. Melting points ranged from 214°C to 220°C; lit. (15), 215-216°C. Concentration of mother liquors gave additional material having an acceptable melting range. Total yield, 7.3g (35%).

3. *1,4-bis(p-tolylglyoxaloyl)benzene*

In a 500 ml 1-neck flask fitted with a magnetic stirrer and a drying tube ($CaSO_4$) was placed 250 ml of dimethylsulfoxide (refluxed over and freshly distilled from CaH_2), 4.5 g (0.0147 mole) of 1,4-bis(p-tolylethynyl)benzene and 10.5 g (0.0588 mole) of N-bromosuccinimide (stored over P_2O_5). The mixture was stirred at room temperature for 4 days at which point solution was complete. The solution was poured into 1500 ml of water and the resulting precipitate removed by filtration and washed with several portions of water. After drying, recrystallization from ethanol with decolorizing charcoal treatment gave 1.79g (30%) of material melting 167-168°C.

Anal. Calcd. for $C_{24}H_{18}O_4$: C, 77.82; H, 4.89
Found: C, 77.91; H, 4.91

C. Polymer Synthesis

1. Poly-p-tolylquinoxaline for Preliminary Evaluation.
In a 200 ml Erlenmeyer flask equipped with a magnetic stirrer was placed 50 ml of m-cresol containing 0.4285g (0.0020 mole) of DAB and 50 ml of m-cresol containing 0.7408g (0.0020 mole) of TGB. The resulting solution was stirred at room temperature for 5 hours and at 60°C for an additional 1 1/2 hours. At this point the inherent viscosity of the solution was 0.46. Pouring into 500 ml of methanol yielded a precipitate which was removed by filtration and washed with several portions of warm methanol. Drying in vacuo at 85°C for 6 hours yielded 0.8915g (87%) of yellow-brown polymer.

Anal. Calcd. for $C_{36}H_{24}N_4$: C, 84.35; H, 4.72; N, 10.93
Found: C, 84.11; H, 4.85; N, 10.97

2. Polymers for Copolymer Study
The following procedure is illustrative of that used for all of the polymers or copolymers prepared in this phase of the study. Only the quantities of tetraketones were changed as per Table 4 to yield the desired copolymers.

TABLE 4
Reactants Used in Polymer Synthesis

EXPT#	Polymer	DAB(g)	PGB(g)	TGB(g)	m-cresol (ml)
1001-57	0% PTQ	0.2143	0.3424	-	24
1001-58	5% PTQ	0.2143	0.3252	0.0185	24
1001-59	10% PTQ	0.2143	0.3081	0.0370	24
1001-61	20% PTQ	0.2143	0.2793	0.0741	24
1001-63	100% PTQ	0.2143	-	0.3704	24

Into a 500 ml 1-neck flask equipped with a magnetic stirrer was poured a solution of 0.2143g (0.001 mole) of DAB in 10.0 ml m-cresol. To this stirred solution was added a solution of 0.3252g (0.0008 mole) of PGB and 0.0185g (0.0002 mole) of TBG in 10.0 ml m-cresol. The resulting reaction mixture was capped with an air condenser and warmed to 100°C over approximately

1 hour. This temperature was maintained for 23 hours. After cooling to ambient temperature, the reaction mixture was poured with stirring into 150 ml of methanol. After stirring for 2 hours, the resulting precipitate was removed by filtration through a fine fritted glass funnel. After washing with several portions of hot methanol, the precipitate was air dried overnight and dried in vacuo at 85°C for 6 hours to yield 0.4663g (96.2%) of 5% PTQ.

D. Characterization and Thermal Analysis

Viscometry was carried out in a Cannon-Ubbelohde dilution viscometer using m-cresol at 30°C as the solvent. Thermogravimetric analyses were performed with a DuPont Model 951 Thermogravimetric Analyzer using a heating rate of 10°C/minute in an atmosphere of static air. Isothermal aging studies were conducted with this equipment in a nitrogen, argon or static air environment as appropriate. Torsional braid analyses were performed with a Chemical Instruments Corporation Model 100-Bl Torsional Braid Analyzer. A controlled heating rate of 4.2°C/minute was provided by a Tetrahedron Associates Model ATC-200 Temperature Indicator Controller in conjunction with a Research Incorporated Model 5310 Data Trak Card Reader. All determinations were conducted in a nitrogen atmosphere with 8 inch multi-filament quartz braids being used throughout.

V ACKNOWLEDGEMENTS

The author gratefully acknowledges the many helpful discussions with Dr. G. Hagnauer and Mr. D. Macaione and the technical assistance of Miss S. Kalian and Mr. R. Cherill. Dr. G. Mulligan is especially acknowledged for her early support of this work. Finally Dr. J. Augl of the Naval Surface Weapons Center is acknowledged for his generosity during all phases of this work.

VI REFERENCES

1. P. M. Hergenrother and H. H. Levine, J. Polym. Sci., Part A-1 5, 1453 (1967).
2. W. Wrasidlo and J. M. Augl, J. Polym. Sci, Part B 7, 281 (1969).
3. M. L. Santelli, Naval Ordnance Laboratory Technical Report 71-187 (1971).
4. S. E. Wentworth and D. P. Macaione, J. Polym. Sci, Polym. Chem. Ed. 14, 1301 (1976).
5. P. M. Hergenrother, Macromolecules 7, 575 (1974).

6. R. F. Kovar, G. F. L. Ehlers and F. E. Arnold, Polym. Prepr, Am. Chem. Soc., Div. Polym. Chem., 16, No. 2, 246 (1975).
7. J. K. Stille, R. G. Nelb and S. O. Norris, Macromolecules 9, 516 (1976).
8. A. L. Landis, N. Bilow, R. H. Boschan, R. E. Lawrence and T. J. Aponyi, Polym. Prepr., Am. Chem. Soc., Div. Polym. Chem., 15, No. 2, 537 (1974).
9. R. W. Vaughn, R. J. Jones, C. H. Sheppard and E. A Burns Space Shuttle Mater., Nat. SAMPE Tech. Conf., 1971, 17
10. S. E. Wentworth, U.S. 3,829,497, (1974).
11. S. Wolfe, W. R. Pilgrim, T. F. Garrard and P. Chamberlain, Can. J. Chem. 49, 1099 (1971)
12. J. M. Augl, J. Polym. Sci., Part A-1 10, 2403 (1972).
13. C. E. Castro, E. J. Gaughan and D. C. Owsley, J. Org. Chem., 31, 4071 (1966).
14. F. Richter ed., "Beilstein's Handbook of Organic Chemistry" 4th ed, 1st Suppl. Vol. 5, p. 247, Springer Verlag, Berlin, 1930.
15. G. Drefahl and G. Plötner, Chem. Ber. 91, 1280 (1958).

THERMOSETTING PLASTICIZERS FOR HIGH TEMPERATURE QUINOXALINE THERMOPLASTICS

Robert F. Kovar
University of Dayton Research Institute
Gerhard F. L. Ehlers and Fred E. Arnold
Nonmetallic Materials Division
Air Force Materials Laboratory

Recent studies in this laboratory have been concerned with a novel approach to the processing of high temperature thermoplastics. A series of bis(ethynylquinoxaline) monomers were prepared to demonstrate the feasibility of using thermosetting plasticizers in the processing of polyphenylquinoxaline thermoplastics.
The monomers were prepared by the reaction of 4-(3-ethynylphenoxy)-o-phenylenediamine with various aromatic 1,2-dicarbonyl compounds in m-cresol. The thermosetting plasticizer lowers the effective softening point of the thermoplastic resin during processing and then becomes dormant by reacting with itself or the host thermoplastic. Mixtures of monomer and thermoplastic were studied with respect to compatibility, Tg depression and plasticizer deactivation.

I. INTRODUCTION

In recent years there has been an increasing interest in the utilization of thermoplastic resins as a means of reducing the processing cost of fiber-reinforced composites. Thermoplastic matrices offer the potential advantage of decreasing the fabrication costs of advanced structures, thereby making them more cost competitive. Cost reductions would become possible because faster, more economical manufacturing procedures could be employed. Manufacturing methods which have been investigated[1-6] for the fabrication of graphite/thermoplastic composites have demonstrated cost savings from 25 to 80% over conventional epoxy composites.

The processing of a thermoplastic material as a fiber reinforced composite involves essentially three steps; the initial formation of stiff, boardy prepreg, consolidation of multi-layered prepreg into sheet stock, and finally, thermo-forming of the sheet stock into structural components. One problem associated with the fabrication process involves the temperatures required to provide adequate flow and wetting of the fibers in both the consolidation and thermoforming operations. Temperatures in excess of 200°-300°F above the glass transition temperature of the thermoplastic material are usually necessary to sufficiently decrease the bulk viscosity for the consolidation process. The problem becomes more critical as the use temperature of the structural composite is extended, since higher use temperatures require thermoplastics with higher glass transition temperatures and consequently higher fabrication temperatures. The disadvantages of using very high processing temperatures (800°-1000°F) include the unfavorable economics of high temperature tooling and the danger of thermal degradation of the polymer during fabrication.

The use of plasticizers represents one approach toward reducing the high temperatures required for fabrication. A plasticizer facilitates the processing of the thermoplastic by lowering the glass transition temperature, and reducing the bulk viscosity. Although plasticizers facilitate the processing of thermoplastics, they also lower the use-temperature of a fabricated structural component. An ideal plasticizer would therefore be one which lowers the effective softening point of the thermoplastic during processing and then undergoes reaction at a slightly higher temperature to a new material of high Tg. The type of reaction utilized to deactivate the plasticizer will undoubtedly effect the ultimate mechanical properties of the structural laminate. For example, a reactive plasticizer which becomes dormant by a reaction with itself would generate a thermoplastic matrix containing an organic filler, whereas one which reacted with itself might form an interpenetrating network of crosslinked plasticizer intertwined with the polymer chains of the thermoplastic. Finally, a plasticizer that was capable of reacting with itself and with the host thermoplastic might give rise to a crosslinked thermoplastic.

In order to be useful in the fabrication of thermoplastic composite materials, a reactive plasticizer would have to exhibit the following combination of properties: (a) be compatible with the thermoplastic polymer, (b) exhibit a low initial Tg, (c) lower the bulk viscosity of the thermoplastic and (d) cure at a reasonable temperature without the evolution of volatiles to a thermally stable material of high Tg.

The success or failure of any plasticizer is primarily dependant upon its compatability with the host thermoplastic. In addition, the cure reaction of the plasticizer must proceed without the evolution of volatiles to prevent the formation of voids which would seriously effect the mechanical properties of the structural component.

It was the objective of this work to synthesize a series of reactive plasticizers of specific molecular structure which would be compatible with a number of high temperature thermoplastic resins. The feasibility of using reactive plasticizers to facilitate the processing of high temperature thermoplastic resins into reinforced composites would then be determined by studying the effects of the above plasticizers on the thermomechanical properties of the thermoplastics both before and after cure.

II. RESULTS AND DISCUSSION

The approach utilized in this work was to structurally tailor the plasticizer to closely resemble the molecular structure of the thermoplastic resin to be studied. This would assure the highest probability of obtaining compatibility within mixtures of the two components. Deactivation of the plasticizer was accomplished by polymerization of the terminal acetylene groups within the molecule, a method that was successfully employed in the ATQ polymer system,[7] which is currently under development as a high temperature, moisture resistant matrix resin. The high temperature thermoplastics chosen for this study were the polyphenylquinoxalines A and B of varying viscosity ranges and glass transition temperatures of 285°C and 350°C respectively.

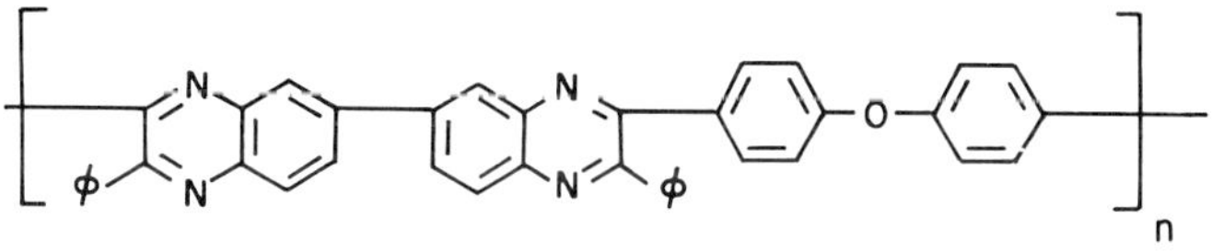

A

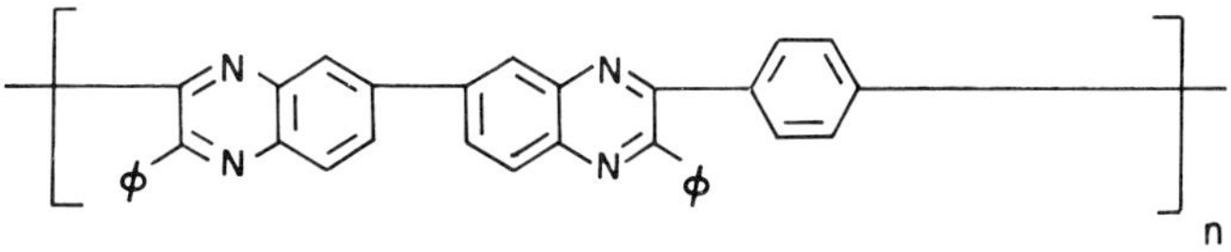

B

A series of bis(phenylquinoxaline) monomers containing terminal acetylene end groups were prepared of varying molecular structure (Table I), in order to obtain polymerizable plasticizers with the lowest initial softening points.

The plasticizers were prepared by the condensation of 3-(3,4-diaminophenoxy)acetophenone (I) with aromatic bis-benzils, giving rise to bis(acetylphenoxy-quinoxaline) intermediates.

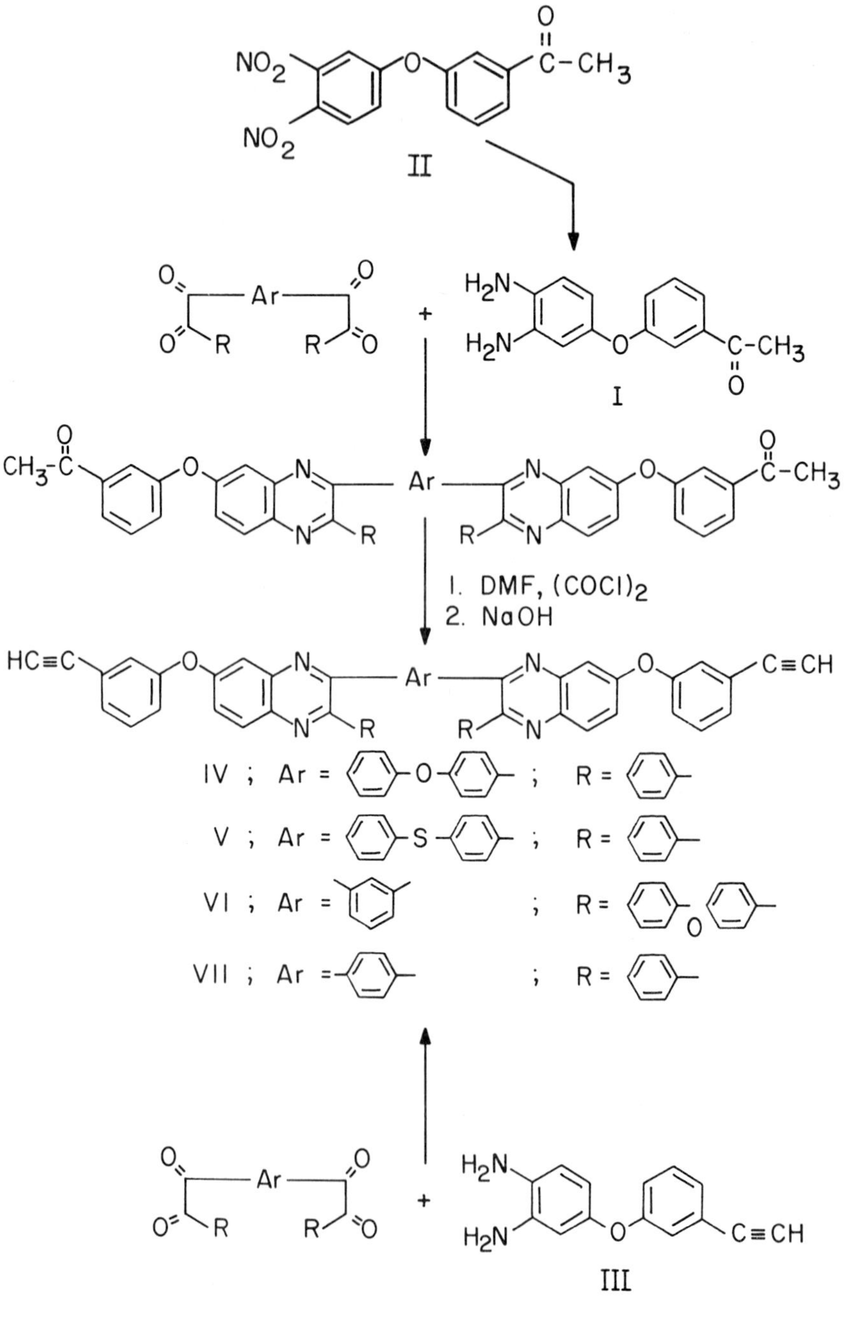

The 3-(3,4-diaminophenoxy)acetophenone was prepared and used in situ by catalytic reduction of 3-(3,4-dinitrophenoxy)-acetophenone (II) with platinum oxide in absolute ethanol. Conversion of the bis-acetyl intermediates to acetylenes was carried out by formation of chlorocinnamaldehyde groups with oxalyl chloride in dimethylformamide (DMF) and their subsequent hydrolysis using aqueous sodium hydroxide. An alternate route to the monomers was provided by the direct condensation of aromatic bis-benzils with 4-(3-ethynylphenoxy) -o-phenylene-diamine (III) in m-cresol. Compound III was used successfully as an end-capping reagent in the synthesis of ATQ oligomers.[7]

Solid phase homopolymerization of the monomers were carried out in the differential scanning calorimeter (DSC) at a fixed heating rate of 20°/min. (Table I) and the temperatures determined at which the polymerizations were

TABLE I

REACTIVE PLASTICIZERS

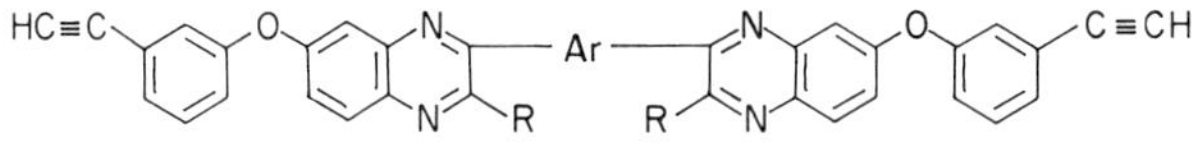

PLASTICIZER	Ar	R	Tg., °C	Tpi,(1) °C	Tp Max(2) °C	Tg(3) °C
IV	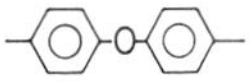	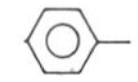	100	220	250	280
V	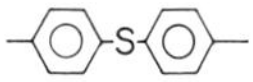	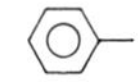	140	225	263	337
VI	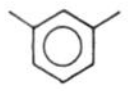	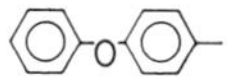	95	180	263	278
VII	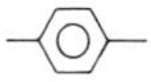	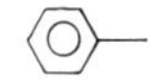	205	205	225	348

(1) Tpi = Temperature of polymerization (initial) as determined by DSC (T = 20°C/min).

(2) Tp max = Temperature of polymerization (maximum) as determined by DSC (T = 20° C/min).

(3) Tg = Glass transition temperature after heating at 280°C for 12 hrs.

initiated and reached a maximum. Samples of each monomer were also heated under nitrogen at 280°C for twelve hours to surmise what Tg could be expected after a complete cure. Two of the four monomers prepared exhibited Tgs in the 100°C range and were used to demonstrate the feasibility of the process. Since it was felt that monomer IV, containing pendant phenyl groups would be more compatible with the PPQ thermoplastics A & B, it was selected for use as the plasticizer in this study.

Samples of plasticizer IV were mixed in various percentages with different molecular weight PPQ thermoplastics. To assure homogeniety in mixing, the plasticizer and thermoplastic were dissolved in chloroform and either coprecipitated into methanol or cast into film by removal of the chloroform.

Film samples of the mixtures were heated at different temperatures and the deactivation of the plasticizer was followed by the disappearance of the acetylenic hydrogen absorption 3.2u in the infrared spectrum. After an eight hour cure at 280°C no acetylenic hydrogen absorption could be detected. The light yellow films containing the plasticizer were transparent, without haze, both before and after heat treatment, which was a good indication of compatibility of the system.

The films, after the heat treatment, were no longer soluble in the solvent from which they were cast. The deactivation reaction of the plasticizer presumably resulted in both reaction with itself and also the host thermoplastic forming a small percentage of crosslinks in the system. The insolubility of the films could also be explained by the fact that the high molecular weight material is entwined in an interpenetrating network structure generated from the plasticizer. Further work will be required to clarify the actual mechanism by which insolubility results.

Further proof of compatibility is provided by the DSC data (Table II). The data indicate only <u>one</u> Tg for the mixture plasticizer/thermoplastic (A). Incompatible components would display their inherent Tg's, while a partially compatible mixture would show a Tg of the mixture along with more or less strong signals for the original Tg's. It should be stated, however, that the extent of compatibility can only be ascertained on the basis of the sensitivity of the method, in this case DSC.

Polymerization temperatures (initial as well as maximum) increase with increasing "dilution" of the reactive plasticizer with the polymer. The Tg's of the cured mixtures are about 20°C higher than that of the polymer, and about 26°C higher than the Tg of the cured plasticizer. This may be the result of entanglement of the cured plasticizer network with the polymer chains, but it may also suggest that some crosslinking between the plasticizer and the polymer has occurred.

TABLE II

OBSERVED EFFECTS OF REACTIVE PLASTICIZER IV ON Tg's

OF THERMOPLASTICS A & B

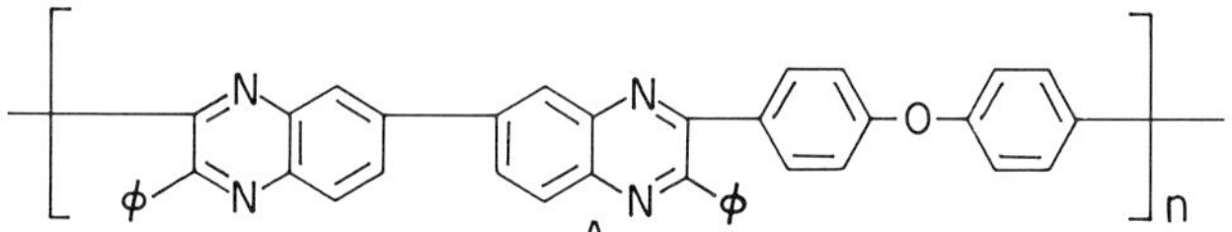

A

N_{inh} [a]	% PLASTICIZER	% PPQ	T_g MIXTURE	T_{pi} [b]	T_{pm} [c]	T_g [d] CURED
2.19	0	100	286°			
	100	0	100°	220°	250°	280°
	20	80	243°	253°	310°	304°
	30	70	226°	235°	310°	307°
0.91	0	100	285°			
	20	80	234°	245°	294°	306°
	30	70	213°	225°	286°	308°

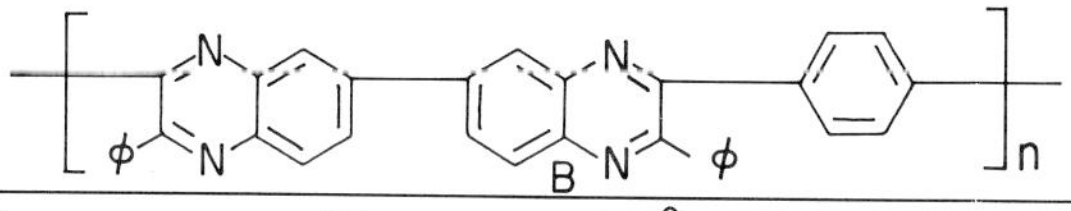

B

2.7	0	100	349°			
	20	80	—	200°	280°	357°
	30	70	—	205°	266°	354°

a) Inherent viscosity determined in m-cresol (0.5 % at 25 °C)

b) T_{pi} = Temperature of polymerization (initial) as determined by DSC, 20 °/min.

c) T = Temperature of polymerization (maximum) as determined by DSC, 20 °/min.

Slightly lower Tg's and polymerization temperatures were observed for the lower molecular weight polymer, but the Tg's of the cured mixtures are practically the same as those of the mixtures with the high molecular weight polymer.

With increasing plasticizer content, the uncured mixtures show decreasing softening temperatures and increasing flow. The cured mixtures not only have a higher Tg, but also exhibit less flow than the polymer itself.

No glass transition temperatures have been found for the mixtures of plasticizer with the polymer (B) in Table II. As a result of the high Tg of the polymer, Tg's of compatible mixtures of this polymer with plasticizer are expected to fall within the polymerization temperature range of the plasticizer and cannot be detected by DSC or TMA. Consolidation of prepregs would not be possible with such a system without premature curing occurring. Excessive amounts of plasticizer would be needed to lower the Tg of the mixture below the onset of polymerization.

III. EXPERIMENTAL

A. Glass Transitions

Glass transition and polymerization temperatures have been determined by differential scanning calorimetry (DSC). Samples were subjected to a heating rate of T = 20°C/min in nitrogen in the Dupont 990 Differential Scanning Calorimeter. The extrapolated onset of the baseline shift was taken as Tg. Onset and peak of the polymerization exotherm were considered as the initial (Tpi) and the maximum (Tpm) temperature of polymerization, respectively.

The cured samples frequently gave unsatisfactory DSC signals. Thermomechanical Analysis (TMA) was used to determine the Tg of the cured samples. These were subjected to programmed heating at T = 20°C/min in air using the Dupont Thermomechanical Analyzer, with the penetration probe and 5g load. The highest rate of penetration (peak of the derivative curve) was taken as Tg.

B. Monomers

p,p'-Bis[3-phenyl-6-(3-ethynylphenoxy)-quinoxalin-2-yl]-diphenylether. IV

1. p,p'-bis(3-phenyl-6-(3-acetylphenoxy)-quinoxaline-2-yl) diphenyl-ether.

To a hydrogenation bottle was added 10.0 g (28.6 mmole) of 3-(3,4-dinitrophenoxy)acetophenone and 250 ml of absolute ethanol. The suspension was purged with nitrogen, and then 150 mg of platinum oxide catalyst was carefully added. The flask was shaken under a hydrogen pressure of 55 psi until no further pressure drop was noticeable (4 hr.). TLC at that point (SiO_2 , eluted with ethylacetate) showed one major spot of reduced product 3-(3,4-diaminophenoxy] acetophenone) and only a small amount of impurty. The solution was filtered under nitrogen pressure, and the filtrate purged with nitrogen for 10 minutes. Then 5.2 g (12 mmole) of p,p'-bis(phenylglyoxaloyl)diphenly ether was added along with 5ml of acetic acid, and the mixture refluxed **under** nitrogen for 1 hour. At that point the solvent was evaporated in vacuo, and the residue refluxed with 25 ml of m-cresol to complete the reaction. The m-cresol was distilled of in vacuo, and the residue dissolved in a minimum volume of methylene chloride. This solution was poured into 50 ml of refluxing ethanol, and the methylene chloride boiled off. The precipitated procuct was filtered and air dried. TCL (S_iO_2-elution with CH_2Cl_2) showed a highly fluorescent first spot of high Rf which was subsequently identified as the product. The solid product was purified by repeated recrystallization from methanol/CH_2Cl_2 mixtures, in which the methylene chloride was boiled away. High purity material was obtained by chromatography on a dry column of silica gel (quartz column). Elution of the column with methylene chloride afforded a first band (fluorescent) containing the product. Evaporation of solvent in vacuo yielded p,p'bis [2-phenyl-6-(3-acetylphenoxy)quinoxaline-2-yl]-diphenylether as an amorphus pale yellow solid, m.p. 100°C. Calc'd for $C_{56}H_{38}N_4O_5$: C, 79.42; H, 4.52; N, 6.62 Found: C, 79.08; H, 4.33; N, 6.51.

2. *p,p'-Bis(3-phenyl-6-(3-ethynylphenoxy)-quinoxaline-2-yl]-diphenylether)*

A 250 ml round bottomed one-necked flask equipped with magnetic stirrer and nitrogen inlet adapter was thoroughly flamed and purged with nitrogen. To this was added 25 ml of anhydrous DMF. The flask was cooled with stirring under nitrogen to -78°C, and then 2.5 g (20 mmole) of freshly distilled oxalyl chloride was added dropwise to the flask to minimize the violent reaction. A white precipitate of Vilsmeyer complex formed in the flask. After the addition the reaction mixture was stirred at 0° for 15 minutes at which time 5.0 g (6.9 mmole) of p,p'-bis[3-phenyl-6-(acetylphenoxy)-quinoxaline-2-yl]-diphenyl ether was added to the flask. The flask was allowed to warm to room temperature, and was then stirred at 50° for one half hour. The contents of the flask were poured into 500 ml of cold, saturated sodium bicarbonate solution, and the crude product which precipitated was filtered, washed with water and dried. The material thus obtained could be used directly for the next step, or could be purified by chromatography on a column of silica gel (elution with methylene chloride).

To a refluxing solution of sodium hydroxide (5 g) in 40 ml of water was added a solution of p,p'-bis[3-phenyl-6-(3-chlorocinnamaldophenoxy)-quinoxaline-2-yl]-diphenylether (4 g) dissolved in 10 ml of dioxane. The mixture was refluxed for one half hour, at which time TLC showed the reaction to be virtually complete. The reaction mixture was poured into 1 liter of water, and the solution acidified with 50% sulfuric acid. The cooled solution was extracted with several portions of methylene chloride, and the combined extracts evaporated to near dryness <u>in vacuo</u>. The residue was chromatographed on a 1" x12" dry column of silica gel (quartz column) (eluted with CH_2Cl_2/hexane). Band 1 (highly fluorescent in UV) contained the desired product, m.p. 98-99°.
Calc'd for $C_{56}H_{34}N_4O_3$: C, 82.95; H, 4.23; N, 6.91
Found: C, 82.53; H, 4.20; N, 6.67

<u>4-(3-Ethynylphenoxy)-o-phenylenediamine III</u>

Compound III was prepared by the reduction of 3-(3,4-dinitrophenoxy) phenylacetylene using sodium dithionite and sodium hydroxide (tenfold excess) in aqueous methanol solution according to a previously described procedure[7].

<u>p,p'-Bis[3-phenyl-6-(3-ethynylphenoxy)quinoxaline-2-yl]diphenylsulfide</u> (<u>V</u>)

To a solution containing 1.25 g (2.77 moles) of 4,4'-(phenylglyoxaloyl)diphenylsulfide and 1 ml of glacial acetic acid dissolved in 25 ml of m-cresol was slowly added, under a nitrogen atmosphere, a solution containing 1.24 g (5.55 mmoles) of 4-(3-ethynylphenoxy)-o-phenylenediamine dissolved in 25 ml of methylene chloride. After completion of the addition, the reaction mixture was heated at reflux for one hour, at which time the methylene chloride was distilled out of the reaction mixture. The mixture was further heated to 150°C and maintained at that temperature for one hour. The cooled reaction mixture was then placed on a rotary evaporator and the cresol was removed under reduced pressure. The residual solid was recrystallized from dioxane/water to give 2 g (87.3%) of product, m.p. 140-141°C. Analysis Calc'd for $C_{56}H_{34}N_4O_2S$: C, 81.33; H, 4.14; N, 6.77 Found: C, 81.53; H, 3.89 N, 6.93

<u>1,3-Bis[3-(p'-phenoxyphenyl)-6-(3-ethynylphenoxy)-quinoxaline-2-yl]benzene (VI)</u>

Monomer IV, m.p. 95°C, was prepared by the reaction of III with m-bis(p'-phenoxyphenylgly-oxalyoyl)benzene according to the procedure previously described for the preparation of V. Calculated for $C_{62}H_{38}N_4O_4$: C, 82.86; H, 4.24; N, 6.20. Found: C, 82.13; H, 4.01; N, 5.91.

<u>1,4-Bis[3-phenyl-6-(3-ethynylphenoxyquinoxaline)-2-yl]benzene (VII)</u>

Monomer VII, m.p. 204-205°C was prepared by the reaction of III with 1,4-bis(phenylglyoxaloyl) benzene according to the procedure previously described for the preparation of V. Calculated for $C_{50}H_{30}N_4O_2$: C, 83.54; H, 4.22; N,7.79. Found: C,83.21; H, 4.23; N, 7.54.

IV REFERENCES

1. J. T. Hoggatt, D180-17531-1 (1973).
2. J. T. Hoggatt and A. D. Von Volkli, D180-18034-3 (1974)
3. J. T. Hoggatt and A. D. VonVolkle, D180-17503-3 (1975
4. J. T. Hoggatt, Nat'l SAMPE Conference Series, Vol. 20, 606 (1975).
5. M. G. Maximovich, Nat'l SAMPE Conference Series, Vol. 19, 262 (1974)
6. C. L. May and R. Gode, AFML-TR-75-111 (1976)
7. R. F. Kovar, G. F. L. Ehlers and F. E. Arnold, Amer. Chem. Prepr. 16 (2) 246 (1975).

THERMOSETTING ARYLETHER MALEIMIDES

G. T. Kwiatkowski, G. L. Brode, L. M. Robeson,
A. W. Bedwin and P. Van Riper
Union Carbide Corporation

Arylimides have been prepared from diamines and oligomer amines containing halogenated phenylene, oxygen, alkylidine, and/or sulfone moieties and maleic anhydride. The arylamine intermediates were derived by reacting the alkali metal salt of para-aminophenol with 4,4'-dichlorodiphenylsulfone or chloroaromatics under nucleophilic substitution reaction conditions. Oligomer amines were prepared by replacing a portion of the para-aminophenol with bisphenols in the condensation process.

The arylimides could be thermally cured to afford heat stable systems possessing high glass transition temperatures (Tg) and high modulus plateaus above the Tg. The addition type curing process circumvents problems associated with the fabrication of conventional polyimide systems since volatiles are not liberated and low-viscosity, high solid solutions can be prepared in low boiling organic solvents.

Thermal, mechanical and fabrication characteristics for the oligomer arylimides are described, including mechanical loss and shear modulus temperature profiles. If the form of B-stage resins, they can be used for the preparation of glass cloth prepregs, molding materials and adhesives which can be thermally converted to the thermoset state.

I. INTRODUCTION

A variety of recently developed heterocylic polymers including polyimides, polybenzimidazoles, polyquinolines, certain polyamide-imides, etc., offer a unique combination of acceptable mechanical properties coupled with outstanding thermo-oxidative stability, but as a class, fabrication difficulties have prevented exploitation, except in a very few application areas. Certain polyimide and polyphenylquinoxaline composites, for example, are projected to have upper use temperatures of 315°C or higher (1), but the intractable nature of such materials has prevented full utilization. The volatile by-products from the tractable precursors of fully cyclized materials on the one hand, and the extremely high melt viscosity of the resulting heterocyclic products on the other, have been responsible for this dilema. Various approaches have been conceived to circumvent these problems, including:

1. spacing the high melting heterocyclic moiety between high softening and thermo-oxidatively stable polymeric units (2,3,4);
2. phenylated polymeric products (5,6,7,8);
3. preparation of low molecular weight heterocyclic oligomers terminated with reactive double bonds (9,10,11,12).

The last approach, in particular, can lead to tractable and soluble compositions which display many of the sought after properties, provided the aliphatic content is controlled at a minimal level. Our investigations have centered on reactive thermosetting maleimides derived from aromatic amines of the polyether sulfone type, I (13,14,15, 16) and more recently, maleimides derived from chloroaromatic ether diamines, II (17). We have referred to the former as arylimides and to the latter as chloroarylimides. This represents an alternate approach to the more conventional reactive olefin derivitization of, for example, oligomeric polyimides or polyamide-imides.

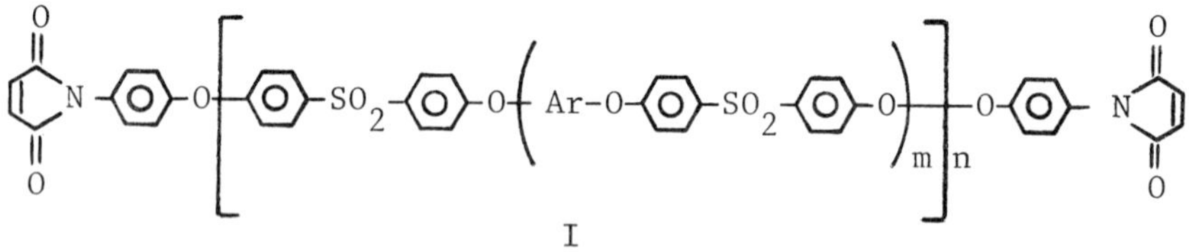

I

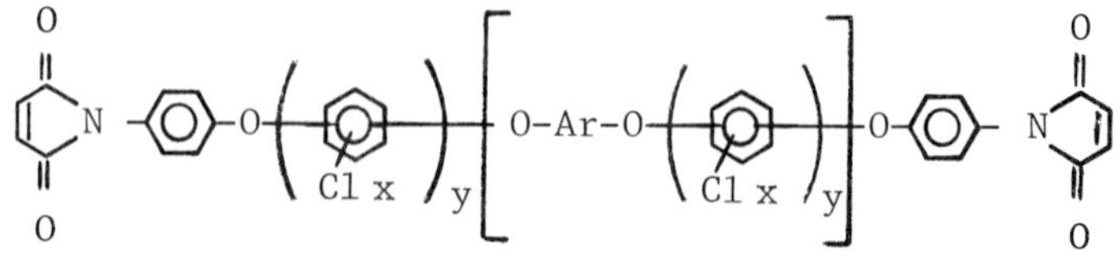

II

II. DISCUSSION

A. Synthesis of Chloroarylimides

The chloroarylimides are prepared by reacting a chloroaromatic amine with maleic anhydride in dimethylacetamide or N-methylpyrrolidinone followed by imidization of the intermediate polyamic-acid with acetic anhydride/sodium acetate. The in situ chemical imidization reaction employed was developed earlier for sulfone polyamide-imides (14). The preferred method for the preparation of chloroarylimides involves the direct conversion of the aromatic amine to the arylimide in situ without isolation of the amine. This series of reactions is delineated in Equations 1-4. The diversity of arylamines and arylimides available through the condensation technology allows the production of thermosets with varying glass transition temperatures (Tg), cross-link densities and modulus plateaus (above the Tg). Table I summarizes a number of the chloroaromatic precursors to the chloroarylamines studied, together with the empirical formulae and molecular weights. Maleimides based on decachloroterphenyl diamine (17), III (from Aroclor 5460[1]) offered the most useful combination of properties.

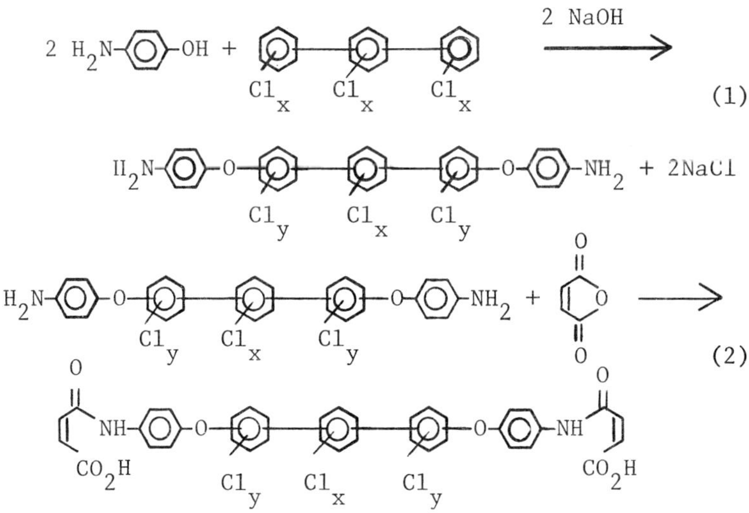

(1)

(2)

[1]A specific product in the generic class of chlorinated polyphenyl compounds previously produced by Monsanto Corp. under the trade name "Aroclor".

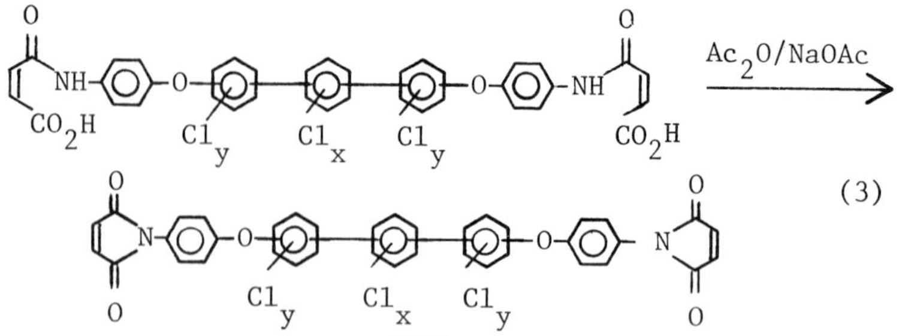

(3)

III

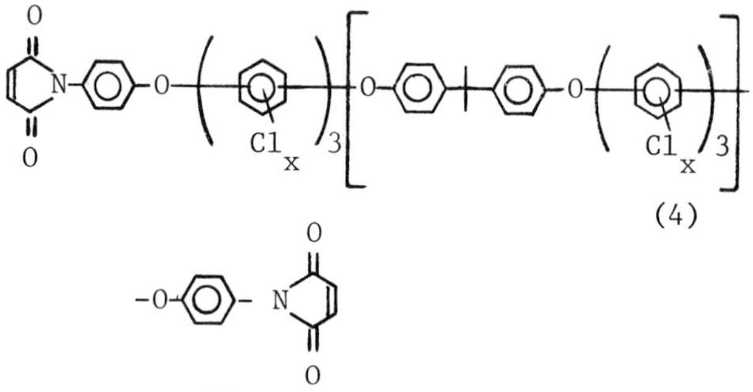

(4)

IV

TABLE I

Chloroaromatic Precursors to Chloroarylamines

Compound	Emperical Formula	Molecular Weight
Pentachlorobenzene	C_6Cl_5H	252
Hexachlorobenzene	C_6Cl_6	285
Decachlorobiphenyl[1]	$C_{12}Cl_{10}$	499
Decachloroterphenyl[1]	$C_{18.9}H_{4.8}Cl_{9.8}$	578
Dodecachloroterphenyl[1]	$C_{18.9}H_{2.6}Cl_{12}$	656

Chloroarylimides prepared in dimethylacetamide or N-methylpyrrolidinone are recovered by coagulation in water in yields of >95%. The vacuum dried products can be used directly without further purification. Ketones, amides and chlorinated hydrocarbons, including methylene chloride, are good solvents for these materials and provide low viscosity solutions at up to 75% solids level.

Range finding toxicity studies on decachloroterphenylarylimide have been completed at Mellon Institute. The material was not toxic by the acute oral, skin penetration, or inhalation routes at the maximum dosage levels attainable in the studies. Twenty-five percent solutions of the maleimide resulted in trace skin irritation and moderate eye injury. No hazards are anticipated from utilization of decachloroterphenylarylimide under normal handling conditions.

B. Chloroarylimide Polymerization

Polymerization of maleimide terminated oligomers can be accomplished through any of several routes including: (a) reaction with amines (18) and phenols; (b) exposure to elevated temperatures; (c) oxidative initiation at temperatures in the 100-150°C range (19). When the chloroarylimides are heated from about 150°C to 300°C, the reactive maleimide end groups are activated and undergo addition type cross-linking reactions, illustrated by Equation 5. As with sulfone based maleimides (14), the cure rate is relatively slow

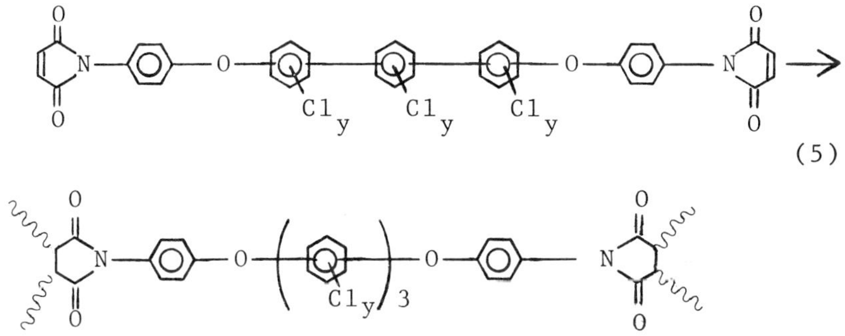

(5)

at 180-220°C and "B-staging" is possible. Since volatile by-products are not liberated during cure, this represents a substantial advantage over state-of-the-art high temperature resin systems and has been employed in most of the chloroarylimide applications investigated to date. Chloroarylimide curing rates can be markedly accelerated by use of free radical initiators. For example, the cure rate of decachloroterphenyl maleimide was increased from >>1 hour at 200°C for total cure, in the absence of peroxide, to under five minutes with 1.5% dicumyl peroxide as an additive. As previously reported with sulfone based arylimides (14), the chloroarylimide cure rates could also be accelerated with phenols, amines and vinyl monomers.

Cure rates in the chloroterphenyl series of maleimides were found to be slower than those in the sulfone ether diamine series, for example, structure III versus structure V, as shown by the data in Table II. This observation,

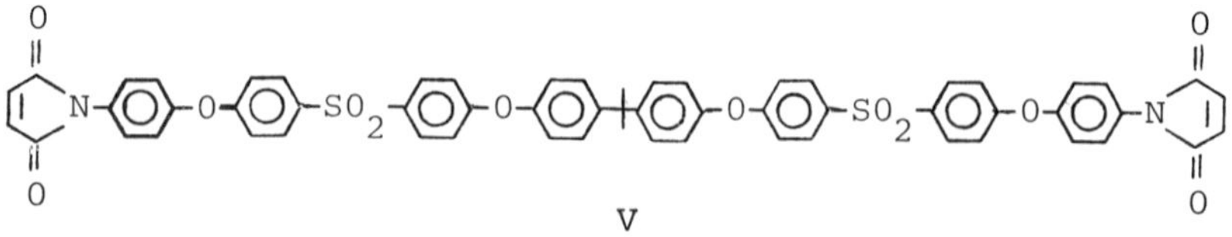

V

namely, a decreased rate with increased electron withdrawing capacity of maleimide substituents, taken together with the accelerated rate of cross-linking observed with peroxide initiators and the substantially increased rate (20-50 times) in the presence of reactive olefins, indicates that the mechanism of thermally induced cure probably involves a free radical polymerization. The relatively modest cure rate acceleration observed when the chloroarylimides are combined with amines and phenolic derivatives, vide infra, indicates that a competing Michael type reaction may also occur in the presence of such compounds.

The curing reaction kinetics for compound III was determined using the torsion pendulum method described in the experimental section. This involved measuring the change in modulus of glass cloth prepregs as a function of temperature. The results are shown in Figure 1 where relative modulus $(C/S)^2$ is plotted as a function of time, at 200°C and 220°C, respectively. As can be seen from Table II and by comparing Figure 1 with the torsion pendulum data for compound V previously published (14), the induction time and cure requirements for sulfone based maleimides (V, etc.) are significantly different than those for the less reactive chloroaromatic amine based maleimides. It is speculated

TABLE II
Sulfone Maleimide vs. Chloroaromatic Maleimide Cure Speed

Temperature	Compound V 180°C	Compound V 200°C	Compound III 200°C	Compound III 220°C
Induction Time (min.)	29	18	110	75
Reaction Completed (min.)	120	80	435	220

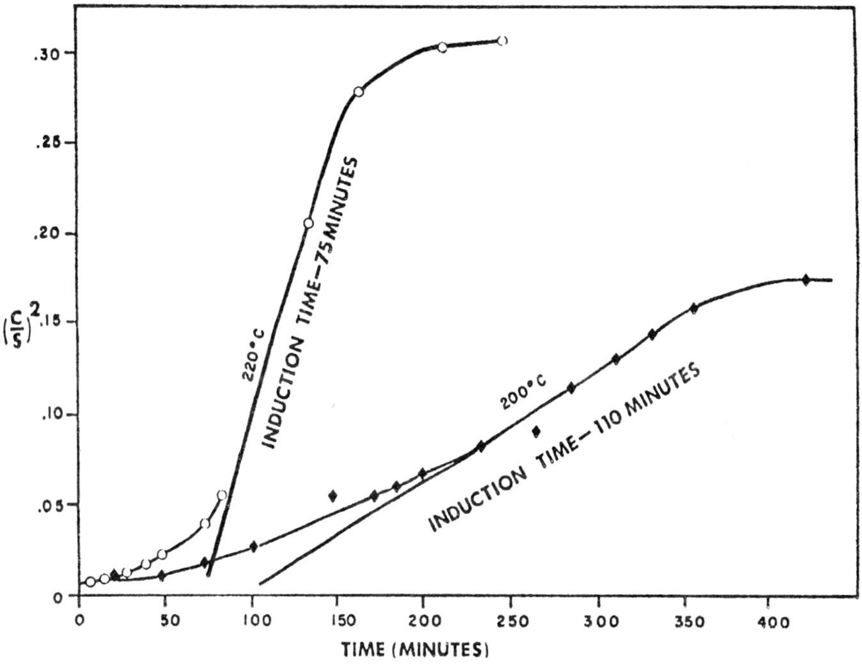

Fig. 1. Normalized Modulus $(C/S)^2$ Versus Time For Compound III Glass Prepeg, (200 and 220°C).

that the slower cure rate of chloroaromatic amine based arylimides is due to a greater electron withdrawal capacity of the chloroaromatic nuclei vs. the sulfone group, which reduces the electron density of the terminal olefin to a greater degree. Whereas a post cure of thirty minutes at 270°C was recommended to attain maximum crosslink density in the sulfone based maleimides(14), a post cure of 100 minutes at 270 °C is required in the case of neat chloroarylimides. Certain composite fabrications involved consolidation under pressure at 220°C followed by post-curing at 260-270°C in an air oven. Shorter times and lower temperatures for total cure can be achieved through the use of select accelerators, additives and fillers. Figure 2 illustrates the effect of glass versus asbestos on chloroarylimide III cure speed.

C. Properties of Chloroarylimides

Some of the mechanical properties on three members of the chloroarylimide series are shown in Table III. The data summarizes the effect of structure on glass transition temperature, tensile modulus and modulus plateau above the Tg. As can be seen, both the Tg and modulus above the Tg, decreased as the bis-phenol A content increased and the high modulus chloroaromatic portion is reduced. Chloroarylimides III and VI (Table III) were studied in most detail as candidates for high temperature applications. The high modulus plateau above the Tg, especially with chloroarylimide III, (Figure 3) allows fabrication of filled and unfilled parts which do not exhibit heat distortion temperatures (264 psi). Figures 4 and 5 show mechanical loss data for oligomer arylimides VI and VII. The oligomer arylimides show significantly lower modulus values above the Tg. An oligomer (n=1) arylimide prepared from nonachlorobiphenyl was also evaluated and shown to possess a Tg at 260°C with a modulus plateau above the Tg of 60,000 psi. However, due to the questionable availability of polychlorinated biphenyls, further work with this system was not pursued.

TABLE III
Properties of Chloroarylimides

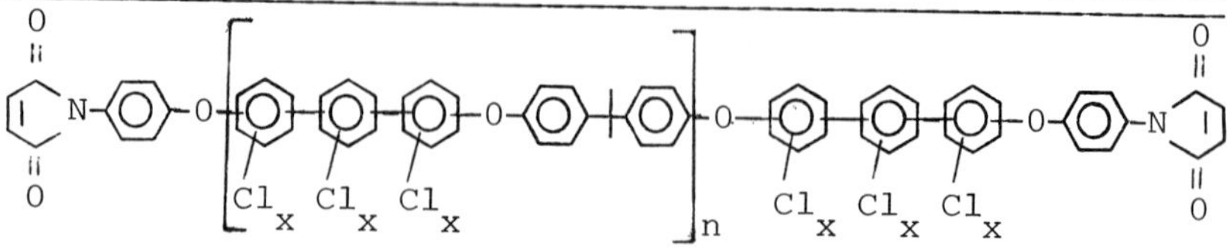

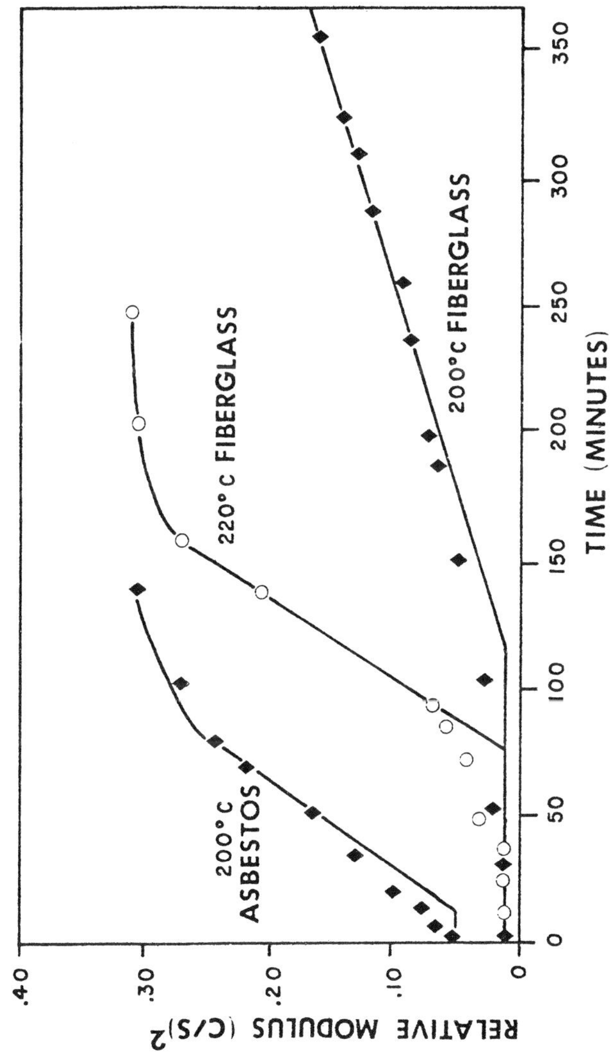

Fig. 2. The Effect of Fillers on the Curing Rate of Chloroarylimide III.

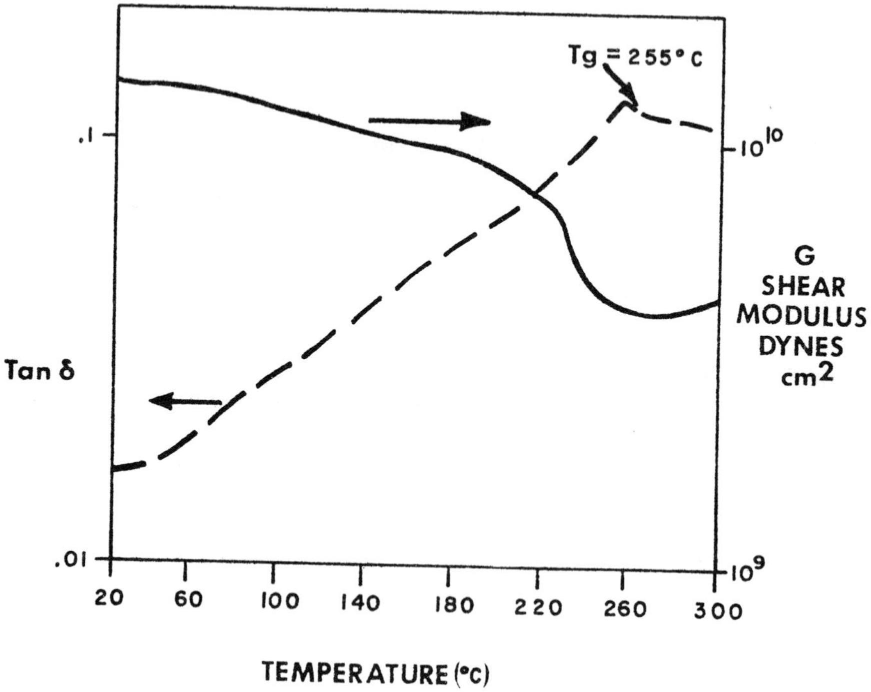

Fig. 3. Mechanical Loss Results for Chloro-arylimide-(III).

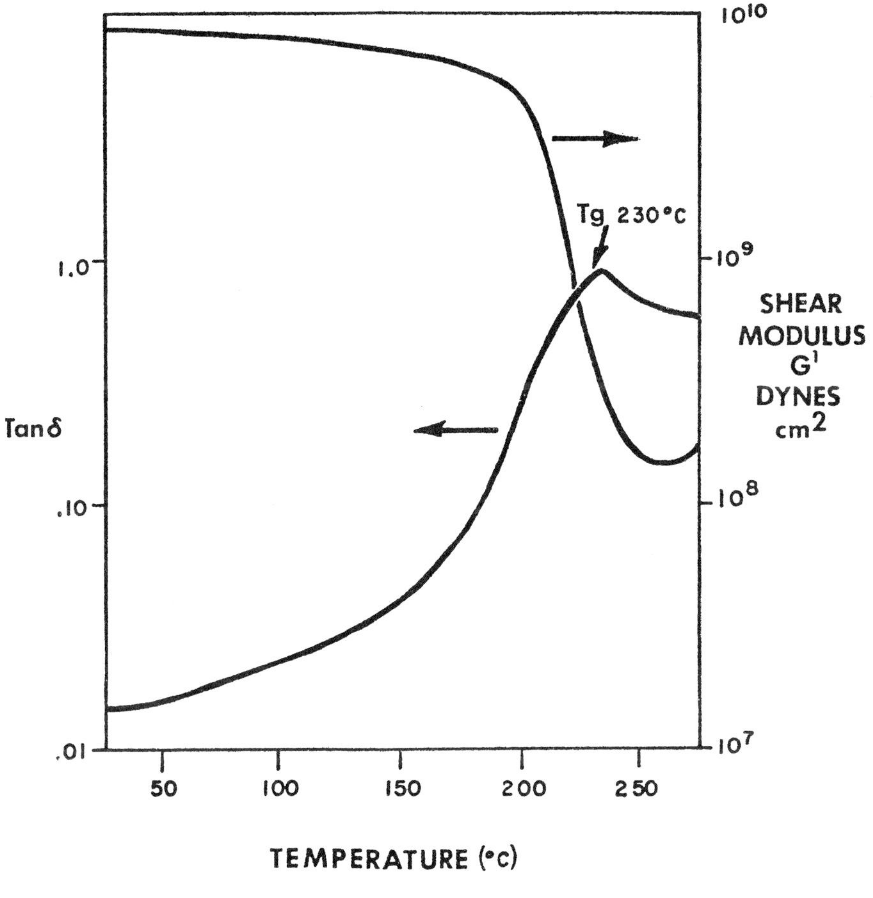

Fig. 4. Mechanical Loss Results for Decachloroterphenyl Maleimide (VI). Oligomer (n=1).

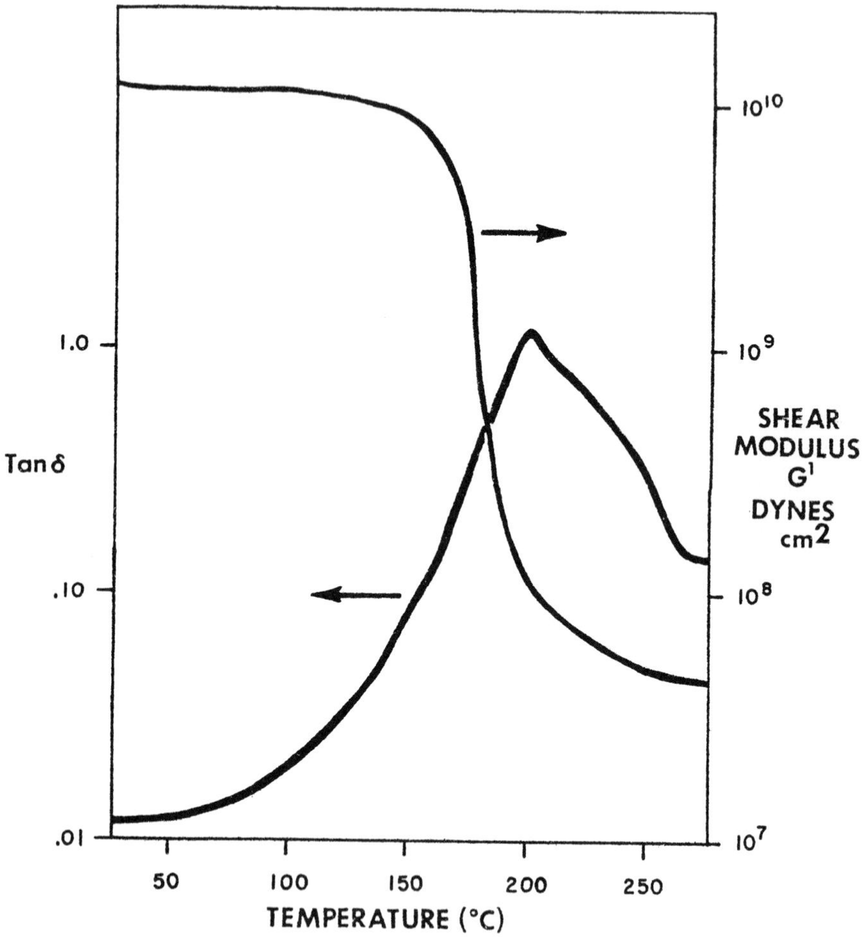

Fig. 5. Mechanical Loss Results for Decachloroterphenyl Maleimide VII. Oligomer (n=2).

Table III (continued)

	III DECACHLORO- TERPHENYL MALEIMIDE	VI OLIGOMER (n=1) DECACHLORO- TERPHENYL MALEIMIDE	VII OLIGOMER (n=2) DECACHLORO- TERPHENYL MALEIMIDE
Molecular Weight (uncured)	900	1550	2200
Tg, °C, Cured	245-255	230	200
Tensile Modulus, psi	500,000	450,000	450,000
Tensile Modulus Above the Tg, psi	218,000	6,500	2,000
Specific Gravity		1.4	

Air aging studies were conducted on chloroarylimide, III, and (n=1) oligomer arylimide, VI. Plaques of the cured resins, after aging at 500°F for 500 hours, showed no decrease in properties (tensile modulus and modulus above the Tg). In fact, under these conditions the Tg′s of the aged samples increased approximately 40°C over the Tg′s of the unaged controls, thus indicating further cure had taken place. A maleimide, VIII, based on a phenol-formaldehyde-aniline resin/dodecachloroterphenyl condensation product was

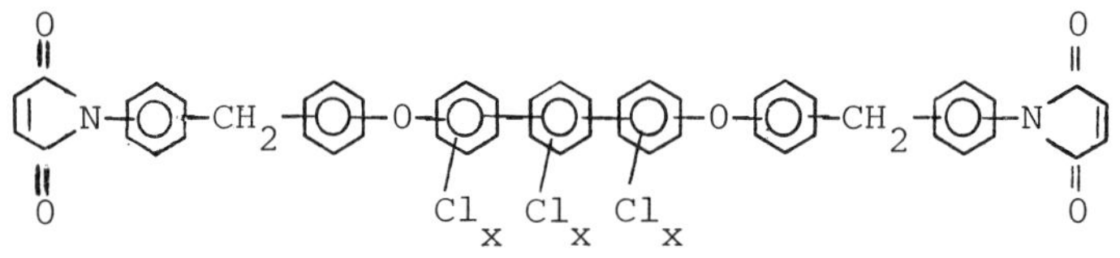

VIII

similarly aged and found to show a significant loss in strength after 250 hours at 500°F. The thermal instability of VIII can be attributed to the diphenylmethane moiety present in the backbone It is anticipated that the maleic moiety will be the temperature limiting component of the chloroarylimide systems.

The flame retardant characteristics[2] of the chloroarylimides are excellent, a feature of significant interest in various applications. The materials are non-burning, a result of their high chlorine content (>30%) and their high cross-link densities. The chloroarylimides possess flame resistant properties which are superior to other related resins tested in graphite composite applications with the possible exception of sulfone etherdiamine polyamide-imide (2).

D. Properties of Chloroarylimide Composites

The properties of chloroarylimide composites (structure III or VI) based on glass, asbestos or carbon fiber, respectively, were evaluated. Mechanical and electrical properties of glass filled composites are shown in Table IV together with other thermoset systems. Tensile strength and elongation values were low, whereas the heat distortion temperatures of the cured composites were quite respectable. Electrical properties appear to be similar to both filled phenolic and epoxy compositions. The excellent electrical properties observed demonstrate that the chloroaromatic structure is not deleterious.

Evaluation of asbestos based composites in friction applications showed that a 15% chloroarylimide modified phenolic binder displayed significantly higher friction levels and greater stability at elevated temperatures (700-900°F) (20) than a corresponding conventional system. Although resin systems with high temperature friction performance generally suffer from having high wear, the subject resin exhibited less wear than a comparably formulated high heat resistant straight two-step phenolic. Extended oven postcure is normally required with phenolic binders. Chloroarylimide III composites, where III was the sole binder, were cured at 535°F for four hours, resulting in good heat resistance and friction properties. A composite including chloroarylimide III plus Cardolite displayed good friction performance after only a 90 minute cure at 520°F (refer to Figure 6). These results are summarized in Table V and Figure 6.

---

[2] It is not the authors intention to correlate laboratory flammability data with performance under actual fire conditions or even to imply such a correlation exists.

TABLE IV
Mechanical and Electrical Properties of Chloroarylimides

	Chloro-arylimide-III 30% Glass	Oligomer Chloro-arylimide-VI 30% Glass	Epoxy(a) Glass	Phenol(a) Formaldehyde Glass Filled	Cyclo-Aliphatic Epoxy No Filler(b)
Tensile Modulus, psi	$16x10^{5}$	$11.1x10^{5}$	$30.4x10^{5}$	$33x10^{5}$	-
Tensile Strength, psi	2500	6110	10,000-30,000	5,000-18,000	-
Elongation @ Break, %	0.2	0.62	4.0	0.2	-
Izod, ft. #/in. notch	1.0-1.5	0.52	10	0.3-18	-
Heat Distortion Temp. (264 psi), °F	>550	480	250-500	300-600	-
Dielectric Strength volts/mil.	477	590	300-400	140-400	-
Dielectric Constant					
60 cps	3.85	3.62	3.5-5.0	7.1	2.8
10^{6} cps	3.94	3.67	3.5-5.0	4.6-6.6	-
Dissipation Factor					
60 cps	0.0027	0.0042	0.01	0.05	0.008
10^{6} cps	0.0062	0.0071	0.01	0.012-0.026	-
Volume Resistivity	$10x10^{15}$	$14x10^{15}$	$>10^{14}$	$7x10^{12}$	$1x10^{13}$

(a) Plastics Properties Chart, Modern Plastics Encyclopedia
(b) Bakelite Cycloaliphatic Epoxides Data Sheets

TABLE V
Chloroarylimide Friction/Wear Test Data

Sample	A	B	C	D
Resin Bond	Std. Phenolic	Chloro Arylimide-III	Chloro Arylimide-III	Std. Phenolic With 15% Chloro Arylimide-III
Formula (wt. %):				
Asbestos 7D	60	60	60	60
Resin Bond	20	20	20	20
Barytes	10	20	10	20
Cardolite NC111	10	-	10	-
Mold Cure:	15min @300°F 2,000 psi	30min @430°F 90min @520°F 4,000 psi	30min @430°F 90min @520°F 4,000 psi	15min @300°F 2,000 psi
Post Cure:	4hrs @300°F +4hrs @360°F	4hrs @530°F	None	4hrs @300°F +4hrs @360°F
Fade Temp. - °F	600	None	700	None
Average Wear (wt./thick) - %	10	-	5.5	3.7

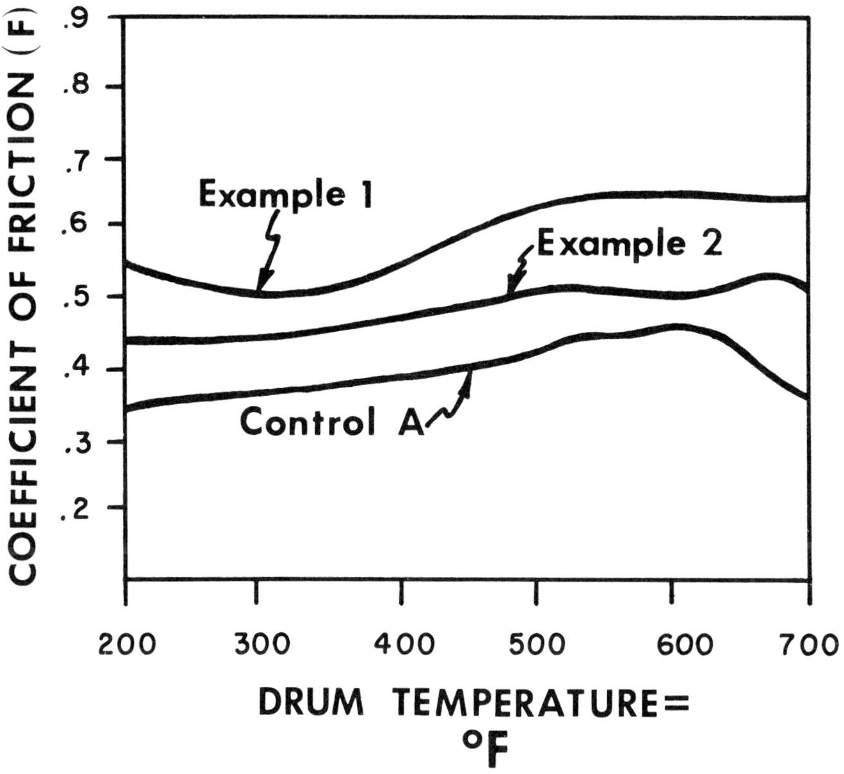

Fig. 6. Friction Performance Test Curves[2] *With Chloro-arylimide-III.*

Example I -Compound-III (20); Barium Sulfate (20); Asbestos Fiber (60).

Example II-Compound III (20); Barium Sulfate (10); Cardolite NC111 (10); Asbestos Fiber (60).

Control A -Two Step Novolac (13.5); Hexa (6.5); Barium Sulfate (10); Cardolite NC111 (10); Asbestos Fiber (60).

III. ACKNOWLEDGEMENT

The authors wish to thank Mr. W. J. D'Allesandro for the data on friction performance. Many stimulating discussions were held with Dr. B. H. Eckstein.

IV. EXPERIMENTAL

A. Oligomer (n=1) Sulfone Ether Diamine Bismaleimide Preparation

An oligomer polysulfone diamine was first prepared as follows. Into a 12-liter flask was charged 716.6 g (3.14 mole) of bisphenol A, 687.5 g (6.38 mole) ρ-aminophenol, 4.2 liters of dimethyl sulfoxide, and 2.5 liters of toluene. After purging with nitrogen, 1003.8 g (12.62 mole) of a 50.2% solution of sodium hydroxide was added, and the pot temperature brought to 110-120°C. Water was removed from the toluene azeotrope by using a Barrett tube, after which the toluene was distilled off until the pot temperature reached 160°C. At this point, the reaction mixture was cooled to 100°C and 1807.5 g (6.28 mole) of dichlorodiphenyl sulfone added as a solid. The pot was reheated to 160°C for 1 hr and then cooled.

After cooling to room temperature the solution was filtered to remove sodium chloride and coagulated in a blender from 2% sodium hydroxide solution containing 1% sodium sulfite. The precipitated diamine was washed with a hot 1% solution of sodium sulfite and methanol and dried in a vacuum oven at 80°C.

The yield of oligomer polysulfone diamine was 2655 g (96.5%) and the equivalent weight was 456 g.

The bismaleimide was then prepared from the above diamine as follows. To a 5-liter, three necked flask equipped with a stirrer, thermometer, and nitrogen inlet tube was charged 900 g (1.0 mole) of oligomer polysulfone diamine and 2 liters of dimethylacetamide. The diamine was allowed to dissolve and the solution then cooled to about 0°C. Maleic anhydride 196 g (2.0 mole) was added as a solid at such a rate as to keep the temperature below 15°C. After 1 hr at 10-25°C, 204 g (2.0 mole) of acetic anhydride and 20 g (0.2 mole) of triethylamine were added in one portion and the mixture stirred for 4 hrs.

The bismaleimide solution obtained thereby was coagulated from 10 parts of water to 1 part of reaction mixture. The tan coagulate which formed was collected by vacuum filtration. The product was repeatedly washed on the filter until the filtrate was neutral and then dried in a vacuum oven at about 85°C. The yield was 98%. The cured maleimide exhibited a Tg of 239°C.

B. Octachloroterphenyl Etheramine Maleimide

To a 2-liter, 4-necked flask equipped with a Dean Stark trap, condenser, nitrogen inlet tube and thermometer was added 110.0 grams (1.008 moles) of p-aminophenol and 500 ml. of toluene. The system was purged with nitrogen and 400 ml. of dimethylsulfoxide added. The system was purged again with nitrogen and 81.05 grams (1.05 moles) of 49.15% aqueous sodium hydroxide added. This solution was heated to 110-120°C and water removed via the toluene/water azeotrope. After complete dehydration (approximately 4-5 hours), toluene was removed until the pot temperature reached 135°C.

A concentrated solution of 274 grams (0.5 mole) decachloroterphenyl in 250 ml. of hot toluene was added via an addition funnel. The remaining toluene was then distilled off. The pot was heated to 160°C and maintained 1 hour before cooling to room temperature.

At room temperature, the reaction mixture was vacuum filtered to remove sodium chloride and coagulated. Coagulation was accomplished by pouring the filtrate slowly into distilled water (1 to 10 of water) contained in a 3-liter blender and stirred at a high speed. Vacuum filtration through a fritted glass funnel afforded a dark colored diamine. The diamine was washed further with hot distilled water, then dried at 60°C under vacuum.

The dried diamine (76% yield) was dark brown in color and had a titrated amine equivalent of 365; the chlorine content by elemental analysis was 36.2%. The melting point was 115-125°C. The mass spectrum indicated the product was composed of 9 amines: $C_{18}H_7Cl_6(OC_6H_4NH_2)$; $C_{18}H_6Cl_7(OC_6H_4NH_2)$; $C_{18}H_5Cl_8(OC_6H_4NH_2)$; $C_{18}H_6Cl_6(OC_6H_4NH_2)_2$; $C_{18}H_5Cl_7(OC_6H_4NH_2)_2$; $C_{18}H_4Cl_8(OC_6H_4NH_2)_2$; $C_{18}H_5Cl_6(OC_6H_4NH_2)_3$; $C_{18}H_4Cl_7(OC_6H_4NH_2)_3$; $C_{18}H_3Cl_8(OC_6H_4NH_2)_3$.

The corresponding thermosetting maleimide was then prepared as follows. To a three liter, three neck flask equipped with a nitrogen inlet tube, stirrer and thermometer was charged 496.4 g (1.36 equivalents) of octachloroterphenyl etheramine and 1.5 liters of dimethylacetamide. Solution was effected under nitrogen while cooling to 0°C. Maleic anhydride 134.24 grams, (1.37 moles), was added while maintaining a temperature of about 15°C. The solution was then stirred for approximately 1 hour at 15-25°C, after which 142.8 grams (1.4 moles) of acetic anhydride and 8.2 grams (0.1 moles) of sodium acetate were added. Stirring was continued for 4-5 hours at room temperature.

The arylimide was isolated from solution via coagulation in 10 parts of water. The tan powdery filter cake was water washed until neutral and then vacuum dried at 85°C to a constant weight. The yield was 600 grams. This product has a molecular weight of about 850 uncured. After curing by heating at 270°C for 30 minutes, this product showed a Tg of 245 °C, a tensile modulus of 500,000 psi and a tensile modulus plateau above the Tg of 180,000-300,000 psi.

C. Oligomer (n=1) Octachloroterphenyl Etheramine Maleimide

To a 2 liter, 4 necked flask equipped with a Dean Stark trap, condenser, nitrogen inlet tube and thermometer was added 60.02 grams (0.55 mole) of ρ-aminophenol, 57.08 grams (0.25 mole) of bisphenol A and 500 ml of toluene. The system was purged with nitogen, 450 ml of dimethylsulfoxide added, and again purged with nitrogen after which 84.64 grams (1.04 moles) of 49.15% aqueous sodium hydroxide was added. The solution was heated to 110-120°C and water removed via the toluene/water azeotrope. After complete dehydration (approximately 4-5 hours), the toluene was removed until the pot temperature reached 135°C.

A concentrated solution of 274 grams (0.5 mole) decachloroterphenyl in 250 ml of hot toluene was introduced via an addition funnel. The remaining toluene was then distilled off. The pot was heated to 160-165°C and maintained 2 hours before cooling to room temperature.

At room temperature, the reaction mixture was vacuum filtered to remove sodium chloride and coagulated. Recovery was accomplished by pouring the filtrate slowly into distilled water (1 to 10 of water) containing 2% sodium hydroxide/1% sodium sulfite contained in a 3 liter blender and stirred at a high speed. Vacuum filtration through a fritted glass funnel afforded a light colored diamine. The diamine was washed further with a hot 1% sodium sulfite solution and isopropanol, then dried at 85 °C under vacuum.

The dried diamine was tan in color and had a titrated amine equivalent of 696. The melting point was 162-169°C. The diamine was converted to the corresponding maleimide as follows. To a one liter, three neck flask was charged 50 grams (0.216 equivalent) of the oligomer arylamine and 300 ml of dry dimethylacetamide. The mixture was cooled to 0°C while under nitrogen and 21.17 grams (0.216 mole) of maleic anhydride added. After stirring for one hour at 0-25°C, 22.03 grams (0.216 mole) of acetic anhydride and 2.2 grams of sodium acetate was added. The mixture was stirred for an additional four hours and then coagulated from water. The product maleimide was collected by vacuum filtration, washed further with water and dried at 80°C for 48 hours. The yield was 151 grams (91%). This product had a molecular weight of about 1560 uncured. After curing by heating at 275°C for about 30 minutes, this product exhibited a Tg of 227°C, a tensile modulus of 400,000 psi and a tensile modulus plateau above the Tg of 6,100 psi.

D. Octachloroterphenyl Etheramine Maleimide

A single-pot synthesis of octachloroterphenyl etheramine maleimide was conducted in which the arylamine and arylimide were consecutively prepared in the same vessel and the same solvent.

A five liter, four neck flask equipped with a condenser, thermometer, Barrett tube, addition funnel, nitrogen inlet tube and stirrer was charged with 225 grams (2.063 moles) of ρ-aminophenol, 560.4 grams (1.023 moles) of decachloroterphenyl, 1200 ml of xylene and 900 ml of N-methypyrrolidonone. After purging with nitrogen, the mixture was brought to reflux (155°C) and 167.55 grams (2.058 mole) of 49.15% sodium hydroxide solution added dropwise over a one hour period. The water was removed azeotropically during the caustic addition. The xylene was recirculated until the dehydration was complete (1.5 hours) and the xylene then removed until the pot temperature reached 165°C.

After cooling to room temperature, 202.2 grams (2.062 mole) of maleic anhydride was added. Stirring was continued for one hour and 213 grams (2.10 mole) of acetic anhydride and 86.1 grams (1.05 mole) of sodium acetate was charged. After stirring for four hours, the solution was coagulated from water and the product recovered by vacuum filtration. Water washing and drying at 80°C for 48 hours afforded 835 grams (96%) of arylimide, m.p. 138-142°C.

E. Thermomechanical Characterization

The reaction kinetics were determined by coating woven fiberglass cloth with a solution of the maleimide precursor from an appropriate solvent. After proper drying, a rectangular section was placed between the grips in a torsion pendulum apparatus similar to the design of Nielsen (21). The chamber was preheated to the test temperature, and after the specimen had been inserted, frequency-time measurements were taken. The relative modulus (frequency^2; $(c/s)^2$) versus time was plotted to determine the induction time for reaction and the time for complete reaction.

The dynamic mechanical properties (mechanical loss: tan δ, shear modulus, G^1, dynes/cm^2) were determined on the maleimide samples prepared by compression molding and curing in a cavity mold.

Using the torsion pendulum, the tan δ and G^1 values as a function of temperature were obtained from the resultant damped sinusoidul wave as described by Nielsen (22). Tensile modulus, E, values (Table III) were estimated from the relationship: $E = 2G(1+\gamma)$, where γ = Poisson's ratio. Values of $\gamma = 0.3$ below the Tg and $\gamma = 0.5$ above the Tg were used for these calculations.

The maleimide fiberglass composites were prepared by melt processing at 200-220 °C on a two roll mill within a time period that the extent of crosslinking was negligible. These composites were then compression molded and cured in an 1/8" cavity mold. The mechanical, thermal and electrical properties were determined using the appropriate ASTM test procedures.

V. REFERENCES

1. T. T. Serafini, NASA Technical Memorandum X-71682, April, 1975.

2. G. L. Brode, J. H Kawakami, G. T. Kwiatkowski and A. W. Bedwin; J. Poly. Sci., 12, 575-587 (1974).

3. G. T. Kwiatkowski, G. L. Brode, J. H. Kawakami and A. W. Bedwin, ibid, 12, 589-601 (1974).

4. G. L. Brode and J. H. Kawakami, Polyamide-Imides, U.S. Patents 3,895,064 (1975) and 3,897,497 (1975), to Union Carbide Corp.

5. H. Mukamal, F. W. Harris and J. K. Stille, J. Poly. Sci., A-1, 5, 2721 (1967).

6. W. Wrasidlo and J. M. Angl, J. Poly. Sci., A-1, 7, 3393 (1969).

7. P. M. Hergenrother and H. H. Levine, J. Poly. Sci., A-1, 5, 1453 (1967).

8. F. W. Harris, W. A. Feld and L. H. Lanier, Polymeric and Polycondensation Processes; N. A. J. Platzer, ed., Interscience Pub. 1975, pp 421-428.

9. T. T. Serafini, P. Delvigs, G. R. Lightsey, J. Appl. Poly. Sci., 16, 4,905-916, (1976).

10. G. F. D'Alelio, U.S. Patent 3,897,395 (1975), to Univ. of Notre Dame.

11. T. T. Serafini, P. Delvigs, G. R. Lightsey, U.S. Patent 3,745,149 (1973) to U.S.A.

12. M. A. J. Mallet, Modern Plastics, 50, 6, 78-81 (1973).

13. J. H. Kawakami, G. T. Kwiatkowski, G. L. Brode and A. W. Bedwin, J. Appl. Poly. Sci., 12, 565-573 (1974).

14. G. T. Kwiatkowski, L. M. Robeson, G. L. Brode and A. W. Bedwin, ibid, 961-972 (1975).

15. G. L. Brode, J. H. Kawakami, G. T. Kwiatkowski and A. W. Bedwin, Advances In Chemistry Series, 1975 Gould, Pub.

16. G. T. Kwiatkowski and G. L. Brode, U.S. Patent 3,839,287 (1974) to Union Carbide Corp.

17. G. T. Kwiatkowski, G. L. Brode and A. W. Bedwin, J. Poly. Sci., 1976, in press.

18. M. Bargain, A. Combet, and P. Grosjian, U.S. Patent 3,878,172, 1975, to Rhone-Poulenc S.A., France.

19. G. F. D'Alelio, U.S. Patent 3,929,713, 1975 to duPont de Nemours & Co.

20. W. J. D'Allesandro and G. L. Brode, U.S. Patent 3,761,441 (1973) to Union Carbide Corp.

21. L. E. Nielsen, Rev. Sci. Instr. 22,690 (1951).

22. L. E. Nielsen, "Mechanical Properties of Polymers and Composites: Vol. 1", Marcel Dekker Inc., New York (1974).

THERMAL AGING OF CURED ETHYLENE/VINYL ACETATE AND ETHYLENE/VINYL ACETATE/VINYL ALCOHOL ELASTOMERS

R. M. Smith, G. K. Baker, and C. H. Smith

The Bendix Corporation

Accelerated aging characteristics of ethylene-vinyl acetate (EVA) and ethylene/vinyl acetate/vinyl alcohol (VCE) elastomers were evaluated after exposure to controlled thermal and atmospheric environments to provide information for predicting the long term stability of the materials. Composite test specimens were prepared by placing discs of the materials in contact with discs of open-cell silicone foam which were then clamped between stainless steel plates. The composite samples were thermally aged at 60°, 80°, and 100°C in closed containers back-filled with either dry air or dry nitrogen for periods of from 2 weeks to 8 months. At the appropriate intervals, samples were subjected to a three-part analysis; (1) measurement of the migration of unbound chemicals between materials by weight change, (2) solvent swell determinations to evaluate the degree of crosslinking, and (3) measurements of residual unbound chemicals by solvent extraction. Little change was found in the VCE samples under the most severe conditions, while the EVA materials degraded considerably as indicated by the dramatic increase in crosslink density and the identification of degradation products. A degradation mechanism was proposed based upon the data collected.

I. INTRODUCTION

One of the design requirements of our customers is that the materials involved maintain their chemical and mechanical functionality and remain compatible with surrounding materials for a long time. As part of a material evaluation program to select a suitable elastomer for part fabrication, two cross-linked polymers were subjected to thermal aging under various conditions. Such accelerated aging tests are necessary to determine the probable effects of long term real time storage. Specific material changes associated with accelerated aging were monitored on the basis of a time-temperature test schedule. Of particular interest were chemical and physical changes and the subsequent formation and migration of chemically unbound material.

The results of this study indicate that the ethylene/vinyl acetate copolymer (EVA) is susceptible to thermal degradation. Although the uncrosslinked polymers are chemically very similar (Figures 1 and 2) the difference in the type of crosslinking accounts for the superiority of the ethylene/vinyl acetate/ vinyl alcohol terpolymer (VCE).

II. EXPERIMENTAL

Test specimens were prepared by die-cutting discs of the materials 38.1 mm diameter and 0.68 mm thick and placing them in contact with die-cut discs of cellular silicone foam 38.1 mm diameter by 0.51 mm thick. Each EVA/silicone or VCE/silicone composite was placed between two stainless steel plates and held together by compression. The composite samples were packaged in cannisters which had been thoroughly flushed with either dry nitrogen or dry air and were then placed in ovens maintained at 60°, 80°, and 100°C. Control samples of each material were packaged separately in containers equipped for gas analysis and placed in the same ovens. The formulation and cure schedule of the materials are presented in Table 1.

III. ANALYSIS

At the scheduled sampling times (Table 2) composite samples were removed from the ovens and subjected to a three part analysis involving material migration by weight change, evaluation of crosslink density by solvent swell measurement, and amount of unbound chemicals by solvent extraction. Major emphasis was placed on the use of dry nitrogen as the storage environment, but a comparison with dry air was also desired.

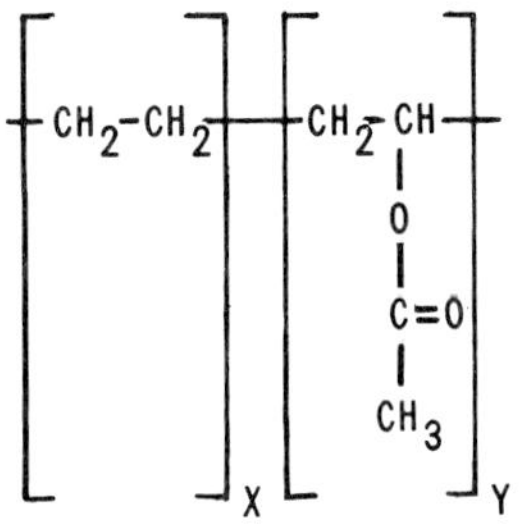

ETHYLENE/VINYL ACETATE (EVA)

WHERE X = 57% WEIGHT

Y = 43% WEIGHT

Fig. 1.

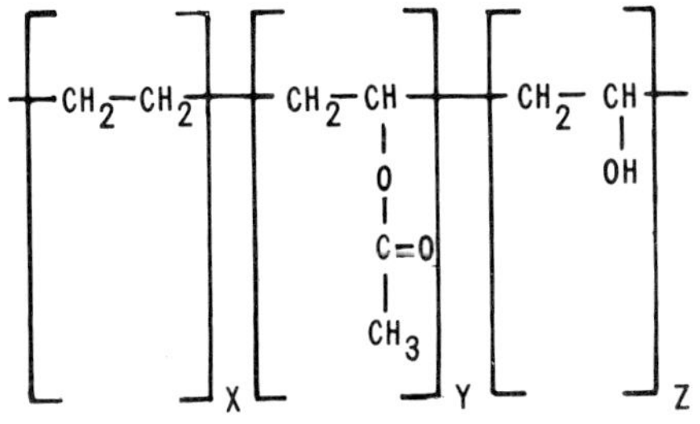

ETHYLENE/VINYL ACETATE/VINYL ALCOHOL (VCE)

WHERE X = 57% WEIGHT

Y = 37% WEIGHT

Z = 6% WEIGHT

Fig. 2.

Table 1. Formulation and Cure Data

Material and Vendor	Curing Agent	Cure	Postcure
EVA from USI Chemicals	Lupersol 101,* 2 phr	30 minutes at 177°C	16 hours at 150°C
VCE from Monsanto Research Corporation	TDID** 12 phr	30 minutes at 125°C	16 hours at 150°C
Cellular Silicone from Union Carbide Corporation	Cadox BSG,† 2.2 phr	30 minutes at 104°C	24 hours at 250°C

*2,5-dimethyl-2,5-(ditertiary butyl-peroxy) hexane
**Toluene diisocyanate dimer
†Contains benzoyl peroxide and silicone oil

Table 2. Sample Storage Conditions in Dry Nitrogen and Dry Air

Exposure Time (Months)	Exposure Temperature		
	60°C	80°C	100°C
0.5			X
1		X	XO
2	X	XO	XO
4	XO	XO	XO
6	X	X	X
8	X	X	X

X is dry nitrogen
O is dry air

IV. DISCUSSION

The first segment of the analysis actually started before the composite samples were prepared. Baseline data were collected on all three materials prior to assembly. Sample weights were recorded to the nearest tenth of a milligram before and after storage. This provided the first indication the materials were significantly different in their thermal stabilities. Over the eight month test period the maximum weight change of the VCE control samples was about 0.06 percent compared to 2.15 percent for the EVA control samples. The small weight change associated with the VCE samples probably was the result of the migration of small amounts of unbound material onto the surfaces of the cannisters.

Similar data were obtained with the VCE/silicone composite samples in which material migration was found to be in the direction of the silicone foam and even onto the stainless steel plates. Other tests were necessary to define the cause of the large weight losses encountered in both the control and composite samples of EVA. The weight change data for all samples are listed in Tables 3 and 4.

Solvent swell measurements using chloroform were performed on all samples to monitor changes in the crosslink density as a function of aging conditions. Solvent swell values, as shown in Tables 5 and 6, are determined by calculating the ratio given.

$$\text{Swell} = \frac{V_p + V_s}{V_p}$$

where:

V_p = Volume of the polymer, and

V_s = Volume of the solvent trapped in the swollen polymer.

Such values are useful in following crosslinking trends and for qualitative comparisons between similar materials. It can be seen intuitively that lower swell values indicate higher crosslink densities.

Table 3. VCE/Silicone Weight Change

Time (Months)	Atmosphere	Material	Weight Change (mg) 100°C	80°C	60°C
0.5	Nitrogen	VCE	-0.4		
		Silicone	+2.3		
1	Nitrogen	VCE	-0.3	-1.4	
		Silicone	+1.4	+0.8	
	Air	VCE	-0.2		
		Silicone	+0.4		
2	Nitrogen	VCE	-1.0	-0.6	-1.1
		Silicone	+0.4	+2.5	+2.1
	Air	VCE	0.0	-0.2	
		Silicone	+4.5	+8.7	
4	Nitrogen	VCE	+1.9	-0.9	-1.1
		Silicone	-3.7	+0.4	+1.4
	Air	VCE	+0.4	-0.2	-0.5
		Silicone	-2.2	0.0	-0.9
6	Nitrogen	VCE	+0.9	0.0	-1.5
		Silicone	-8.3	-0.6	+1.6
8	Nitrogen	VCE	+0.3	-0.3	-2.1
		Silicone	-10.0	-1.7	+1.1
8*	Nitrogen	VCE	-0.9	+0.1	+0.5
		Silicone	-0.9	0.0	
	Air	VCE	+0.2	0.0	+0.7
		Silicone	-0.3	+0.5	

*Controls

Table 4. EVA/Silicone Weight Change

Time (Months)	Atmosphere	Material	Weight Change (mg) 100°C	80°C	60°C
0.5	Nitrogen	EVA	+0.4		
		Silicone	+2.0		
1	Nitrogen	EVA	-8.6	-1.0	
		Silicone	+2.1	+0.8	
	Air	EVA	-1.0		
		Silicone	0.0		
2	Nitrogen	EVA	-15.5	-6.7	-0.2
		Silicone	+4.0	+6.5	+0.8
	Air	EVA	-6.7	-2.1	
		Silicone	+9.3	+3.6	
4	Nitrogen	EVA	-8.4	-1.3	+0.2
		Silicone	-2.1	+0.5	+0.5
	Air	EVA	-22.2	-1.4	-0.7
		Silicone	-3.6	-10.7	0.0
6	Nitrogen	EVA	-10.8	-5.6	-2.0
		Silicone	-5.8	-10.6	+1.9
8	Nitrogen	EVA	-14.2	-7.8	-1.8
		Silicone	*	-0.7	+1.3
8**	Nitrogen	EVA	-36.0	-16.0	-0.3
		Silicone	-0.9	0.0	
	Air	EVA	-32.5	-11.5	+0.1
		Silicone	-0.3	+0.5	

*Sample completely destroyed during disassembly.
**Controls.

Comparing the two materials on the basis of apparent changes in crosslink densities showed that VCE was highly crosslinked initially (indicated by the baseline swell value of 1.78) but did not change significantly under the most severe conditions. The swell values for both the control and composite samples were 1.66 after exposure to 100°C for eight months. Conversely, EVA had a somewhat lower crosslink density initially (swell value of 2.22), but at the end of eight months at 100°C, the swell value had dropped to as low as 1.03. Such a value was considered to indicate extreme crosslinking resulting from chemical degradation within the polymer yielding free radicals which recombined to form new crosslinks.

Table 5. VCE/Silicone Solvent Swell

Time (Months)	Atmosphere	Material	Solvent Swell Values 100°C	80°C	60°C
Baseline	Ambient	VCE*			
		Silicone**			
0.5	Nitrogen	VCE	1.72		
		Silicone	2.49		
1	Nitrogen	VCE	1.69	1.73	
		Silicone	2.51	2.62	
	Air	VCE	1.69		
		Silicone	2.62		
2	Nitrogen	VCE	1.71	1.78	1.74
		Silicone	2.56	2.46	2.46
	Air	VCE	1.71	1.73	
		Silicone	2.69	2.67	
4	Nitrogen	VCE	1.75	1.79	1.70
		Silicone	2.58	2.54	2.51
	Air	VCE	1.64	1.70	1.72
		Silicone	2.55	2.57	2.46
6	Nitrogen	VCE	1.66	1.71	1.70
		Silicone	2.48	2.55	2.50
8	Nitrogen	VCE	1.66	1.69	1.69
		Silicone	***	2.56	2.61
8†	Nitrogen	VCE	1.66	1.73	1.79
		Silicone	2.55	2.67	
	Air	VCE	1.68	1.71	1.76
		Silicone	2.42	2.44	

*Solvent swell at ambient temperature was 1.78 which represents an average of three trials.
**Solvent swell at ambient temperature was 2.42 which represents an average of four trials.
***Sample was completely destroyed during disassembly.
†Controls.

Table 6. EVA/Silicone Solvent Swell

Time (Months)	Atmosphere	Material	Solvent Swell Values 100°C	80°C	60°C
Baseline	Ambient	EVA*			
		Silicone**			
0.5	Nitrogen	EVA	1.76		
		Silicone	2.57		
1	Nitrogen	EVA	1.37	2.45	
		Silicone	2.49	2.59	
	Air	EVA	1.78		
		Silicone	2.48		
2	Nitrogen	EVA	1.30	1.98	2.68
		Silicone	2.67	2.52	2.50
	Air	EVA	1.32	2.25	
		Silicone	2.56	2.50	
4	Nitrogen	EVA	1.24	1.43	2.58
		Silicone	2.67	2.65	2.62
	Air	EVA	1.44	2.36	2.20
		Silicone	2.59	2.53	2.58
6	Nitrogen	EVA	1.29	1.47	2.08
		Silicone	2.54	2.54	2.55
8	Nitrogen	EVA	1.67	1.66	1.90
		Silicone	***	2.70	2.58
8†	Nitrogen	EVA	1.09	1.42	2.68
		Silicone	2.55	2.67	
	Air	EVA	1.03	1.52	2.27
		Silicone	2.42	2.44	

*Solvent swell at ambient temperature was 2.22 which represents an average of three trials.
**Solvent swell at ambient temperature was 2.42 which represents an average of four trials.
***Sample was completely destroyed during disassembly.
†Controls.

On the basis of the data available at that time, a mechanism was proposed which accounted for the differences in the thermal stabilities of the two filled materials.

EVA uses a peroxide curing agent, Lupersol 101, 2,5-dimethyl-2, 5-(ditertiary butyl peroxy) hexane, which thermally dissociates to form tertiary butoxy radicals. The tertiary hydrogen on the vinyl acetate group is abstracted by one of the radicals to form tertiary butyl alcohol and a radical site on the polymer which reacts with another radical polymer site to form the carbon-carbon crosslink. These steps are illustrated in Reactions 1, 2, and 3. This represents what is believed to be the crosslinking mechanism involved in the peroxide cure of EVA.

The crosslinking of VCE uses the reaction of the vinyl alcohol group with toluene diisocyanate dimer (TDID) to form the urethane linkage (Reaction 4). At this point, one major difference in the crosslinked structures of EVA and VCE becomes apparent. In Reaction 3, it can be seen that during crosslinking some of the vinyl acetate groups have been converted from secondary to tertiary groups, while in VCE the status of the secondary acetate groups has not been altered. Since less energy is required to break the C-O bond in tertiary butyl acetate than in secondary butyl acetate, the differences in thermal stabilities appear to be strongly related to the type and position of the crosslink site.

A study of the thermal decomposition of poly(vinyl acetate) was conducted by N. Grassie (*Trans. Faraday Soc.*, *48*, *379*, *1952*) who reported that the polymer is stable up to 190°C in a vacuum. Above that temperature it decomposes into acetic acid and polyacetylene as shown in Reaction 5. Grassie explains the mechanism for the formation of acetic acid as being a chain reaction initiated by the loss of an acetic acid molecule at some random point along the polymer backbone as a result of thermal scission of the C-O bond. Since the C-O bonds are weaker than C-C bonds, those bonds break first. According to this mechanism, the break of the C-O bond is accompanied by the abstraction of a hydrogen atom from an adjoining carbon which results in the formation of a double bond in the chain. Acetate groups on either side of the double bond are now weaker than others on the chain so they break next and the process proceeds by chain reaction.

Gilbert and Kipling (*Fuel*, *XII*, *249*, *1962*) studied the thermal degradation of poly(vinyl alcohol). They noted the evolution of water and assumed the degradation followed the same mechanism as proposed for poly(vinyl acetate).

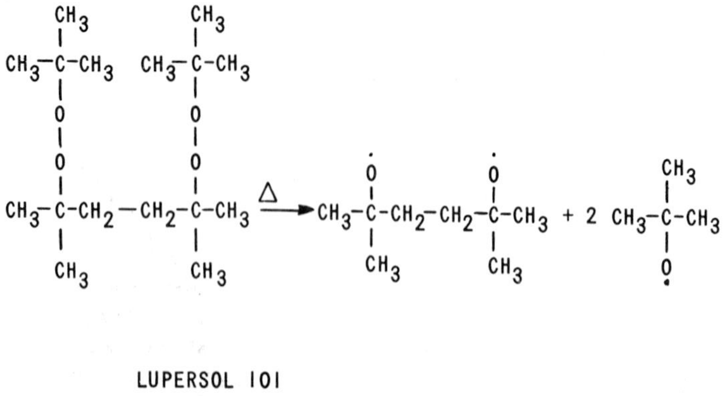

Reaction 1.

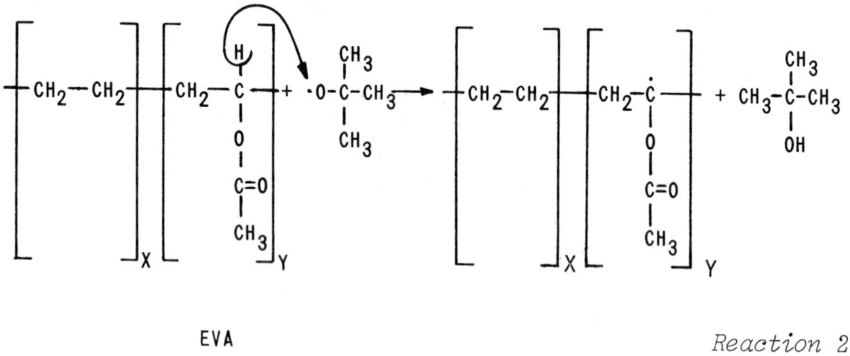

Reaction 2.

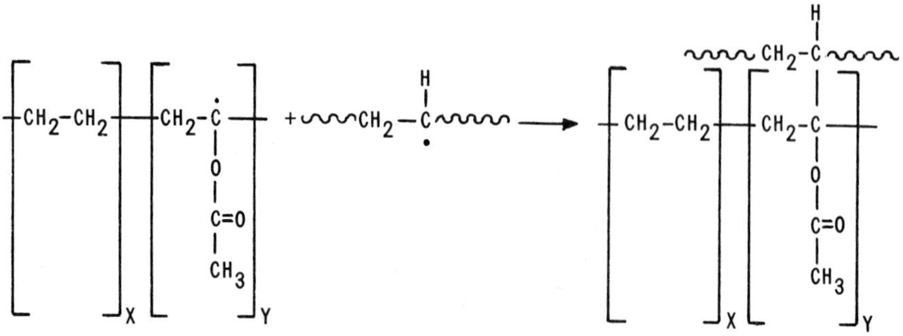

Reaction 3.

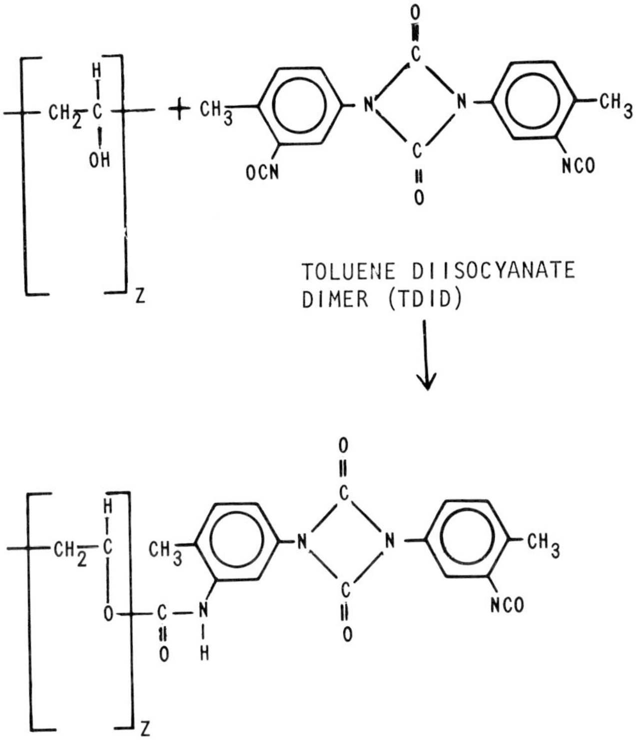

Reaction 4.

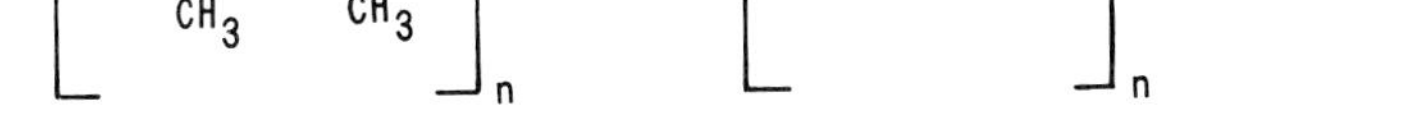

Reaction 5.

After analyzing the data collected for this study, an alternate mechanism was proposed to account for the loss of acetate groups and the apparent increase in crosslink density. Acetic acid was found to be the primary degradation product in the aged EVA samples. It was detected in the material which migrated into and through the cellular silicone cushion and onto the stainless steel plates. Thermogravimetric analyses of selected samples also confirmed the loss of the acetate groups during aging.

As discussed earlier, some of the acetate groups are changed from secondary to tertiary during the crosslinking mechanism in EVA. The tertiary groups would be the most likely to undergo the thermal scission of the C-O bond since more energy is required to break a secondary C-O bond. The main point of this alternate mechanism centers around the assumption that the acetate group leaves as a free radical and abstracts a hydrogen from some other point on the chain, at the same time leaving a radical site on the position vacated. This radical site on the chain could then react with some other site on the chain to produce an additional crosslink. As thermal scission of the tertiary acetate groups progress, so does the increased crosslinking.

One of the main areas of interest was the dramatic increase in the crosslink density, as indicated by the solvent swell test. Closer examination of the test and the possible polymeric degradation products showed that either mechanism seemed to fit the data. If the crosslink density of the polymer does increase so dramatically, then the swell data can be interpreted directly. However, if the degradation product is actually polyacetylene, then the values are actually indicating the increase in the hydrocarbon nature of the polymer backbone. Since linear hydrocarbons such as polyethylene do not exhibit solvent swell in chloroform, this test can be used to monitor the increase in the hydrocarbon fraction of the polymer. No attempt has been made to determine the actual degradation product since the VCE material was shown to be an acceptable production material, at least on the basis of thermal stability.

Finally, Soxhlet extractions using chloroform as a solvent were performed on all samples to determine the amount of unbound chemicals present in the elastomer materials and cellular silicone cushion. These data are presented in Tables 7 and 8. Prior to aging, the VCE baseline samples contained 1.11 percent by weight unbound material as compared to 3.64 percent for the EVA samples. These values were of considerable interest since material migration during storage is a vital concern.

Table 7. VCE/Silicone Extractable Levels

Time (Months)	Atmosphere	Material	Percent Soluble Material 100°C	80°C	60°C
Baseline	Ambient	VCE*			
		Silicone**			
0.5	Nitrogen	VCE	1.25		
		Silicone	2.66		
1	Nitrogen	VCE	1.69	1.73	
		Silicone	2.86	3.17	
	Air	VCE	1.69		
		Silicone	3.31		
2	Nitrogen	VCE	1.52	1.06	1.28
		Silicone	3.82	2.76	2.79
	Air	VCE	1.21	1.13	
		Silicone	2.52	2.25	
4	Nitrogen	VCE	1.48	1.01	1.33
		Silicone	3.63	2.30	2.34
	Air	VCE	1.15	1.28	1.24
		Silicone	2.89	2.29	2.97
6	Nitrogen	VCE	1.56	0.92	1.16
		Silicone	8.09	2.32	2.24
8	Nitrogen	VCE	1.32	0.57	1.25
		Silicone	***	3.94	2.27
8†	Nitrogen	VCE	1.56	1.41	1.41
		Silicone	1.55	1.61	
	Air	VCE	1.59	1.41	1.49
		Silicone	1.38	1.90	

*Extractable level at ambient temperature was 1.11 which represents an average of three trials.

**Extractable level at ambient temperature was 1.43 which represents an average of four trials.

***Sample was completely destroyed during disassembly.

†Controls.

Table 8. EVA/Silicone Extractable Levels

Time (Months)	Atmosphere	Material	Percent Soluble Material 100°C	80°C	60°C
Baseline	Ambient	EVA*			
		Silicone**			
0.5	Nitrogen	EVA	1.76		
		Silicone	4.97		
1	Nitrogen	EVA	1.37	2.45	
		Silicone	3.13	3.02	
	Air	EVA	1.78		
		Silicone	3.02		
2	Nitrogen	EVA	1.19	7.50	3.58
		Silicone	3.32	3.71	3.13
	Air	EVA	0.91	2.47	
		Silicone	4.39	2.33	
4	Nitrogen	EVA	0.96	3.08	3.42
		Silicone	3.78	2.76	2.36
	Air	EVA	1.96	2.42	2.60
		Silicone	3.42	2.99	2.09
6	Nitrogen	EVA	0.77	2.42	3.08
		Silicone	5.11	3.65	3.06
8	Nitrogen	EVA	1.26	2.00	2.90
		Silicone	***	3.18	2.06
8††	Nitrogen	EVA	0.40	1.94	2.84
		Silicone	1.55	1.61	
	Air	EVA	0.73	1.52	†
		Silicone	1.38	1.90	

*Extractable level at ambient temperature was 3.64 which represents an average of three trials.
**Extractable level at ambient temperature was 1.43 which represents an average of four trials.
***Sample was completely destroyed during disassembly.
†Sample severely degraded during swell test.
††Controls.

V. CONCLUSIONS

Two crosslinked polymers were subjected to accelerated aging conditions and were analyzed in a three-part test program. There is a considerable difference in the relative thermal stabilities between the ethylene/vinyl acetate copolymer and the ethylene/vinyl acetate/vinyl alcohol terpolymer, apparently because of the type of crosslinking agent used and the position at which the crosslink occurs.

VI. ACKNOWLEDGEMENTS

The authors wish to express their appreciation to O. A. Krueger and C. J. Cook for their contributions to this investigation, to the Energy Research and Development Administration for funding this work, and to The Bendix Corporation for assisting with the publication.

ULTRAVIOLET (UV) CURE OF MODIFIED STARCH COATINGS AND ADHESIVE BINDERS

A. H. Young, F. Verbanac and T. F. Protzman
A. E. Staley Mfg. Co.
dedicated to Professor John E. Willard on the occasion of his 70th birthday

UV Curing of acrylamidomethyl starch with water soluble monomers has been studied. Other modified starches containing vinyl groups have been copolymerized with this starch. The films have water insolubility. Their water sensitivity is greatly reduced by irradiation with UV in the presence of crosslinking resins which cure thermally. Preliminary application studies indicate the starch containing coatings have good flexibility and offer potential for water resistant coatings for aluminum, bonderized steel, paper, textiles and as a UV curable adhesive for paper and nonwoven fabrics. The starch has the initial high solids/viscosity relationship characteristic of a dextrin, but can be cured with UV light in less than one second to a water insoluble state. Coatings can also be cured with thermal initiator systems.

I. INTRODUCTION

A modified starch containing acrylamidomethyl groups, Starch-$OCH_2NHCOCH{=}CH_2$, capable of polymerization to produce crosslinking within the starch and by copolymerization with water-soluble acrylate monomers to produce an acrylic network has been developed in our laboratories.

This paper describes some of the properties of acrylamidomethyl starch (AAMS) and its potential for use in the water borne coatings industry (1). Coatings for paper, textiles, metal, glass and plastic have been formulated for UV and thermal cure. Coatings have been pigmented with clay. Others have been given increased water resistance by curing at ambient temperature with methylated urea formaldehyde (MUF) resins and at elevated temperature with methylated melamine formaldehyde (MMF) resins.

II. EXPERIMENTAL

A. Initiator

Hydrogen peroxide at 1.5 to 3 wt.% was the photoinitiator. The system was initiated thermally using a redox persulfate-bisulfite couple at 0.2 wt.% of the coating.

B. Coating Preparations

AAMS was solubilized at 24-53 wt.% solids in distilled water for 15 min. at 99°C., and cooled to ambient. Monomer was dissolved with agitation, followed by initiator or conversely without noticeable difference. Coatings were cast with a 3 inch width Boston Bradley adjustable blade set at 1.5 mils or with a #10 wire-wound rod on 4 inch wide glass plates or on other substrates affixed to the glass plates.

C. UV Irradiator

A Hanovia 679A 100 watt/inch lamp contained in an Alzak aluminum reflector was mounted laterally 1.5 inches over a Sears Craftsman belt sanding machine, whose speed was controlled with a Morse adjustable speed drive, between 20 ft./min. and 200 ft./min. A 6 inch diameter pulley replaced the 2 inch pulley on the belt drive shaft. The 3450 RPM AC motor was replaced by a 1725 RPM DC motor. One pass at 20 ft./min. was equivalent to 0.18 seconds exposure based upon the 0.71 inch diameter of the mercury lamp. Six passes gave an exposure of 1.1 seconds.

D. Solubility of Coatings

Solubility of films was determined in distilled water at 75°C. and 10 wt.% solids.

E. Weight Swelling Ratio of Insolubles

Swelling ratios of the insolubles were determined from the expression,

$$WSR = \frac{I}{O - S}$$

where: WSR = Weight Swelling Ratio; I = Weight Swollen Insolubles; O = Weight Original Sample; S = Weight Solubles.

F. Tensile Properties

Tensile strength and elongation at break were measured by a Tinius-Olsen Universal Tester.

G. Reverse Impact Resistance

Coatings were applied to BONDERITE[1] 37 (zinc phosphate galvanized chemical treated) steel panels using a #10 wire-wound rod and resistance to reverse impact was determined using a Gardner Light-Duty Variable Impact Tester.

H. Flexibility Resistance

Coatings on BONDERITE 37 were measured for resistance to flexibility using a Gardner Conical Mandrel.

I. Water Resistance

A drop of distilled water was allowed to remain on the coating for 30 min. under ambient conditions.

J. Detergent Resistance

A drop of aqueous 1% Tide[2] detergent solution was allowed to remain on coating for 60 min. under ambient conditions.

K. Scotch[3] Tape Adhesion

A 1" x 3/4" area of tape was rapidly peeled across the coating to determine whether any coating was removed.

---

[1] BONDERITE is a registered trademark of the Parker Co., Detroit, Mich.

[2] Tide is a registered trademark of the Procter & Gamble Co., Cincinnati, Ohio.

[3] Scotch is a registered trademark of the 3M Co., Saint Paul, Minn.

III. RESULTS

A. UV Curable Modified Starch Coating

An example of a UV curable coating is shown by the copolymerization of AAMS and hydroxyethyl acrylate (HEA) aqueous coating when formulated with hydrogen peroxide as a photoinitiator, Table 1. On drying, the 1.5 mil wet film is converted from a brittle, chalk-white useless coating to a tough, water clear flexible film with only one pass at 20 ft./min. (0.2 sec. exposure) under the UV lamp.

TABLE 1

Photopolymerization AAMA/HEA

	Parts
Acrylamidomethyl Starch (AAMS) (0.6% N, 0.075 D.S.)	19
Distilled Water	52
Hydrogen Peroxide (30% H_2O_2)	10
Hydroxyethyl Acrylate (HEA)	19

Total Solids, 38 Wt.% Gardner Viscosity @ 25°C. B-C

Passes at 20 ft./min.[a]	*Exposure*	*After Irradiation*	*After 2 Hrs.*
0	0 sec.	fluid	chalk white, brittle
1	0.2	gel	clear, flexible
6	1.1	firm, film	clear, flexible

a. 1.5 mil wet film cast on glass

The decrease in solubility after UV curing of the 0.075 D.S. (Degree of Substitution) modified starch nearly equals that of the 0.15 D.S. starch, Fig. 1.

During preparation the 0.15 D.S. modified starch was slightly crosslinked as shown by the higher weight swelling ratio of the insoluble fraction when compared with that of the 0.075 D.S. starch, Fig. 2. UV irradiation reduces the swelling of the modified starch HEA film. Both total solubility and swelling of the insoluble fraction decrease with increasing degree of substitution and level of UV irradiation.

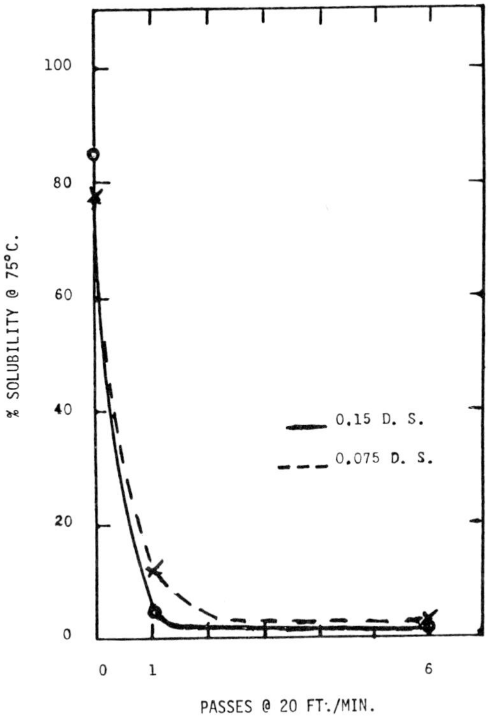

Fig. 1. Solubility acrylamidomethyl starch/HEA and UV irradiation.

B. UV Curable Starches

Other modified starches containing unsaturation may be homopolymerized or copolymerized with each other or with water soluble acrylate monomers, Table 2. These include (3-allyloxy-2-hydroxy)propyl starch (AHPS) and the half ester of maleic anhydride and starch (MS) shown in Table 2 with the copolymerizable water soluble monomers: hydroxyethyl acrylate (HEA), 2-hydroxypropyl acrylate (HPA), acrylamide (AAm), acrylic acid (AA) and methacrylic acid (MAA) which copolymerizes much more slowly than the acrylates. Conventional starches are high in molecular weight and give high viscosity coatings, but they can be hydrolyzed to give low viscosity products which allow greater solids to be formulated into the coating.

C. Tensile Properties of UV Cured Starch-Monomer Films

AAMS/HEA films adhere too strongly to glass to allow tensile measurements. Measurements for some of the other

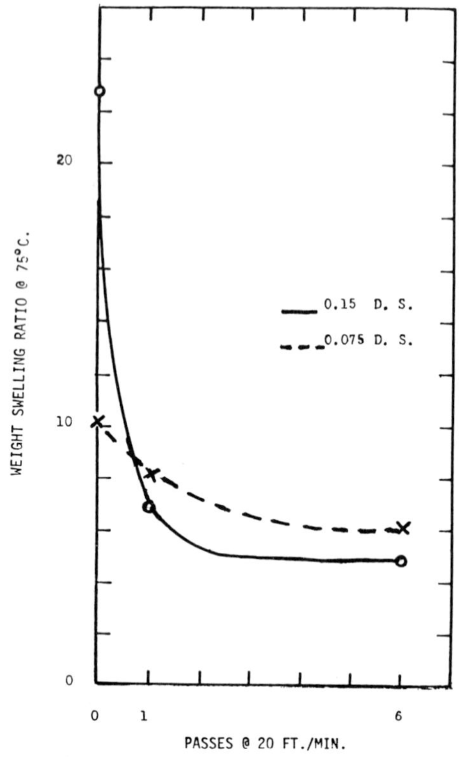

Fig. 2. Weight swelling ratio acrylamidomethyl starch/ HEA and UV irradiation.

TABLE 2

Polymerizable Starches and Water Soluble Comonomers

Starch-$OCH_2CH(OH)CH_2OCH_2CH{=}CH_2$	(AHPS)
Starch-$OCH_2NHCOCH{=}CH_2$	(AAMS)
Starch-$OCOCH{=}CHCO_2H$	(MS)
$CH_2{=}CHCO_2CH_2CH_2OH$	(HEA)
$CH_2{=}CHCO_2CH_2CH(OH)CH_3$	(HPA)
$CH_2{=}CHCONH_2$	(AAm)
$CH_2{=}CHCO_2H$	(AA)
$CH_2{=}C(CH_3){-}CO_2H$	(MAA)

copolymerizable starches and monomer combinations are shown in Table 3. In general the AHPS/HEA films give tensile strengths

TABLE 3

Tensile Properties

Film[a]	*Film Thickness*	*Tensile Strength*	*Elongation*
Amylopectin	4.6 mils	6,570 psi	4%
AHPS	1.6	1,500	3.5
AHPS/HEA 50/50			
1 pass @ 20 ft./min.	1.6	2,550	5
6 passes @ 20 ft./min.	3.0	2,090	19
AHPS/HPA 50/50	2.8	2,850	30
MS	2.2	4,850	3.5
MS/HEA 50/50	3.5	2,210	5

a. Irradiation, 6 passes at 20 ft./min. unless indicated otherwise, 12 pounds full scale, grip separation 2 inches, sample width 0.5", drive load 2"/min., recorder chart speed 2"/min. 50% R.H. and 23°C.

of the order of 2600 psi and elongation at break of 25%. The tremendous change in the tensile properties of the AHPS as a result of copolymerization with HEA is shown by Fig. 3. The area under the stress-strain tensile curve is proportional to film toughness. The AHPS film is quite brittle showing little elongation and tensile strength. When this modified starch is copolymerized with either HEA or HPA, the toughness greatly increases due to higher elongation and tensile strength.

D. Adhesion to Substrates

To increase the coating solids the AAMS was further hydrolyzed and formulated with an equal weight of HEA into a coating containing 62% solids whose viscosity was only 20-30 cps, Table 4. Coatings which contain hydrogen peroxide photoinitiator have adequate stability for use on a coating machine. But on prolonged standing, the system gels.

The coatings have good adhesion to BONDERITE 37, aluminum, polyester and glass. The coating on BONDERITE 37 gives a pencil hardness of H, passes the 1/8 inch conical mandrel test and gives a reverse impact resistance greater than 90 inch-pounds.

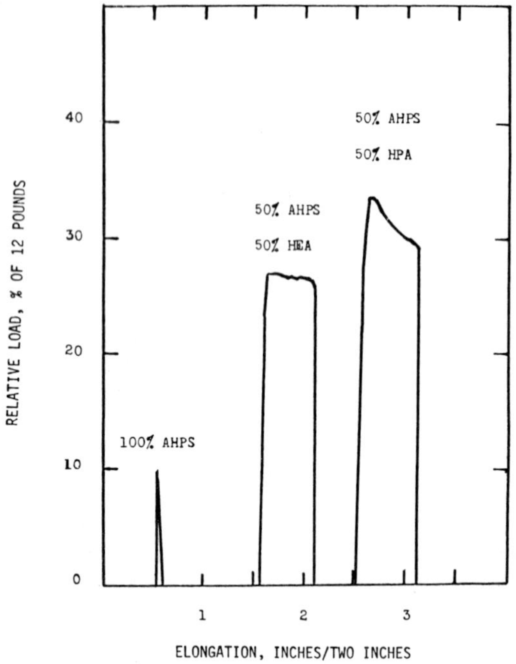

Fig. 3. Tensile Curves (3-allyloxy-2-hydroxy)propyl starch and hydroxyethyl and hydroxypropyl acrylates.

TABLE 4

Adhesion of High Solids Hydrolyzed AAMS/HEA Coating

	Parts
Hydrolyzed AAMS	31
Distilled Water	28
HEA	31
Hydrogen Peroxide (30% H_2O_2)	10

Gardner viscosity @ 25°C. A_2-A_1
Coat substrate with #1 wire-wound rod
6 passes at 20 ft./min.

Substrate	*Scotch Tape Adhesion*
BONDERITE 37	P(ass)
Aluminum	P
PLEXIGLASS[1] (polymethacrylate)	F(ail)
CELANAR[2] (polyester)	P
Glass	P

1 PLEXIGLASS is a registered trademark of the Rohm & Haas Co., Phila., Pa.
2 CELANAR is a registered trademark of the Celanese Plastics Co., Newark, N.J.

E. Increased Water Resistance with Methylated Urea Formaldehyde Resin

BEETLE 65[1] (MUF) was used to improve the water resistance of the AAMS/HEA, Table 5. As low as 13 wt.% dry solids basis (dsb) of MUF gives water resistance on curing at ambient conditions. However, the coating lacks detergent resistance. Twenty five percent of MUF resin gives both water resistance and detergent resistance. The film containing no MUF is destroyed rapidly by water.

With methylated melamine formaldehyde (MMF), the dried film lacks water resistance even after 90 hours at ambient (25°C.). It acquires good water resistance after heating to 177°C. (350°F.) for 10 minutes. The advantage of the MUF curing agent is that it develops water resistance at 25°C. in 18 hours without heating.

In Fig. 4, MUF reduces the reverse impact resistance and conical mandrel elongation of the coatings on BONDERITE 37 steel panels.

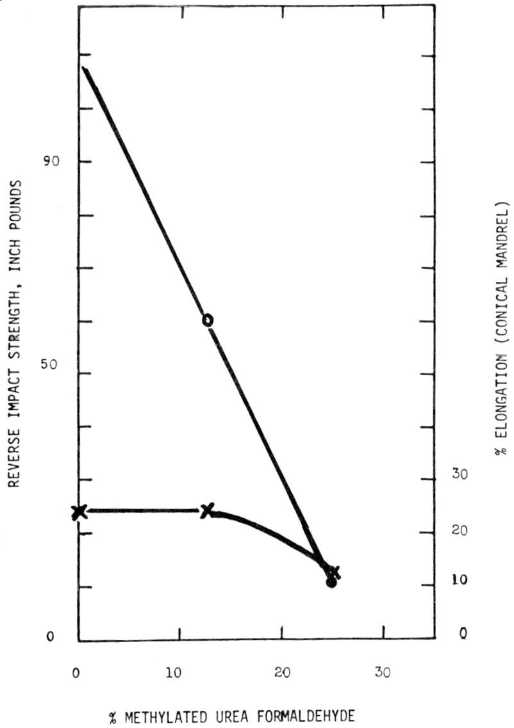

Fig. 4. Reverse impact (O) and conical elongation (X) acrylamidomethyl starch/HEA and methylated urea formaldehyde.

[1] BEETLE 65 is a registered trademark of the American Cyanamid Co., Wayne, N.J.

TABLE 5

Increasing Water Resistance with Methylated UF & MF Resins

Wt.% Crosslinker, dsb	*0*	*13*	*25*	*13*
AAMS	20	17	16	17
Distilled Water	50	46	43	46
HEA	20	17	16	17
Hydrogen Peroxide (30% H_2O_2)	10	9	9	9
Methylated UF Resin[a]	-	5	11	-
Hexamethoxymethyl melamine[b]	-	-	-	5
p-Toluene Sulfonic Acid (20% in isopropanol)	-	6	5	6
Solids, wt.%	40	40	44	40
Gardner viscosity, 25°C.	B-C	B-C	E-F	C-D
				25°C. / 177°C.
Water Resistance[c]	F(ail)	P(ass)	P	F / P
Detergent Resistance	F	F	P	

a. BEETLE 65, American Cyanamid Company, Wayne, N.J.
b. CYMEL[1] 301, American Cyanamid Company, Wayne, N.J.
c. Coatings applied on BONDERITE 37 with #10 wire-wound rod. 6 passes at 20 ft./min.

[1] CYMEL is a registered trademark of the American Cyanamid Co., Wayne, N.J.

F. Paper Coating

In Table 6 is the formulation of a pigmented UV cure paper coating that has been applied at 60 wt.% solids. The hydrogen peroxide photoinitiator was present at only 1.5% of the coating.

TABLE 6

Pigmented Paper Coating[a]

	Parts
AHPS	4
Distilled Water	35
HEA	4
Clay HT, predispersed	52
Hydrogen Peroxide (30% H_2O_2)	5

a. Coat white paper with #10 wire-wound rod. 6 passes at 20 ft./min., 1.5 inches under lamp.

G. Nonwoven Binder

The MUF coatings of Table 5 have been applied to a rayon web sandwiched between two plastic screens using a padder. Six passes at 20 ft./min. (1.1 sec.) under the UV produced 170% add-on. An adhesive pattern can be applied to a nonwoven web by gravure, silk screen, or offset lithographic processes and cured to give nonwoven fabric possessing good hand and flexibility. An alternate process is to saturate the web with a UV curable coating and then irradiate through an open screen possessing the desired pattern. Cure occurs where the web is exposed through the screen openings.

H. Thermal Initiated Polymerization

A formulation similar to one in Table 5 without cross-linker was thermally cured at room temperature using an equal molar ammonium persulfate/sodium bisulfite redox initiation at 0.2 wt.% of the coating. The coating begins copolymerization within 30 seconds with a large evolution of heat. Although thermal polymerization is slower than radiation curing, the level and type of initiator can control the rate at which a thermal system will cure.

IV. DISCUSSION

Hydrogen peroxide is corrosive but it can be used at lower levels than the 1.5-3.0 wt.% reported in this initial work. Electron beam initiation would require no photoinitiator.

HEA and HPA are toxic and require proper ventilation.

Both ultraviolet light (2) and electron beam (3) initiation of coatings and adhesives from hydrophobic oil based systems have been reviewed. The technology reported in this paper makes use of the coating and adhesive properties of water soluble starches either alone or in combination with water soluble monomers and/or aqueous resin emulsions. The insolubilization of these compositions can be initiated by ultraviolet light, electron beam, or heat in coating, binder, adhesive or laminate applications. The addition of MUF or MMF resins will increase water resistance by post curing.

With the shortages and accompanying high cost of petrochemical based raw materials there is now an opportunity to develop raw materials for water borne coatings and adhesives from starch and natural based products. High solids coatings containing up to 45% starch and possessing low viscosity can be formulated that would require lower energy for volatilizing lower levels of water solvent. In increasing solids from 20% to 60% the amount of water per pound of solids that must be evaporated decreases six-fold (4).

The problem with high hydroxyl containing polymers to achieve water solubility is their water sensitivity. When they are crosslinked with MUF or MMF resins they become excessively brittle. The brittle character of the hydrolyzed, low molecular weight starch dextrins is overcome by copolymerization with acrylic monomers such as HEA or other water soluble monomers to create internal plasticization. This technology has the advantage of utilizing the good rheological flow properties of the dextrins at high solids and then restoring the toughness of high molecular weight polymers through copolymerization. Substrates such as paper can be coated with controlled penetration. Rapid insolubilization by UV cure keeps the high solids, low viscosity coating on the surface. Water borne coatings containing a high percentage of replenishable starch with high water resistance are promising for use in industrial coatings, adhesives and printing inks.

V. REFERENCES

1a. T. J. Miranda, in "Water Soluble Polymers" (N. M. Bikales, Ed.), p. 187. Plenum Press, New York, 1973.

b. Industrial Finishing, 51, (4), 48 (1975).

1c. Ibid, 51, (8), 42 (1975).
d. Ibid, 51, (9), 49 (1975).
2. S. H. Schroeter in "Nonpolluting Coating Processes" (J. L. Gardon and J. W. Prane, Eds.), p. 109. Plenum Press, New York, 1973.
3. K. H. Morganstern, Ibid, p. 169.
4. D. I. Lunde and W. J. Freund, Industrial Finishing, 51, (5), 24 (1975).

INTERPENETRATING POLYMER NETWORKS

H. L. Frisch
State University of New York at Albany

K. C. Frisch and D. Klempner
University of Detroit

We present a concise, pedagogical review of the chemistry and physics of interpenetrating polymer networks.

I. INTRODUCTION

Interpenetrating polymer networks (IPN's) are more or less intimate mixtures of two or more distinct crosslinked polymer networks which cannot be physically separated. IPN's can be of various chemical types and can be synthesized in a variety of ways. Interest centers in these materials for many reasons but we shall focus here on the following three:

(1) IPN's represent a mode of blending of two or more polymers to produce a mixture which is not completely phase separated. On the scale of sizes of low molecular weight compounds (angstroms to tenths of angstroms) most IPN's are heterogeneous mixtures of phase domains rich in one or more of the polymer components of the IPN. On a colloidal scale (tenths of microns to tens of microns) many IPN's appear to be "compatible", more or less homogeneous, blends of the component crosslinked networks. IPN formation, like graft or block copolymerization, can be considered another technique for inducing polymer blend compatibility through polymer structure modification.

(2) IPN's represent a special example of topological isomerism[1] in macromolecules.[2] Some permanent entanglements between the different crosslinked networks are inevitable in any sufficiently intimate mixture of the crosslinked networks.

These represent examples of catenation in polymer systems, i.e. different ways of imbedding these molecules in three dimensional space. Permanent entanglements are hindering constraints on the motion of segments and ought to simulate covalently bound chemical crosslinks.[3] Simplified theoretical models of such permanent entanglements[4] exhibit a surprisingly large non-linear elastic restoring force unlike that expected with chemical crosslinks from ideal rubber elasticity theory.

(3) The possibility of combining varied chemical types of polymeric networks in different compositions, often resulting in controlled different morphologies has produced IPN compositions with synergistic behavior. For example if one polymer is elastomeric and one polymer is a glass at use temperature one obtains a reinforced rubber if the elastomer phase predominates or an impact resistant plastic if the glassy phase predominates.[5] IPN's have been synthesized with intermediate maxima versus network composition bulk properties such as tensile strength[6] and minima in surface properties such as the critical surface tension. The latter results have not yet been published by us. Certain of these synergistic properties of IPN's like the above one must reflect their special architecture. Other desirable properties, e.g. thermal resistance, may simple be consequences of the fact that IPN's are usually blends of different chemical types of networks and may have little to do with their special structure.[6]

We shall present first a short historical review of the synthesis of IPN's, their classification and morphology. After we have done this we shall consider the physical properties of the IPN's concentrating particularly on those which exhibit maxima or minima with composition and those which have been employed to study IPN structure.

II. SYNTHESIS, CLASSIFICATION AND MORPHOLOGY

In an excellent recent review of IPN's Sperling[7] points out that ..."the IPN topology was long known and apparently "rediscovered" several times." He cites[7] patents dating from the forties in great Britain and the fifties in the United States. Thus e.g. Staudinger and Hutchinson[8] describe the use of IPN's to produce smooth sheets of bulk polymerized homopolymers while Solt[9] somewhat later described the use of anionic and cationic IPN's as ion exchange resins. The term IPN was introduced by Millar,[10] who also studied <u>homo-IPN's</u>

in which both polymer networks were composed of polystyrene crosslinked with divinyl benzene. Millar prepared a series of these IPN's by allowing the first crosslinked polystyrene network to imbibe a calculated amount of a suitable mixture of styrene and a 50% divinyl benzene-toluene solution, containing catalyst and then polymerizing the imbibed monomers within the original polymer network. Millar found a small increase in density of the resultant network which he ascribed to interpenetration. Such homo-polymer IPN's are sometimes referred to a Millar IPN's.

Shibayama and Shibayama and Suzuki studied the viscoelastic properties of such polystyrene home-IPN's prepared in a manner similar to Millar.[10] Contrary to Millar they found practically no difference in density between a control simple polystyrene network and the IPN. They found much larger crosslink densities in the IPN's. Besides additional crosslink formation by chain transfer and extension of the original network, these authors ascribed the increase in crosslink density to the increase in entanglements caused by the superposition of the network. They found as expected an increase in rubber modulus, a decrease in swelling tendency (in agreement with Millar), while the glass transition temperature and the viscoelastic properties in the glass-to-rubber transition region were not much altered. Other such mono IPN's were synthesized by Shibayama and coworkers[12,13] and more recently by Clark.[14]

A number of different IPN nomenclature schemes have been introduced. A very simple scheme[15] is based on morphology, topology and method of synthesis. According to this scheme essentially all of the above examples of IPN's are sequential interpenetrating polymer networks (SIPN). SIPN are formed by the swelling method outlined above; they are termed sequential since one material is completely polymerized and crosslinked while the other is still a monomer. In this scheme Millar homo IPN's are called interpenetrating homopolymer networks (IHPN). A much more extensive classification scheme has been recently developed[16] which considers the nature of the reactive unit (e.g. monomer, crossliker, etc.) the operation involved (e.g. polymerization of monomer, grafting, etc.) and most importantly the sequence of operations.

Since 1969, two groups independently developed systematically the concept of IPN's composed of two or more chemically different polymers. Initially Frisch et al.[17,18] produced a latex interpenetrating polymer network (LIPN) by mixing emulsions, for example of a urethane-urea and a polyacrylate. This was followed by casting a film and crosslinking. The polyacrylate was essentially crosslinked through sulfur and double bonds by a free radical process. The urethane polymer was crosslinked thermally by reaction with triols. This system was particularly chosen for two reasons: (1) the difference in crosslinking mechanism of the two polymers and (2) the ability of the urethane network to be selectively hydrolyzed at its ether linkages. Thus films of the IPN were hydrolyzed with dilute hydrochloric acid, leaving still an integral polymer film. Weight loss and infrared spectroscopy showed that almost all of the urethane component was hydrolyzed and separated. This chemical structure proof suggested strongly that a considerable part of the individual networks were not chemically bound to each other, but indeed topologically interlocked . Subsequent work[19,20] showed that these materials appear to exhibit two distinct Tg's when studied by a Vibron viscoelastometer but only one Tg could be resolved by differential scanning calorimetry (DSC) measurements. Other examples of such LIPN were prepared;[17] since most of these were two different elastomeric networks Sperling refers to these materials as interpenetrating elastomeric networks (IEN).

Sperling and his collaborators[21-24] prepared, as early as 1969, a series of SIPN. While the SIPN made from poly (ethyl acrylate) and polystyrene[27] still exhibited two distinct Tg's somewhat shifted towards one another, the SIPN, made from the polymers with zero heat of mixing, poly (ethyl acrylate) and poly (methyl methacrylate, exhibited only one broadened Tg.[22] In view of the further mechanical, solubility and thermal studies there is little doubt that these results can only be satisfactorily be explained on the basis of interpenetration and not simply chain transfer crosslinking. These materials were synthesized to provide rather more than less compatible polymer blends, whose phases would remain finely divided without the need for further mechanical mixing.

The earliest osmium tetroxide staining of the IPN's carried out on the LIPN samples followed by thin section electron microscopy appears to indicate phase domains and structures on the order of magnitude of a micron to a tenth of a micron.[19] These structures are about a factor of ten smaller than the latex particles in the original lattices. At certain compositions the micrographs appear not to be inconsistent with a structure in which both phases are continuous. Interpenetration perhaps occurs primarily at the interface between both continuous structures. Subsequent electron microscopic studies of the SIPN morphology revealed that depending on the compatibility of the separate polymers two phased systems were formed. In the case of the most compatible networks only a fine structure of the order of 100Å remains.[25] In others much larger cellular domains are evident in accord with a conjectured modified "fringed micelle" morphology.[25] Presumably the sequential mode of synthesis of the SIPN provide the electron microscopic "cellular" and "fine" structure. Similarly the underlying size of the latices and the difficulty of overcoming both the surface and bulk forces keeping the particles apart prevent a uniform morphology with very small domain sizes up to submolecular dimensions. To overcome this both Sperling and his coworkers and Frisch and their collaborators developed the simultaneous interpenetrating networks (SIN).

The method employed by Sperling and coworkers to form the SIN's involved mixing and simultaneous reaction of epoxy resin formulations (cross-linked via a condensation reaction) and acrylic formulations (crosslinked through an addition reaction). The smallest phase domains and the largest extent of mixing was obtained with reaction conditions where both polymers geled almost simultaneously. Frisch et al. prepared a variety of SIN's by combining linear prepolymers, together with crosslinking agents and catalysts, casting films and subsequently curing them in situ. Care was taken to employ a step reaction with a chain reaction, or two step reactions which did not interfere with one another. In this fashion binary SIN's composed of polyurethane (PU) poly epoxy (EP), polyurethane (PU) - polyester (PE) and polyurethane (PU) - polyacrylate (PA) networks were formed. Many of these SIN preparations were very compatible. DSC often revealed only one Tg or two inwardly shifted Tg's. Electron microscopy for example of the PU - poly (methyl methacrylate) SIN showed domains in the range from 500 - 5000A. We will stop here and not review the properties of semi IPN's, threaded macrocycles, DNA catenanes, latex IPN related materials, etc. Instead of doing this we shall briefly discuss some properties of these fascinating materials.

III. PHYSICAL PROPERTIES OF IPN'S

The following physical properties of the IPN's have been investigated:

(i) Electron microscopy - in particular using Kato's staining and sectioning techniques.[19,25,26]

(ii) Density[10,11,17,27] and equilibrium swelling

crosslink density.[17,18]

(iii) Thermal measurements - (a) differential scanning calorimetry[5,7,20,29] (DSC); (b) differential thermal gravimetric analysis[28] (DTA and DTGA); gas chromatography.[30]

(iv) Mechanical measurements - (a) Viscoelastic measurements[11,12,19,21] (e.g. Vibron), (b) Ultimate strength[17,19,22,25] (Tensile strength and ellongation, lapshear, peel strength hardness, impact resistance, etc.) (c) stress-strain curve[31] (d) acoustical damping.[32]

(v) Electrical measurements - electrical resistance.[33]

(vi) Surface properties - wetting studies through contact angle measurements and critical surface tension.

(vii) Barrier properties - water permeability, diffusion coefficient and sorption.

We have already discussed briefly the variety of morphologies revealed by electron microscopy of these systems. These studies together with the initial chemical structure proof and evidence from the glass transition temperature behavior were employed as a basis for the postulated topology in these compounds. Further attempts to substantiate interpenetration and the resultant expected increased crosslink density, were carried out by equilibrium swelling measurements.[18] While these measurements exhibited maxima at network compositions which were consistent with maxima as exhibited by tensile strength versus composition, the heterogeneity of the networks prevents a strict interpretation of these measurements. Thus they are at best gross approximations. Until recently no direct, reproach free estimate of the crosslink density in these materials was available. Recently Lipatov and his collaborators[30] have applied a thermodynamic method of obtaining the crosslink density of an IPN (PU - polystyrene) from the measured retention volume in gas chromatography on the IPN.

Broadly speaking the physical properties of at least binary IPN's fall into two classes: The first class contains those properties which vary monotonically as the composition is varied from one pure network to the other. Examples are the glass transition temperature or temperatures, density, elongation to break and water vapor permeability. While an IPN depending on compatability and resultant morphology can exhibit one, two or two shifted or even three (and in principle more) Tg's all of the reported Tg's lie at or between the Tg's of the pure networks. The second class of properties are those which at least in certain IPN's can exhibit maxima or minima at an intermediate composition between the two networks.[6,18] Thus for example the tensile strength at break in certain PU IPN's appears to exhibit this property. On the other hand this does not appear to be the case with the systems studied by Sperling and his collaborators.[7] It appears that the PU IPN's which exhibit such a maximum do this both when the apparent more continuous phase is more rubbery or less rubbery than the remaining phase. Thus it is possible that this maximum is a true reflection of an optimal extent of interpenetration.

Other properties which fall in this second class are lapshear and peel strength. (Unpublished data by H. L. Frisch, H. Yoon, K. C. Frisch and D. Klempner.) Since the failure in these materials is easily seen to be cohesive in the polymer phase and since both peel strength and lapshear are probably proportional to the tensile strength it is not surprising that the maximum in these ultimate strength properties reflects the maximum in the tensile strength. More astonishing is the observed minimum in the critical surface tension γ_c obtained from measured advancing contact angles of homologous series of liquids in a PU-EP, SIN-type IPN's. An example is shown in Figure 1.

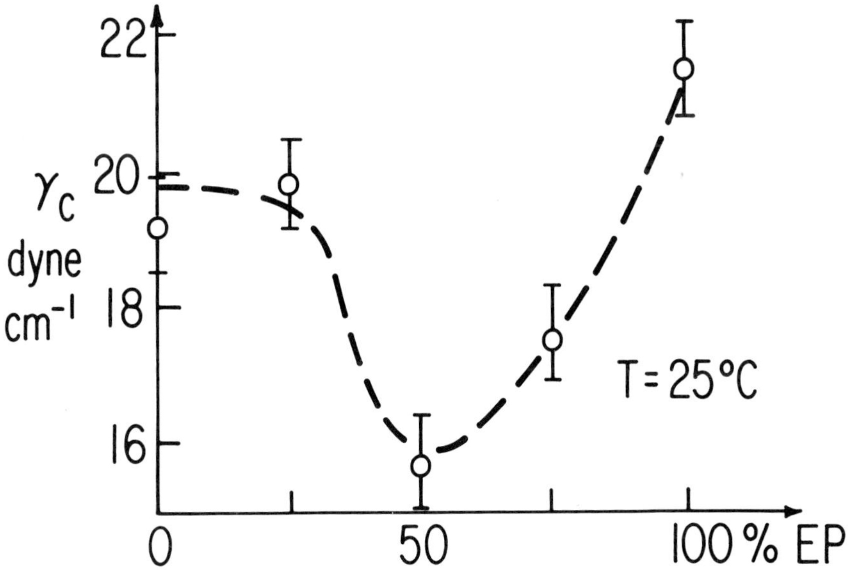

Fig. 1. Critical surface tension versus IPN composition for a caprolactam PU - EP SIN type IPN.

The minimum occurs at the composition where the ultimate strength exhibits a maximum. Further work is in progress by us on attempts to verify whether contact angle hysterisis is present and whether other IPN's exhibit this behavior which would potentially be of interest in making adhesive coatings from these materials.

Recent, as yet unpublished, water vapor permeability studies on some PU - EP IPN show an S - shaped curve versus EP network concentration, see e.g. Figure 2.

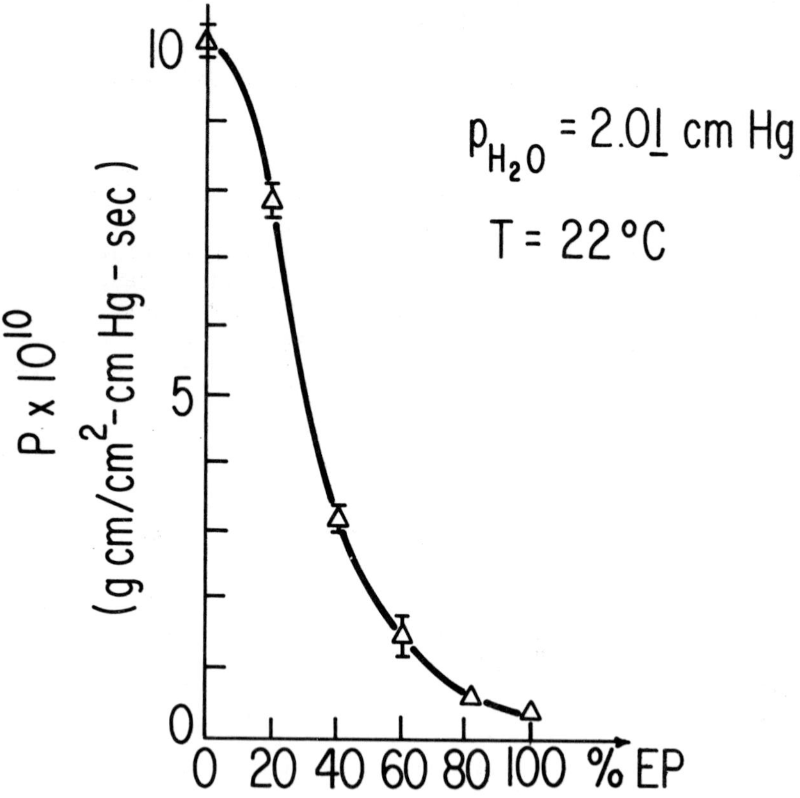

Fig. 2. Water vapor permeation vs IPN network composition of a polyether PU - EP SIN type IPN.

The inflection point occurs around 30% weight EP and results from a sharply decreasing diffusion coefficient combined with a more slowly rising solubility coefficient between 20 - 40 weight % EP. The shape of this curve is what would be expected from two interpenetrating continuous phases. Thus, for example the curvature of this curve would not be consistent with a relatively impenetrable epoxy network suspended as a collection of discrete, discontinuous, convex domains in a continuous PU network, or vice versa. Such studies of diffusion and sorption with a variety of vapors could provide additional means of studying IPN's.

Other desirable properties of IPN's are the toughening and increased impact resistance observed when one component network is glassy and the other elastomeric.[5] The very broad glass transition region observed in some of the semi-compatible IPN's yield damping materials and acoustical damping coatings suitable for a wide variety of use temperatures.[32] We have already mentioned the fact that a number of IPN combinations exhibit significant improvement in thermal resistance over the component networks.[28]

The authors would like to acknowledge support of the National Science Foundation and American Chemical Society Petroleum Research Fund.

IV. REFERENCES

1. H. L. Frisch and E. Wasserman, J. Amer. Chem. Soc. 83, 3789 (1961).
2. H. L. Frisch and D. Klempner, "Advances in Macromol. Chem.", 2, 149 (1970).
3. P. J. Flory, Chem. Rev. 35, 51 (1944).
4. S. Prager and H. L. Frisch, J. Chem. Phys., 46, 1475 (1967).
5. A. J. Curtins, M. J. Covitch, D. A. Thomas and L. H. Sperling, Polym. Eng. Sci. 12, 101 (1972).
6. For a review see K. C. Frisch, D. Klempner, H. L. Frisch and H. Ghiradella "Topologically Interpenetrating Polymer Networks" in "Recent Advances in Polymer Blends, Grafts and Blocks," L. H. Sperling, editor; Plenum Press, New York, 1974.
7. L. H. Sperling, Macromolecular Review, (in press).
8. J. J. P. Staudinger and H. M. Hutchinson, U.S. 2, 539, 376 and U. S. 2, 539, 377 (1951).
9. G. S. Solt, Brit. Pat. No. 728, 508 (1955)
10. J. R. Millar, J. Chem. Soc., 1311 (1960).
11. K. Shibayama, Kobunshi Kogatu, 19, 219 (1962); ibid., 20, 221 (1963) and Zairyo, 12, 362 (1963).
12. K. Shibayama and Y. Suzuki, Kobunshi Kogatu, 23, 24 (1966).

13. K. Shibayama and M. Kodama, Kobunshi Kogaku, 24, 104 (1967).
14. H. A. Clark, U. S. 3, 527 942 (1970).
15. D. Klempner, K. C. Frisch and H. L. Frisch, J. Elastoplastics, 5, 196 (1973).
16. L. H. Sperling in "Recent Advances in Polymer Blends, Grants and Blocks", L. H. Sperling, editor, Plenum Press 1974; in Advances in Chemistry Series, "Toughness and Brittleness in Polymers", R. D. Deanin, editor (in press); L. H. Sperling and K. B. Ferguson, Macromolecules, 8, 691 (1975).
17. H. L. Frisch, D. Klempner and K. C. Frisch, J. Polym. Sci., B7, 775 (1969).
18. D. Klempner, H. L. Frisch, and K. C. Frisch, J. Polym. Sci. A-2, 8, 921 (1970).
19. D. Klempner, T. K. Kwei, M. Matsuo and H. L. Frisch, Polym. Eng. Sci., 10, 327 (1970).
20. D. Klempner and H. L. Frisch, J. Polym. Sci. B, 8, 525 (1970).
21. L. H. Sperling and D. W. Friedman, J. Polymer Sci. A-2, 7, 425 (1969).
22. L. H. Sperling, D. W. Taylor, M. L. Kirckpatrick, H. F. George and D. R. Bardman, J. Appl. Polym. Sci., 14, 73 (1970).
23. L. H. Sperling, H. F. George, Volker Huelck and D. A. Thomas, J. Appl. Polym. Sci., 14, 2815 (1970).
24. L. H. Sperling, Volker Huelck and D. A. Thomas in "Polymer Networks: Structure and Mechanical Properties", S. Newman and A. J. Chompff, editors. Plenum Press, New York, (1971).
25. Volker Huelck, D. A. Thomas and L. H. Sperling, Macromolecules, 5, 340, 348 (1972) and for a review see also A. A. Donatelli, D. A. Thomas and L. H. Sperling in "Recent Advances in Polymer Blends, Grants and Blocks", L. H. Sperling, editor., Plenum Press, New York, (1974); R. E. Touhsaent, D. A. Thomas and L. H. Sperling, J. Polym. Sci., 46c, 175 (1974).
26. S. C. Kim, D. Klempner, K. C. Frisch, W. Radigan and H. L. Frisch, Macromolecules, 9, 258 (1976) also H. L. Frisch, K. C. Frisch and D. Klempner, Polym. Eng. Sci., 14, 562 (1974).
27. S. C. Kim, D. Klempner, K. C. Frisch and H. L. Frisch, Macromolecules, 9, 263 (1976).
28. K. C. Frisch, D. Klempner, S. K. Mukherjee and H. L. Frisch, J. Appl. Polym. Sci., 18, 689 (1974); K. C. Frisch, D. Klempner, S. Migdal and H. L. Frisch, J. Polymer Sci. A12, 885 (1974); K. C. Frisch, D. Klempner, T. Antczak and H. L. Frisch, J. Appl. Polym. Sci., 18, 683 (1974).

29. S. C. Kim, D. Klempner, K. C. Frisch, H. L. Frisch and H. Ghirdella, Polym. Eng. Sci., 15, 339 (1975); K. C. Frisch, D. Klempner, S. Migdal, H. Ghirdella and H. L. Frisch, Polym. Eng. Sci., 14, 76 (1974).
30. Y. Lipatov et al., J. Polymer Sci. (in press).
31. A. A. Donatelli, L. H. Sperling and D. A. Thomas, (in press).
32. L. H. Sperling, D. A. Thomas, J. E. Lorenz and E. J. Nagel, J. Appl. Polym. Sci., 19, 2225 (1975) and J. A. Gates, D. A. Thomas, E. C. Hickey and L. H. Sperling, J. Appl. Polym. Sci., 19, 1731 (1975).
33. S. C. Kim, D. Klempner, K. C. Frisch and H. L. Frisch, J. Appl. Polym. Sci. (in press).

ISOMERIC GRAFT COPOLYMERS AND INTERPENETRATING POLYMER NETWORKS. CURRENT STATUS OF NOMENCLATURE SCHEMES

L. H. Sperling
Lehigh University

There are literally hundreds of distinguishable multipolymer combinations in the scientific and patent literature. For the most part, these materials are now designated as "blends", "grafts", or IPN's. Two possible nomenclature schemes based on group and ring theory are presented and reviewed, along with examples. While neither of the nomenclature schemes fit the exact format of formal group and ring theory, sufficient analogy exists to make use of existing theorems and concepts. Both of these schemes offer a general way to name the many now existing polymer blend, graft, or IPN combinations.

The proposed nomenclature also suggests novel chemical experiments in polymer science. As an example, the decrosslinking of a simple polymer network is briefly described. Polystyrene was synthesized with acrylic acid anhydride (AAA) *as a crosslinking agent. Upon soaking in ethylene diamine, the* AAA *bonds were broken. The resulting linear polymer had the same molecular weight as the product prepared without crosslinking agent. The relationships between the chemical steps and the ring theory nomenclature scheme are explored.*

I. INTRODUCTION

At the present time, the scientific and patent literature describes over 200 distinguishable ways of organizing two kinds of polymer molecules in space.[1,2] While such materials encompass the polymer blends, grafts, blocks, and interpenetrating polymer networks (IPN's), the largest number of compositions actually synthesized are classified as graft copolymers. With the present nomenclature, a graft copolymer can be named poly(A-g-B), where the A and B represent the two initial monomers,[3,4] and the first mentioned symbol represents the backbone chain while the second represents the side chain. The symbol g stands for "graft". However, the order of the synthetic steps, the presence or absence of cross-linking, and the actual mode of grafting have received inadequate attention in part because of an inadequate nomenclature.

A good nomenclature system, in general, serves two purposes:

(1) The chemical nomenclature of the material must accurately describe its composition to any interested party, and

(2) The system should include predictive elements, useful for research purposes. With the current chemical nomenclature, for example, it is easy to acertain if all of the chlorine derivatives of toluene have been prepared in a given series of experiments. The group theory nomenclature of crystal structures describe exactly what arrangements of atoms in space are possible, and their number. Although Mendelyeev had probably never heard of group theory, his periodic table incorporates many of its principles. The "holes" in his table, as is well known, generated many major research programs to discover, isolate, and study the remaining elements.

Besides the intrinsic value of accurate detail per se, the morphology of the materials so formed and hence their physical and mechanical properties are strongly influenced by the synthetic sequence. The present paper has the dual purpose of describing a proposed blend, graft copolymer, and IPN nomenclature, and presenting the results of a computer-based study on the use of this nomenclature to generate some of the possible, but not yet synthesized, combinations. Although the schemes to be outlined below remain woefully incomplete, some tens of thousands of distinct possibilities are shown possible. For general reader use, small samplings of the more interesting synthetic possibilities are included below. First, group theory concepts[4a] will be used to present a nomenclature scheme that tends to yield exact details of synthesis but is somewhat pedestrian in suggesting novel systems. The second scheme involves the ring-like[4b] characteristics of the various combinations. The ring-like nomenclature omits considerable detail. Such detail in some cases is unnecessary, hence the ring theory appears significantly more elegant in its approach in comparing molecular structures.

As will be emphasized below, neither the group nor the ring approach fulfills all of the axioms for groups and rings. Certain rules must be taken with "a grain of salt" at present. But the schemes and concepts presented below are not finished either. They are presented to the reader as an interim report on a search for a better nomenclature. Perhaps work in this laboratory or elsewhere will eventually evolve a much more useful, complete scheme, which satisfies some exact mathematical axioms.

In presenting a proposed nomenclature scheme, it is appropriate to mention a few of the many papers to which it would apply. Recent symposia have been edited by Ceresa,[5] Burke and

Weiss,[6] Aggarwal,[7] Molau,[8] Gould,[9] Platzer,[10] and Sperling.[11] Manson and Sperling have recently reviewed the field.[11a] Works by Rogers,[12] Frisch[13-15] Ryan,[16] Amagi, Ohya, Shuki, and Yusa,[17] Johnson and Labana,[18] Vollmert,[19] and Sperling[20,21] bear on the problem. Klempner and Frisch[13] have also provided an independent nomenclature scheme.

The present theoretical development remains incomplete, however, special symbols being required in writing nomenclature for the AB cross-linked copolymers of Bamford, Eastmond, and Whittle,[22] and the star-block copolymers of Bi and Fetters.[23]

II. GROUP THEORY NOMENCLATURE

As basic elements, we will consider monomer 1, monomer 2, . . ., monomer n, which can be polymerized to form various polymers and copolymers. As the basic reactive units, we designate the following in Chart I. The operations employed are designated in Chart II. Polymerization will be assumed to be linear unless the operation C is specified. Most importantly, the present group is noncommutative, and the time sequence of events must be preserved. For the group theory nomenclature, time advances from left to right. Thus, the order of the operations must be maintained. One of the key findings to be explored below is that we must increase our sensitivity to the order of the operations in more complex cases, and not assume, for example, that cross-linking followed by grafting is identical with grafting followed by cross-linking.

The operations and the reactive units must be clearly distinguished. To differentiate between operations and the objects upon which the group acts (the reactive units), capital and lower case letters will be employed, respectively. For example, the addition of monomer will be designated as m. The addition of monomers capable of inducing grafting or cross-linking, e.g., divinylbenzene, will be designated by g and c, respectively. The operations of grafting and cross-linking, which may come much later in the reaction sequence, will be specified by the capital letters.

We must also consider a series of inverse operations.[1,2]

CHART I

Reactive Unit	Interpretation
m_1	monomer 1
m_2	monomer 2
c_1	cross-linker 1
c_2	cross-linker 2
g_1	grafting agent for 1
g_2	grafting agent for 2

CHART II

Operation	Interpretation
P_1	polymerization of monomer 1
P_2	polymerization of monomer 2
C_1	cross-linking of 1
C_2	cross-linking of 2
G_{12}	grafting of 2 to 1
G_{21}	grafting of 1 to 2

Thus, P^{-1} is introduced as depolymerization, G^{-1} as degrafting, C^{-1} as decross-linking. In this context, C and C^{-1} are inverses. Thus, $CC^{-1} = I$, where I represents the mathematical identity. In more chemical terms, the reaction was reversed.

As discussed elsewhere,[1,2] simultaneous operations can be placed in parentheses. Thus, parentheses will be used to distinguish operations which happen at the same time from those that occur sequentially in time. Square brackets will be employed to distinguish separate polymerizations, whose products are later mixed and/or reacted.

In a formal sense, the brackets constitute a binary operation in their own right. The use of brackets is, in fact, identical to the o_1 binary operation introduced below in the ring-like corresponding theory. For simplicity, neither inverse operations nor brackets will be considered in the computer study. The polymer molecule will be associated with the designated operation with the use of the subscripts 1, 2, etc. Thus, P_1 indicates polymerization of m_1. The operation G will be specified by both subscripts, the order of the subscripts indicating respectively the backbone and the branch side chain. (Identical subscripts could, of course, be used to indicate homopolymer branching.)

A few examples are in order. The combination

$$[m_1P_1][m_2P_2] \tag{1}$$

represents a mixture of two linear polymers, as in a simple mechanical blend. A simple graft copolymer may be written

$$m_1P_1m_2(P_2G_{12}) \tag{2}$$

The combination

$$m_1(P_1C_1)m_2(P_2G_{12}) \tag{3}$$

refers to a simple semi-IPN of the first kind. A semi-IPN is a graft copolymer where one, but not both, constituent is cross-linked. Note that the order of the operations is important. For example,

$$m_1P_1m_2(P_2G_{12})C_1 \neq m_1(P_1C_1)m_2(P_2G_{12}) \quad (4)$$

the left-hand side indicating a post-cross-linking operation for polymer 1, and the right-hand side indicating that the cross-links in polymer 1 are introduced during polymerization.

III. REACTIVE UNITS AND OPERATIONS SEQUENCES

In the following, several approximations have been made for simplicity.

TABLE I

Reactive Unit Combinations (with m_1 and m_2)

1.	m_1	17.	$m_1c_1g_1m_2$	33.	m_2
2.	m_1c_1	18.	$m_1c_1g_1c_2$	34.	m_2c_1
3.	m_1g_1	19.	$m_1c_1g_1g_2$	35.	m_2g_1
4.	m_1m_2	20.	$m_1c_1m_2c_2$	36.	m_2c_2
5.	m_1c_2	21.	$m_1c_1m_2g_2$	37.	m_2g_2
6.	m_1g_2	22.	$m_1c_1c_2g_2$	38.	$m_2c_1g_1$
7.	$m_1c_1g_1$	23.	$m_1g_1m_2c_2$	39	$m_2c_1c_2$
8.	$m_1c_1m_2$	24.	$m_1g_1m_2g_2$	40.	$m_2c_1g_2$
9.	$m_1c_1c_2$	25.	$m_1g_1c_2g_2$	41.	$m_2c_2g_2$
10.	$m_1c_1g_2$	26.	$m_1m_2c_2g$	42.	$m_2g_1c_2$
11.	$m_1g_1m_2$	27.	$m_1c_1g_1m_2c_2$	43.	$m_2g_1g_2$
12.	$m_1g_1c_2$	28.	$m_1c_1g_1m_2g_2$	44.	$m_2c_1g_1c_2$
13.	$m_1g_1g_2$	29.	$m_1c_1m_2c_2g_2$	45.	$m_2c_1c_2g_2$
14.	$m_1m_2c_2$	30.	$m_1g_1m_2c_2g_2$	46.	$m_2c_1g_1g_2$
15.	$m_1m_2g_2$	31.	$m_1c_1g_1c_2g_2$	47.	$m_2g_1c_2g_2$
16.	$m_1c_2g_2$	32.	$m_1c_1g_1m_2c_2g_2$	48.	$m_2c_1g_1c_2g_2$

TABLE II

Combinations of Operations

101.	P_1	122.	$P_1P_2C_1$	143.	$P_1P_2C_1G_{12}$
102.	P_2	123.	$P_1P_2C_2$	144.	$P_1P_2C_1G_{21}$
103.	C_1	124.	$P_1P_2G_{12}$	145.	$P_1P_2C_2G_{12}$
104.	C_2	125.	$P_1P_2G_{21}$	146.	$P_1P_2C_2G_{21}$
105.	G_{12}	126.	$P_1C_1C_2$	147.	$P_1P_2G_{12}G_{21}$
106.	G_{21}	127.	$P_1C_2G_{12}$	148.	$P_1C_1C_2G_{12}$
107.	P_1P_2	128.	$P_1C_1G_{21}$	149.	$P_1C_1C_2G_{21}$
108.	P_1C_1	129.	$P_1C_2G_{12}$	150.	$P_1C_1G_{12}G_{21}$
109.	P_1C_2	130.	$P_1C_2G_{21}$	151.	$P_1C_2G_{12}G_{21}$
110.	P_1G_{12}	131.	$P_1G_{12}G_{21}$	152.	$P_2C_1C_2G_{12}$
111.	P_1G_{21}	132.	$P_2C_1C_2$	153.	$P_2C_1C_2G_{21}$
112.	P_2C_1	133.	$P_2C_1G_{12}$	154.	$P_2C_1G_{12}G_{21}$
113.	P_2C_2	134.	$P_2C_1G_{21}$	155.	$P_2C_2G_{12}G_{21}$
114.	P_2G_{12}	135.	$P_2C_2G_{12}$	156.	$C_1C_2G_{12}G_{21}$
115.	P_2G_{21}	136.	$P_2C_2G_{21}$	157.	$P_1P_2C_1C_2G_{12}$
116.	C_1C_2	137.	$P_2G_{12}G_{21}$	158.	$P_1P_2C_1C_2G_{21}$
117.	C_1G_{12}	138.	$C_1C_2G_{12}$	159.	$P_1P_2C_1G_{12}G_{21}$
118.	C_1G_{21}	139.	$C_1C_2G_{21}$	160.	$P_1P_2C_2G_{12}G_{21}$
119.	C_2G_{12}	140.	$C_1G_{12}G_{21}$	161.	$P_1C_1C_2G_{12}G_{21}$
120.	C_2G_{21}	141.	$C_2G_{12}G_{21}$	162.	$P_2C_1C_2G_{12}G_{21}$
121.	$G_{12}G_{21}$	142.	$P_1P_2C_1C_2$	163.	$P_1P_2C_1C_2G_{12}G_{21}$

(1) Only two types of monomer, cross-linker, and grafting agent are permitted, designated by subscript 1's and 2's.

(2) Each reactive unit can be added only once, and each operation can be carried out only once.

(3) Random copolymerization between the 1's and 2's is prohibited. (Different polymerization modes, such as addition and condensation, must be assumed when m_1 and m_2 appear together.)

(4) No inverse reactions are included.

(5) No blending operations requiring brackets are included.

(6) Grafting and cross-linking reactive groups are always explicitly written. In practice, grafting and cross-linking may or may not require specific reactive units. In addition, the operations of grafting or cross-linking may occur before, during, or after polymerization.[24,25] Grafting or cross-linking before polymerization has the meaning of forming the pertinent site first, to be followed by polymerization.

TABLE III

Addition of Monomer 1 and Other Reactive Units after Monomer 2 has Already Been Added

m_1	m_1g_2	$m_1c_2g_1$	$m_1c_1c_2g_2$
m_1c_1	$m_1c_1c_2$	$m_1c_2g_2$	$m_1c_1g_1g_2$
m_1c_2	$m_1c_1g_1$	$m_1g_1g_2$	$m_1c_2g_1g_2$
m_1g_1	$m_1c_1g_2$	$m_1c_1c_2g_1$	$m_1c_1c_2g_1g_2$

TABLE IV

Addition of Monomer 2 and Other Reactive Units after Monomer 1 has Already Been Added

m_2	m_2g_2	$m_2c_2g_1$	$m_2c_1c_2g_2$
m_2c_1	$m_2c_1c_2$	$m_2c_2g_2$	$m_2c_1g_1g_2$
m_2c_2	$m_2c_1g_1$	$m_2g_1g_2$	$m_2c_2g_1g_2$
m_2g_1	$m_2c_1g_2$	$m_2c_1c_2g_1$	$m_2c_1c_2g_1g_2$

A combination of symbols representing reactive units is written first, followed by a possible combination of operations. A combination of reactive units disjoint with the first is then introduced, followed by a second combination of possible operations disjoint with the first combination. The process is repeated until all possible reactions have been carried out. The sequence, if interrupted at any point, also yields a viable, realistic material (but then, not necessarily a graft copolymer!). Such a material may or may not contain little molecules, however, depending on the sequence and point of interruption.

The combinations of reactive units to be initially chosen are shown in Table I. The collection of the combinations of operations to be added next is shown in Table II. (The computer program, as in real life, was written so that only possible combinations of operations followed the reactive units. For example, P_1 could not appear unless m_1 had been previously introduced.) As shown in Appendix I, Tables III, IV, and V may be employed for subsequent selection of reactive units.

Table VI samples the results of the computer program. Since many thousands of possibilities exist, even for this simplified treatment, no attempt at completeness was made in constructing Table VI. The reader is referred to ref 1 and 2 for many other examples.

It may be that future readers would wish to employ the numbering system that accompanies the reactive units and operations in Tables I-V. For example, the last sequence in Table VI could be written.

$$20\text{-}142\text{-}51\text{-}105\text{-}52\text{-}106 \qquad (6)$$

Numbers below 100 refer to reactive units, and numbers between 101 and 199 refer to operations.

TABLE V

Reactive Unit Combinations Excluding Monomers

49. c_1	54. c_1g_1	59. $c_1c_2g_1$
50. c_2	55. c_1g_2	60. $c_1c_2g_2$
51. g_1	56. c_2g_1	61. $c_1g_1g_2$
52. g_2	57. c_2g_2	62. $c_2g_1g_2$
53. c_1c_2	58. g_1g_2	63. $c_1c_2g_1g_2$

TABLE VI

A Short List of Possible Reaction Sequences

1. $m_1P_1c_1C_1m_2P_2c_2C_2g_1G_{12}g_2G_{21}$
2. $m_1P_1c_1C_1(m_2c_2g_1g_2)(P_2C_2G_{12})$
3. $(m_1c_1m_2)P_1c_2C_2g_1G_{12}C_1$
4. $(m_1c_1m_2)(P_1C_1)(c_2g_2)G_{21}g_1(P_2G_{12})$
5. $m_1P_1c_1C_1(m_2g_2)(P_2G_{21})g_1G_{12}c_2C_2$
6. $(m_1c_2g_2)P_1(m_2c_1g_1)(P_2C_1G_{12})$
7. $(m_1c_1m_2c_2)(P_1P_2C_1C_2)g_1G_{12}g_2G_{21}$

IV. RINGS AND BINARY NOTATION

A system with ring-like characteristics has two binary operations, which in ordinary algebra are addition and multiplication.[5] We take all binary polymer combinations not involving bonding between them as the "addition", and its binary operation will be designated o_1. Thus:

$$P_2 o_1 P_1 = M_{12} \qquad (7)$$

means a blend of polymers 1 and 2, read from right to left. (The group theory notation read from left to right.) In important ways the binary operation symbol o_1 replaces the brackets used in the group theory, above, which stood for blending or mixing of previously polymerized materials.

The combinations involving chemical bonding between polymers will be the "multiplication", and its binary operation will be designated o_2. Thus:

$$P_1 o_2 P_1 = C_1 \tag{8}$$

indicates a crosslinked polymer I, and

$$P_2 o_2 P_1 = g_{12} \tag{9}$$

indicates the grafting of polymer 2 onto a polymer I backbone.

Two simplifications must be made from the group theory concepts:

(1) The use of reactive unit symbolism will be discarded, and

(2) Materials that are slightly or accidentally grafted will be considered as blends for the present discussion. Only systems that are intentionally or extensively grafted will be so considered.

Tables for o_1 and o_2 are shown in Figure I. For comparison, the simple tables for ordinary addition and multiplication are included. The tables for the polymer structures are infinite in size in the general case, as are the arithmetic tables, with very complex structures possible. Two specific points should be noted: (1) In the Blends table, the commutative law of addition holds, and $M_{12} = M_{21}$, where M stands for mixture or blend. (2) Coefficients are omitted. In general $xP_1 o_1 yP_1 = (x+y)P_1$, etc. However, simple combinations of the two tables are more illustrative. For example:

$$P_2 o_2 (P_2 o_1 P_1) = P_2 o_2 M_{12} = C_2 o_1 G_{12} \tag{10}$$

which makes use of the distributive property of multiplication over addition, shows some of the characteristics of the notation. It should be noted that the acidentally or slightly grafted polymer combinations fit the blend table better than the graft-crosslink table. Thus, most of the IPN's synthesized to date may be considered analogous to a blend of two crosslinked polymers (a chemical blend, not a mechanical one):

$$C_1 o_1 C_2 = I_{21} \tag{11}$$

where I stands for an IPN.

Besides the symbols defined above, it is also convenient to introduce the semi-IPN, represented by S. A semi-IPN has one polymer crosslinked, and one linear. In general, the notation S_{ik}^{h} is a semi-IPN of polymers i and k, and h is 1 or 2 , depending on whether the first or the second polymer so introduced contains the crosslinks. It is obvious that much more complicated symbols could be evolved. For simplicity, however, combinations of existing symbols will be employed, as in the right hand side of equation (5).

In Figure I, the elements in the left hand columns are employed first, and are "multiplied" by the elements in the top rows. This specifies the time order of the operations. (In ordinary arithmetic, the time order is irrelevent.) Upon examination of the Tables, a striking symmetry becomes apparent. Elements on either side of the diagonal running from the upper left to the lower right are clearly related. For example, the qualitative relationship between G_{12} and G_{21} is obvious, but now we observe that they are quantitatively related in the Grafts and Crosslinks Table in Figure I, lying in symmetric positions across the diagonal. In fact, a function, γ, may be defined, which will cause the element to be moved to its corresponding position across the diagonal, and physically adopt its new structure. In general, there are two γ functions: γ_1 for the Blends Table, and γ_2 for the Grafts and Crosslinks Table. The transformation of element X into element Y by the function γ is shown in Figure 2. Thus:

$$\gamma_2 G_{12} = G_{21} \qquad (12)$$

γ_2 transforms G_{12} to G_{21} within Graft-Crosslink Table.

Since the patent literature contains numerous multipolymer systems, some of those relating to IPN's and IPN-like materials are abstracted in Table VII. This table shows both the new and the old notation. Also included are more complex notations, such as

$$\begin{pmatrix} P_2 \\ \sigma_2 \\ P_1 \end{pmatrix} \begin{matrix} \sigma_2 \\ \\ \sigma_2 \end{matrix} \begin{pmatrix} P_1 \\ \sigma_2 \\ P_2 \end{pmatrix} \qquad (13)$$

Equation (13) is read both vertically and horizontally, with time sequences moving from right to left. Quantities within the parentheses are taken simultaneously. Equation (13) permits a fair (but still not entirely complete) representation of an AB-crosslinked copolymer, (7) as distinguished from the simple graft copolymer analog, which does not constitute a network.

V. LIMITATIONS OF THE RING-LIKE FORMAT

The system described above does not fulfill all of the

RING THEORY TABLES

ORDINARY ADDITION

0_1	1	2	....
1	2	3	
2	3	4	
⋮			

ORDINARY MULTIPLICATION

0_2	1	2	....
1	1	2	
2	2	4	
⋮			

POLYMER BLENDS

0_1	P_1	P_2	....
P_1	P_1	M_{12}	
P_2	M_{21}	P_2	
⋮			

GRAFTS AND CROSSLINKS

0_2	P_1	P_2	....
P_1	C_1	G_{12}	
P_2	G_{21}	C_2	
⋮			

(COEFFICIENTS OMITTED)

Fig. 1. Ring theory tables for polymer blends and grafts are compared with their equivalent tables for ordinary arithmetic.

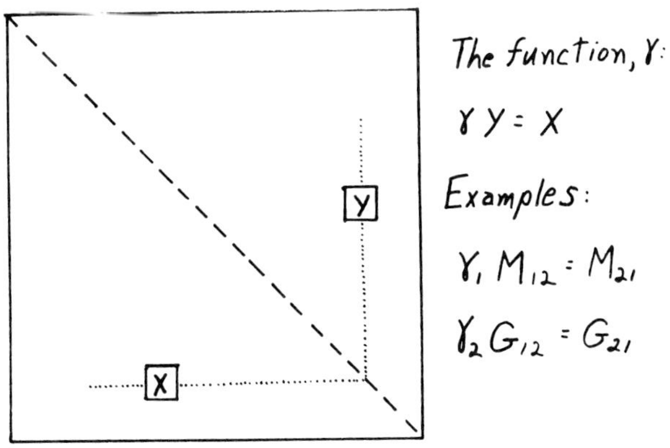

Fig. 2. The function γ moves an element to its symmetric position across the diagonal. In this case, elements X and Y are interchanged.

TABLE VII

Application of Group and Ring-like Nomenclature to Selected IPN-Related Patent Literature

Reference	Common Designation	Group Theory Designation	Ring-like Designation
M. J. Hatch U.S. 3,041,292 (1962)	Semi-I	$(m_1 c_1)(P_1 C_1) m_2 P_2$	$P_2 o_1 C_1$
T. A. Solak and J. T. Duke U.S. 3,426,102 (1969)	Graft Copolymer	$m_1 P_1 m_2 (P_2 G_{12})$	$P_2 o_2 P_1$
R. D. Hibelink and G. H. Peters U.S. 3,657,379 (1972)	IPN	$[m_1 P_1][(m_2 P_2)(c_1 m_3)]$ $(C_1 P_3 G_{23})$	$\begin{pmatrix} P_1 \\ o_1 \\ P_3 \end{pmatrix} \begin{matrix} o_2 \\ \\ o_2 \end{matrix} \begin{pmatrix} P_1 \\ o_1 \\ P_2 \end{pmatrix}$
F. G. Hutchinson Br. 1,239,701 (1971)	Semi-IPN	$(m_1 c_1 m_2)(P_1 C_1) P_2$	$P_2 o_1 C_1$
J. M. Hawkins Br. 1,197,794 (1970)	Semi-IPN	$[m_1 P_1][m_2 P_2] C_1$	$P_1 o_2 \begin{pmatrix} P_1 \\ o_1 \\ P_2 \end{pmatrix}$

TABLE VII (CONT'D)

Reference	Common Designation	Group Theory Designation	Ring-like Designation
G. S. Solt Br. 728,508 (1955)	IPN	$(m_1c_1)P_1(m_2c_2)P_2$	$C_2\sigma_1C_1$
W. H. Parrkiss and R. Orr Br. 786,102 (1957)	IPN	$[m_1P_1(m_2c_3)P_2G_{12}]$ $[m_3P_3]C_3$	$P_3\sigma_2P_3\sigma_1\begin{pmatrix}P_2\\ \sigma_2\\ P_1\end{pmatrix}\begin{matrix}\sigma_2\\ \\ \sigma_2\end{matrix}\begin{pmatrix}P_1\\ \sigma_2\\ P_2\end{pmatrix}$
J.J.P. Staudinger and H.M.Hutchinson U.S. 2,539,376 (1951)	Semi-I	$(m_1c_1)P_1m_2P_2$	$P_2\sigma_1C_1$
J.J.P. Staudinger and H.M.Hutchinson U.S. 2,539,377 (1951)	IPN	$(m_1c_1)P_1(m_2c_2)P_2$	$C_2\sigma_1C_1$

formal axioms for a ring. Examination of the theorems in Chapter 2 of McCoy's book[5] reveals both useful and apparently applicable theorems for the present case, and also some important non-applicable theorems.

For an example of an applicable theorem, (McCoy's theorem 2.6) "If a and b are elements of a ring R, the equation $a o_1 X = b$ has in R the unique solution $X = b o_1 (-a)$." In this case, $-a$ serves as an inverse. The inverse quantities also show the limitations of the ring-like characteristics, however. For example:

$$(-P_2) o_2 P_1 \neq -(P_2 o_2 P_1) \qquad (14)$$

Ordinary addition and multiplication, Figure I, have both a zero and a unity. In form ring theory as a minimum, both kinds of tables in general, are required to have the zero, but some rings do exist without the unity. In the present case, the graft-crosslink table (o_2), Figure I, has a unity, but the zero has no meaning. In the blends table (o_1), the zero is present, but the unity has no meaning. (Consider that zero reacted with P_1, $0 o_2 P_1$, yields P_1 if anything, not zero. However, zero blended with P_1 obviously yields P_1, but $1 o_1 P_1$ is not defined as such.) Thus the zero and the unity, strangely, are not transferable between o_1 and o_2 in the present case. While inverses should be considered real, obviously negative algebraic quantities (such as inverses alone) lead to imaginary physical quantities. Until the special theorems relating to the present case are worked out, the readers sense of possible chemical operations must prevail.

VI. DECROSSLINKING AND DEGRAFTING

As with the group theory mode of presentation, a most important aspect involves the concepts of decrosslinking and degrafting. The symbol $(-G_{12})$ implies removal of both polymers and the graft site. What is really needed is a symbol to change from one binary table to the other*, as a degrafted polymer becomes a blend. To meet this need, we define two functions, α and β, which move combinations of elements from the o_1 table to the o_2 table, and vice versa, respectively.

---

* Of course, in moving from one table to another, we really change from o_1 to o_2, or vice versa in the reaction equations.

For example;

$$\alpha M_{12} = \alpha(P_2 o_1 P_1) = P_2 o_2 P_1 = G_{12} \tag{15}$$

$$\beta G_{12} = \beta(P_2 o_2 P_1) = P_2 o_1 P_1 = M_{12} \tag{16}$$

$$\beta C_1 = \beta(P_1 o_2 P_1) = P_1 o_1 P_1 = P_1 \tag{17}$$

Equation (17) yields $2P_1$, or just P_1 in the sense of Table I, omitting the coefficient.

The relationships among α, β, and γ may be seen more clearly with the aid of Figure 3. In Figure 3 are shown ways in which two polymers may be grafted, degrafted, and regrafted. While structure I must go through either II or III to reach IV from a chemical point of view, the effect is to apply the function of γ_2 in a conceptual way to go directly from structure I to structure IV.

VII. SYSTEMATIC EVOLUTION OF POSSIBLE COMBINATIONS

Noting that binary operations o_1 and o_2 bear a simple analogy to ordinary addition and multiplication Figure I, it was desired to develop a computer program to systematically evolve and number combinations specified by certain rules. One such program is shown in Appendix II, which reads out all combinations of one, two, and three elements.

The number of combinations generated was a function of the number of elements allowed to combine, as shown in Table VIII. Inclusion of all combinations requires a summation. For example, all combinations of one, two, and three elements is 15 + 450 + 13500 = 13965.

The numbering of the combinations is useful for nomenclature purposes. The general rules for going back and forth between the physical combinations and their corresponding base 10 numbers are shown in Appendix III. The procedure calls forth memories of the joke about joke numbers, where the joke number not heard before is funniest: In this case, here-to-fore unknown combinations are thus called into being, and await being made.

The physical combinations are reduced to a modulo 10 number via an intermediate step which requires the use of Table IX. Table IX numbers the basic elements, and the combinations of the elements and an associated operation. Three polymers, and their various crosslinked, grafted, and blended combinations are specified. Table X gives examples of encoding and decoding.

Clearly the combinations specified by the present computer program are limited to those capable of being represented

TABLE VIII. THEORETICAL NUMBER OF COMBINATIONS

No. of Elements in combination	No. of Different Combinations Possible
1	15
2	450
3	13,500
4	405,000
5	12,150,000
6	364,500,000
7	10,935,000,000

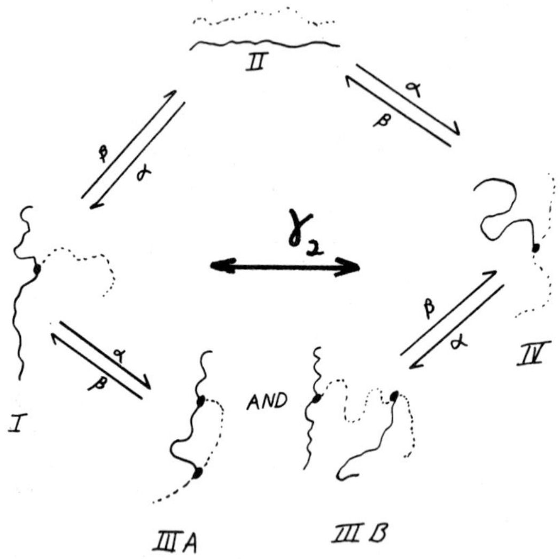

Fig. 3. An illustration of the interrelations among the polymer blend and graft functions α, β, and γ.

TABLE IX. NUMERICAL COMBINATIONS FOR ENCODING AND DECODING

Initial Polymer Elements		Polymer Elements Under o_1 and o_2			
N_1	Nomenclature Symbol	N_2, N_3, etc.	Nomenclature Symbols	Continued	
1	P_1	0	$P_1 o_1$	15	$P_1 o_2$
2	P_2	1	$P_2 o_1$	16	$P_2 o_2$
3	P_3	2	$P_3 o_1$	17	$P_3 o_2$
4	C_1	3	$C_1 o_1$	18	$C_1 o_2$
5	C_2	4	$C_2 o_1$	19	$C_2 o_2$
6	C_3	5	$C_3 o_1$	10	$C_3 o_2$
7	G_{12}	6	$G_{12} o_1$	21	$G_{12} o_2$
8	G_{13}	7	$G_{13} o_1$	22	$G_{13} o_2$
9	G_{21}	8	$G_{21} o_1$	23	$G_{21} o_2$
10	G_{23}	9	$G_{23} o_1$	24	$G_{23} o_2$
11	G_{31}	10	$G_{31} o_1$	25	$G_{31} o_2$
12	G_{32}	11	$G_{32} o_1$	26	$G_{32} o_2$
13	M_{12}	12	$M_{12} o_1$	27	$M_{12} o_2$
14	M_{13}	13	$M_{13} o_1$	28	$M_{13} o_2$
15	M_{23}	14	$M_{23} o_1$	29	$M_{23} o_2$
				30	*blank*

represented on one horizontal line, and do not include the two dimensional reaction schemes developed in Table VII. Also, parentheses are omitted for simplicity, and of course, the combinations are limited by the kinds of elements introduced. (In particular, the *S* and *I* elements are omitted from the program, although many of the combinations of basic elements generate *S* and *I* topologies.) The more general cases obviously would have many more combinations than specified by Table IV.

VIII. DECROSSLINKING OF POLYSTYRENE NETWORKS

Experiments both in the field of grafting and degrafting, and crosslinking and decrosslinking are in progress in this laboratory, making use of the concepts developed above. As a simple example of equation (12), the decrosslinking of a polystyrene network is presented below.

1. Linear polystyrene, and polystyrene containing 0.2% W/W acrylic acid anhydride (AAA) were thermally polymerized in bulk under similar conditions.

2. The two samples were placed in contact with toluene. The non-AAA containing sample dissolved, while the AAA-containing sample swelled approximately 10 times its initial volume.

This indicates that the AAA introduced chemical crosslinking.

3. After soaking the crosslinked sample in ethylene diamine, it was found that the sample dissolved in toluene. This indicates that the ethylene diamine caused the hydrolysis of the acid anhydride bond.

4. The intrinsic viscosities of the two dissolved polymers were determined, and M_v calculated for both polymers using the Mark-Houwink relationship ($[\eta] = KM^a$), with constants from the Polymer Handbook.[8] The results are shown in Table XI.

These results identical within experimental error, indicate that the original polymerization kinetics were not significantly affected by the presence of the AAA, except to introduce crosslinking.

5. The Flory-Rehner equation was employed to estimate M_c, the molecular weight of the sub-chains between crosslinks.

Based on the increase in weight of the swollen sample, v_2 was found to be 0.0802. Based on the increase in length, $v_2 = 0.102$. Using $X_1 = 0.47$, the M_c values were then estimated, and compared with the values calculated from the known addition of AAA. See Table XII.

Reasonable agreement (at least in order of magnitude) was obtained, in view of the precision and accuracy inherent

TABLE X. EXAMPLES OF ENCODING AND DECODING FOR TWO AND THREE ELEMENT COMBINATIONS.

Physical Combination	Modulo-30-30-15	Modulo 10
$P_3\sigma_2G_{23}\sigma_2M_{13}$	17-24-14	08024
$M_{12}\sigma_1G_{21}\sigma_2G_{12}$	12-23-7	05752
$G_{21}\sigma_1G_{12}\sigma_1M_{13}$	8-6-14	03704
$G_{23}\sigma_1G_{13}\sigma_1P_2$	9-7-2	04157
$M_{23}\sigma_1G_{21}\sigma_1M_{12}$	14-8-13	06433
$C_3\sigma_1G_{31}\sigma_1G_{23}$	5-10-10	02410
$C_1\sigma_2C_2\sigma_2G_{32}$	18-19-12	08397
$G_{21}\sigma_2M_{23}\sigma_2M_{13}$	23-29-14	10799
$M_{23}\sigma_2G_{31}\sigma_2G_{13}$	14-25-8	06683
$M_{23}\sigma_2P_3$	30-29-3	13938

TABLE XI. POLYSTYRENE MOLECULAR WEIGHTS

Polymer	M_v
Linear Polystyrene	3.3×10^5 gm/mole
PS with AAA, Hydrolyzed	3.2×10^5 gm/mole

TABLE XII. MOLECULAR WEIGHT OF CHAIN SEGMENTS BETWEEN CROSSLINKS.

Method	V_2	M_c
Weight increase	0.0802	1.1×10 gm/mole
Length increase	0.102	4.5×10 gm/mole
Calculated	--	3.4×10 gm/mole*

* Infinite chain length assumed.

in the measurements and calculations.

6. Probably the "weight increase" technique above is more accurate than the "length increase" method. However, the crosslink levels were very low, making accurate assessments via the Flory-Rehner equation difficult.

7. Ordinarily, the swelling method yields values for M_c smaller than those estimated from organic syntheses proportions, because of the presence of physical crosslinks (i.e., chain entanglements). The inverted situation suggests that either the AAA is inefficient (resulting in dangling unreacted groups, or both vinyls being incorporated in the same chain), or that some of the anhydride bonds were hydrolyzed before the final measurements. Hydrolysis is the more probable cause.

IX. DISCUSSION

The objective of this paper was to present a comparative review of the group and ring-like methods of describing many types of two polymer combinations. The group theory approach is richer in chemical detail, but does not provide the insight into the interrelationships among polymer blends, grafts, and IPN's that the ring theory approach yields. Both approaches yield a usable nomenclature. Examination of the mathematical formalism in both cases yields the specific concepts of decrosslinking and degrafting.

The current literature is very rich in combinations of two or more polymers.[3-6,8-11a,12-23,30] While naturally the scientific literature gives more insight into the chemical and physical processes involved, a review of the patent literature often reveals far more complicated structures. In addition to the patents described in Table VII, other patents may be cited[31-48]. Examination of a recent issue of the Patent Gazette revealed 18 patents on multipolymer combinations. Many of these had one or more polymers in the crosslinked state.

Classical organic and inorganic chemistry has developed an enormously complex nomenclature; a description of the fruits of modern chemical research would be impossible without it. The hundreds of different multipolymer combinations now merely described as "blends" or "grafts" show the need for improvements in the nomenclature.

The present work is not complete. Block copolymers and star blocks are not described, and a few structures such as the AB crosslinked copolymers are only poorly described. While the group theory notation yields more detail, the use of ring-like notation yields greater versatility, and enhances algebraic manipulation.

The author would appreciate comments from the readers relating to errors, inconsistencies, or possible improvements in the proposed nomenclature.

X. ACKNOWLEDGMENT

The authors wish to acknowledge the financial support of the National Science Foundation Through Grant No. DMR73-0255 A01.

XI. REFERENCES

1. (a) L. H. Sperling, "Recent Advances in Polymer Blends, Grafts, and Blocks", L. H. Sperling, Ed., Plenum Press, New York, N. Y., 1974; (b) L. H. Sperling, Polym. Prepr., Am. Chem. Soc., Div. Polym. Chem., 14, 958 (1973).
2. L. H. Sperling, Adv. Chem. Ser., in press.
3. R. J. Ceresa, "Block and Graft Copolymers", Butterworths, London, 1962, Chapter 1.
4. W. J. Burland and A. S. Hoffman, "Block and Graft Polymers", Reinhold, New York, N. Y., 1960, Chapter 1.
4a. L. H. Sperling and K. B. Ferguson, Macromolecules, 8, 691 (1975).
4b. L. H. Sperling, K. B. Ferguson, J. A. Manson, E. M. Corwin, and D. L. Siegfried, accepted, Macromolecules.
5. R. J. Ceressa, Ed., "Block and Graft Copolymerization", Vol. 1, Wiley New York, N. Y., 1973.
6. J. J. Burke and V. Weiss, Ed., "Block and Graft Copolymers", Syracuse, 1973.
7. S. L. Aggarwal, Ed., "Block Polymers", Plenum Press, New York, N. Y., 1970.
8. G. E. Molau, Ed., "Colloidal and Morphological Behavior of Block and Graft Copolymers", Plenum Press, New York, N. Y., 1971.
9. R. F. Gould, Ed., Adv. Chem. Ser. No. 99 (1971).
10. N. Platzer, Ed., Adv. Chem. Ser., No. 142 (1975).
11. L. H. Sperling, Ed., ref 1a.
11a. J. A. Manson and L. H. Sperling, "Polymer Blends and Composites", Plenum, 1976.
12. (a) C. E. Rogers and M. I. Ostler, Polym. Prepr. Am. Chem. Soc., Div. Polym. Chem., 14, 587 (1973); (b) C. E. Rogers, B. Kupka, S. Yamada, and M. I. Ostler, Coatings Plastics Prepr., 34(1), 485 (1974).
13. D. Klempner and K. C. Frisch, J. Elastoplast., 5, 196 (1973).
14. D. Klempner, H. L. Frisch, and K. C. Frisch, J. Polym. Sci., Part A-2, 8, 921 (1970).
15. S. C. Kim, D. Klempner, K. C. Frisch, W. Radigan, and H. L. Frisch, Macromolecules, 9, 258 (1976).

16. C. F. Ryan, U. S. Patent 3,678,133 (1972).
17. Y. Amagi, M. Ohya, Z. Shuki, and H. Yusa, U. S. Patent 3,671,610 (1972).
18. O. B. Johnson and S. S. Labana, U. S. Patent 3,659,003 (1972).
19. B. Vollmert, U. S. Patent 3,055,859 (1962).
20. V. Huelck, D. A. Thomas, and L. H. Sperling, Macromolecules, 5, 340 (1972).
21. J. A. Grates, D. A. Thomas, E. C. Hickey, and L. H. Sperling, J. Appl. Polym. Sci., 19, 1731 (1975).
22. C. H. Bamford, G. C. Eastmond, and D. Whittle, Polymer, 16, 377 (1975).
23. L. K. Bi and L. J. Fetters, Macromolecules, 8,90 (1975).
24. G. J. Mantell, U. S. Patent 2,837,512 (1958).
25. J. L. Gardon, U. S. Patent 3,125,405 (1964).
26. N. H. McCoy, "Fundamentals of Abstract Algebra", Allyn and Bacon, 1972.
27. H. L. Frisch, D. Klempner, and K. C. Frisch, J. Polym. Sci., B7, 775 (1969).
28. C. N. Bamford and G. C. Eastmond, in "Copolymers, Polyblends, and Composites", Advances in Chemistry Series No. 142, American Chemical Society, 1975, N. A. J. Platzer, Ed.
29. J. Brandrup and E. H. Immergut, Eds., Polymer Handbook 2nd Ed., Wiley-Interscience, 1975.
30. J. E. Lorenz, D. A. Thomas, and L. H. Sperling, Chapter 20 in Emulsion Polymerization", I. Piirma and J. L. Gardon, Eds., ACS Symposium Series 24, American Chemical Society, 1976.
31. Celanese Coatings Co., Br. 1,205,682 (1970).
32. Matsushita Denko Kabushiki Kaisha Br. 1,185,665 (1970).
33. Ciba, Ltd., Br. 1,136,260 (1968).
34. Standard Oil Co., Br. 1,100,542 (1968).
35. General Electric Co., Br. 1,003,975 (1965).
36. Westinghouse International Co., Br. 794,541 (1958).
37. Armstrong Cork Co., Br. 784,565 (1957).
38. Naamlooze Vennootschap de Bataafsche Petroleum Maatschappij, Br. 736,457 (1955).
39. W. J. McKillip and C. N. Impola, U. S. 3,396,210 (1968).
40. K. Jellinek and R. Oellig, U. S. 3,928,287 (1975).
41. V. A. Aliberti, U. S. 3,928,494 (1975).
42. W. D. Waters, U. S. 3,928,491 (1975).
43. J. M. Seahy, G. E. Cremeans, and M. Luttinger, U. S. 3,928,266 (1975).
44. D. F. Lohr, Jr., and J. W. Kang, U. S. 3,928,282 (1975).
45. S. H. Feairheller, A. H. Korn, E. H. Harris, Jr., E. M. Filachione, and M. M. Taylor, U. S. 3,843,320 (1974).
46. J. J. Falcetta, G. D. Friends, and G. C. C. Niu, Ger. Offen. 2,518,904 (1975).
47. L. T. C. Lee and K. J. Liu, U.S. 3,948,823 (1976).
48. P. Stamberger, U. S. 3,383,351 (1968); reissued 28,715 (1976).

APPENDIX I

Brief Program Description

1. Pick reactive unit combination from Table I.
2. Pick a permissible operation unit combination from Table II.
3. Pick further permissible reactive unit combination from Tables III-V.
4. Pick further permissible operation combination from Table II.
5. Repeat steps 3 and 4 until each reactive unit and operation unit has been chosen once and only once. There are now N combinations.
6. Print this combination.
7. Replace the N-th combination with a new permissible combination from the appropriate table.
8. Print this new combination.
9. Repeat steps 7 and 8 for all permissible combinations.
10. Replace the $N - 1$ combination with a new permissible combination.
11. Print this combination.
12. Add a new permissible combination to this combination.
13. Print resulting combination.
14. Replace this combination with a different permissible combination.
15. Print resulting combination.
16. Repeat steps 14 and 15 for all combinations.
17. Repeat steps 12 to 16 for all combinations.
18. Repeat steps 10 to 17 for all combinations.
19. Let $N = N - 1$ and return to step 10.
20. Repeat steps 10 to 19 until all permissible combinations have been formed.

APPENDIX II

In a computer program used to generate all the combinations possible for a particular system, two variables must be specified. These two variables are (1) the binary operations to be used, in our study it was o_1 and o_2, and (2) the number of elements in the system such as P_1, C_2, G_{23}, M_{13} etc. Once these are specified the writing of a program is a simple matter. The program should count in a modulo equal to the number of elements times the number of operations.

First data arrays are read in. All the elements are read in under an alphanumeric format, then all the elements with each binary operation to the right of it are read into the computer followed by a blank card.

Next various counters are initialized and the first set of combinations are printed out, then the counters are incremented in their respective modulo and these results are printed. This is repeated until all values are printed.

The program employed is detailed in Ref. (4b).

APPENDIX III

Rules for Encoding and Decoding Physical Combinations to and from $Base_{10}$

(General Case)

I. From a $Base_{10}$ Number to Physical Nomenclature:

Step 1. Identify the number of elements in the combination (duplicates count) and designate this as i

Examples $P_1 O_1 P_2 O_2 P_3$ i = 3

$P_1 O_1 P_1 O_2 P_2$ i = 3

2. If i = 2 Go to Step 7

3. Divide $Base_{10}$ number by $(30^{(i-2)} \times 15)$

4. Designate Ni as the number to the left of the decimal point.

5. Subtract Ni × $(30^{(i-2)}$ × 15 from the $base_{10}$ number and designate this as the new $base_{10}$ number.

6. i = i - 1, Go to Step 2

7. Divide $Base_{10}$ number by 15

8. Designate N2 as the number to the left of the decimal point.

9. Subtract N2 × 15 from the $base_{10}$ number

10. Designate this number as N1

11. If N1 = 0, then N2 = N2 - 1 and then N1 = 15

12. Using Table V convert N1, N2, ... Ni to nomenclature symbols.

13. Write combination right to left starting with N1 and ending with Ni.

II. Physical Nomenclature to $Base_{10}$ Number:

Step 1. Identify Polymer numbers N1, N2, N3, ... Ni using Table V.

2. $Base_{10}$ number is given by the formula:

$$N_{10} = \left(\sum_{j=3}^{i} (Nj) \times 30^{(j-2)} \times 15 + (N2 \times 15) + N1 \right)$$

POLYURETHANE-POLYACRYLATE PSEUDO-INTERPENETRATING NETWORKS

D. Klempner, H. K. Yoon, and K. C. Frisch
University of Detroit

H. L. Frisch
State University of New York

Two component interpenetrating polymer networks (IPN's) of the SIN type (simultaneous interpenetrating networks), pseudo IPN's (only one component crosslinked), and linear blends composed of a polyurethane and an acrylic copolymer were produced. They were prepared by combining the urethane prepolymers together with chain extender and crosslinking agent with the acrylic prepolymer (20-30% conversion) containing crosslinking agent, mixing thoroughly, casting between glass plates lined with Teflon film, and curing at 130°C for three hours and 120°C for twenty hours.

The morphology of these materials was determined by a glass transition (Tg) analysis. The Tg's were measured by differential scanning calorimetry. The systems were all found to be heterophase. The stress-strain properties and hardness of these systems were also measured and related to the morphology and extent of interpenetration of the networks. Comparisons with a similar IPN system synthesized previously using a commercially available acrylic polymer (similar to the present acrylic only employing a different crosslinking mechanism which potentially could interfere with the urethane cure) were made. In addition, the effect of kinetics on the degree of interpenetration was studied by varying the reaction rates of the curing reactions.

I. INTRODUCTION

Interpenetrating polymer networks (IPN's) are a novel type of polyblend consisting of two (or more) crosslinked polymers. They are produced either by swelling a crosslinked polymer with monomer and crosslinking agent of another polymer, and curing the swollen polymer in situ (1-14), or by mixing the linear polymers, prepolymers, or monomers in some liquid form (latex [15-20], solution [21-25], or bulk [26-28], together with crosslinking agents, evaporating the vehicle (if any), and curing the component polymers simultaneously. In this manner, polymeric "catenanes", or IPN's are produced, the amount of interpenetration being a function of the morphology. The systems have generally been selected so as to minimize chemical bonding (interreaction) between the component polymers. In addition, one of the polymers is usually a glass and the other a rubber. This facilitates a morphological analysis by glass transition behavior as well as provides opportunity for reinforcement.

Most of the IPN's reported so far involve heterogeneous systems, usually, as mentioned above, one phase rubbery and the other phase glassy. This combination of rubbery and glassy polymer networks gives a rather interesting situation where a particular IPN system can range from a filler-reinforced elastomeric material to a rubber-modified, high impact plastic material, depending on which component becomes the continuous phase.

The morphology of IPN's depends on the method of synthesis, compatibility of the polymer systems employed, crosslink density, and on the relative rates of formation of each network. IPN's reported so far can be classified as having large domain structures with domain sizes of a few microns (15-18), intermediate structures with sizes around 1000 Å (9, 11), and no resolvable domain structures at all (1-5, 23, 24).

The nature of interpenetration is believed to vary systematically with the morphology from partial interpenetration, mostly at the boundaries of the dispersed phase (in the cases of large domain structure IPN's), to a super-molecular mixing where the domain size is in the same order of magnitude as the distances between the crosslinks of the polymer network (a domain size of 100 Å corresponds roughly to a distance of about 200 mers between crosslinks) (11, 28) and to a molecular level mixing (homogeneous IPN's).

In sequential IPN's, the network first formed is most likely to be the continuous network. Its crosslink density is a controlling factor in determining the morphology of the system. Sperling et al (14) observed a finer domain size (800-1000 Å) in their poly(styrene-co-butadiene)-polystyrene sequential IPN's when the first formed network, poly(styrene-co-butadiene), was crosslinked with 0.2% dicumyl peroxide, compared to a domain size of 1600-1800 Å when the first formed network was crosslinked with 0.1% dicumyl peroxide. The domain size was believed to be related to the distances between neighboring crosslink sites. Similar phenomena occur in latex and simultaneous IPN's, although the relative rates of formation of each network (as well as the compatibilities) partially control the morphology.

It has not been clearly shown whether permanent, topological interpenetration (chain entanglements between the two polymers made "permanent" by crosslinking both polymers) controls the morphology and the resulting properties of the IPN's. In an earlier study (23, 24) with IPN's composed of various polyurethanes and a polyacrylate, single phase morphologies resulted. The polyacrylate was a commercial material which consisted of a random copolymer of butyl methacrylate, ethyl methacrylate, hydroxyethyl acrylate, methacrylic acid, and styrene. It crosslinked by reaction of a butylated melamine-formaldehyde resin with the pendant hydroxyls catalyzed by the methacrylic acid. A variety of polyurethanes were employed. They were all made by the prepolymer technique, in which an isocyanate terminated prepolymer is prepared by reacting two equivalents of a diisocyanate with one equivalent of a hydroxy terminated polyol. The prepolymer is then chain extended and crosslinked by reacting with a combination of diols and triols. The IPN's were formed by mixing the urethane prepolymer, in solution with its chain extending and crosslinking agents, in various ratios with the polyacrylate-melamine solution, casting films, and thermally curing them. In order to minimize interreaction between the polymers, the isocyanate terminated prepolymer was blocked by reacting with 2-butanoneoxime, thereby rendering the isocyanate nonreactive at the temperature necessary to cure the polyacrylate. Higher temperature curing results in deblocking and crosslinking of the polyurethane. However, the acrylic cure is very rapid at this temperature and occurs before the urethane is deblocked, thus reducing the chances of coreaction between the two polymers. One possibility of interreaction still occurs, however, in the reaction between the butylated melamine-formaldehyde resin and the hydroxyl-terminated chain extender for the polyurethane.

Apparent single phase morphologies, as evidenced by the presence of one intermediate glass transition (Tg) and electron microscopy, occurred. An enhancement in certain mechanical properties, such as stress-strain and impact, also resulted.

In order to determine the effects of topological interpenetration on the morphologies and properties of the IPN's, pseudo-IPN's (only one polymer crosslinked) and linear blends of the above polymers were prepared in this study. If interpenetration was responsible for these effects, heterophase behavior would be observed. In addition, IPN's were prepared from a polyurethane and a polyacrylate synthesized in our laboratories. This polyacrylate, however, was designed to crosslink by means of a free radical mechanism. Thus, the possibilities for interreaction which existed for the previous polyacrylate are not present. Pseudo-IPN's and linear blends of this system were also prepared. The latter blends would theoretically result in temporary entanglements rather than permanent entanglements which occur in the IPN's. These temporary entanglements can readily be interrupted by the diffusion of the polymers due to their thermodynamic incompatibility resulting from their chain extension.

The mechanical properties and glass transition behavior of these polymer alloys were compared. In addition, for the latter IPN's, the kinetics of polymerization of the component polymers were measured and varied by changing the concentration of catalysts in order to determine the effect of polymerization rates on the morphology of the IPN's.

A. Materials

The materials used and their descriptions are listed in Table I. Poly(1,4-oxybutylene glycol), M.W.=1017 (Polymeg 1000) was dried at 80°C for five hours under a vacuum of 1 mm Hg. All vinyl monomers were purified by washing with a 0.5% sodium hydroxide solution and vacuum distilled at 1 mm Hg. All other materials were used without further purification.

B. Preparation of Networks

1. *Polyurethane (PU) Prepolymer*

The prepolymer (NCO/OH = 2:1) was prepared at 80°C under nitrogen. 508.6 g (1 equivalent) Polymeg 1000 (M.W.=1004.2) were added slowly with stirring to 262 g (2 equivalents) of 4,4'-methylene bis(cyclohexyl isocyanate)(Hylene W) in a one liter resin kettle. The reaction was carried out until the theoretical isocyanate content (determined by the di-n-butyl amine method) (29) was reached.

2. *Commercial Polyacrylate (PA)*

The material used was a 50% solution and consisted of a copolymer of butyl methacrylate, ethyl methacrylate, styrene, methacrylic acid, and hydroxyethyl acrylate. It crosslinks by reaction of the pendant hydroxyl groups with a butylated melamine-formaldehyde resin (also supplied in solution). The methacrylic acid was present only in small amounts ($<1\%$) and served as catalyst for the melamine cure. To 14 g of the acrylic solution were added 5 g of the melamine solution. They were thoroughly mixed, films cast on glass panels with a

TABLE I
Materials

Designation	*Description*	*Source*
Polymeg 1000	Poly(1,4-oxybutylene) glycol [Poly(tetramethylene)glycol] MW=1004, hydroxyl number 111.8	Quaker Oats, Inc.
TMP	Trimethylolpropane	Celanese Chem. Corp.
Hylene W	4,4'-Methylene bis(cyclohexyl isocyanate)	E.I. duPont de Nemours & Co., Inc.
T-12	Dibutyltin dilaurate	M & T Chem., Inc.
Acrylic 342-CD 725	Random copolymer of butyl methacrylate, ethyl methacrylate, methacrylic acid, styrene and hydroxyethyl acrylate, 50% solution in xylene: Cellosolve acetate (1:1); hydroxyl number 60.0; acid number 13.5	Inmont Corporation
Melamine RU 522	Butylated melamine formaldehyde resin; 60% solution in xylene: Cellosolve acetate (1:1)	Inmont Corporation
	n-Butyl methacrylate	Fisher Chem. Company
	Ethyl methacrylate	Fisher Chem. Company
EGDMA	Ethylene glycol dimethacrylate	Polyscience, Inc.
	Styrene	Dow Chemical Corp.
	Benzoyl peroxide	Fisher Chem. Company

doctor blade, and cured at 110°C for 24 hours. The linear polyacrylate was formed by omitting the melamine. In addition, however, the pendant hydroxyls were completely reacted with phenyl isocyanate to render them nonreactive with the urethane prepolymer during the formation of pseudo-IPN's.

3. *Acrylate Copolymer (AC)*

A copolymer of eight parts of n-butyl methacrylate, one part of ethyl methacrylate and one part of styrene was prepared. 800 g of n-butyl methacrylate, 100 g of ethyl methacrylate and 100 g of styrene were heated with stirring in a 2000 cc three-necked flask, equipped with a reflux condenser and nitrogen inlet. The reaction was carried out at 80°C until a prepolymer of syrupy consistency was obtained. The polymer was very similar in nature to the polyacrylate previously described except that it contained no pendant hydroxyl or carboxyl groups needed for the melamine-formaldehyde cure.

4. *Linear Blends*

a. *Commercial polyacrylate (PA).* The PU prepolymer, 1,4-butanediol, and 0.02% T-12 were mixed thoroughly with the blocked PA. Films were cast on glass and cured as above. Combinations composed of 20%, 40%, 60%, and 80% PU by weight were made.

b. *Acrylate copolymer (AC).* The PU prepolymer and 1,4-butanediol were mixed thoroughly with the acrylate copolymer syrup. 0.02% T-12 (by wt. of PU) and 1% benzoyl peroxide (by wt. of AC) were used as catalysts. The mixture was cast between two glass plates provided with rubber seals around the edges, and subsequently polymerized at 110°C for 24 hours. Combinations composed of 20%, 40%, 60% and 80% PU by weight were made.

5. *Pseudo-IPN's (PDIPN's)*

Two types of pseudo-IPN's were prepared with each acrylate, one from a linear PU/crosslinked AC or PA (PDIPN-2), and the other from a linear AC or PA/crosslinked PU (PDIPN-1).

a. *Commercial polyacrylate.* The PDIPN-1 was made by mixing the PU prepolymer, admixed with 1,4-butanediol and trimethylolpropane, with the blocked PA, casting films on glass, and curing as above. For the PDIPN-2, (PU-linear), the PU had to be completely chain extended in solution before mixing with the PA and the melamine in order to prevent interreaction between the two components. The fully polymerized PU was then mixed in solution with the PA and the melamine-formaldehyde resin, films cast and cured as above.

b. *Acrylate copolymer (AC).* The PDIPN-2 was prepared from the mixture of the linear polyurethane component (PU prepolymer + 1,4-butanediol) and the acrylate copolymer syrup with ethylene glycol dimethacrylate (EGDMA). The calculated molecular weight between crosslink sites ($\overline{M}c$) was 6500. The mixture of acrylate copolymer syrup and the PU prepolymer admixed with 1,4-butanediol and trimethylolpropane (crosslinking agent) resulted in the PDIPN-1. The curing conditions and compositions were the same as in the linear blends.

6. *IPN's*

IPN's were prepared only for the case of the acrylate copolymer, since IPN's with the commercial PA had been studied earlier (23, 24). They were prepared from the mixture of acrylate copolymer syrup with EGDMA and PU prepolymer with 1,4-butandiol and trimethylolpropane. The curing conditions and compositions were the same as those for the linear blends. The calculated crosslink densities of both polymers were the same ($\overline{M}c$=6500).

C. Measurements

For the commercial PA IPN's, only glass transition measurements were made.

1. *Stress-Strain Properties*

The tensile strengths and elongations at break were measured on an Instron Tensile Tester at room temperature with a crosshead speed of 2 in/min. Specimens were 0.125 inch wide dumb bells.

2. *Glass Transition Temperature*

The glass transition temperatures were measured on a Perkin-Elmer Differential Scanning Calorimeter, DSC-2. Measurements were carried out from -120°C to +60°C under helium at a scanning rate of 10°C per min. Specimen sizes were on the order of 20 mg.

3. *Hardness*

The hardness was measured by means of Shore A and D durometers according to ASTM 2240-75.

4. *Kinetic Measurements*

Three different catalyst concentrations were employed for each polymer, i.e., 0.5%, 1% and 2% of benzoyl peroxide in the acrylate copolymer; 0.02%, 0.1% and 0.5% of T-12 in the polyurethane.

One g of each sample was poured into a glass tube (12 cm long, 8 mm diameter). The tubes were subsequently sealed. These sample capsules were heated in an oil bath at 110°C. The samples were taken out at various intervals and were quenched in a dry ice-acetone bath and examined for flowability. The gel time was taken as the time at which the polymerizing mass did not flow at room temperature.

III. RESULTS AND DISCUSSION

A. Morphology

1. *Commercial Polyacrylate*

The morphology, as indicated by the glass transition behavior, was heterophase. Since this material is not the main impetus of this study, the data are not shown for the sake of brevity. Suffice it to say that the pseudo-IPN's and linear blends all exhibited 2 Tg's virtually identical to the Tg's of the component polymers. This indicates the role played by interpenetration, since the full IPN's (23, 24) all showed one intermediate Tg. This still does not rule out the possibility of interreaction between the polymers contributing to the single phase morphology, since there was a much higher possibility of interreaction with the full IPN's than with the pseudo-IPN's or linear blends. Studies with the free radical curing polyacrylate (below) indicate that interreaction probably does play a role in compatibilizing the polymers, since even the full IPN's showed phase separation.

2. *Acrylate Copolymer*

The morphology, as indicated by the glass transition behavior (Table II) was heterophase.

TABLE II
Glass Transitions (°K)

	PU 100%	*80*	*60*	*40*	*20*	*0*
	AC 0%	*20*	*40*	*60*	*80*	*100*
Full IPN		317.2	318.5	319	319	320.5
	208	209	211.2	212	212.5	
PDIPN-1		313	314	316	318	318
	208	209	210	211.5	212.5	
PDIPN-2		318	318	319	319.5	320.5
	210	210.5	211	211	211.5	
Linear Blend		306	306	307.5	312	318
	210	209	209	210	211.5	

In all cases, two Tg's, corresponding to the Tg's of the component polymers, resulted. However, the Tg's were shifted inwards, indicating some phase mixing (interpenetration), most likely at the phase boundaries. In the case of the linear blends, a large unaccountable inward shift for the acrylic component occurred. This may be a molecular weight effect. In the case of the full IPN's, intermediate Tg's occurred (not shown in the table) depending on the thermal history of the material. This would indicate a third phase, i.e. an interpenetrating region. The PDIPN's and linear blends showed no indication of this intermediate phase. Preliminary dynamic mechanical property measurements indicate that the loss peaks corresponding to the Tg's of the component polymers were very broad for the full IPN's, and much sharper for the PDIPN's, with the linear blends showing peaks very similar to the homopolymers. These studies are being pursued. Further studies should clarify this situation.

As mentioned above, this also indicates the role of grafting, since the IPN's synthesized using the vinyl curing polymer did show heterophase behavior, as opposed to the single phase morphology of the IPN's synthesized using the melamine cured polyacrylate, in which interreaction between the polymers was more probable.

B. Mechanical Properties

The tensile strengths and breaking elongations of the IPN's as a function of composition are shown in Tables III and IV, respectively. The IPN's show a significant enhancement in tensile strength, particularly at PU/AC = 80/20. The PDIPN's and the linear blends show little or no enhancement.

TABLE III
Tensile Strength of IPN's (PSI)

	PU 100%	*80*	*60*	*40*	*20*	*0*
	AC 0%	*20*	*40*	*60*	*80*	*100*
Full IPN	6100	7100	6525	5000	3720	2570
PDIPN-1	6100	5880	6300	3130	2230	1610
PDIPN-2	5600	4430	5220	3600	3020	2570
Linear Blend	5600	1830	3620	3410	2120	1610

TABLE IV
Elongation of IPN's (% at Break)

	PU 100%	80	60	40	20	0
	AC 0%	20	40	60	80	100
Full IPN	640	780	540	270	180	15
PDIPN-1	640	540	260	140	120	12
PDIPN-2	610	550	520	280	210	15
Linear Blend	610	640	360	130	195	12

In all cases measured, the tensile strengths of the IPN's are greater than those of the pseudo-IPN's and the linear blends at the same compositions. In addition, the tensile strengths of both of the pseudo-IPN's are greater than those of the linear blends at the same compositions. The enhancement in tensile strength is most likely due to the higher level of mixing in the IPN's and to greater adhesion between the dispersed and continuous phases. The IPN's should exhibit more complete mixing (less phase separation) and greater phase adhesion due to the permanent entanglements (interpenetration) at the phase boundaries. However, in the case of pseudo-IPN's, the phase mixing is less due to the presence of temporary entanglements, since only one polymer is crosslinked. In the case of the linear blends, even less mixing would be expected, since there are no topological constraints at all, for neither polymer is crosslinked. Electron microscopic studies should shed more light on the situation by revealing the change in domain sizes.

The elongation, as shown in Table III, shows a significant increase from 100% PU to 80% PU in the IPN's, indicating the exceptional toughness of this IPN. Little or no increase occurs for the PDIPN's and the blends. A sharp drop in elongation takes place at 60% PU, which indicates that a phase inversion occurs around this composition. The Shore A and D hardnesses, shown in Table V, show a rapid increase between 80% PU and 40% PU, which again indicates the phase inversion between 80% and 40% PU content. Dynamic mechanical properties should shed more light on this behavior.

C. Kinetic Measurements

The gel times of the polymers, shown in Table VI, show

the expected trend, i.e. increasing catalyst concentration decreases the gel time.

TABLE V
Hardness of IPN's (Shore A)

	PU 100% / *AC 0%*	*80* / *20*	*60* / *40*	*40* / *60*	*20* / *80*	*0* / *100*
Full IPN	*68 (32)	70 (35)	85 (38)	92 (53)	94 (63)	100 (72)
PDIPN-1	68 (32)	78 (33)	86 (38)	94 (49)	95 (55)	100 (68)
PDIPN-2	73 (31)	81 (37)	91 (43)	93 (53)	96 (65)	100 (72)
Linear Blend	73 (31)	75 (30)	87 (35)	92 (48)	95 (58)	100 (68)

* *Hardnesses in parentheses are measured by Shore D.*

TABLE VI
Gel Times of Crosslinked Polymers at Different Catalyst Concentrations (Minutes)

AC	*Time*	*PU*	*Time*
AC-1	4.25	PU-1	12.30
AC-2	4.00	PU-2	7.25
AC-3	3.20	PU-3	3.15

AC-1 (0.5% BPO) PU-1 (0.02% T-12)

AC-2 (1% BPO) PU-2 (0.1% T-12)

AC-3 (2% BPO) PU-3 (0.5% T-12)

The glass transition behavior of these IPN's (Table VII) shows that as the rate of the respective polymerizations increases, the Tg's shift inward, indicating less phase separation. This is most likely due to the fact that increasing the reaction rate lowers the diffusion time allowed for phase separation. The initial prepolymer mixture is single phase, since the molecular weights are low enough to allow complete mixing.

TABLE VII
Glass Transition Temperatures of IPN's: Kinetic Results

	AC 40 - PU 60 Tg (°K)		AC 60 - PU 40 Tg (°K)	
IPN 1.1*	212.2	318.5	212	319
IPN 1.2	211	318	210	318
IPN 1.3	215	314	214	314
IPN 2.1	212	317	211	318
IPN 2.2	212.5	316	214	315.5
IPN 2.3	216	313	215	315
IPN 3.1	211	314	211.5	316
IPN 3.2	214	308	215	307
IPN 3.3	219	293	220	298

* *IPN 1.1 (IPN from AC-1 and PU-1).*

As the polymers are cured, they phase separate due to their thermodynamic incompatibility. This phase separation is naturally diffusion controlled and requires time. If the curing reactions are accelerated, less time will be available for diffusion and subsequent phase separation to occur. When fully crosslinked, further phase separation cannot take place due to topological constraints imposed by the crosslinking of the component polymers. Thus, faster crosslinking would be expected to yield less phase separation. The maximum shift in Tg occurs in the IPN 3 series, in particular IPN 3.3. In this case, both polymers gel at almost the same time. This is in agreement with Sperling's results (28), which showed that the smallest domain size of epoxy-acrylic IPN's occurred when the respective curing reactions were closest to simultaneity. The degree of phase mixing, as deduced by the shifts in Tg, are confirmed by the transparency of the IPN films. The transparency increases as the reaction rate increases.

Acknowledgment is made to the donors of the Petroleum Research Fund, administered by the American Chemical Society, for partial support of this research. We also wish to acknowledge the National Science Foundation Grant No. ENG 7401954 for partial support of this study.

IV. REFERENCES

1. J. R. Millar, J. Chem. Soc., 1311 (1960).
2. K. Shibayama and Y. Suzuki, Kobunshi Kagaku, 23, (249), 24 (1966).
3. K. Shibayama, Zairyo, 12, 363 (1963).
4. K. Shibayama, Kobunshi Kagaku, 19, 219 (1962).
5. K. Shibayama, Kobunshi Kagaku, 20, 221 (1963).
6. L. H. Sperling and D. W. Friedman, J. Polym. Sci., A-2, 7, 425 (1969).
7. L. H. Sperling, D. W. Taylor, M. L. Kirkpatrick, H. F. George and D. R. Bardman, J. Appl. Polym. Sci., 14, 73 (1970).
8. L. H. Sperling, H. F. George, Volker Huelck and D. A. Thomas, J. Appl. Sci., 14, 2815 (1970).
9. L. H. Sperling, D. A. Thomas, M. J. Covitch and A. J. Curtius, Polym. Eng. Sci., 12, 101 (1972).
10. L. H. Sperling, T. W. Chiu, C. P. Hartman and D. A. Thomas, Intern. J. Polym. Mater., 1, 331 (1972).
11. L. H. Sperling, D. A. Thomas and V. Huelck, Macromolecules, 5, 340 (1972).
12. L. H. Sperling and H. D. Sarge III, J. Appl. Polym. Sci., 16, 3041 (1972).
13. L. H. Sperling and E. N. Mihalakis, J. Appl. Polym. Sci., 17, 3811 (1973).
14. L. H. Sperling, T. W. Chiu and D. A. Thomas, J. Appl. Polym. Sci., 17, 2443 (1973).
15. K. C. Frisch, H. L. Frisch and D. Klempner, Polym. Letters, 7, 775 (1969).
16. K. C. Frisch, H. L. Frisch and D. Klempner, J. Polym. Sci., A-2, 8, 921 (1970).
17. D. Klempner, K. C. Frisch and H. L. Frisch, J. Elastoplastics, 3, 2 (1971).
18. H. L. Frisch, D. Klempner, T. K. Kwei and M. Matsuo, Polym. Eng. Sci., 10 (6), 327 (1970).
19. L. H. Sperling, D. A. Thomas, J. E. Lorenz and E. J. Nagel, J. Appl. Polym. Sci., 19, 2225 (1975).

20. J. A. Grates, D. A. Thomas, E. C. Hickey and L. H. Sperling, J. Appl. Polym. Sci., 19, 1731 (1975).
21. K. C. Frisch, H. L. Frisch, D. Klempner and S. K. Mukherjee, J. Appl. Polym. Sci., 18, 689 (1974).
22. K. C. Frisch, H. L. Frisch, D. Klempner and T. Antczak, J. Appl. Polym. Sci., 18, 683 (1974).
23. K. C. Frisch, H. L. Frisch, D. Klempner and S. Migdal, J. Polym. Sci., A-1, 12 (4), 885 (1974).
24. K. C. Frisch, H. L. Frisch, D. Klempner, H. Ghiradella and S. Migdal, Polym. Eng. Sci., 14, (1) 76 (1974).
25. H. L. Frisch, K. C. Frisch and D. Klempner, Polym. Eng. & Sci., 1, 17 (9), 646 (1974).
26. K. C. Frisch, H. L. Frisch, D. Klempner and S. Kim, Paper B-4.2, SIM, IUPAC Conf., Brazil, 1974.
27. K. C. Frisch, H. L. Frisch, D. Klempner and S. Kim, Polym. Eng. Sci., 15 (5), 339 (1974).
28. P. L. Touhsaent, D. A. Thomas and L. H. Sperling, J. Polym. Sci., 46, 175 (1974).
29. E. J. Malec and D. J. David, "Analytical Chemistry of Polyurethanes," (D. J. David and H. B. Staley, Eds.), John Wiley, New York, p. 1087, 1969.

CASTOR OIL BASED INTERPENETRATING POLYMER NETWORKS. III CHARACTERIZATION AND MORPHOLOGY

G. M. Yenwo, L. H. Sperling, and J. A. Manson
Lehigh University

A. Conde
Universidad Industrial de Santander

Interpenetrating polymer networks (IPN's) based on castor oil and polystyrene have been synthesized using 2,4 tolylene diisocyanate (TDI), 80/20 : 2,4/2,6 tolylene diisocyanate, and hexamethylene diisocyanate as crosslinkers for the castor oil component. The crosslink level of the polystyrene phase was maintained at 1% divinyl benzene (55%). The NCO/OH ratio for incipient infinite network formation was determined by experiment to be 0.64.

Electron microscopy revealed a cellular structure with the polystyrene phase sizes varying from about 250Å - 550Å. The Donatelli, et al. equation predicts domain sizes between 300Å and 450Å, in good agreement with the experimental results. The polystyrene domain size decreases with increasing crosslink level of the castor oil phase and with increasing polystyrene content. The chemical structure of the castor oil crosslinker showed no apparent influence on the morphology of the IPN's.

I. INTRODUCTION

The combination of two different materials to form a composite of superior properties has long been practiced. In modern times, many such materials involve a polymer and a non-polymer, e.g. an epoxy resin with glass fibers. In other systems, such as the one described in this paper, novel properties

---

The authors wish to thank the National Science Foundation for support under Grant No. GF-42712, and Colciencias in Colombia, Mr. F. Naughton of N L Industries for his many helpful discussions, and Mr. R. Korastinsky for his help in the electron microscopy.

are achieved by combining together two different polymers, generally termed a polyblend (1-6).

Plastics and elastomers can be modified by the incorporation of another polymer as a second phase. The blending of rigid, brittle plastics with modest amounts of elastomer, for example, can improve the toughness without undue loss of rigidity, as with high-impact polystyrenes. The properties of the improved materials depend very much on the morphology as well as the inherent properties of the two individual components (1-4,7-10).

Interpenetrating polymer networks, IPN's, are a special kind of polyblend. They are synthesized by swelling a pre-existing polymer network (I) with monomer (II) plus its cross-linker and initiator and polymerization of monomer II in situ (11,12,13). The term IPN describes a limiting case of high compatibility between the two polymers where both networks may be visualized as continuous throughout the macroscopic sample. If the two polymers are chemically distinct, incompatibility and some degree of phase separation usually occurs (14-16).

The use of castor oil as a co-monomer has been described by Cassidy and Schwank (17). It is also used in the preparation of sebacic acid (18,19), nylon-11 (20,21), castor oil based polyurethane elastomers (22-25) and for medicinal purposes (27,28). The chemistry and some important industrial applications have been reviewed (17,26).

This paper describes the characterization and morphology of IPN's based on castor oil. The effect of crosslink level on the average molecular weight between crosslinks, M_c, of the elastomer is studied via swelling tests. Transmission electron microscopy reveals the morphology of the IPN's. The experimentally determined phase domain sizes is compared to those predicted by the Donatelli, et al. equation. The following paper (27) will discuss the physical properties and engineering behavior of the IPN's.

II. EXPERIMENTAL

A. Synthesis

The synthesis of castor oil-urethane elastomers using 2,4 tolylene diisocyanate has been described earlier (28,29). Other elastomers were prepared using the 80/20 : 2,4/2,6 tolylene diisocyanate and hexamethylene diisocyanate. The latter reaction was rather slow and thus dibutyltin dilaurate (0.001 gm per gm of hexamethylene diisocyanate) was used as a catalyst. In brief, prepolymers were prepared from castor oil and an excess of the various diisocyanates, at ambient conditions.

More castor oil was then added and the mixture reacted between glass plates for two hours at 130°C. The materials were allowed to cool and the products separated.

The IPN synthesis has also been described earlier (28,29). In brief, the elastomers were swollen with styrene monomer plus 1% divinyl benzene and 0.4% benzoin. The styrene was polymerized by ultraviolet irradiation for two days. Tables 1, 2, and 3 describe the various samples prepared.

TABLE 1*
*CO/PS*** *IPN's (Crosslinker 2,4 TDI)*

Sample	*NCO/OH Ratio*	*Composition, CO/PS*
1	0.95	32/68
2	0.95	40/60
3	0.95	53/47
4	0.85	36/64
5	0.85	40/60
6	0.85	50/50
7	0.75	29/71
8	0.75	36/64
9	0.75	50/50

* *Included from Paper I for comparison.*
** *Castor oil-urethane/polystyrene.*

TABLE 2
CO/PS IPN's (Crosslinker 80/20 : 2,4/2,6 TDI)

Sample	*NCO/OH Ratio*	*Composition, CO/PS*
1	0.95	38/62
2	0.95	40/60
3	0.95	46/54
4	0.85	37/63
5	0.85	38/62
6	0.85	46/54
7	0.75	31/69
8	0.75	34/66
9	0.75	51/49

TABLE 3
CO/PS IPN's (Crosslinker: HDI)

Sample	*NCO/OH Ratio*	*Composition, CO/PS*
1	0.95	36/64
2	0.95	38/62
3	0.95	62/38
4	0.85	33/67
5	0.85	35/65
6	0.85	54/46
7	0.75	29/71
8	0.75	31/69
9	0.75	55/45

B. Instrumentation and Measurements

1. *Swelling Tests*

Several specimens of known dimensions and weight were cut from the elastomers and swollen in several solvents for two weeks at ambient conditions. The purpose of this experiment was to measure the average molecular weight between crosslinks, and the number of polymer network chains per unit volume. The data were also used to determine the minimum NCO/OH ratio for the formation of infinite networks.

2. *Electron Microscopy*

A Philips 300 transmission electron microscope (TEM) was used for all microscopy work. The technique for preparing samples for electron microscopy has already been described (18). In brief, specimens about 2 x 2 x 20 mm were cut from the IPN's and one end of each sample was trimmed to a truncated pyramid of sides approximately 0.1mm. They were exposed to osmium tetroxide vapor for five days and then placed in a vacuum for twenty-four hours. A Porter-Blum MT-2 ultramicrotome equipped with a diamond knife was used to obtain sections of about 600Å thickness. They were then observed directly in the electron microscope.

III. RESULTS AND DISCUSSION

A. Swelling Tests

The solubility of a polymer in a given solvent depends on the polymer-solvent interaction forces. Solvents with like solubility parameters are likely to dissolve the same solutes. This provides an indirect method for determining the solubility parameter, δ, of a polymer. If the polymer-solvent interaction forces are stronger than the polymer-polymer forces, the polymer will dissolve and as the polymer chain expands with solvent "goodness", the viscosity of the solution will increase. When the solubility parameters of the polymer and solvent are substantially equal, maximum expansion will occur and the highest viscosity will be attained. Thus by measuring the viscosities of the polymer in various solvents, it is possible to determine the solubility parameter of the polymer (30). Blanks and Shah (31) have used this method to determine the solubility of styrene-acrylonitrile copolymers.

For a crosslinked network, however, the polymer cannot dissolve but individual segments will solvate to give a swollen gel. The maximum swelling will occur when the solubility parameters of the solvent and polymer are substantially equal, for the same reasons as for the linear polymer.

In order to determine X, the polymer-solvent interaction parameter, Bristow and Watson (32) derived the following semi-emperical equation:

$$X = \beta_1 + \frac{V_1}{RT}[\delta_1 - \delta_2]^2 \qquad (1)$$

where δ_1 and δ_2 relate to the solvent and polymer respectively. β_1 is the lattice constant, usually 0.35 ± 0.1.

Figure 1 shows the swelling curve of an elastomer prepared from 2,4 tolylene diisocyanate, in various solvents of known δ_1 values. The curve peaks when δ equals 9.2 $(cal/cm^3)^{1/2}$. At this point δ_1 equals δ_2 and thus X equals β_1. Appendix 1 presents a summary of all of the swelling data for elastomers with NCO/OH ratios of 0.75, 0.85, 0.95. The average molecular weight between crosslinks, M_c, and the number of polymer chains per unit volume, N, were calculated from the Flory-Rehner equation (33) given below:

$$\ln(1 - v_2) + v_2 + X_1 v_2^2 = -NV_1(v_2^{1/3} - \frac{2v_2}{F}) \qquad (2)$$

where v_2 is the volume fraction of polymer in the swollen gel at equilibrium, V_1 is the molar volume of solvent, and F is the functionality of the system which in this case is 3. N and M_c

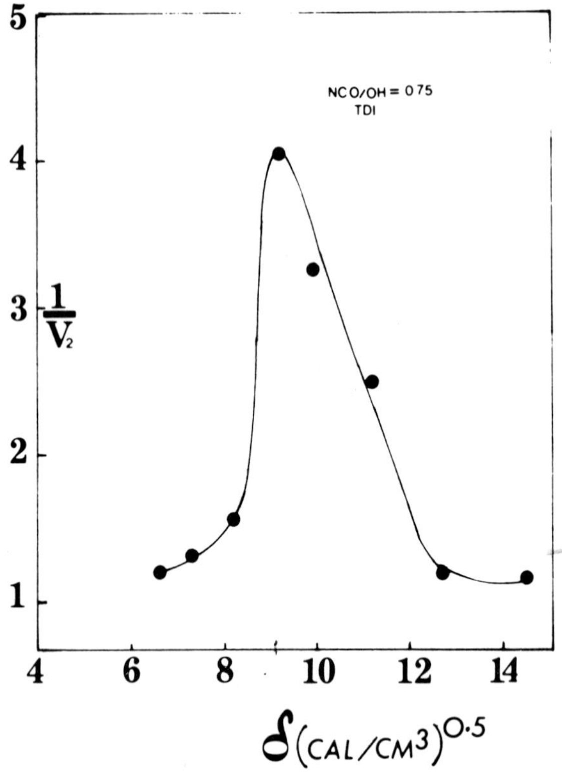

Fig. 1. Swelling data for castor oil-urethane elastomer, NCO/OH = 0.75, in various solvent of differing δ levels.

are related by the density, d:

$$N = d/M_c \quad (3)$$

Table 4 summarizes the results. The relatively small M_c values indicate rather dense crosslinking of the elastomers. Many elastomers have M_c values near 7500 gm/mole, as opposed to the present values of 1000 - 2000 gm/mole.

TABLE 4
Values of M_c for Castor Oil-Urethanes

NCO/OH	$N \times 10^4$ ($\frac{\text{Polymer Chains}}{\text{Unit Vol.}}$)	M_c, g/mole
0.75	3.7	2947
0.85	7.0	1328
0.95	9.5	964

Figure 2 shows a plot of N versus NCO/OH ratio. The curve crosses the NCO/OH ratio axis at 0.64, i.e. below this point, a branched, finite molecular weight polymer should be obtained and above it, an infinite network should exist. The structure of one of the two possible isomers of the equivalent linear polymer is illustrated in Figure 3. The other isomer arises when the -OH of the middle acid residue is reacted.

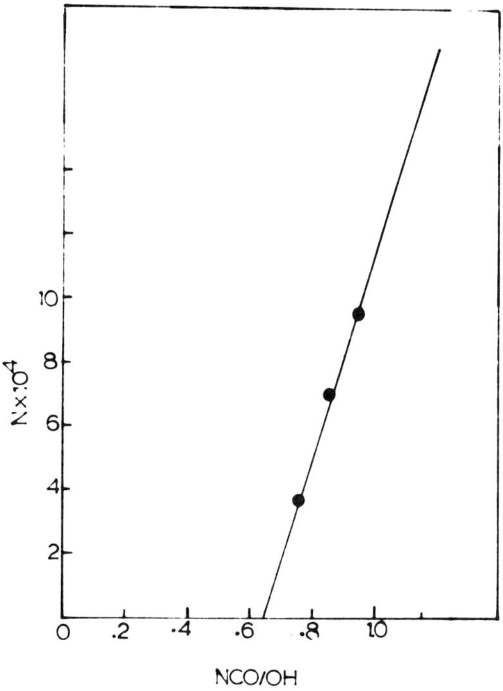

Fig. 2. Number of polymer network chains per unit volume versus crosslink ratio.

B. Morphology

The optical appearance of the IPN's varied from reasonably clear at high polystyrene content to translucent at high elastomer content. There are two possible explanations for this optical clarity (34,35,36): first, the indices of refraction of the two phases may be equal; second, and more likely, the dispersed phase may exist in domains which are too small relative to the wavelength of visible light, so that the amount of visible radiation scattered is small. The scattered radiation is proportional to the square of the differences in refractive index, and the 6th power of the domain diameters.

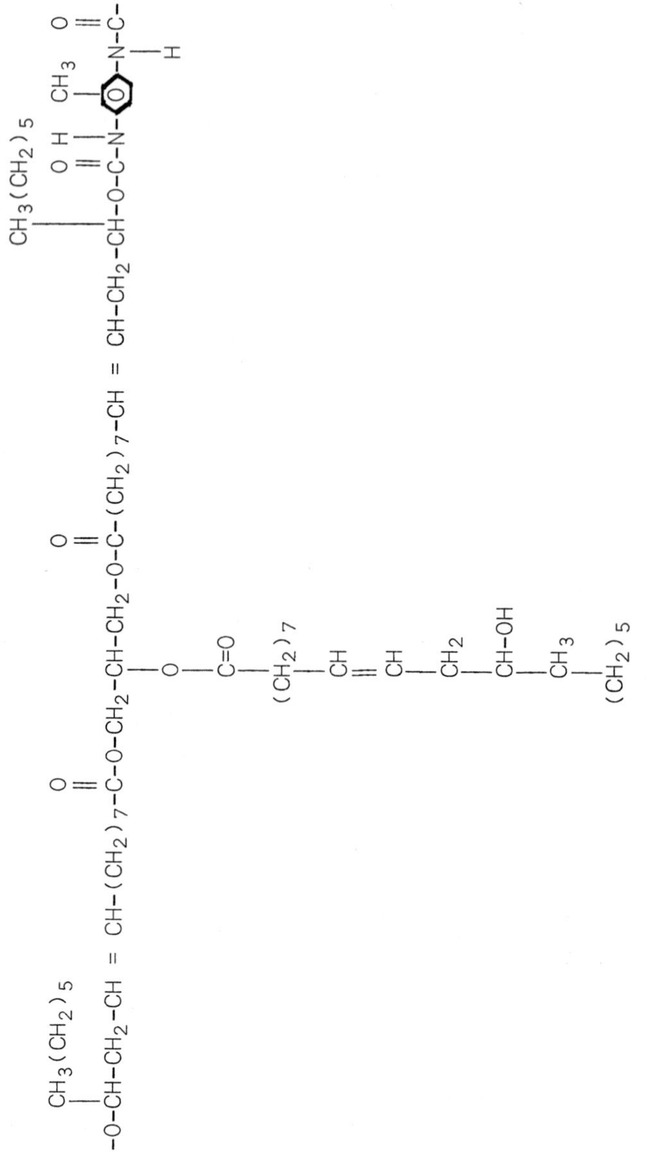

Fig. 3. The structure of the castor oil-urethane equivalent linear polymer.

The morphology of the IPN's is shown in Figures 4-6. The characteristic cellular domain structures noted earlier on other IPN's appear here, but are smaller than before. The domain structures range from about 300Å to 500Å in diameter. In each figure the size of the polystyrene phase decreases with increasing NCO/OH ratio and with increasing polystyrene

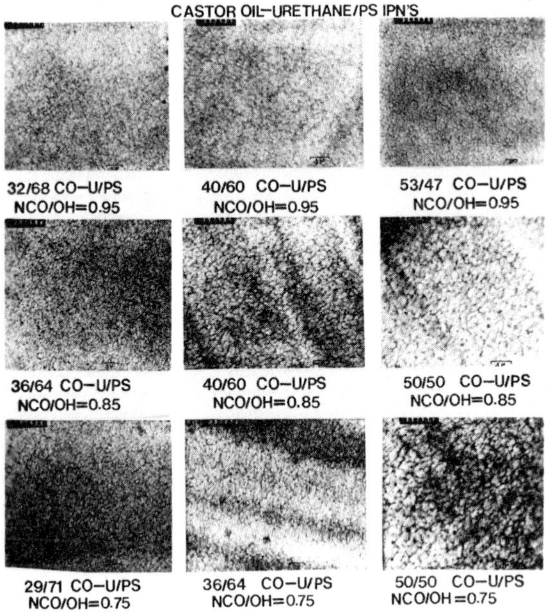

Fig. 4. Morphology of castor oil-urethane/polystyrene IPN's. Crosslinker: 2,4 Tolylene diisocyanate (included from paper I for comparison).

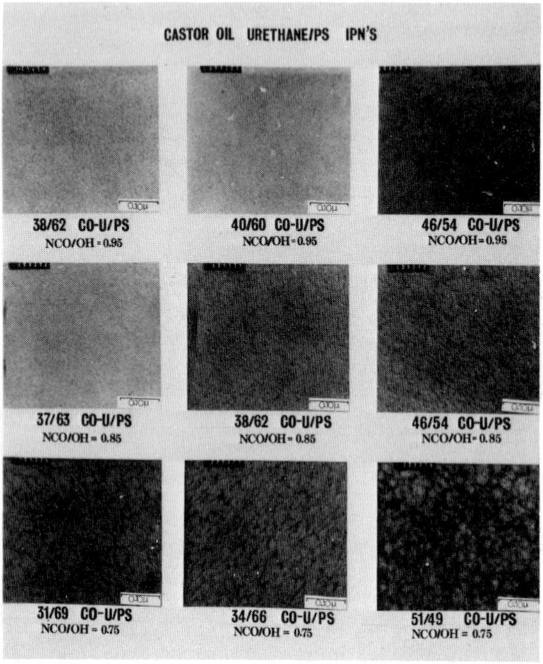

Fig. 5. Morphology of castor oil-urethane/polystyrene IPN's. Crosslinker: 80/20 : 2,4/2,6 Tolylene diisocyanate.

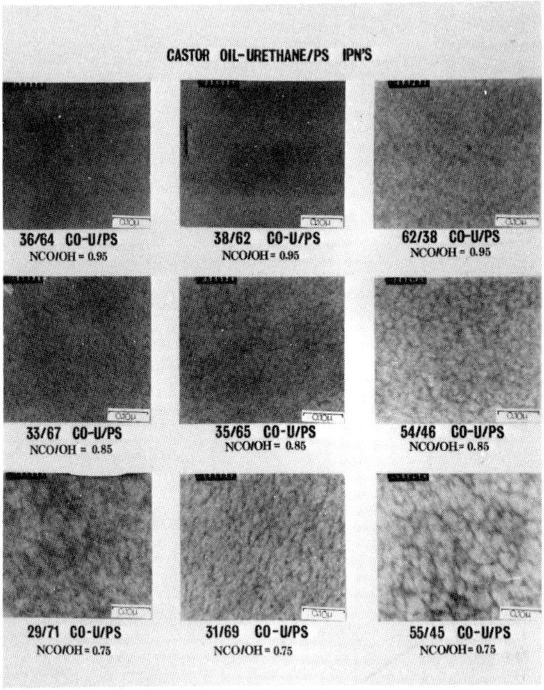

Fig. 6. Morphology of castor oil-urethane/polystyrene IPN's. Crosslinker: Hexamethylene diisocyanate.

content. The cellular structure shown by these micrographs reflect the dense crosslinking developed in the castor oil-urethane networks. The M_c values of Table 4 also suggest that the morphology would be a small cellular structure (see below). In all three cases, the morphology is not appreciably affected by the chemical structure of the crosslinker, i.e., the same morphology is obtained by using tolylene diisocyanate or hexamethylene diisocyanate. The continuity of the phases depends on the amounts of each component present. At low polystyrene levels the castor oil-urethane phase appears continuous; at high polystyrene levels, the polystyrene phase attains continuity.

C. Domain Size Prediction

Since domain sizes play an important role in the mechanical properties of a given polymer/polymer combination, it would be useful to be to predict these domain sizes for optimum properties before the composite is made. Donatelli, et. al. (37,38) derived the following equation for semi-IPN's and interpenetrating polymer networks, which predicts the diameter of the polymer II domains:

$$\left(\frac{\nu_1}{C^2K^2}\right)\left(\frac{\nu_1}{1 - \mathcal{W}_2} + \frac{2}{M_1}\right)\mathcal{D}_2^{\,3} + \left(\frac{\mathcal{W}_2}{M_2} - \frac{\nu_1}{2}\right)\mathcal{D}_2 = \frac{2\gamma\mathcal{W}_2}{RT} \qquad (4)$$

where ν_1 = crosslink density of polymer I
M_1 = primary molecular weight of polymer I
$\mathcal{D}_2$ = domain size of polymer II
M_2 = molecular weight of polymer II
$\mathcal{W}_2$ = weight fraction of polymer II
γ = interfacial energy between polymers I and II
C = constant
K = $r_o/M^{1/2}$ = constant available for most polymers
R = universal gas constant
T = absolute temperature.

With a value of $C = \sqrt{2}$, and M_1 and M_2 taken as infinite (37), equation (4) was applied to the present IPN system, see Table 5. Because γ is not known experimentally for the present system, and K cannot be determined for the elastomer (the equivalent linear polymer is difficult to synthesize), a series of values were assumed and values of $\mathcal{D}_2$ calculated. While values of γ = 5 dynes/cm and K = 800 (Å - mole$^{1/2}$)gm$^{1/2}$ are the probably the most realistic, theoretical, column (2), values of γ = 15 dynes/cm and K = 1300 (Å - mole$^{1/2}$)gm$^{1/2}$ theoretical, column (1), gave the best comparison with experiment, see Table 5. In fact γ and K are slow moving

TABLE 5
Polystyrene Domain Sizes

IPN* Sample	NCO/OH Ratio	wt Fraction PS	Polystyrene Domain Size, Å Experimental**	Theoretical (1)***	Theoretical (2)***
1	0.95	0.68	250	323	303
2	0.95	0.60	300	325	303
3	0.95	0.47	370	327	304
4	0.85	0.64	300	344	306
5	0.85	0.60	350	345	306
6	0.85	0.50	430	347	307
7	0.75	0.71	350	432	323
8	0.75	0.64	410	443	325
9	0.75	0.50	550	452	328

* *The castor oil phase in all the above IPN's was crosslinked with 2,4 TDI.*
** *Estimated from Fig. 4.*
*** *Theoretical, from equation (4).*

functions through all realistic values. The value of K may be larger than average noting the foliage present in Fig. 3.

It can be seen that the theoretical results agree reasonably with the experimental results. In fact, considering the difficulty involved in measuring the domain sizes experimentally and also the fact that the original equation was derived for a semi-IPN and not a full IPN, better agreement was achieved than expected.

IV. CONCLUSIONS

The synthesis of castor oil-urethane/polystyrene interpenetrating polymer networks yielded a two phase structure with polystyrene phase domain diameters of 300Å to 500Å. The Donatelli et. al. analysis yielded values that compared well with the experimental values. The solubility parameters for the castor oil-urethane elastomer was found to be 9.2 $(cal/cm^3)^{1/2}$ from swelling tests. The minimum NCO/OH ratio required to form an infinite network was found to be 0.64.

V. REFERENCES

1. Polymer Modification of Rubbers and Plastics, Keskkula Ed., (1968), Interscience.
2. Colloidal and Morphological Behavior of Blocks and Graft Copolymers, G. E. Molau, Ed., Plenum, 1971.
3. Composite Materials, Plueddemann, E. P., Ed., Academic, 1974.
4. Mechanical Properties of Polymers and Composites, L. E. Nielsen, New York, Marcel Dekker, 2 vols. (1974).
5. C. G. Bragaw, in Multicomponent Polymer Systems, R. F. Gould, Ed., American Chemical Society Publications, 1971.
6. J. A. Manson, and L. H. Sperling, Polymer Blends and Composites, Plenum, 1976.
7. J. A. Manson and R. W. Hertzberg, CRC Crit. Rev. in Macromol. Sci., 1, 433 (1973).
8. R. P. Kambour and R. E. Robertson, in Polymer Science, A Materials Science Handbook, A. D. Jenkins, Ed., N. Holland Publishing Co., 1972.
9. Platzer, N. A. J., Ed. (1971) Multicomponent Polymer Systems (Adv. Chem. Series 99), ACS, Introduction.
10. Kambour, R. P. and Russel, R. R. (1971), Polymer 12, 237.
11. L. H. Sperling, D. A. Thomas, E. J. Lorenz, and E. J. Nagel, J. Appl. Polym. Sci., 19, 2225 (1975).
12. Volker Huelck, D. A. Thomas, and L. H. Sperling, Macromolecules, 5, 340, 348 (1972).
13. A. A. Donatelli, D. A. Thomas, and L. H. Sperling, in "Recent Advances in Polymer Blends, Grafts, and Blocks", L. H. Sperling, Ed., Plenum, 1974.
14. S. C. Kim, D. Klempner, K. C. Frisch, H. L. Frisch, and H. Gheradella, Polym. Engn. Sci., 15(5), 339 (1975).
15. S. C. Kim, D. Klempner, K. C. Frisch, W. Radigan, and H. L. Frisch, Macromolecules, 9, 258 (1976).
16. S. C. Kim, D. Klempner, K. C. Frisch, and H. L. Frisch, Macromolecules, 9, 263 (1976).
17. P. E. Cassidy and G. D. Schwank, J. Appl. Polym. Sci., 18, 2517 (1974).
18. U. S. Pat. 2,734,916 (Feb. 14, 1956), D. D. Bolley (to Baker Castor Oil Co.).
19. U. S. Pat. 2,851,492 (Sept. 9, 1958), F. C. Naughton (to Baker Castor Oil Co.).
20. Rilsan, B. General Properties, ATO Chemie Bulletin 1052, Aug. 1973, p. 7.
21. Encyclopedia of Polymer Science and Technology, Vols. 3 and 4, pp. 21-25, and 524-533, respectively.
22. J. H. Saunders and K. C. Frisch, Polyurethanes: Chemistry and Technology, Part I, 1962, Interscience, p. 48-54.
23. J. H. Saunders and K. C. Frisch, "Polyurethanes: Chemistry and Technology", Part II, Interscience, p. 340-341.

24. T. C. Patton, A. Ehrlich, and M. K. Smith, Rubber Age, 86, 639 (1960).
25. R. F. Landel in Polymer Networks: Structure and Mechanical Properties, A. J. Chompff and S. Newman, Eds., Plenum, 1971.
26. F. C. Naughton, J. Am. Oil Chemists Soc., 51, 65 (1974).
27. G. M. Yenwo, L. H. Sperling, J. Pulido, J. A. Manson, A. Conde, and N. Devia-Manjarrés, in preparation.
28. L. H. Sperling, J. A. Manson, G. M. Yenwo, A. Conde, and N. Devia-Manjarrés, Polymer Preprints, 16(2), 604 (1975).
29. G. M. Yenwo, J. A. Manson, J. Pulido, L. H. Sperling, A. Conde, and N. Devia-Manjarrés, Accepted, J. Appl. Polym. Sci., 1976.
30. F. Rodriquez, Principles of Polymer Systems, McGraw-Hill, 1970, p. 20.
31. B. F. Blanks, and B. N. Shah, Polymer Preprints, 17(2), 407 (1976).
32. G. M. Bristow and W. F. Watson: Trans. Faraday Soc., 54, 1731 (1958).
33. J. P. Bell, J. Polym. Sci., A-2, 8, 417 (1970).
34. L. Bohn, Rubber Chem. Technol., 41(2), 495 (1968).
35. B. D. Gesner, J. Appl. Polym. Sci., 11, 2499 (1967).
36. S. L. Rosen, Polym. Engr. Sci., 7(2), 115 (1967).
37. A. A. Donatelli, L. H. Sperling, and D. A. Thomas, Accepted, J. Appl. Polym. Sci.
38. A. A. Donatelli, L. H. Sperling, and D. A. Thomas, Macromolecules, 9, 671, 676 (1976).

VI. APPENDIX 1

Elastomer Swelling Data

Solvent	δ, $(cal/cm^3)^{1/2}$	$1/v_2$ NCO/OH = 0.75	0.85	0.95
n-decane	6.6	1.22	1.19	1.16
n-hexane	7.3	1.29	1.30	1.30
cyclohexane	8.2	1.58	1.55	1.52
benzene	9.2	4.08	3.04	2.70
acetone	9.9	2.57	2.18	2.02
furfural	11.2	2.50	2.09	1.93
nitromethane	12.7	1.19	1.19	1.19
methanol	14.5	1.22	1.22	1.21

v_2 = *volume fraction of polymer in swollen gel.*

GRAFT CURING WITH A MODIFIED BUTYL RUBBER

F. P. Baldwin
I. J. Gardner
Exxon Chemical Company

We have recently prepared a polyisobutylene backboned elastomer containing low levels of conjugated diene functionality. This polymer is capable of participating in free radical copolymerization with simple monomers which provides for the preparation of complex networks with interesting physical and chemical properties. The networks are prepared by contacting the elastomers with free monomer, adding a free radical initiator and conducting the copolymerization in a pressurized heated mold. The process resembles a bulk polymerization and engages the kinetic benefits of the Trommsdorff effect. A crosslinked network is developed in which elastomer chains are interconnected by and interwoven with chains of the added monomer. Thus, the final products are composed of simple and complex grafts of the added monomer on the elastomer. Choice of monomer type, concentration and desired crosslink density in the composite provides broad preparative and property flexibility. The network constraints imposed during the crosslinking process impart to the final products unique and interesting physical characteristics. In practical terms, this process can be viewed as one initially employing efficient, low molecular weight "plasticizers" which on "curing" become an integral part of the product network.

I. INTRODUCTION

The synthesis of a polyisobutylene elastomer containing conjugated diene functionality has been reported earlier (1). The elastomer was prepared by the dehydrohalogenation of a commercial elastomer, CHLOROBUTYL as shown schematically below. One route to the synthesis has been reported (2).

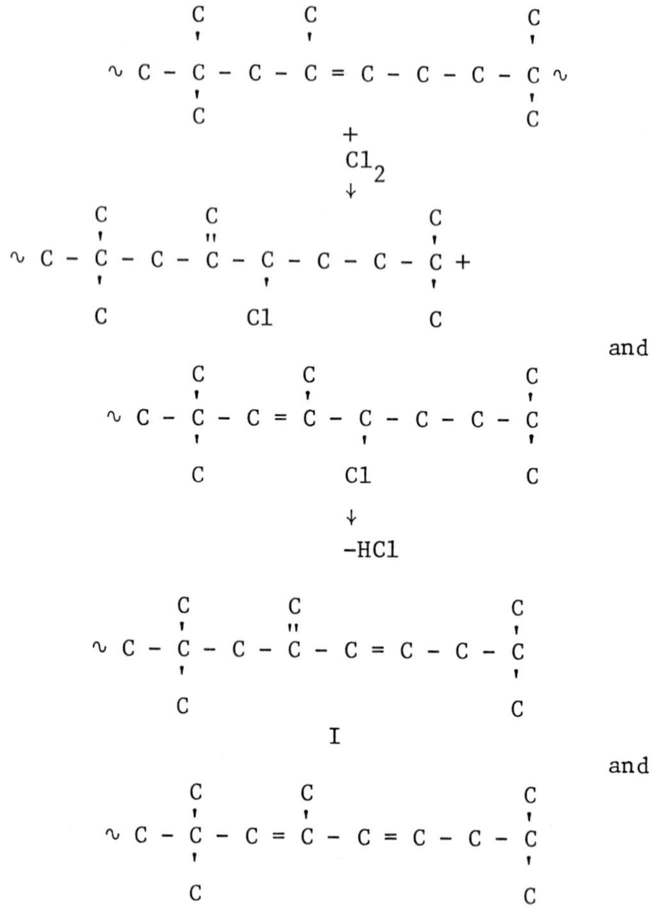

This new elastomer (CDB=conjugated diene butyl) is thought to contain two predominant diene structures in various configurations though structural details have not been completely worked out. The basic structures I and II are shown above with structure I being the most reactive in diene (e.g. Diels-Alder) and free radial polymerization reactions.

This elastomer might be considered as a polyfunctional macromonomer and accordingly be employed in radical initiated copolymerizations with simple mono and polyfunctional monomers. Since crosslinking of the elastomer by chains derived from the added monomer would be the likely consequence of such a copolymerization, it was clear that the copolymerization would have to take place during a molding operation to be useful. As the final product structure would appear to have been both grafted onto and crosslinked, we refer to the copolymerization as "graft curing."

Two illustrations of this process are shown in Figures 1 and 2. In the simplest case employing a single monofunctional monomer or mixture thereof (Fig. 1), we would anticipate several elastomer molecules being linked by single chains derived from the monomer(s), elastomer chains containing simple and complicated grafts and some free homopolymer. In a variation employing some polyfunctional monomer along with the monofunctional monomer (Fig. 2), the chains derived from the latter would be themselves crosslinked.

There are two important features of this graft curing process which make it potentially useful. First, the ultimate level of crosslinking of the elastomer is controlled by having only limited reactive functionality present. The CDB employed in our experiments contained some 1.4 mole % diene about half of which was of structure I. Second, the fact that our "solvent" for the free monomer is a viscous elastomer coupled with the fact that crosslinking occurs during polymerization automatically reduces the rate of termination of the high molecular weight radical chains so that the rate of polymerization is high (Trommsdorff effect) (3).

II. EXPERIMENTAL

CDB was purified for these experiments by *(a)* acetone precipitation from hexane solution then vacuum drying @ ∿ 50°C followed by cold storage or *(b)* steam stripping of freshly prepared CDB followed by hot mill drying and then cold storage. For experiments with compatible monomers the elastomer was cut into small cubes and placed in ointment jars. Monomer (s) was then added, the jars flushed with nitrogen, capped and the monomer allowed to diffuse into the CDB by overnight soaking at ∿ 23°C. Final homogenization occurred when other reagents were added to the CDB monomer solution in a Baker-Perkins or Brabender mixer. The addition of highly polar-incompatible monomers such as methacrylic acid was accomplished by pre-adsorbing the insoluble monomer onto a minor quantity of high surface area fumed silica or other appropriate adsorbent and incorporating the adsorbed material during the final homogenization steps. Mixtures were stored in capped jars under nitrogen. Molding was accomplished in aluminum molds between silicone coated mylar film in an electrically heated press.

Elastomer + Monomer $\xrightarrow[\Delta]{\text{CAT.}}$

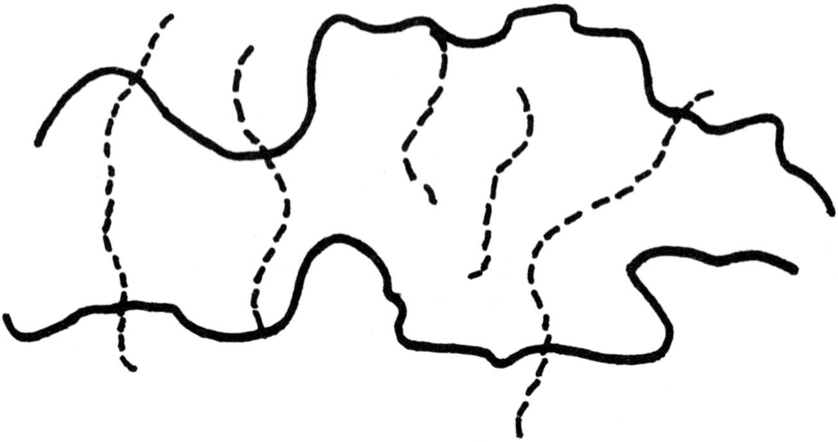

Fig. 1. Graft Curing Concept.

Elastomer + Monomer + XL Monomer $\xrightarrow[\Delta]{\text{CAT.}}$

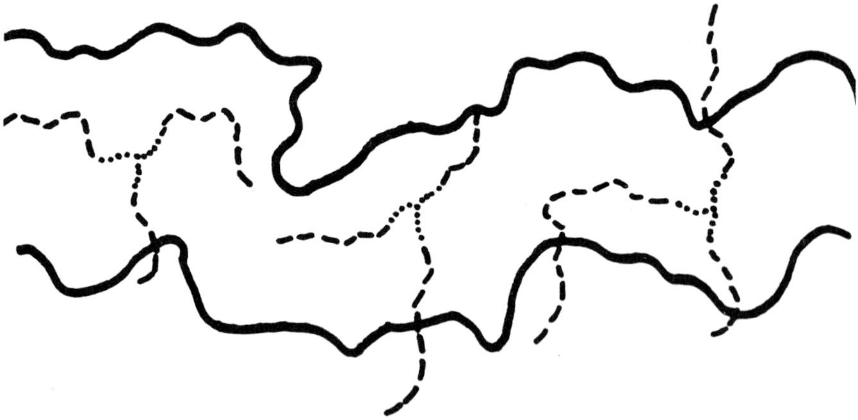

Fig. 2. Theme Variation.

Physical testing was carried out employing the applicable ASTM test specifications.

III. RESULTS AND DISCUSSION

A. Comparison of CDB and Regular Butyl Rubber

Experience has taught that high molecular weight olefin homopolymers and copolymers of α and internal olefins (of >3 carbon atoms) with other monomers cannot be made via simple free radical initiation because of the intrusion of chain transfer reactions involving hydrogen on α-carbon atoms. With internal olefins, the situation is at its worst because the number of α-carbon positions and hydrogens thereon is greater than for α-olefins.

Thus, if monomer M is polymerized in the presence of butyl, the primary reactions with butyl would be:

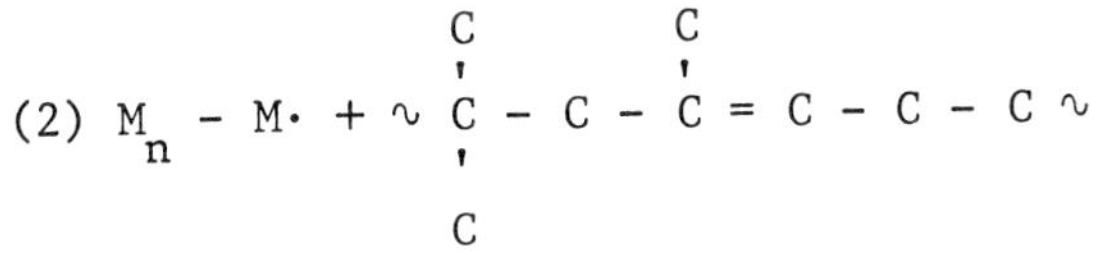

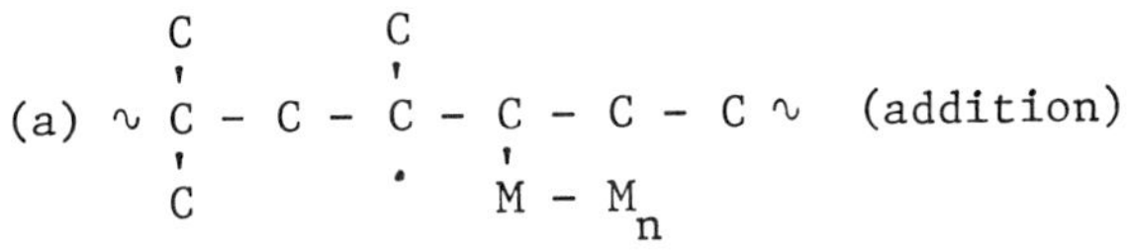

or

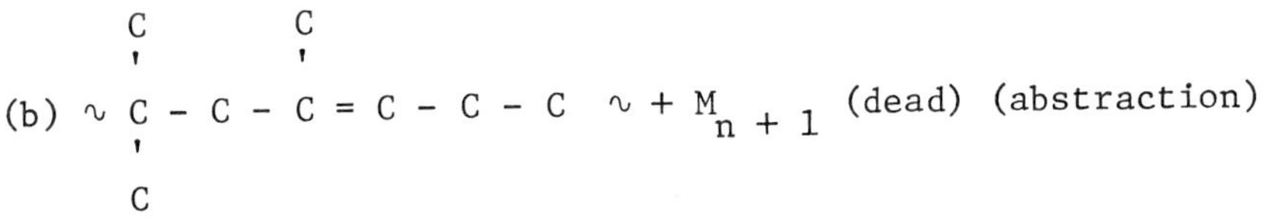

The radical produced in (a) is rather sterically hindered as regards further propagation and is less stable than the allyl radial produced in (b). Thus reaction (b) would be more favored than (a), the more so since the hydrogen abstraction reaction (b) can take place at as many as three but at least at two positions offering five accessible hydrogens on α-carbons. Thus, one could expect some grafting as a result of initiation of polymerization at the radical site produced in reaction (b) but not much growth of a polymer chain through a butyl chain, hence, little crosslinking. It is for these reasons that radical copolymerization of many reactive monomers with simple olefins do not yield high molecular weight products. If the growing chain of the reactive monomer interacts at all with the olefin, the chain transfer process dominates.

On the matter of initiation of polymerization at the site of an isoprene residue by a radical generator, the large excess of free monomer initially present makes this highly unlikely at this point in the (batch polymerization) process, and, if during the process few or no chains of M have grown through the butyl comonomer, then at the end of the process there is little free monomer present to grow from an initiation site on the butyl molecule.

With the conjugated diene, the concentration of reactive sites on the elastomer is still low relative to added monomer, but radical addition to the conjugated system is quite facile (relative to simple aliphatic olefins) and the resulting allyl radical is capable of adding a monomer molecule just as it would be in reaction (b). Thus

(3)

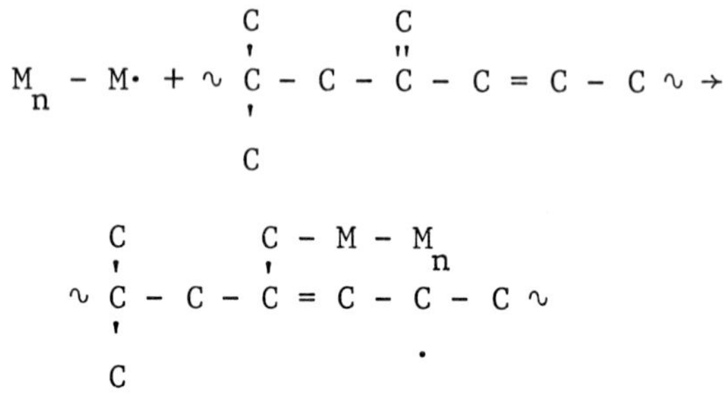

True, after this addition and further propagation have taken place, one again is left with a simple olefin residue, but in this case it is after the desired reaction has occurred, not before. Moreover, after propagation, the hydrogens on α-carbon are fewer in number (than in butyl) and more sterically hindered.

An illustration of this concept is provided by a comparison between regular butyl rubber containing ∿ 1.6 mole % of 1, 1, 2 trisubstituted olefinic functionality; CHLOROBUTYL containing 1.28 wt. % chlorine in addition to the olefinic functionality and CDB. Mixtures were prepared to contain (by wt.) elastomer - 100, styrene - 43, lauroyl peroxide - 0.64. Molding conditions were 40 min. at 100°C. On removal from the mold the pads prepared with butyl and CHLOROBUTYL were opaque, sticky to the touch and easily deformable. The

CDB specimen was clear, dry and obviously crosslinked. Immersion in toluene resulted in complete dissolution of the butyl and CHLOROBUTYL samples and production of a swollen gel with the CDB. The gel represented 96.2 wt. % of the specimen and its swelling ratio (swollen wt.-dry wt.)/dry wt., was 3.30. Additional results are given in Table 1.

TABLE 1
Graft Curing - Comparison of Butyl and CHLOROBUTYL with CDB

Polymer	Lauroyl Peroxide, g	Swelling Ratio[1]/% Insolubles[2,3] MEK	Cyclohexane	Toluene
Butyl	0.102	--	∞/0	∞/0
	0.203	--	∞/0	∞/0
	0.454	--	∞/0	∞/0
CHLOROBUTYL HT-1068	0.454	--	∞/0	∞/0
CDB-82	0.102	0.34/92.1	4.33/92.1	--
	0.203	0.36/94.4	3.81/95.2	3.30/96.2
	0.454	0.36/95.8	3.40/97.2	--
CDB-84C	0.454	0.32/97.4	3.49/96.2	3.95/99.5

1. (Swollen Weight - Dry Weight/Dry Weight) = S.R.
2. (Dry Weight/Original Weight) x 100 = % insolubles.
3. 72 hours at 25°C.

B. Composite Morphology

The clarity of the CDB derived specimen was unanticipated and suggested that if phase separation had occurred, the polystyrene particle diameter must be appreciably less than the wavelength of visible light. No Tg other than that associated with the elastomer (-59°C) could be found after repeated DTA experiments which included attempts at sample annealing. Mechanical spectra also revealed only one Tg, a broadened tan δ spectrum associated with the elastomer Tg.

The absence of a second Tg may be rationalized if one presumes that there has been no macro phase separation. Such a presumption is supported by our electron microscopy experiments in which no second phase has been detected under conditions yielding resolutions of ∿ 20 Å (OsO_4) staining). Secondly, the method of Conaghan and Rosen for determining particle size in two phase system indicates that, based upon the difference in refractive indices (polystrene N_D = 1.59 - 1.60; butyl rubber N_D = 1.5081) and concentration of polystyrene in the graft cures, the maximum particle size of the polystyrene dispersed phase is less than 150 Å (4). In this experiment we have employed a molar ratio of free styrene monomer to reactive functionality in the elastomer of about 30, therefore, the number average molecular weight of the unperturbed styrene sequences (assuming complete reaction of all functional groups and no homopolymer) would be about 3,400 maximum. Furthermore, the perturbations in these sequences are massive when they do occur (i.e. $\overline{M}n$ between points of active functionality in CDB = 8,000) and most of the polystyrene chains are constrained at least at one end and often at two ends by being part of a three dimensional network. This idea of a "homogeneous network" (inhomogenities are on a micro scale) is supported by the physical properties of the specimen - Tensile Strength - 2.6 MPa, Breaking Elongation - 355% - very much like an amorphous gum elastomer vulcanizate. Higher levels of styrene yield higher tensile products (viz.: 60 phr styrene: TS = 14.8 MPa, E = 260%).

This specimen clarity is not just peculiar to the CDB/styrene system. Specimens prepared from CDB, styrene and methacrylic acid are also transparent and display only Tg's and Tan δ related to the elastomer (Table 2). The DSC curve and tan δ plot for a graft cure containing CDB-100; styrene - 30; methacrylic acid - 15 are shown in Figures 3 and 4. The DSC scan was performed on a PE-DSC-1B and the Tan δ data obtained using a Rheovibron (Courtesy of Prof. W. MacKnight, U. Of Mass.).

TABLE 2

T_g [1] and Tan δ [2] of CDB/Styrene/Methacrylic Acid Graft Cures

Compound, phr	A	B	C	D	E	42	Control[3]
CDB (1.28 mole % CD)	100	100	100	100	100	100	100
Styrene	30	30	30	-	-	30	-
Methacrylic Acid	15	30	22	30	30	-	-
HDDMA[4]	-	-	8	-	8	-	-
t-Butyl Peroctoate	1.3	1.4	1.4	1.2	1.2	1.2	-
Percadox-16	0.2	0.2	0.2	0.1	0.1	0.1	-
Cure Conditions			40' @110°C				
Tg °C	-63	-60	-60	-62	-61	-	-60
$T_{\tan\delta}$ Max. °C	-25		-29		-25	-25	

1. Dupont DTA-900.
2. Rheovibron (data of W. MacKnight) 110 Hz
3. CDB gum elastomer - no additives - not crosslinked
4. 1, 6-Hexane diol-dimethacrylate.

C. Physical Properties

In the following 6 tables we illustrate some of the physical properties of these graft cure systems. The systems may be prepared to contain inert plasticizers, fillers, fibers and other compounding ingredients. Properties can be altered appreciably by kinds and amounts of monomers employed together with other compounding ingredients.

Table 3 illustrates representative tensile-elongation properties of several CDB-styrene-methacrylic acid graft cures including one containing a polyfunctional crosslinking agent hexane diol dimethacrylate. Other CDB graft cures utilizing maleic anhydride, alkyl acrylates and methacrylates, acrylo-

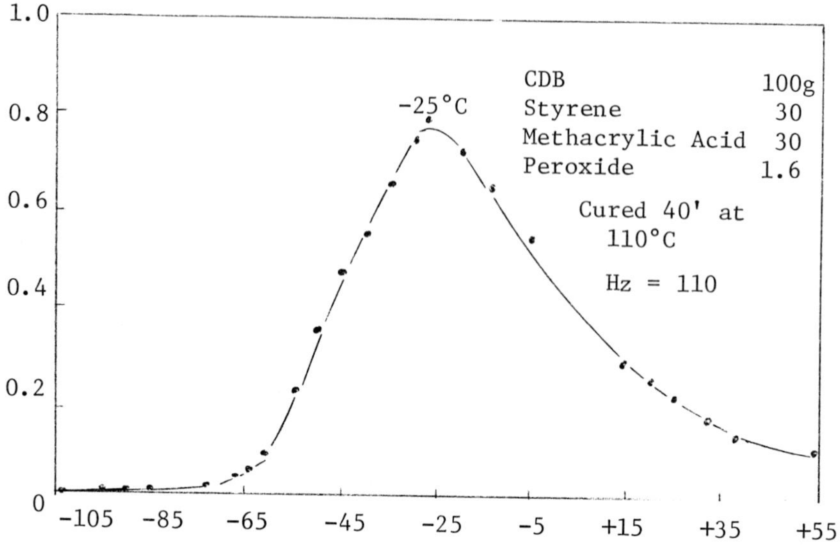

Fig. 3. Tan δ vs temp. Temp., °C

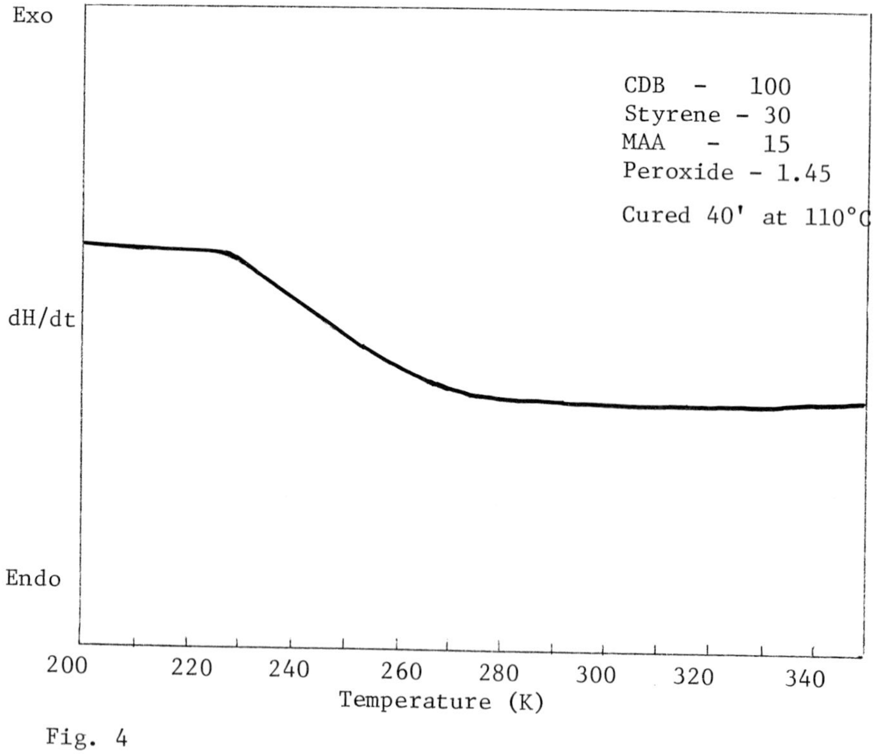

Fig. 4

nitrile, divinylbenzene, vinylpyridine and polyfunctional monomers have been successfully utilized in our studies.

In the case of graft cures containing polar monomers, the enhanced tensile strength may be attributed to the visco-elastic contributions of the polar monomer chains with some possible reinforcement from micro-domains. Clearly there will be a monomer concentration at and above which obvious separation must occur, even if only because all active functionality in the elastomer is consumed and considerable homopolymer is formed.

Table 4 illustrates the response of these graft cures to 70 hours exposure at 100°C in ASTM Oil #3.

Tables 5 and 6 illustrate the excellent electrical properties of various unfilled graft cures. In the particular case of heat aged graft cures containing methacrylic acid, the acid groups tend to dehydrate yielding an anhydride or ketone

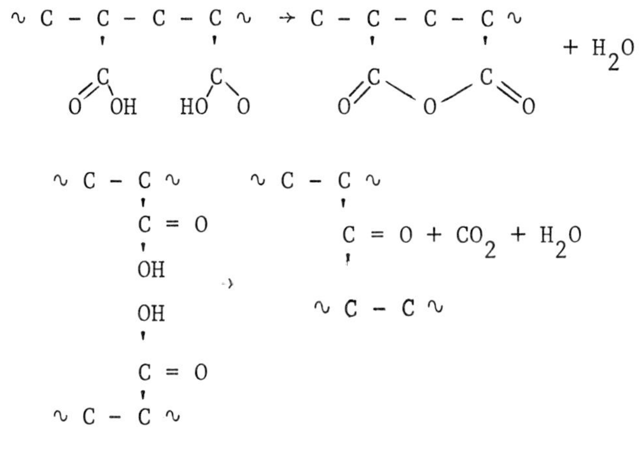

and the generation of a tacky surface. This tack can be eliminated without affecting the normal aging behavior by inclusion of a stoichometric amount of zinc oxide in the formulation. Presumably the formation of the zinc methacrylate salt effectively eliminates the dehydration reaction. However, in this case the cured materials are opaque.

TABLE 3
Physical Properties of CDB/Styrene/Methacrylic Acid Graft Cures

Compound, phr	A	B	C	D	E
CDB (1.28 mole % CD)	100.0	100.0	100.0	100.0	100.0
Styrene	30.0	30.0	30.0	--	--
Methacrylic Acid	15.0	30.0	22.0	30.0	30.0
HDDMA[1]	--	--	8.0	--	8.0
t-Butyl Peroctoate	1.30	1.44	1.44	1.17	1.24
Percadox-16	0.15	0.16	0.16	0.13	0.14
Cure Conditions			40' @ 110°C		
Physical Properties					
Tensile, MPa	11.71	18.05	13.37	14.00	12.13
Elongation, %	210	270	130	200	120
Shore A	68	78	78	83	85

1. 1,6 - Hexanediol Dimethacrylate.

TABLE 4
Volume Swell of CDB/Styrene/Methacrylic Acid Systems in ASTM #3 Oil at 100°C

CDB/S/MAA/XL*/P	% Volume Swell in ASTM #3 Oil 70 Hrs. @ 100°C
100/30/15/0/1.45	143
100/30/30/0/1.60	123
100/30/22/8/1.60	107
100/0/30/0/1.30	96
100/0/30/8/1.38	82
Polychloroprene Type W (GUM)	140
Polychloroprene Type W (40 phr HAF Black)	82
HT-1068 (Gum)**	400-500
HT-1068 (50 phr Black)**	350-400

*Hexanediol dimethacrylate. 1,6 - Hexane diol dimethacrylate

**Toluene - 25°C.

TABLE 5
Heat Aging Resistance of CDB Graft Cures

Compound		
	CDB	100 phr
	Styrene	60
	TMPTMA	3.6
	t-Butyl Perbenzoate	1.6
	Irganox 1010	0.24
	DLTDP	0.48
	CYASORB UV 5411	0.30

	Original	Air Aged 6 Wks. @ 130°C
Tensile, MPa (psi)	12.9 (1875)	13.6 (1945)
Elongation, %	195	180
100% Modulus, MPa (psi)	7.2 (1050)	7.8 (1125)
Shore A	85	88
Dielectric Constant	2.45	2.45
Power Factor	0.09	0.11
Volume Resisistivity x 10^{-17} ohm cm	2.29	>11.30
Dielectric Strength, Volts/mil	1610	1350
Transparency (% Light thru 0.16 cm pad)	84.4	76.3
Weatherometer Aging - 1000 hrs.		Clear and Colorless

TABLE 6
The Electrical Properties of CDB Graft Cures

Compound:	CDB 100, Styrene 30, Methacrylic Acid 30	CDB 100, Methacrylic Acid 30	EPM[1]
Dielectric Constant 50 Hz, 0.19 cm pad	2.44	2.45	2.8
Power Factor, % 0.19 cm pad	0.18	0.37	1.0
Dielectric Strength 25°, 0.08 cm pad, 500 v/sec, TPC treated Volts/.0025 cm	1200	1344	1200

1. Ethylene Propylene high voltage industrial gum compound.

The low viscosities of these graft cure masterbatches and the opportunity to incorporate selected monomers suggest their use as adhesives for a variety of substrates. Table 7 illustrates lap shear adhesion results for aluminum and stainless steel adherends at 25°C and 121°C as well as peel adhesion for aluminum adherends at 25°C (Table 7).

Finally in Table 8 we present moisture vapor transmission rates of CDB graft cures. The preservation of butyl rubber's traditional low rate of moisture transmission was unanticipated but welcome.

TABLE 7
CDB Graft Cures as Adhesives for Aluminum and 302 Stainless Steel

Compound		
CDB	100 phr	100
Styrene	5	5
Methacrylic Acid	25	25
SRF Black	--	50
Aerosil 200	3	3
Peroxide	1.6	2.3
Physical Properties (Cured 10' @ 110°C)		
Tensile, MPa	17.9	12.7
Elongation, %	295	210
Shore A Hardness	78	85

Lap Shear Adhesion MPa (psi)				Peel Adhesion to Aluminum kN/m (lb/inch)
Al to Al		SS to SS		
25°C	121°C	25°C	121°C	25°C
14.4 (2100)	5.2 (755)	13.4 (1950)	5.3 (775)	13.3 (76)

TABLE 8
Moisture Vapor Transmission Rates of CDB Graft Cures

Compound[1]	Film Thickness mils	MVTR[2] g H_2O/645.2 cm^2/24 hours
A. CDB/Styrene/SR 350	25	0.074
B. CDB/Styrene/DVB	26	0.060
C. CDB/Styrene	23	0.102
D. CDB/Styrene/EMA	27	0.067
E. CDB/Styrene/MAA	29	0.026
F. Polyisobutylene		0.4 - .1

1. Test performed on 17.8 cm x 17.8 cm x .064 cm pad (7" x 7" x .025") cured 60' at 110°C.
2. g H_2O/100 in^2/24 hours.

IV. CONCLUSIONS

Advantages for the system reside in the lower viscosity of the monomer swollen elastomer which permits compounding in relatively low power equipment together with the variety of property alteration intrinsic in the nature of the process. Potential applications areas are in spread coatings, electrical equipment potting, adhesives, ordinary and reinforced moldings and lay-ups and modification of conventional polyester bulk and sheet molding compounds.

V. ACKNOWLEDGMENTS

The assistance of R. E. Clayton and J. M. Rehberger in this research program was greatly appreciated as was commentary and Rheovibron data supplied by Dr. W. J. MacKnight.

VI. BIBLIOGRAPHY

1. 1. U.S. Patent 3,816,271, June 11, 1974.
2. U.S. Patent 3,775,387, November 27, 1973.
3. P. J. Flory, Principles of Polymer Chemistry, Cornell University Press (1953), Chapter IV-1a.
4. R. F. Conaghan, and S. L. Rosen, Poly. Eng. & Sci., 12, 134 (1972).
5. U. S. Patent 3,968,185, July 6, 1976.

A REVIEW OF THE RELATION BETWEEN THE PHYSICAL STRUCTURE AND MECHANICAL RESPONSE OF EPOXIES[1]

Roger J. Morgan and James E. O'Neal
McDonnell Douglas Research Laboratories

The effects of cure conditions, curing agent and thermal history above and below T_g on the network structure, microvoid characteristics, failure modes and mechanical properties of amine-cured bisphenol-A-diglycidyl ether based epoxies are reviewed. The mechanical properties and fracture topographies are reported as a function of strain rate and temperature. Electron microscope studies of carbon-platinum surface replicas, thin films and fracture topographies reveal that these glasses contain regions of heterogeneous crosslink density. The flow involved in the craze fibrillation process is controlled by the size and concentration of highly crosslinked regions and the free volume of the material interconnecting such regions. The presence of epoxy monomer crystalline regions in a room-teperature, partially cured glass produces microvoids and a poor network structure in the post-cured glass.

I. INTRODUCTION

Crosslinked glasses, primarily epoxies, are utilized by diverse industries in the form of matrices for composite materials, adhesives, coatings and foams. The increasing use of epoxies in extreme service environments requires a knowledge of their lifetime in such environments. To predict the lifetime of these glasses in a service environment requires knowledge of (1) the chemical structure and the physical arrangement of the crosslinked network structure in the bulk, (2) how such structural parameters affect the failure processes, (3) the effect of the failure processes on the mechanical properties, and (4) how these structural parameters are modified by fabrication procedures and the service environment.

The mechanical response of a polymer glass depends on the amount of flow occurring during the failure process, either microscopically via crazing or shear banding or macroscopically via necking (1-13). This flow absorbs energy during the failure process and enhances the toughness of the polymer glass. Any phenomenon that inhibits flow will embrittle the glass and

1 This research was conducted under the McDonnell Douglas Research and Development Program.

seriously limit its use. The major parameters controlling the flow processes in uncrosslinked polymer glasses are the free volume (14-19) and the stress-raising microvoid characteristics of the glass (17, 20, 21).

In the case of crosslinked glasses, such as epoxies, the presence of crosslinking is an additional structural parameter affecting the flow processes. Generally, the cure process and final network structure of epoxies have been determined from the chemistry of the system, if the curing reactions were known and assumed to go to completion, and from experimental techniques such as infrared spectrometric, swelling, dynamic mechanical, thermal conductivity and differential scanning calorimetry measurements (22-37). There have, however, been no systematic studies relating the chemical and physical structure of epoxies to their mechanical response.

In this paper, we report the effects of cure conditions, curing agent and thermal history above and below T_g on the physical structure, microvoid characteristics, failure modes and mechanical properties of amine-cured bisphenol-A-diglycidyl ether (DGEBA) based epoxies.

II. EXPERIMENTAL

A. Material

Epon 828 (Shell) and DER 332 (Dow) difunctional bisphenol-A-diglycidyl ether epoxide monomers (DGEBA) were used in this study. DER 332 is the pure DGEBA epoxy monomer of molecular weight 340, whereas Epon 828 contains ~10% higher molecular-weight oligomers and has an average molecular weight of 370 - 384. Diethylene triamine, DETA (Eastman), m-phenylene diamine, MPDA (Eastman), and an aliphatic polyamide (General Mills Versamid 140) were used as the curing agents.

B. Experiments

The tensile mechanical property tests of the epoxies were performed in a table-model tensile tester (Instron TM-S-1130). A scanning reflection electron microscope (JEOL model JEM-100B) and optical microscope (Zeiss Ultraphot II) were used for fracture topography studies. Transmission electron microscopy was used for thin-film and carbon-platinum surface replica studies. Infrared spectrometric analysis and dielectric loss measurements were performed on a infrared spectrophotometer (Perkin-Elmer 457) and an automatic dielectrometer (Tetrahedron Audrey II) respectively.

III. RESULTS AND DISCUSSION

A. Epoxy Monomer Crystallization

An understanding of the structure-property relations of epoxies requires a knowledge of the effect of cure conditions on the network structure and microvoid formation. Inhomogeneous mixing of the epoxy monomer and curing agent could modify the network structure and microvoid characteristics and, therefore, the mechanical response of epoxies. Pure DGEBA epoxy monomer (DER 332) crystallizes at room temperature resulting in crystals that are suspended in the higher molecular-weight liquid. In Epon 828, the crystal sizes are ~10 μm and predominantly in the form of square platelets or rods. For cold-cured epoxies, the presence of these crystallites can result in microvoids in the post-cured resin. Partially curing Epon 828 with 25 parts per hundred (phr) polyamide (Versamide 140) at room temperature leaves the crystals embedded in the glass. Post-curing this epoxy at higher temperatures produces ~10 μm microvoids and associated stresses in the glass as a result of melting the crystals and subsequent volatilization of the resultant liquid. The formation of these microvoids and stresses from the original crystals was monitored directly in the optical microscope. Figure 1 shows the light scattering patterns, under polarized light, associated with the stress fields surrounding the microvoids in an Epon 828-polyamide system that was post-cured at 95°C for 24 h. The presence of the microvoids and associated stresses in the epoxy, however, do not significantly deteriorate the mechanical properties; for example, the room-temperature toughness of such a glass is only ~15% lower than that of a void-free epoxy prepared from non-crystalline Epon 828 for the same chemistry and cure conditions. This

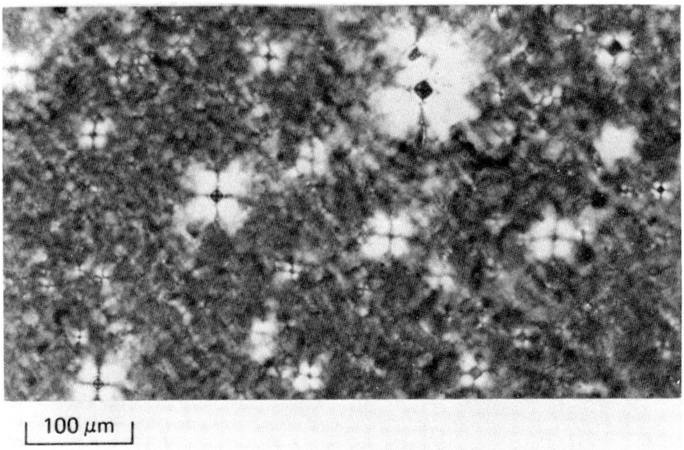

Fig. 1. Light scattering patterns, under polarized light, produced by microvoids and surrounding stress-fields in Epon 828-polyamide epoxy.

observation suggests that the stresses and associated oriented material surrounding these microvoids together with the ductility of the glass inhibit crack growth.

The unreacted DGEBA epoxy monomer in a room-temperature, partially cured resin recrystallizes over several weeks. Epon 828 was heated to 60°C to melt the crystals and was then partially cured at room temperature with 25 phr polyamide. The epoxy was stored at room temperature for three weeks, and the room-temperature mechanical properties were measured. After exposing this epoxy to 48°C for 2 h, which melts any crystals present in the glass, the toughness of the glass increased six fold, and macroscopic shear bands were observed under polarized light. This enhanced toughness was caused by the melting of epoxy monomer crystals, which subsequently plasticized the partially cured resin. Post-curing the resin containing regions of recrystallized epoxy monomer in the 80 - 130°C range causes the unreacted epoxy to melt and volatilize producing a glass with half the toughness of a similar epoxy system that originally did not contain crystalline regions. Scanning electron micrographs of the fracture topography of these epoxies revealed that the epoxy monomer recrystallizes between microgel regions of high crosslink density and/or high molecular weight. Post-curing, which causes the monomer crystals to melt and subsequently volatilize, results in a poor network structure interconnecting the microgel regions. The poor network structure, illustrated in the scanning electron micrograph of the fracture topography in Fig. 2, causes the brittle mechanical behavior. These observations suggest that microgel regions of high crosslink density form prior to the formation of a macrogel during the network formation.

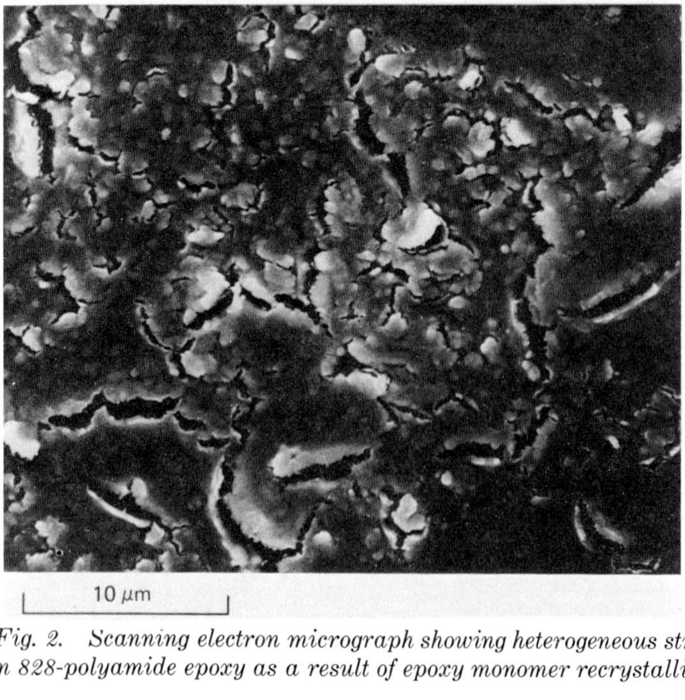

Fig. 2. Scanning electron micrograph showing heterogeneous structure of Epon 828-polyamide epoxy as a result of epoxy monomer recrystallization.

B. Effect of Post-Curing on Mechanical Properties

The room-temperature mechanical properties of amine (DETA, polyamide, MPDA)-cured DGEBA epoxies do not vary as a function of post-cure temperature when post-cured for 24 h in vacuum at 80° - 180°C. The ultimate extension of these epoxies can reach ~18%, 30°C below T_g, indicating that they are not highly crosslinked glasses, despite being prepared from a stoichiometric mixture of epoxy and amine. Exposure to temperatures above 180°C for 24 h causes the epoxies to embrittle because of the onset of complex oxidative crosslinking reactions. Differential infrared analysis of an epoxy post-cured above 180°C relative to a standard epoxy post-cured at 150°C reveals an additional broad absorption band in the 700 - 1800 cm^{-1} region. The intensity of this absorption increased with exposure time and increasing temperature, in the 180° - 300°C range, and increased more rapidly in air than in vacuum. A strong infrared absorption at 1725 cm^{-1} appears during the initial stages of the degradation process, which indicates the formation of carbonyl groups. Such groups could result from oxidation of unreacted epoxide rings to form α-hydroxyl aldehyde and carboxylic acid (38). Degradation causes the epoxies to change from colorless to brown to cherry red with an accompanying increase in free-radical formation as monitored by electron paramagnetic resonance. Jain (39) first detected free-radical formation during thermo-oxidative degradation of epoxies. Ovenall (40), in more detailed studies of epoxies, concluded that at 180°C in air, the formation and decay of radicals occur by oxidative scission and molecular diffusion interaction between radicals respectively. Later studies have suggested that resonance-stabilized free radicals occur in the thermal degradation of epoxies (41, 42). These data indicate that complex oxidative degradation reactions start to occur in DGEBA epoxies near 180°C and cause detectable embrittlement above ~200°C. (Absorbed oxygen present in the epoxies allows such reactions to occur even when post-curing under vacuum.)

C. Effect of Initial Epoxy:Amine Ratio and Thermal History

The room-temperature yield stress of a series of DGEBA-polyamide epoxies cured with 20, 25 and 33 phr polyamide was found to be independent of the initial epoxy:amine ratio and crosslink density. This constant yield-stress implies that the strength of interaction between the entities involved in the flow processes during failure is not affected by the overall changes in crosslink density. This phenomenon can be explained by hypothesizing that islands of high crosslink density remain intact and move past one another during the processes.

The free volume of the lightly- or non-crosslinked material interconnecting these regions of high crosslink density is therefore a primary factor controlling the flow processes. The free volume of this material depends on the previous thermal history of the epoxy above and below T_g. A typical volume-temperature plot for a polymer is shown in Fig. 3. Changes in free volume, or local order, in the glassy state can occur as a result of extension to temperatures below T_g of packing changes associated with the liquid state. The liquid volume-temperature plot extrapolated to below T_g in Fig. 3 represents the lower free-volume, equilibrium state of the glass. The time necessary to achieve the equilibrium state at a given temperature below T_g depends on the glassy-state mobility. Below a certain temperature, the glassy-state mobility is too small to allow any changes in free volume. A decrease in free volume that occurs in the glassy state results in inhibition of the flow processes that take place during deformation and a more brittle mechanical response. Rapidly cooling from above T_g, however, produces a glass with a larger free volume.

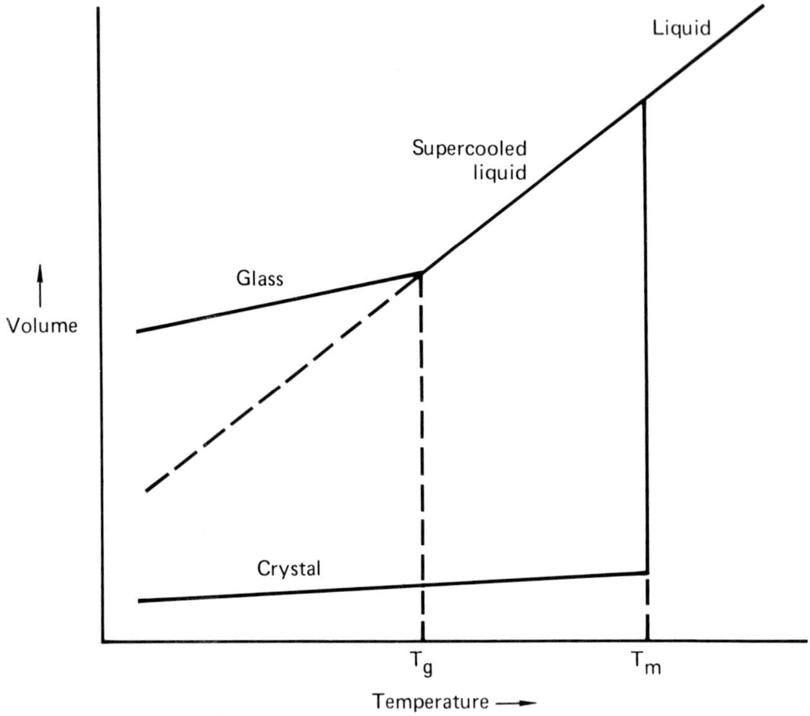

Fig. 3. A schematic volume-temperature plot for a polymer.

Table 1 shows the effect of thermal history on the mechanical properties of a DETA-cured DGEBA epoxy ($T_g \sim 116$°C). [This epoxy, from stoichiometric considerations, should be a highly crosslinked glass (26).] The modifications of the yield stress and ultimate elongation with thermal history, which are reversible, indicate that the flow processes in this glass are controlled by the free volume of regions of lightly- or non-crosslinked material.

In Fig. 4, a plot is shown of the effect of annealing [5°C below T_g (125°C)] on the temperature and strain-rate dependence of the yield stress of DETA (11 phr)-cured DGEBA epoxy. The general increase in the yield stress at all temperatures and strain-rates on annealing below T_g further illustrates the free-volume dependence of these epoxies.

TABLE 1

Effect of thermal history on the room-temperature tensile mechanical properties (strain rate ~10^{-2}/min) of DETA (9 phr)-cured DGEBA epoxy.

Thermal history	Yield (Y) or fracture (F) stress (kg/cm^2)	Ultimate elongation (%)
1) Cured 24 h, 23°C; 24 h, 150°C; cooled 2°C/min to room-temperature	(Y) 840 ± 10	11 ± 1
2) 111°C - 1 day	(Y) 870 ± 10	11 ± 1
3) 111°C - 2 days	(Y) 880 ± 10	11 ± 1
4) 111°C - 4 days	(F) 770 ± 10	9 ± 1
5) 171°C, 10 min; quenched in ice water	(Y) 770 ± 10	14 ± 1

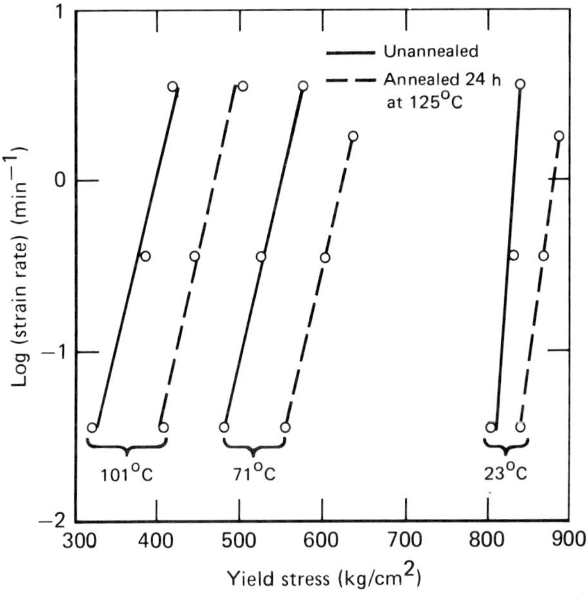

Fig. 4. Log (strain-rate) versus yield stress of DETA (11 phr)-cured DGEBA epoxy as a function of temperature and thermal history.

D. Network Structure and Failure Modes

Our studies of the effects of epoxy monomer crystallization, initial epoxy:amine ratio and thermal history on the mechanical behavior of amine-cured epoxies suggest that these glasses can contain regions of heterogeneous crosslink density. Ordered and/or highly crosslinked regions from 60 Å to 10 μm have been observed in crosslinked resins (17, 24, 43-56). The conditions for formation of a heterogeneous rather than a homogeneous system depend on polymerization conditions (i.e., temperature, solvent and/or chemical composition). The ordered regions have been described as agglomerates of colloidal particles (48, 49) or floccules (51) in a lower molecular-weight interstitial fluid. Solomon et al. (50) suggested that a two-phase system is produced by mirogelation prior to the formation of a macrogel. Kenyon and Nielsen (24) suggested that the highly crosslinked microgel regions are loosely connected during the latter stages of the curing process. The ordered regions have been reported to be only weakly attached to the surrounding matrix (48, 49, 51), and their size varies with cure conditions (48), proximity of surfaces (51, 52) and the presence of solvents (24, 50).

Transmission electron micrographs of thin films (~500 Å) and carbon-platinum surface replicas of acetone-leached surfaces of amine-cured epoxies suggest that these glasses contain heterogeneous regions of high crosslink density (17, 54). Carbon-platinum surface replicas of acetone-leached surfaces revealed 200 - 500 Å regions of apparent high crosslink density (Fig. 5). Bright-field transmission electron microscopy, however, reveals that such regions are aggregates of interconnected ~75 Å entities.

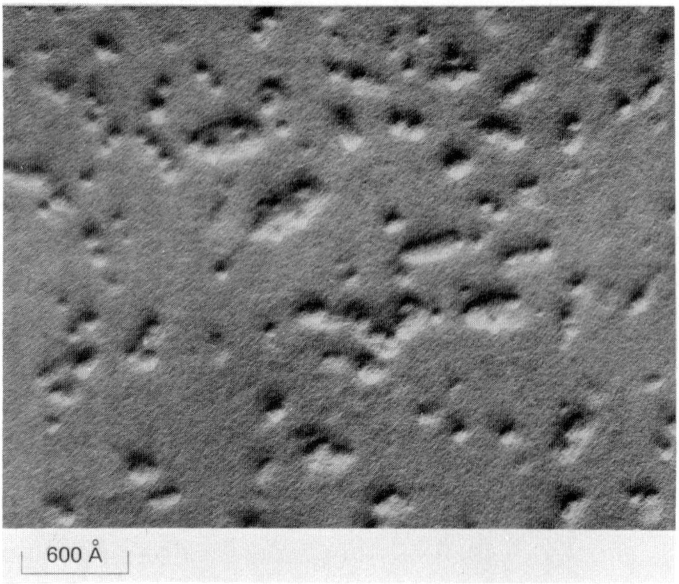

Fig. 5. Carbon-platinum surface replica of acetone-leached surface of DETA (11 phr)-cured DGEBA epoxy.

The relation between the network structure and failure processes of epoxies has received little attention. Localized plastic flow has been reported to occur during the failure processes of epoxies (52, 54, 57, 58), and in a number of cases, the fracture energies have been reported to be a factor of 2 or 3 times greater than the expected theoretical estimate for purely brittle fracture (58-62).

We investigated the microscopic failure processes of the amine-cured DGEBA epoxies in relation to their physical structure by several techniques. Epoxy films were strained on a metal substrate, and the failure processes were monitored by electron microscopy of carbon-platinum surface replicas. The epoxies fail by a crazing process. The crazes initiate by the formation of ~100 Å voids, which are produced by tensile dilatational stress fields. These voids coalesce to form larger voids up to 1000 Å separated by 300 to 600 Å diameter fibrils. Further from the craze tip, ~300 Å diameter fibrils break as their length approaches ~3000 Å. The latter observation may be a consequence of the poor structural integrity of the replica.

Bright-field transmission electron microscopy of strained thin films ($\lesssim$ 1 μm thick) reveals more detailed information of the crazing process. Figure 6 shows apparent regions of high crosslink density at the edge of a craze, which suggests that the craze fibrillation process may be inhibited by these regions. The inhibition of the drawing of new material across the craze-boundary interface increases the possibility of strain hardening and fracture of the fibrils and, therefore, enhances crack propagation.

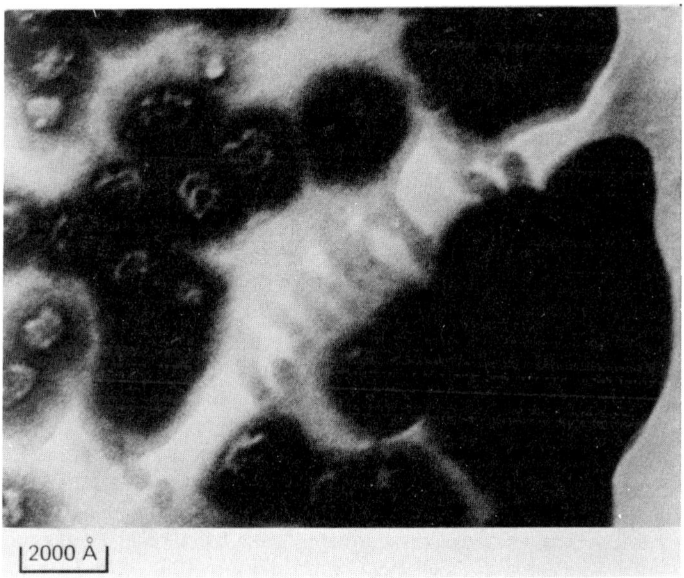

Fig. 6. Bright-field transmission electron micrograph of apparent regions of high crosslink density at edge of craze in DETA (11 phr)-cured DGEBA epoxy.

Bright-field transmission electron microscopy was also used to study the crazing process of epoxy films strained directly in the electron microscope. The inhomogeneous deformation of the craze fibril shown in Fig. 7 further indicates the heterogeneous distribution of crosslink density in these epoxies. The structure breaks into ~75 Å entities, which we suggest are highly crosslinked molecular domains.

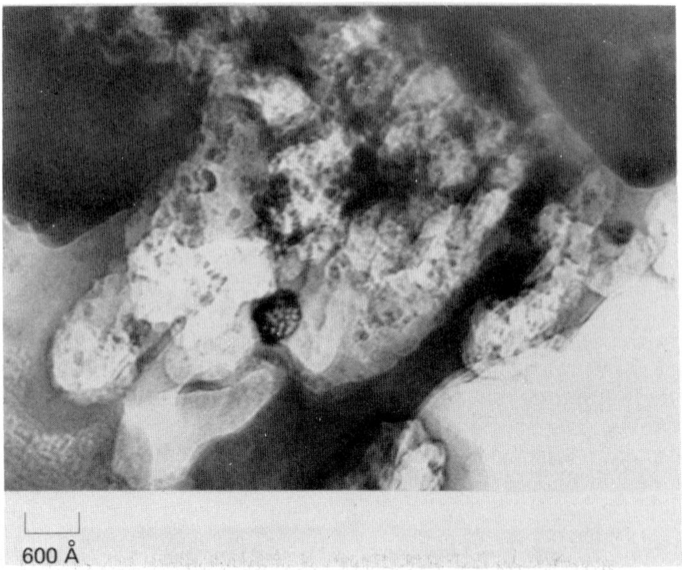

Fig. 7. Bright-field transmission electron micrograph illustrating the inhomogeneous deformation within a craze fibril in DETA (9 phr)-cured DGEBA epoxy.

The fracture topographies of the amine-cured DGEBA epoxies can be interpreted in terms of a crazing failure process. The coarse initiation region of the fracture topography of these epoxies, which has a mica-like appearance, is illustrated in the scanning electron micrograph in Fig. 8. This region is at the center of a cavity and is surrounded by a smooth, mirror, slow crack-growth region. Fracture topography studies of amine-cured epoxies of various thermal histories, which were fractured as a function of temperature and strain-rate, revealed that the mica-like structure can 1) cover a relatively small region in the center of the initiation cavity, 2) cover the entire cavity or 3) irregularly cover parts of the cavity (63). The smooth, mirror region covers the whole fracture surface 30°C below the T_g of these glasses. There is evidence from studies on polystyrene that the initial stages of void growth and coalescence within a craze involve fracture through the center of the craze (64, 65). In addition, the coarseness of the craze fibrils has been reported to decrease with increasing craze width and thickness (65). These facts suggest that the mica-like structure results from void growth and coalescence through the center of a simultaneously growing, poorly developed craze, which consists of coarse fibrils. The diameter of the broken fibrils will depend on the relative rates of craze and void propagation. The smooth, mirror region results from crack propagation either through the center or along the craze-matrix boundary interface of a thick, well-developed craze consisting of fine fibrils (63).

Hence, amine-cured DGEBA epoxies are not highly crosslinked, and there is a heterogeneous distribution in the crosslink density of these glasses. These epoxies fail by a crazing process in which the flow processes are controlled by (1) the size and concentration of regions of apparent high crosslink density and (2) the free volume of the material interconnecting such regions.

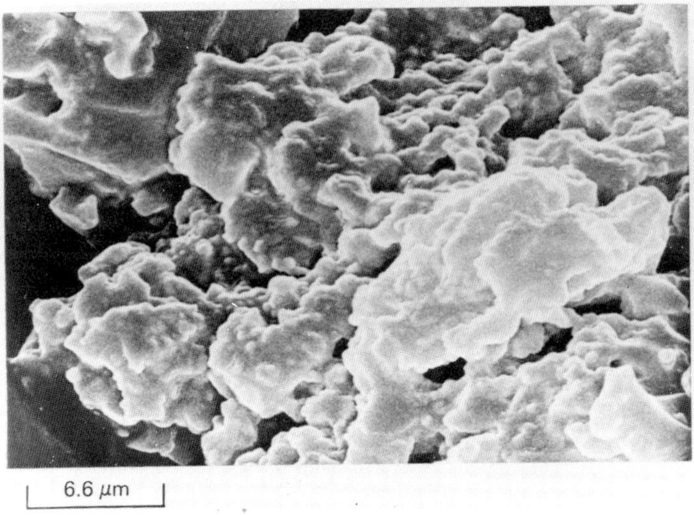

Fig. 8. Scanning electron micrograph of the fracture topography of the initiation region in an amine-cured DGEBA epoxy.

REFERENCES

1. J. P. Berry, J. Polym. Sci. 50, 107 (1961).
2. J. P. Berry, J. Polym. Sci. 50, 313 (1961).
3. R. F. Boyer, Rubber Chem. Technol. 36, 1301 (1963).
4. R. P. Kambour, J. Polym. Sci. A 3, 1713 (1965).
5. R. P. Kambour, Polym. Eng. Sci. 8, 281 (1968).
6. R. P. Kambour, Appl. Polymer Symposia 7, 215 (1968).
7. J. Heijboer, J. Polym. Sci. C, 16, 3755 (1968).
8. E. H. Andrews, "Fracture in Polymers", Elsevier, New York, 1968.
9. S. M. Aharoni, J. Appl. Polym. Sci. 16, 3275 (1972).
10. S. Rabinowitz and P. Beardmore, in "Critical Reviews in Macromolecular Science", Vol. 1, p. 1. Chem. Rubber Co., Cleveland, 1972.
11. R. J. Morgan, J. Polym. Sci. (Phys. Ed) 11, 1271 (1973).
12. J. R. Kastelic and E. Baer, J. Macromol Sci. - Phys. B7(4), 679 (1973).
13. R. J. Morgan and L. E. Nielsen, J. Macromol. Sci. - Phys. B9(2), 239 (1974).
14. A. J. Kovacs, Adv. Polym. Sci. 3, 394 (1964).
15. M. H. Litt and A. V. Tobolsky, J. Macromol. Sci. - Phys, B1(3), 433 (1967).
16. R. F. Boyer, Polym. Eng. Sci. 8, 161 (1968).
17. R. J. Morgan and J. E. O'Neal, Polym. and Plast. Tech and Eng. 5(2), 173 (1975).
18. S. E. B. Petrie, in "Polymeric Materials: Relationships Between Structure and Mechanical Behavior" (E. Baer and S. V. Radcliffe, Eds.), p. 55. Am. Soc. for Metals, 1975.
19. R. J. Morgan and J. E. O'Neal, J. Polym. Sci. (Polym. Phys. Ed.) 14, 1053 (1976).

20. A. N. Gent, J. Mater. Sci. 5, 925 (1970).
21. E. H. Andrews. in "The Physics of Glassy Polymers" (R. N. Haward, Ed.) Chp. 7. Applied Science Publishers Ltd., 1973.
22. D. Katz and A. V. Tobolsky, Polymer 4, 417 (1963).
23. T. K. Kwei, J. Polym. Sci. A-1, 2977 (1963).
24. A. S. Kenyon and L. E. Nielsen, J. Macromol. Sci. - Chem. A3(2), 275 (1969).
25. R. P. Kreahling and D. E. Kline, J. Appl. Polym. Sci. 13, 2411 (1969).
26. J. P. Bell, J. Polym. Sci. A-2, 8, 417 (1970).
27. T. Murayama and J. P. Bell, J. Polym. Sci. A-2, 8, 437 (1970).
28. M. A. Acitelli, R. B. Prime and E. Sacher, Polymer 12, 335 (1971).
29. R. G. C. Arridge and J. H. Speake, Polymer 12, 443 and 450 (1972).
30. P. V. Sidyakin, Vysokomol. soyed. A14, No. 5, 979 (1972).
31. T. Hirai and D. E. Kline, J. Appl. Polym. Sci. 16, 3145 (1972).
32. R. B. Prime and E. Sacher, Polymer 13, 455 (1972).
33. P. G. Babayevsky and J. K. Gillham, J. Appl. Polym. Sci. 17, 2067 (1973).
34. T. Hirai and D. E. Kline, J. Appl. Polym. Sci. 17, 31 (1973).
35. E. Sacher, Polymer 14, 91 (1973).
36. O. A. Whiting and D. E. Kline, J. Appl. Polym. Sci. 18, 1043 (1974).
37. J. K. Gillham, J. A. Benci and A. Noshay, J. Appl. Polym. Sci. 18, 951 (1974).
38. J. P. Bell and W. T. McCarvill, J. Appl. Polym. Sci. 18, 2243 (1974).
39. P. L. Jain, J. Polym. Sci. 31, 210 (1958).
40. D. W. Overall, J. Polym. Sci. B, 1, 37 (1963).
41. M. A. Keenan and D. A. Smith, J. Appl. Polym. Sci. 11, 1009 (1967).
42. D. A. Smith, Amer. Chem. Soc. Div. Org. Coat. Plast. Preprints 27, 321 (1967).
43. T. S. Carswell, "Phenolplasts," Interscience, New York, 1947.
44. T. G. Rochow and F. G. Rowe, Anal. Chem. 21, 261 (1949).
45. R. A. Spurr, E. H. Erath, H. Myers, and D. C. Pease, Ind. Eng. Chem. 49, 1839 (1957).
46. E. H. Erath and R. A. Spurr, J. Polym. Sci. 35, 391 (1959).
47. T. G. Rochow, Anal. Chem. 33, 1810 (1961).
48. E. H. Erath and M. Robinson, J. Polym. Sci. C No. 3, 65 (1963).
49. H. P. Wohnsiedler, J. Polym. Sci. C No. 3, 77 (1963).
50. D. H. Solomon, B. C. Loft, and J. D. Swift, J. Appl. Polym. Sci. 11, 1593 (1967).
51. R. E. Cuthrell, J. Appl. Polym. Sci. 11, 949 (1967).
52. B. E. Nelson and D. T. Turner, J. Polym. Sci. (Phys. Ed.) 10, 2461 (1972).
53. L. G. Bozveliev and M. G. Mihajlov, J. Appl. Polym. Sci. 17, 1963 and 1973 (1973).
54. R. J. Morgan and J. E. O'Neal, Polymer Preprints 16, No. 2, 610 (1975).
55. K. Selby and L. E. Miller, J. Materials Sci. 10, 12 (1975).
56. J. L. Racich and J. A. Koutsky, Bull. Am. Phys. Soc. 20, 456 (1975).
57. R. L. Patrick, in "Treatise on Adhesion and Adhesives" (R. L. Patrick, Ed.), Vol. 3, p. 163. Dekker, New York, 1973.
58. L. J.Broutman and F. J. McGarry, J. Appl. Polym. Sci. 9, 609 (1965).
59. S. Mostovoy and E. J. Ripling, J. Appl. Polym. Sci. 10, 1351 (1966).
60. S. Mostovoy and E. J. Ripling, J. Appl. Polym. Sci. 15, 611 (1971).

61. A. T. DiBennedetto and A. D. Wambach, Int. J. Polym. Mater. 1, 159 (1972).
62. W. D. Bascom, R. L. Cottington, R. L. Jones and P. Peyser, J. Appl. Polym. Sci. 19, 2545 (1975).
63. R. J. Morgan and J. E. O'Neal, Unpublished.
64. J. Murray and D. Hull, J. Polym. Sci. A-2, 8, 1521 (1970).
65. P. Beahan, M. Bevis and D. Hull, J. Materials Sci. 8, 162 (1972).

BOUNDARY LAYERS IN THERMOSETS

James L. Racich and James A. Koutsky
University of Wisconsin-Madison

The two phase morphology of rigid thermosets is depicted, and possible reasons for the change in this morphology near interface are presented and discussed. A consistent relation is observed between nodule size and curing agent concentration for epoxy resins based on the diglycidyl ether of bisphenol A (DGEBA) and cured by tertiary or poly-amines. As the concentration of curing agent increases, the nodule size decreases, and at high concentrations, nodules become less defined. Based on this, suggestions for engineering improved properties into thermoset adhesive and composite systems are presented.

I. INTRODUCTION: PROBLEMS IN THE ENGINEERING OF THERMOSETS

Rigid thermosets are seeing increasing use in their traditional adhesive and binding applications, as well as in the new, so-called second-generation high property composites (e.g., aramid- or inorganic-fiber filled epoxy). Many other large new areas of usage, such as wide-scale replacement of on-site mechanical-fastener assembly of housing structures, are conceivable in the near future.

Despite the considerable body of information available on the chemical and mechanical characterization of thermosetting resins, several significant questions remain in their engineering property prediction. The theoretical strength of cured thermosets has been estimated to be several orders of magnitude higher than any value experimentally obtained (1). Extrapolation of short term adhesive performance to long times has been extremely difficult for these materials, and seldom seems to correlate with actual lab- or weatherexposure data for long times (2-5). One reason for this lack of correlation seems to be unpredictability of attack of the thermoset-adherent interface by the environment. Several studies, indeed, strongly implicate a change in thermoset properties near interfaces (6-10) ("boundary layers") in the explanation of this preferential locus of failure in filled thermosets.

This paper attempts to resolve some of these issues from the viewpoint of micro-morphology.

II. EXPERIMENTAL SYSTEMS AND TECHNIQUES

Table 1 depicts the thermoset systems studied, and Table 2 the substrate systems used. The chemistry of condensation crosslinking of epoxies is complicated (11) and differs depending upon the various thermoset composition and cure recipes used. We note that a wide range of chemical-kinetic and mechanical-property characteristics is represented by these systems.

The bulk of data presented are electron micrographs obtained through two-stage, polyacrylic acid -- platinum/carbon replication of thermoset surfaces. In one-stage replication, the thin Pt-C film is applied directly to the surface, and removed with the mechanical help of a poly-acrylic acid "backing". In two-stage replication, the 25% aqueous solution of polyacrylic acid is the actual replicating medium. One- and two-stage replication methods were found comparable in particle size resolution and qualitative depiction of surfaces. One-stage replication, however, frequently gave higher-resolution images.

III. BULK MORPHOLOGY OF THERMOSETS

As previously described, the apparent bulk structure of rigid thermosets is nodular in character (12). Most nodules seem to be between 100 and 400 Å in size, and generally, but not always, spheroidal in shape. The exception applies to those nodules themselves showing the "dimpled" fine structure previously mentioned. This fine structure results in a spiral shape for these nodules, as shown in Figure 1. Bulk fracture reveals extremely clear, well-defined nodules on either side of the fracture surface. The absence of either a liquid-like or hazy layer on either fracture surface, and the apparent absence of fragments of nodules, suggests that resin fracture is between nodules,

TABLE 1

Thermoset Characterization

A. Chemistry

1 DGEBA (di-glycidyl ether of bisphenol A) resin

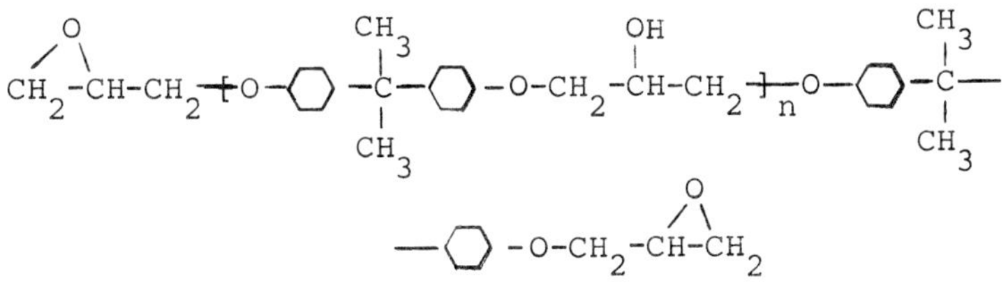

Shell Chemical Co.'s Epon® 828 and Epon® 825 were used. Both resins contain, predominantly, monomeric DGEBA (n = 0). Epon 825 contains a higher percentage of the monomer, and crystallizes more readily.

2 DETA (diethylene triamine) curing agent

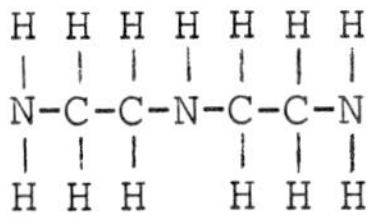

3 BDMA (benzyldimethylamine) curing agent

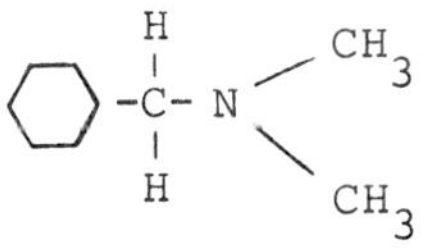

B. Composition and Cure

	Composition		*Cure*
1	*Epon 828, 100 pbw (parts by weight) + DETA, 11 pbw*	1.A.	*2 1/2 to 4 hr at 70-80 C*
			-or-
		B.	*2 1/2 to 4 hr at 70-80 C, then 24 hr at 130-150 C*
2	*Epon 825, 100 pbw + BDMA, 5 pbw (except where noted)*	2.	*18 hr at 80-85 C*

TABLE 2

Substrate Surfaces

	Substrate	Source & Characterization	Preparation	Usage
1.	Hollow glass microspheres	Emerson & Cuming Eccospheres® R, size mostly 40 to 125 μm in diameter	Cleaned in Chromerge® cleaning solution (room temp., > 24 hr stirring), washed with large amounts of distilled water, oven dried.	Spheres added to resin during stir-mixing of the resin components
2.	Silicone rubber	Ted Pella Co. #110 & 111, microtome sample embedding molds. Molds also prepared from Dow Corning Silastic L® resin.	Cleaned with Alconox® detergent, acetone, distilled water	Resin poured into mold cavities. Cured block manipulated out of mold.
3.	Teflon® PTFE film	duPont "TFE"® film, approx. 3 mils thick	Cleaned with Alconox detergent, acetone, distilled water.	Resin applied between PTFE films
4.	Al foil	3 mil smooth Al stock	Cleaned in trichloroethylene, acetone, detergent, distilled water.	Used as adherend. Peeled back, in most cases, to reveal Al-epoxy interface.
5.	Copper wire	#10 gauge electrical wire (with plastic insulation)	Insulation stripped from wire, wire cleaned in trichloroethylene, acetone, detergent, distilled water.	Used as spacer and adherend in several joints.

rather than through them. We also draw from this data the corollary statement that the nodules are higher in nodulus than internodular material, assuming that the resin as a whole fractures through the lowest-modulus region.

Fig. 1. Shape of "Dimpled" Nodules.

Definitive identification of nodules with higher molecular weight material is essential to the selection of a proper model among the many proposed to explain two-phase morphology in thermosets (13-16). One dilemma that the successful model should resolve is the apparent insensitivity of nodule size to post-curing of thermoset resins, seen in our work as well as that of Sukhareva et al. (17). Post-curing is generally accepted to strongly determine mechanical properties (18).

Microscopic examination of a thermoset elastomer supplied by Professor C. W. Macosko (University of Minnesota) did not reveal nodular morphology comparable to that obtained from even partly-cured epoxy thermosets[1]. Erath and Spurr (20) drew similar conclusions from microscopic examination of a silicone resin. Thus, it appears that some unique aspect of rigid thermosets is associated with nodular morphology. Unfortunately, at this stage, we cannot conclusively identify which one, for high overall crosslink density (or low molecular weight between crosslinks), high degrees of intra-molecular (as opposed to intermolecular) crosslinking, and high glass transition temperature of the matrix, could each be identified as the key variable.

[1] (We again mention that structure in amorphous thermosets is markedly more distinct, and usually much larger in size, than that reported by Yeh and others (19) for polymer elastomers and amorphous glasses.)

IV. FORMATION OF BOUNDARY LAYERS AT ADHERENDS OR INTERFACES

Previous studies have implicated the existence of boundary layers in thermosets. Kardos presented morphological evidence in a glass-filled epoxy that could be interpreted in terms of migration of curing agent to the glass-epoxy interface (6). From water diffusion experiments, Kwei (9) and Kumins _et al._ (8) deduced the existence of a region approximately 1000 A thick around filler particles in epoxy resins, the epoxy polymer in this boundary layer having significantly less molecular mobility than that in the bulk. From calculation of viscoelastic relaxation-time spectra in filled epoxies, Lipatov _et al._ (7) notice a similar reduction in molecular mobility in thermoset boundary layers[2].

Microscopic examination of additional thermoset-adherent interfaces and free surfaces leads us to modify previous statements about the effect of inclusions on nodular morphology. We now assert that most of our previous and present micrographic data from epoxy resins is consistent with the concept that nodule size is controlled by catalyst concentration[3] (this idea previously advanced by Kardos) (6). A local deficiency of catalyst relates to large morphology (300-600 Å), while an excess of catalyst relates to small morphology (75-250 Å). This assertion is based on the following data:

1. Free surfaces (of resins cured in contact with air) show larger morphology than that seen on bulk fracture surfaces of the same specimen. Presumably there is loss of catalyst at the free surface (Figure 2).

---

[2]It should be recognized that reduction in molecular mobility near rigid inclusions has been seen in amorphous, non-thermosetting polymers as well (10,21-23).

[3]We use "catalyst" loosely here. In Epon 812-based epoxies, the BDMA is truly present in small quantities, and essentially acts as a catalyst, not entering into the primary-chemical-bonded crosslinked network. However, DGEBA (Epon 825, Epon 828) consumes, via chain termination and other mechanisms, considerable amounts of tertiary (BDMA) or poly-amines (DETA) when used as sole curing agents (24).

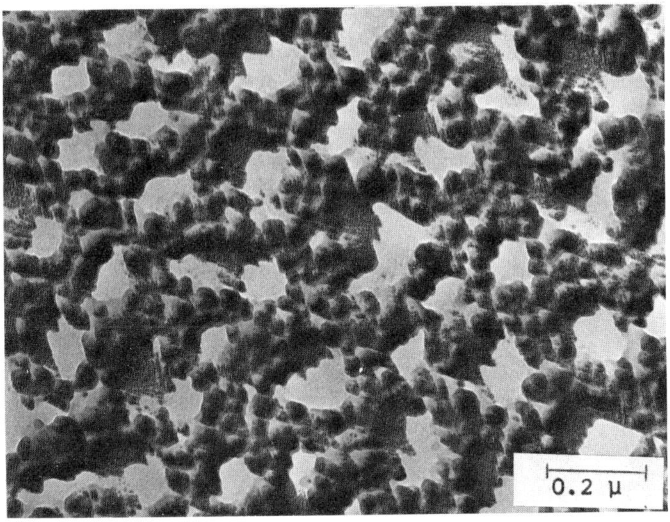

Fig. 2A. Free surface, Epon 825 + 5% BDMA

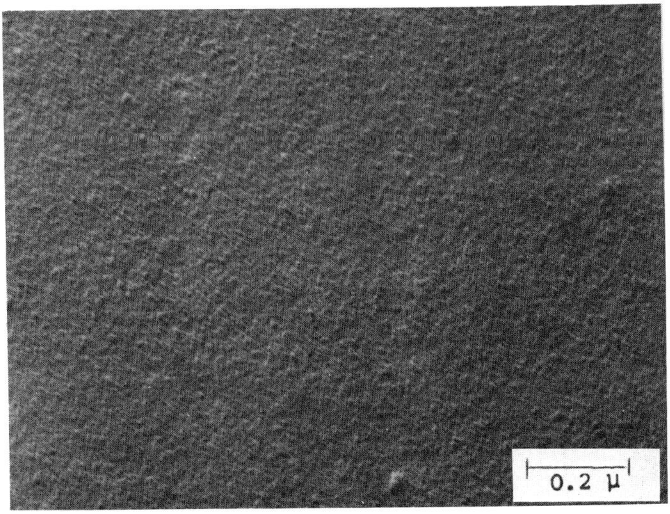

Fig. 2B. Fracture surface, Epon 825 + 5% BDMA

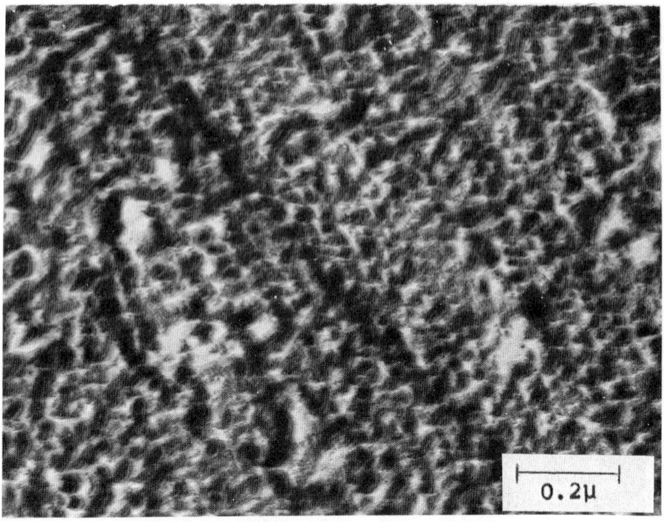

Fig. 3. Fracture surface, epoxy-copper interface, Epon 828 + 11% DETA.

Fig. 4. Free surface, hollow glass-filled epoxy, scratched, Epon 812-based resin (see reference 12). Reprinted by permission of J. Applied Polymer Science.

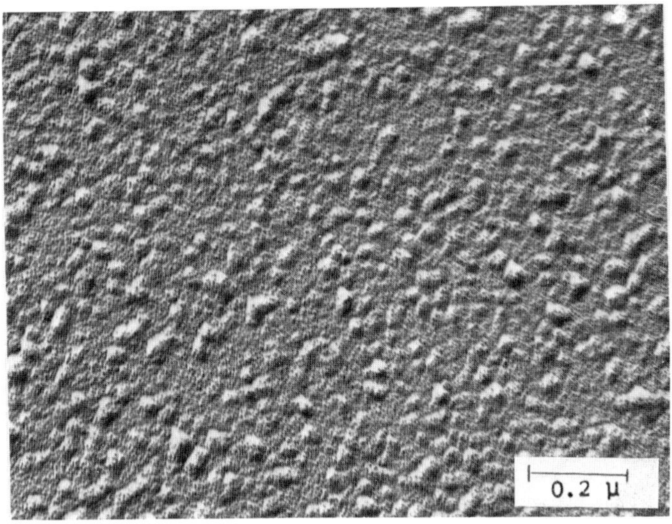

Fig. 5A. Free surface, undercatalyzed epoxy, Epon 825 + 2% BDMA.

Fig. 5B. Free surface, overcatalyzed epoxy, Epon 825 + 20% BDMA.

2. Relatively polar materials, or metal adherends, apparently generate two boundary layers. Directly adjacent to the adherend is a layer or two of closely packed very small nodules (Figure 3), while very slightly further away (~ 1000 A) from the adherend is a layer of larger morphology (previously reported with glass-and-copper-contacted epoxy surfaces (12) and shown in Figure 4). The polar adherend seems to strongly attract catalyst from the resin to the resin-adherend interface, creating a catalyst-rich region directly at this interface, while also apparently depleting catalyst in the adjacent boundary layer. Sukhareva et al. have obtained similar results and made similar interpretations (17).

3. Resins cured with excess catalyst (Figure 5), and resins cured in the presence of saturated vapor of the curing agent (Figure 6), show very small morphology (less than 150 Å). Figure 5 also permits comparison of the widely different morphology exhibited in under-catalyzed and over-catalyzed resins.

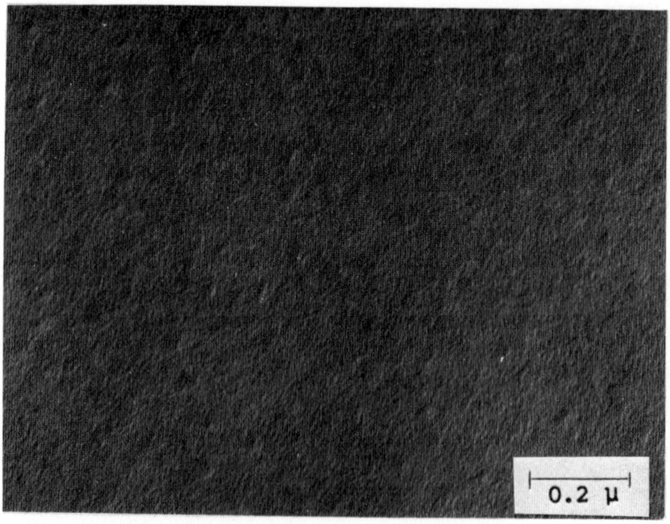

Fig. 6. Fracture surface, epoxy cured in presence of saturated vapor of curing agent (BDMA). Epon 825 + 5% BDMA.

In summary, a schematic plot of nodule size versus curing agent concentration is presented in Figure 7.

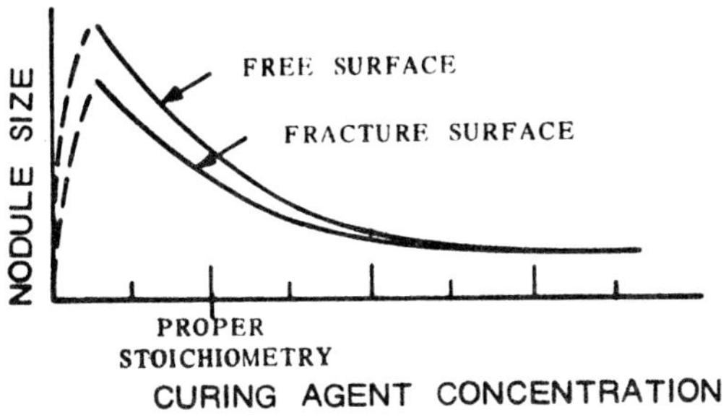

Fig. 7. Nodule Size vs Catalyst Concentration.

Non-microscopic evidence that catalyst concentration can be important and difficult to control include the following:

1. Epoxy resins cure more rapidly when contained in a closed silicone mold, than when contained in an open silicone mold (i.e., a free surface of epoxy exists). The slower cure in an open mold presumably relates to loss of curing agent.

2. One uncatalyzed DGEBA epoxy resin (enclosed in an open silicone mold) was made to cure considerably beyond gelation when it was placed in an atmosphere saturated with BDMA at 80°C. (The free surface and bulk structure of this specimen are shown in Figure 8). The ease of transfer of catalyst <u>into</u> the resin, even through the free surface (which would be expected to cross-link first and form a tough skin), implies the comparable ease with which catalysts may be <u>lost</u> from resins (see also Table 3). Similar conclusions can be drawn from our "parfait"

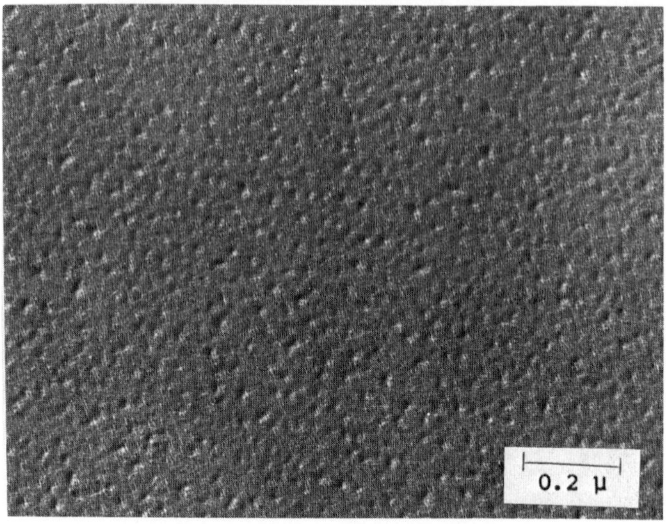

Fig. 8A. Free surface, epoxy cured solely by BDMA vapor, Epon 825.

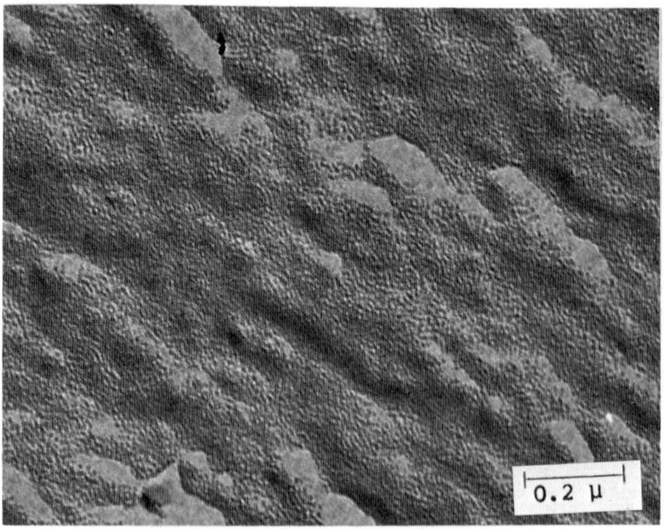

Fig. 8B. Fracture surface, epoxy cured solely by BDMA vapor, Epon 825.

experiments. A layer of BDMA or DETA curing agent was carefully placed over a layer of Epon 825 resin, both within a closed glass tube. A cured layer several millimeters thick was formed with both resins and with 23° and 72°C cures.

TABLE 3

*Vapor-Pressure Estimations for Curing Agents**

T, °C	*P, mm, BDMA*	*P, mm, DETA*
25	1	0.6
50	5	3
80	24	16
150	308	234

estimated by methods of Reid and Sherwood (43) solely on knowledge of boiling temperature at atmospheric pressure.

Other data is more difficult to interpret. Epoxy morphology seen against Teflon sheet (presumed to be largely impermeable to catalyst diffusion) and silicone rubber appears on close examination to be very small and indistinct directly at the interface, while the second boundary layer seems characterized by few, very large nodules (12). The Teflon conceivably is not well wet by the epoxy-catalyst mixture. The silicone rubber probably acts as a semi-permeable barrier to catalyst loss, and the concentration of catalyst at the interface of epoxy contacted with catalyst-swollen silicone may be rather high.

Mechanical tests were not convincing in establishing the magnitude of importance of thermoset boundary layers. Ultimate-shear tests, using the general arrangement of Bell (25,26) (see Figure 9), were performed on various epoxies. Pronounced morphological boundary layers were seen, and the locus of failure was consistently at the boundary layer. However, no relation between ultimate mechanical strength and morphology could be deduced. Torsional pendulum testing of unfilled and glass filled epoxies was also attempted (see Figure 10), with the hope of discovering a relation between morphology and the low temperature transitions (around -50 C) widely reported in DGEBA epoxies (27-31). Unfilled epoxies showed a very

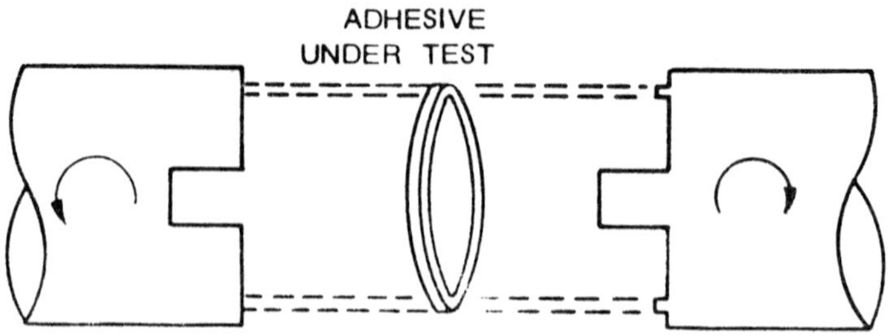

Fig. 9. Ultimate-Shear Test.

"Shear rate"	0.1 to 3.0 °/min
Test environment	72°F, 50% R.H.
Adhesive dimensions:	inner diameter: 1.125" ± .001"
	outer diameter: 1.250" ± .001"
	thickness: .010"
Fixtures:	Type 347 stainless steel, cleaned with acetone, Alconox detergent, distilled water before bonding.

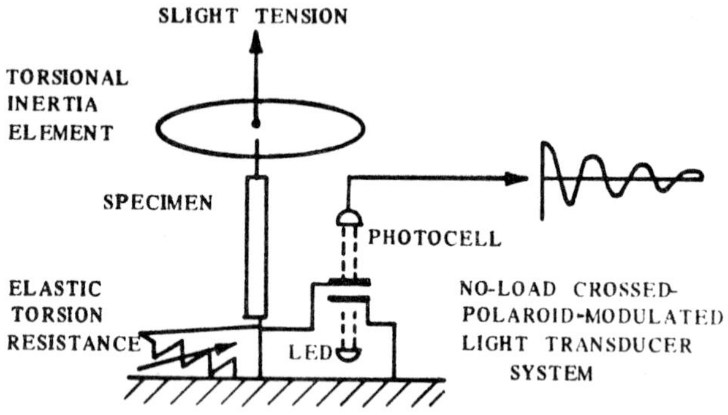

Fig. 10. Freely-Oscillating Torsional Pendulum

Frequency:	0.4 to 1.0 Hz
Temperature	-170 to 125 C
Heating rate:	1.0-1.2°C/min
Specimen dimensions:	.032" x .375" x L
	1.2" < L < 4"
Initial deformation	< 30°
Atmosphere	N_2 gas

broad double peak around -55 and -40 C, while glass filled epoxies showed similar but predictably lower amplitude transitions. Varying degrees of decay of the slope of these damping peaks were noted, but insufficient data were taken for a proper interpretation.

Three reasons for the seeming failure of mechanical tests to reveal much about nodular morphology come to mind. First, the weight fraction of "boundary layer" was very small in both these tests. Second, post curing has been demonstrated to have a strong effect on mechanical properties (18), but (apparently) only a small effect on morphology. Third, Bryant and Dukes (32) have reported considerable plastic strain in ultimate-torsion-strength testing of epoxies. Large degrees of plastic deformation could be expected to strongly determine measured strength values and swamp subtle changes in strength attributable to boundary layer effects. However, our microscopy of these highly crosslinked resins and their boundary layer morphology did not reveal large amounts of plastic deformation.

In summary, we note that high concentrations of curing agent apparently initiate locally high(er) crosslink densities at more sites, resulting in densely packed small nodules. Low concentrations of catalyst, conversely, generate a morphology of large, widely spaced, less closely packed (usually scattered) nodules.

V. MORPHOLOGY AND ADHESION STRENGTH

Bikerman's (33) principal citation of the WBL (weak boundary layer) has been in the context of low molecular weight impurities migrating from the bulk of adhesives and depositing onto adherends. With thermosets, it appears that, with polar adherends and polar, mobile catalysts, a boundary layer can contain highly crosslinked material. Either way, discontinuity of mechanical properties in the boundary region between thermoset matrix and high-modulus reinforcement results in favorable disposition toward boundary layer failure (34-36). Bascom (36) has recently reported a stress focusing phenomenon in adhesive joints suggesting further potential mechanical vulnerability at boundary layers.

Kargin and co-workers (37,38) believe that all "amorphous" polymers can be found in at least two states, one having supermolecular structure (macro-organization of polymer chain configurations), and the other having no such structure. Further, he asserts that the state of the smallest, or of no supermolecular structure generally give the best properties, e.g., strength, durability, etc. Our findings on rigid thermoset morphology seem consistent with Kargin's ideas, and we are tempted to propose that the perfectly formed condensation crosslinked network would have no nodular morphology. Unfortunately, there are two problems. First, Pt-C surface replication does not permit easy resolution of structure below 75 Å, so that if we <u>had</u> achieved a non-nodular, featureless structure, it would have gone undetected. Second, our micrographs showed non-zero nodule sizes even in the presence of great excesses of catalyst (see Figure 5B, for instance).

Regardless of the possibility of existence of a non-nodular, perfectly formed network, our data reveal a marked correlation between nodule size and curing agent concentration, and strongly suggest that control of the curing agent concentration, so as to obtain uniform, small morphology, should be tractable. These assertions are consistent with the following evidence:

1. Small nodules have been seen

    a) in the bulk of resins, where the catalyst stoichiometry is presumably near the intended, optimum level

    b) at interfaces with high-surface-energy adherends generally accepted to be bonded strongly by expoxies

    c) throughout resins cured with an excess of catalyst.

2. Large nodules have been seen

    a) near high-energy-substrate interfaces, where it is possible that the chemisorption or physisorption of the substrate could have depleted catalyst from far into the resin

    b) in the bulk of a specimen cured solely by BDMA vapor.

VI. CONTROL OF BULK AND BOUNDARY LAYER MORPHOLOGY

We now consider those variables which, by implication of either theory or experiment, should have an effect on rigid-thermoset morphology. We review, first, the factors associated with the perfection of the thermoset network in the bulk, and then discuss the perturbations on this perfection of the bulk caused by inclusions or interfaces.

A. Bulk Network Perfection

Solomon (15) has described how rates of crosslinking higher than the rates of diffusion necessary to establish thermodynamic equilibrium among reaction products and reactants (i.e., oligomers and monomers) can result in non-homogeneous, imperfect networks incapable of reaching a complete extent of reaction. Megson (39) and Pritchett (40) have also established that steric hindrance can have an analogous effect, namely, keeping condensable reactive groups from meeting. On both accounts, then, the micro- and macro-mixing of resin and catalyst (i.e., maintenance of concentration equilibrium among reaction products and reactants) should be of concern.

Inadequate macro-dispersion of catalyst into resin can result in large concentration gradients. Proper design for micro-mixing must consider the molecular mobility of the resin (i.e., molecular configuration, viscosity, and molecular weight) as well as that of the catalyst. The size of the catalyst molecule, its vapor pressure, its dispersive-polar interaction-energy parameters, and its reactive functionality are interrelated variables important in micro-mixing optimization.

Other parameters for design of a high degree of network perfection are the overall level of catalyst concentration and the reaction chemistry. Optimal thermoset properties are obtained with stoichiometric ratios of curing agent and resin (41). Maintenance of this ratio throughout the bulk resin is an obvious design goal. The most apparent means is the addition of the appropriate amount of catalyst. However, loss or addition of catalyst may occur through absorption by porous substrates, evaporation from free surfaces, or "conduction" of catalyst along paths of preferential exit (such as continuous fiber reinforcements in composites). Reaction chemistry relates to network perfection in several ways. Epoxy thermosets are subject to competing chemical mechanisms of cure, each with subsequent differences in intra- or intermolecular cross-linking, ester or ether linkage formation, and extents of steric hindrance. The chemical nature of functionality, and the multi-functionality of thermoset constituents can possibly determine the amount of network perfection possible.

B. Effect of Inclusions and Interfaces

The mutual interaction of filler, catalyst, and resin should also be considered in the control of boundary layers. Wetting of inclusions by the adhesive is prerequisite to the generation of a strong bond and "proper" interfacial morphology. However, if the liquid surface tension of the catalyst and resin are markedly different, chemical segregation of the two at the interface may result, with possible deleterious effects on interface properties. A boundary layer likewise formed at a substrate whose surface energy was so high as to adsorb out catalyst from the bulk of the resin, as glass apparently is able to do. However, such strongly interactive substrates may also chemically immobilize some active groups (possible with a glass surface rich in hydroxyl groups).

VII. OTHER RIGID THERMOSET SYSTEMS

We have also studied the morphology of thermosets prepared from triglycidyl ethers of glycerol (Shell Chemical Co.'s Epon 812, cured by acid anhydrides and catalyzed by tertiary amines), and from phenolic and urea-modified phenolic resins. The three and four-component glycerol-based epoxies (see ref. 12 for details) cure by much more complex mechanisms. We hesitate to relate cured-thermoset morphology to catalyst (BDMA) concentration for this reason.

Phenolic resins cure by mechanisms (42) inappropriately depicted by those used in our discussion of epoxies. Proper extrapolation of our analysis to phenolic systems hinges on the isolation and identification of the network parameter(s) directly related to nodular morphology. However, the size of morphology in the bulk of these other thermosets, and the effect of high-energy and low-energy substrates on this morphology, are nearly identical to those seen with DGEBA-amine epoxies.

The correspondence of nodule size across systems of such different chemistry remains a mystery, and it suggests some equivalence in reaction conditions during the early stages of crosslinking. Another mystery continues to be the apparent lack of small-angle x-ray scattering from DGEBA-amine systems demonstrated to give well-defined electron-microscopic structure (12).

VIII. CONCLUSIONS

We have demonstrated that curing agent concentration strongly affects the character of the bulk and interfacial two-phase morphology in DGEBA epoxy resins cured solely with tertiary or poly-amines. We suggest that systems demonstrating the smallest morphology may have the most perfectly formed network and may demonstrate the highest adhesion strengths. These suggestions are highly tentative, and definitive relationship of molecular-weight inhomogeneities during cure with nodular morphology, and conclusive mechanical characterization of thermosets known to be different in nodular morphology must be demonstrated before the suggestions become technologically useful.

IX. ACKNOWLEDGEMENTS

We gratefully recognize the financial and technological support received from the U.S. Forest Products Laboratory, U.S. Dept. of Agriculture. Drs. Robert Gillespie, Harold Tarkow, Daniel Caulfield, and Irving Sachs have provided invaluable FPL input to this project. We also thank the Weyerhaueser Company for financial support.

X. REFERENCES

1. T. S. Carswell, "Phenoplasts", p 141, Interscience, New York, 1947.
2. R. H. Gillespie, Forest Products J., 15(9), 369 (1965).
3. R. H. Gillespie, Forest Products J., 18(8), 35 (1968).
4. A. F. Lewis, Adhesives Age, 15(6), 38 (1972).
5. "Characteristics of Load-Bearing Sandwich Panels for Housing", Ch. 8 ("Durability"). NTIS Document PB-220-899/9--1973.
6. J. L. Kardos, Trans. N.Y. Acad. of Sciences, II, 35(2), 136 (1973).
7. Yu. S. Lipatov, V. F. Babich, and V. F. Rosovizky, J. Appl. Polym. Sci., 20, 1787 (1976).

8. C. A. Kumins and J. Roteman, J. Polym. Sci., A1, 527 (1963).
9. T. K. Kwei, J. Polym. Sci., A3, 3229 (1965).
10. J. A. Manson and E. H. Chiu, Polymer Preprints, 14, 469 (1973).
11. Y. Tanaka and T. F. Mika, in "Epoxy Resins: Chemistry and Technology" (C. A. May and Y. Tanaka, Eds), Ch 3. Marcel Dekker, New York, 1973.
12. J. L. Racich and J. A. Koutsky, J. Appl. Polym. Sci., 20(8), 0000 (1976).
13. R. Houwink, Trans. Faraday Soc., 36, 22 (1936).
14. H. Stäger, R. Sänger, and W. Siegfried, Helv. Phys. Acta, 12, 561 (1939).
15. D. H. Solomon, J. Macromol. Sci. (Rev.), C1, 179 (1967).
16. S. S. Labana, S. Newman, and A. J. Chompff, in "Polymer Networks" (A. J. Chompff and S. Newman, Eds.), p. 453. Plenum Press, New York, 1971.
17. L. A. Sukhareva, V. A. Voronkov, and P. I. Zubov, Vysokomol. soedin, A11, 407 (1969).
18. J. Delmonte, in "Epoxy Resins: Chemistry and Technology" (C. A. May and Y. Tanaka, Eds.), pp. 611-612. Marcel Dekker, New York, 1973.
19. G. S. Y. Yeh, CRC Critical Revs. in Macromol. Sci., 1(2), 173 (1972).
20. E. H. Erath and R. A. Spurr, J. Polym. Sci., 35, 391 (1959).
21. Yu. S. Lipatov, E. G. Moisya, and G. M. Semenovich, Polymer, 18, 582 (1975).
22. R. J. Morgan, J. Mat. Sci., 9, 1219 (1974).
23. S. Kaufman, W. P. Slichter, and S. D. Davis, J. Polym. Sci., A2, 9, 829 (1971).
24. H. Lee and K. Neville, "Handbook of Epoxy Resins", p. 5-5, McGraw-Hill, New York, 1967.
25. C. J. Lin and J. P. Bell, J. Appl. Polym. Sci., 16, 1721 (1972).
26. W. T. McCarvill and J. P. Bell, J. Adhesion, 6, 185 (1974).
27. A. S. Kenyon and L. E. Nielsen, J. Macromol. Sci., A3, 2, 275 (1969).
28. T. K. Kwei, J. Polym. Sci., A2, 4, 943 (1966).
29. E. Cuddihy and J. Moacanin, J. Polym. Sci., A2, 8, 1627 (1970).
30. D. E. Kline, J. Polym. Sci., 47, 237 (1960).
31. F. R. Dammont and T. K. Kwei, J. Polym. Sci., A2, 5, 761 (1967).
32. R. W. Bryant and W. A. Dukes, in "Adhesion: Fundamentals and Practice", p. 230. Gordon and Breach, New York, 1969.

33. J. J. Bikerman, J. Adhesion, 3, 333 (1972).
34. L. H. Sharpe, J. Adhesion, 4, 51 (1972).
35. R. J. Good, J. Adhesion, 4, 133 (1972).
36. W. D. Bascom, C. O. Timmons, and R. L. Jones, J. Materials Sci., 10, 1037 (1975).
37. V. A. Kargin, Russian Chemical Revs., 35, 427 (1966).
38. A. N. Neverov, N. A. Birkina, Yu. V. Zherdev, and V. A. Kozlov, Vysokomol. soedin, A10, 463 (1968).
39. N. J. L. Megson, "Phenolic Resin Chemistry", pp. 10-11, 233-239. Academic Press, New York, 1958.
40. E. G. K. Pritchett, Chem. Ind., 1949, 25.
41. H. Lee and K. Neville, op. cit., p. 7-7.
42. N. J. L. Megson, "Phenolic Resin Chemistry", Academic Press, New York, 1958.
43. R. C. Reid and T. K. Sherwood, "The Properties of Gases and Liquids", 2nd edition, Ch. 4. McGraw-Hill, New York, 1966.

MECHANICAL BEHAVIOUR OF POLY(2-HYDROXYETHYLMETHACRYLATE)-GLASS BEAD COMPOSITES

L. Nicolais
University of Naples

J. Kolarik and J. Janacek
Czechoslovak Academy of Sciences

The mechanical and dynamic relaxation behaviour of model two-phase system poly(2-hydroxyethylmethacrylate)-glass beads was studied by means of an Instron machine and a free oscillating torsional pendulum. The effect of the filler content on the storage and loss moduli of composites could be described in terms of the modified Kerner equation in complex form. At temperature below the glass transition temperature of the matrix, the agreement between experimental and theoretical data was satisfactory after correction to thermally induced stress due to different thermal expansion coefficients of matrix and filler. In presence of filler the capacity of matrix to store and dissipate energy increases, but the character of molecular motions underlying the dispersion observed is preserved because the temperature of dispersions remains unchanged. Tensile properties and stress relaxation of these materials at different filler content have been studied below and above Tg both in the dry and the equilibrium water-swollen state.

I. INTRODUCTION

Composites consisting of a polymer matrix and a particulate filler can be regarded as ordinary multiphase polymer systems. A number of equations based on theoretical models (1-5) were derived in order to calculate their properties, such as the modulus of elasticity, mechanical damping, electrical and thermal conductivity, etc. from the respective properties of the components. However, verification of the models and their further refinement requires extensive and reliable experimental data. So far rather few data have been collected on particulate composites, where the matrix and filler are in the glassy state. It has been the objective of this work to find out what effect the volume fraction of glass beads has on the temperature and intensity of the PHEMA dispersions and on the viscoelastic behaviour in the dry and swollen state.

II. EXPERIMENTAL

The samples were prepared by the crosslinking polymerization of 2-hydroxyethylmethacrylate with 1.5% by wt. of ethylene dimethacrylate as the crosslinking agent; 0.5% benzoyl peroxide related to monomer was used as the initiator of radical polymerization. The polymerization proceeded at 90°C until a sufficiently viscous pregel was obtained, such as to prevent sedimentation of glass beads during subsequent operations. The polymerization was then stopped by fast cooling of the pregel. A given amount of glass beads (Ballotini Europe type, 3000 CP/01, 10, 20, 30 and 40 vol. parts related to the dry polymer) cleaned and sieved (spheres with diameter below 30 mm were used) was added to the pregel and the mixture was mechanically stirred for three minutes. The polymerization at 80°C in an inert CO_2 atmosphere was completed within an hour.

The samples used for stress relaxation and dynamic mechanical measurements were cut from filled plates swollen in water to equilibrium in the shape of strips 150 x 10 x 1 mm in size with two indicated points for optical measurements of deformation which in all cases was $\varepsilon = 0.14$ and which was attained at the rate of deformation $\dot{\varepsilon} = 9\ \text{min}^{-1}$. The samples for tensile measurements were cut in the shape of dumbbells, the width and length of the working part of the samples were 4.1 and 22.5 mm respectively. All samples were then extracted with distilled water at 100°C for 8 h. The samples intended for use in the swollen state were swollen in water to equilibrium while the others were dried to constant weight over P_2O_5 at a temperature c. 90°C; before measurement the samples were annealed at 130-140°C and slowly cooled to room temperature.

The dynamic mechanical properties were measured with a torsional pendulum having digital recording of free damped oscillations (6); an average increase in temperature with time was 1°C/2 min.

Stress relaxation and stress-strain curves were measured by means of the universal Instron apparatus. During measurements the swollen samples were immersed in distilled water while the dry samples were kept in paraffin oil. The temperature was maintained with an accuracy of 1°C. The temperature range was 5-80°C for swollen samples and 110-170°C for dry samples.

The glass transition temperatures of PHEMA filled with various amounts of glass beads were recorded by means of a differential scanning calorimeter (Perkin-Elmer DSC-1) at a heating rate of 16°C/min.

The degree of swelling in water, v_2, was determined by using the relationship $v_2 = (G_d/\rho d)/(G_s/\rho_s)$, where G_d, G_s are weights and ρ_d, ρ_s are densities of dry and swollen samples respectively. The equilibrium degree of swelling of a filled system related to the pure polymer, v_2^P, was defined by $v_2^P = [(G_d/\rho_d)-(G_f/\rho_f)]/[(G_s/\rho_s)-(G_f/\rho_f)]$, where G_f is the weight of the filler in the sample and ρ_f is its density (for glass beads, ρ_f is its density (for glass beads, ρ_f = 2.45 g/cm^3). The sample densities were determined by double weighing: the dry samples were weighed in cyclohexane and in air, the swollen ones in water and in air.

III. RESULTS AND DISCUSSION

A. Time Dependent Moduli in the Dry and Swollen States

By using the time-temperature superposition principle (7) of stress relaxation moduli E(t) the data were reduced to form a single generalized curve shown in Fig. 1.

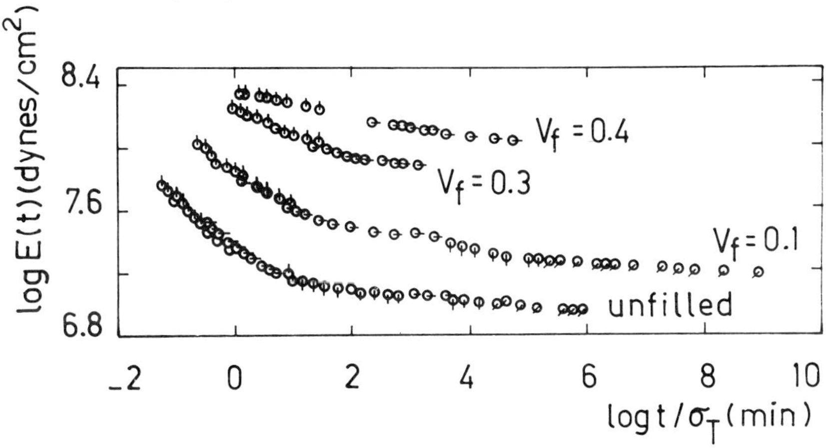

Fig. 1. Relaxation Master curves for dry PHEMA-glass bead composites at various filler content, v_f. Experimental temperatures T: (⦶) 110°; (⦶) 117°; (⦶) 125°; (⦶)135°; (⦶) 145°; (⦶) 170°. The reference temperature is 110°C.

In Table 1 the shift factors used for this superposition are reported.

The reinforcement effect of the filler is time-dependent above the glass transition temperature. Similarly, Kraus et al. (8) observed for the styrene-butadiene rubber filled with polystyrene that the filler leads to a broadening of the main transition region.

TABLE 1
Shift Factors, log a_T, Used for Time Temperature Superposition

V_f	log a_T at various temperatures, °C						
	110	117	125	135	145	170	Tg°C
0	0	0.654	1.431	2.176	3.176	5.176	106[a]
0.1	0	-	1.698	-	4.398	6.654	109
0.3	0	-	1.845	-	-	-	113
0.4	0	-	3.397	-	-	-	113

[a]data obtained using the Clash-Berg torsional stiffness tester

The effect of the filler upon the elastic modulus of the matrix has been predicted by a number of various theoretical relationships already summarized by Chen (9).

In Fig. 2 exp. data are compared with the theoretical curve obtained from Takayanagi's model (4) which has been used successfully earlier for the description of the properties of polymerix mixtures. The equation for such a model is

$$E_c = \left[\frac{\Phi}{(1 - \lambda)E_o + \lambda E_f} + \frac{1 - \Phi}{E_f} \right]^{-1} \qquad (1)$$

E_f is the modulus of the filler, λ and Φ are parameters representing the state of the mixture, of which only one is independent while the other must be calculated from the relationship $\lambda\Phi = v_f$. In Fig. 2 predicted time-dependent moduli $E_c(t)$ and $E_o(t)$ (Eq. 1) using values $\Phi = 0.610$, 0.867 and 0.916 for $v_f = 0.1$, 0.3 and 0.4 are plotted. The same Figure also gives theoretical dependencies obtained from Eq. (1) for special values

$$\lambda = (2 + 3v_f)/5 \quad \text{and} \quad \Phi = 5v_f/(2 + 3v_f) \qquad (2)$$

which were derived for spherical filler particles from the condition that Kerner's equation (5) and Eq. (1) should yield identical results at identical times. However, as has been found by Kraus (8), the use of such values of the parameters λ and Φ does not provide good agreement with the experimental data. It can also be pointed out that predictions based on Kerner's equation and on the Hashin-Shtrikman (10) theory are virtually identical. Thus, best results were obtained by using suitable chosen values of the parameters and of Takayanagi's model.

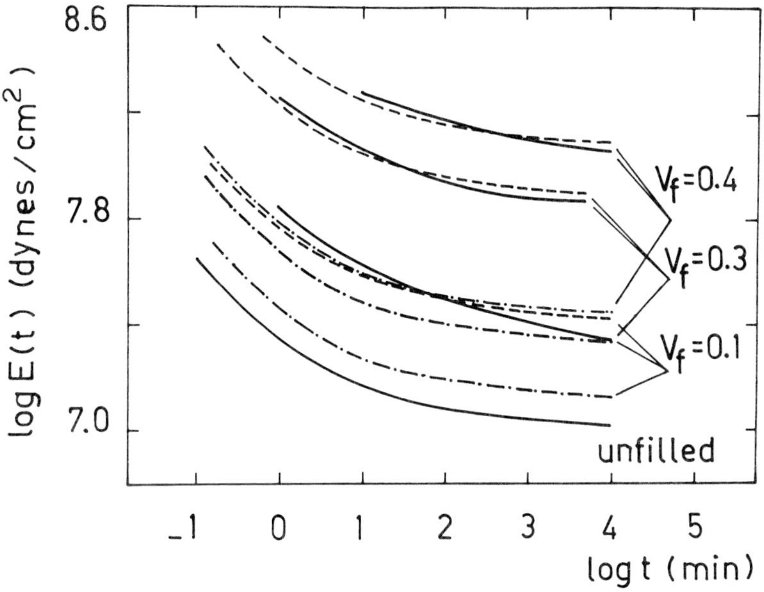

Fig. 2. Log E(t) vs. log t. Comparison of measured (------) (cf. Fig. 1) and calculated by means of Kerner's theory (-.-.-) and calculated using Takayanagi's (- - - -) values.

In order to investigate the effect of filler on the chain mobility of polymer, the glass transition temperature of the system PHEMA-glass beads was measured; the results are summarized in Table 1. Small differences between the observed Tg values are probably due to changes in the specific heat and thermal conductivity of the system and not to changes in chain mobility or in the free volume. Similar conclusions were reached also for other heterogeneous systems (11).

Effect of filler concentration on E_c/E_o in the dry and swollen state.

Fig. 3 contains values of the relative moduli E_c/E_o of dry PHEMA together with those calculated from Kerner's equation (5). Similarly to the results of stress relaxation, the theoretical values are lower than the experimental ones. It seems that for the composites system investigated in this paper the effect of reinforcement due to the filler is always stronger than the values predicted by the existing theories. Analogous results can be obtained for the results published in (12) and concerning filled PHEMA-SiO_2 systems. Figure 3 again presents elastic moduli of dry PHEMA-glass bead

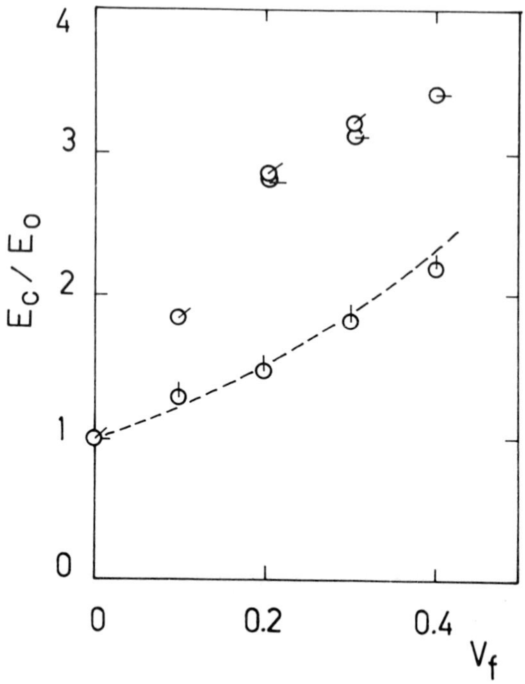

Fig. 3. E_c/E_o plotted vs. filler content for dry PHEMA-glass bead composites. Experimental temperatures T: (ɸ) 50°; (ɣ) 145°; (φ) 170°C. The dashed line corresponds to Kerner's equation.

composites obtained at T = 50°C, i.e., in the glassy state, along with the results of Kerner's equation which indicates that in this region Kerner's equation very adequately describe values of the initial modulus.

The dependencey of Young's modulus on the filler content for the swollen systems PHEMA-glass beads is given in Fig. 4 v_f' is defined by:

$$v_f' = \frac{v_f}{1 + (1-v_f)\left[(1-v_2^P)/v_2^P\right]} \qquad (3)$$

in which v_f is the volume fraction of beads in the dry filled polymer. In this figure it is shown that the increasing filler fraction leads to a decrease in the moduli. This behaviour can be described by Kerner's equation modified for a system in which the filler has zero modulus. This result can be explained by a stress analysis around the inclusions (12,13). In fact due to the swelling of the polymer, tensile

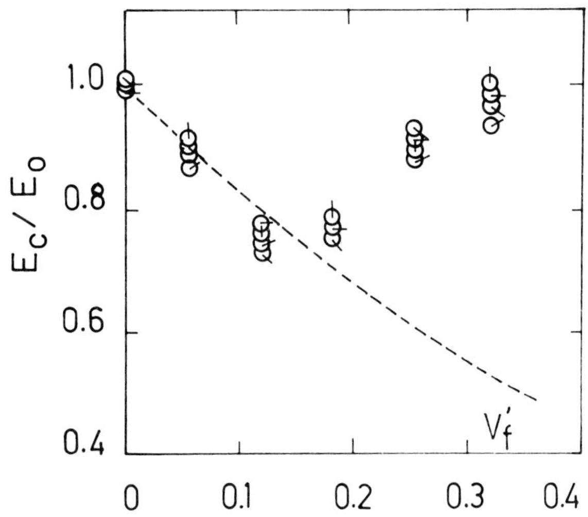

Fig. 4. E_c/E_o *plotted vs. filler content for swollen PHEMA-glass bead composites. Experimental temperatures T: (⦶) 4°; (⊘) 25°; (⊖) 46°; (Q) 80°C. The dashed line corresponds to modified Kerner's equation (cf. text).*

stresses are built up at the filler-matrix interface causing dewetting of the filler and consequently a decrease in the modulus. It may be assumed that this phenomenon is dependent on the size of the filler.

B. Effect of Thermally Induced Stress

The level of the storage modulus of composites increases with the content of glass beads within the whole temperature range of the glassy state investigated. At the same time the filler modifies the shape of the temperature dependency of the storage modulus, so that the relative modulus $G'_{rs} = G'_{cs}/G'_m$ (index m denotes the unfilled matrix) decreases with decreasing temperature. The cause of this frequent phenomenon is seen (13-15) in a thermally induced stress arising in the composite during cooling because of the different thermal expansion coefficients of components. Under these assumptions, the following equation has been derived (13) for the temperature dependency of the relative modulus

$$\frac{d(G'_{cs}/G'_m)}{dT} = K(G'_c/G'_m)\frac{(\alpha_m - \alpha_b)\ f(v_f)}{\varepsilon_{ym}} \qquad (4)$$

where G'_{cs} and G'_c respectively denote the shear modulus of the composite in the presence and absence of the thermally induced stress, α_m and α_b are the linear thermal expansion coefficients of matrix and filler, ε_{ym} is the matrix elongation at yield, and K is a factor dependent of the shape of the filler particles. K = 0.71 (13).

Since at temperatures deeply below the glass transition temperature Tg the samples are destructed before reaching the yield point, ε_{ym} should be regarded only as a parameter of eq. (4) expressing the decrease in the matrix modulus with increasing deformation. Such ε_{ym} is not connected with the real ultimate properties of PHEMA and their dependency on temperature. With respect to data published for polymethacrylates 16 we chose ε_{ym} = 0.03. The values calculated by means of eq. (16) in ref. (13) were used for the function $f(v_f)$.

Although only approximate values of the above terms were used, the good agreement between the experimental and calculated $d(G'_{cs}/G'_m)/dT$ values (Fig. 5) suggest that the above causes of the temperature dependence of G'_{rs} included in eq. (4) can be regarded as real.

C. Effect of Filler on the Storage and Loss Moduli

To correlate the data obtained from dynamic mechanical measurement a modified Kerner equation (17) has been used in complex form

$$\frac{G^*_c}{G^*_m} = \frac{1 + A\,B^*\,v_f}{1 - B^*\psi\,v_f} \qquad (5)$$

where $A = (7-5\nu_m)/(8-10\nu_m)$ $B^*=[(G^*_f/G^*_m)-1]/[(G^*_f/G^*_m)+A]$ and the empirical function $\psi = 1 + [(1 - v_{max})/v^2_{max}]v_f$ represents correction to the maximum possible filling. Using simplifying assumptions $G''_f = 0$, $G'_f = 0$, $G'_f \geq 10\,G'_m$, $G'_m \geq 10\,G''_m$ one can with good accuracy, write

$$B^* = B' + iB'' = [(G'_b/G'_m) - 1]/[(G'_b/G'_m) + A]$$
$$-i[(A + 1)(G''_m/G'_b)]/[1+(AG'_m/G'_b]^2$$

and from Eq. (5) derive approximate relationships:

$$G'_c = G'_m = \frac{1 + A\,B'v_f}{1 - B'\psi\,v_f} \qquad (6)$$

$$G''_c = G''_m\,\frac{1 + A\,B'v_f}{1 - B'\psi\,v_f} - G'_m\,\frac{(A + \psi)B'v_f}{(1 - B'\psi\,v_f)^2} \qquad (7)$$

$$tg\delta_c = tg\delta_m - \frac{(A + \psi)B''v_f}{(1 + A\,B'v_f)(1 - B'\psi\, v_f} \quad (8)$$

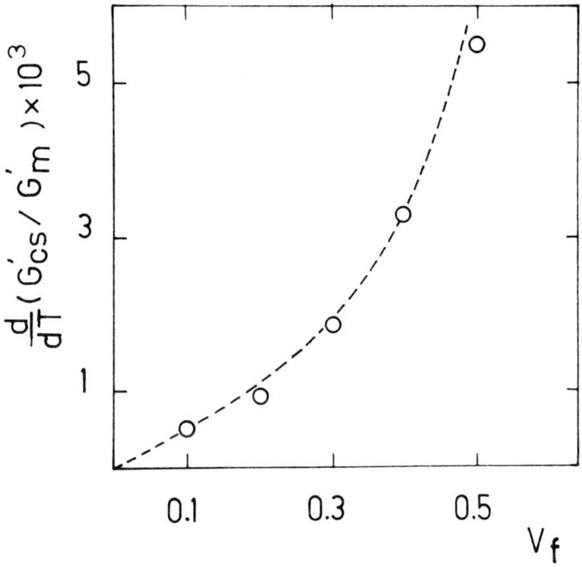

Fig. 5. Effect of filler content on slope of temperature dependence of relative modulus of composites.

In Fig. 6 experimental G'_c data are reported together with the plot of Equation 5.

The glass beads in PHEMA also considerably influence the magnitude of energy losses (Fig. 7): the height of the γ maximum increases from 15.7 x 10^8 dyn/cm^2 for composites with the filler fraction $v_f \geq 0.2$; at temperature above -100°C one can see an increase in the level of the loss modulus with the filler content. Thus, it is obvious that the dissipating capacity of the composite is enhanced with the filler content similarly to the storage modulus. To compare the experimental values of the loss modulus and tgδ with the theoretical ones, calculations were carried out using eqs. (7) and (8) for three characteristic temperatures; Tγ, -60°C (at which the loss modulus passes through a minimum), and Tα. As follows from Table 2, calculated G''_γ's increase with the filler content and are all higher than the experimental ones. To eliminate the effect of thermally iduced stress, calculated $\bar{G}''_\gamma$'s were multiplied by the factor $G'_{rs}(T_\gamma)/G'_r(T_\alpha)$ expressing the decrease in the relative modulus of the composite owing to the thermally induced stress. The corrected loss moduli $(\bar{G}''_\gamma)_{cor}$ then agree well with the experimental data (Table 2). A similar situation is found for the loss modulus $\bar{G}''(-60°)_{cor} = \bar{G}''(-60°C)\ \chi\ [G'_{rs}(-60°C)/G'_r(T_\alpha)]$ at the minimum of mechanical losses.

TABLE 2

Parameters of Dispersions of Poly(2-hydroxyethyl Methacrylate) - Glass Beads Composites

Low-Temperature Dispersion				
v_f [a]	T_γ [b] °C	$\bar{G}''_\gamma$ 10^{-8} dyn/cm^2	$\bar{G}''_\gamma$ 10^{-8} [d] dyn/cm^2	$(\bar{G}''_\gamma)_{cor}10^{-8}$ [e] dyn/cm^2
0	-132	15.7	15.7	15.7
0.1	-132	17.2	17.9	16.7
0.2	-130	20.0	20.9	18.5
0.3	-131	20.3	24.6	20.1
0.4	-130	19.5	29.1	21.0
0.5	-130	21.0	33.5	21.0

tg^δ_γ 10^2 [c]	$\bar{tg}^\delta_\gamma$ 10^2 [f]	Q_γ [i]	G"(-60°C)10^{-8} [c] dyn/cm^2	G"(-60°C)$_{cor}$ 10^{-8} [e] dyn/cm^2
5.2	5.2	0.180	4.0	4.0
4.8	4.9	0.175	5.6	4.5
4.7	4.7	0.180	6.0	5.1
3.9	4.4	0.170	7.0	6.0
3.6	3.9	-.175	7.5	6.6
3.2	3.2	0.185	8.5	8.2

a. volume fraction of glass beads in composite
b. temperature dispersion read off for the loss peak
c. experimentally determined height of loss maximum or minimum
d. value calculated using eq. (7)
e. corrected value (explanation in text)
f. value calculated using eq. (8)
g. value obtained by extrapolation of experimental data
h. value calculated using eq. (6)
i. parameter of the distribution of relaxation times (explanation in text.

Table 2 (continued)

Parameters of Dispersions of Poly(2-hydroxyethyl Methacrylate - Glass Beads Composites

Main Dispersion

v_f [a]	T_γ [b] °C	G'_{re} [g]	$\bar{G}'_r$ [h]	$G''(T)\ 10^{-8}$ [c] dyn/cm	$G''_r(T)$ [c]	$\bar{G}''(T)\ 10_2^{-8}$ [d] dyn/cm
0	103	1.00	1.00	11	1.00	11.0
0.1	102	1.45	1.22	18	1.6	13.4
0.2	102	1.70	1.53	19	1.7	16.6
0.3	101	2.20	1.99	27	2.5	21.4
0.4	102	2.70	2.76	30	3.7	29.2
0.5	104	3.50	4.31	45	4.1	45.0

a. volume fraction of glass beads in composite
b. temperature dispersion read off for the loss peak
c. experimentally determined height of loss maximum or minimum
d. value calculated using eq. (7)
e. corrected value (explanation in text)
f. value calculated using eq. (8)
g. value obtained by extrapolation of exp. data
h. value calculated using eq. (6)
i. parameter of the distribution of relaxation times (explanation in text)

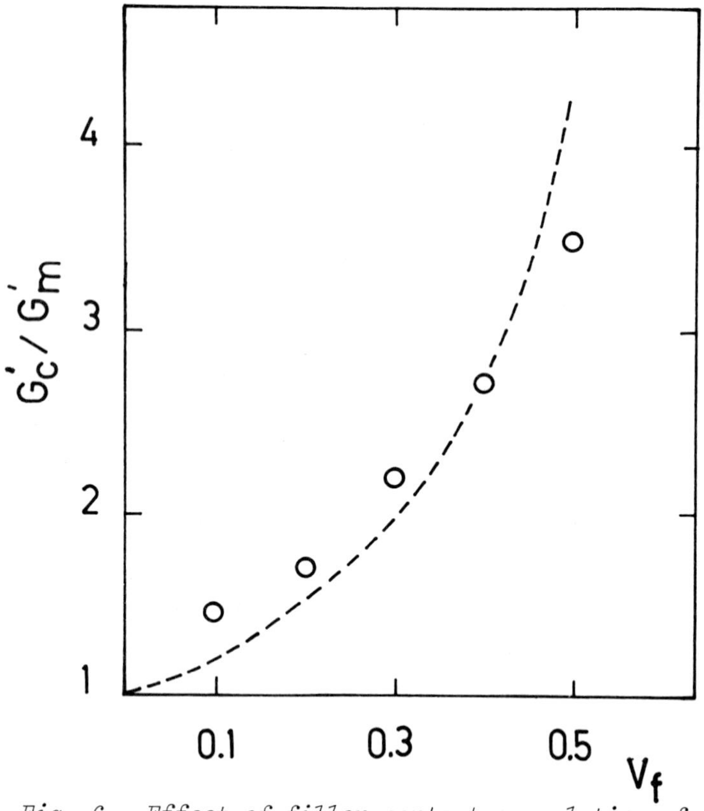

Fig. 6. Effect of filler content on relative of composites.

It can be said consequently that the thermally induced stress depresses the corresponding moduli G'_{cs} and G''_{cs} to the same extent. This is also indicated by the fact that $tg\delta_c = G''_{cs}/G'_{cs}$ (Table 2) fits in fairly well with the theoretical data without correction. As follows from Table 2, the relative magnitude of α of the loss maximum $G''_r(T\alpha) = G''_c(T\alpha)/G''_m(T\alpha)$ increases with the filler content virtually identically with the extrapolated relative modulus G'_{re}. Only for v_f = 0.5 $G''_r(T\alpha)$ is higher than G'_{re} and approaches the theoretical values. The satisfactory agreement between the experimental and calculated data for $G''_r(T\alpha)$ also justifies the assumption that thermally induced stress is negligible at $T\alpha$.

Data in a number of papers (14, 15, 17-20) indicate that $tg\delta_c$'s of filled systems are higher than corresponds to the volume fraction of the matrix in composites in which the filler particles do not participate in the dissipation of mechanical energy. In other words it means that the empirical equation (17,20)

$$tg\delta_c = v_m\, tg\delta_m \qquad (9)$$

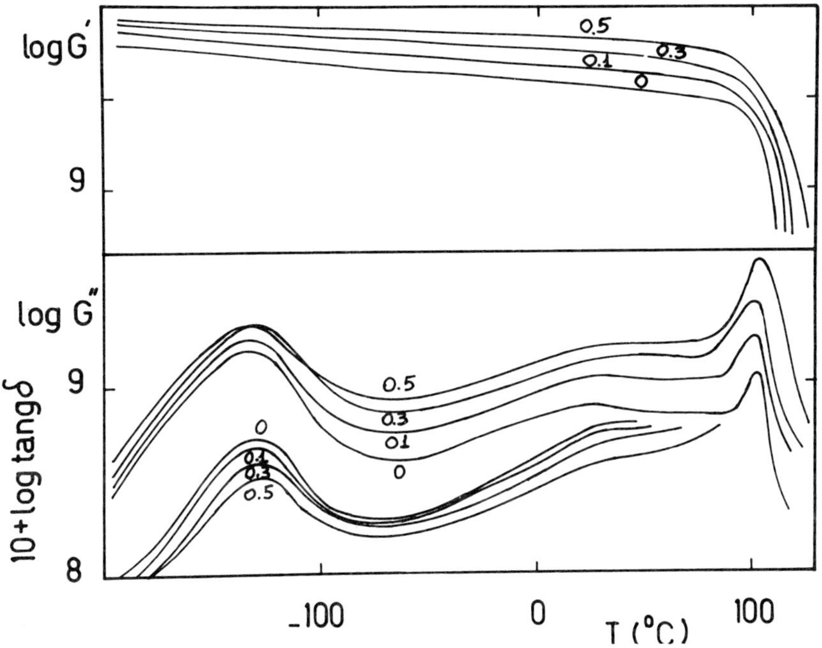

Fig. 7. Temperature dependence of moduli G' and G" (dyn/cm²) and tg of poly(2-hydroxyethyl methacrylate) - glass bead composites. Number at curve gives volume fraction of filler.

is not fulfilled. An analogous linear relationship approximately holds for a number of copolymers of PHEMA with other methacrylic comonomers (Fig. 8), which do not exhibit low-temperature dispersions above the liquid nitrogen temperature. For the two-phase system PHEMA-glass beads, all the values of tgδ are higher than corresponds to eq. (9) (Fig. 8) and their concentration dependence is rather described by eq. (8). It can be inferred that the inequality $tg\delta_c > v_m tg\delta_m$ cannot generally be regarded as a sufficient proof of the presence of additional dissipation mechanism in composites (interparticular friction, friction at the interphase boundary, etc.). It seems that before these mechanisms are used - more or less speculatively - to interpret the experimental data, one should find out, if possible, whether the changes in G', G" and tgδ due to the filler are or are not correlated with each other.

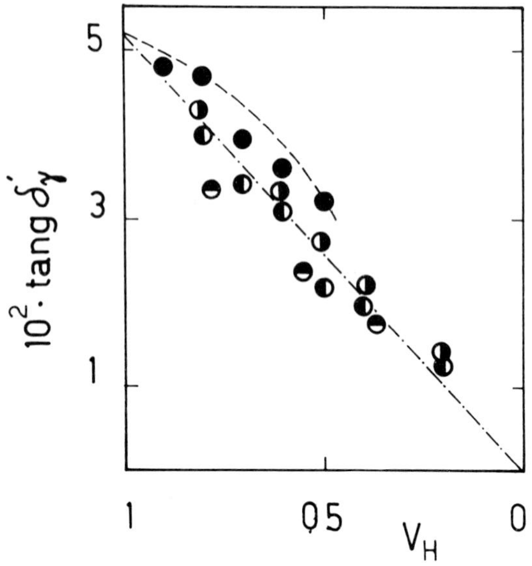

Fig. 8. Effect of volume fraction of poly(2-hydroxyethylmethacrylate) v_H in composites (●) and in copolymers with methyl methacrylate (◓), methacrylamide (◐) and acrylamide (◑) on the height of low temperature maximum.

V. CONCLUSIONS

The above results allow us to conclude that the filler enhances the capacity of the matrix both to store and to dissipate mechanical energy. The dependence of the moduli of composite, G'_c and G''_c , on the filler content is described satisfactorily by the corresponding equations (6) and (7); at temperatures well below the glass transition temperature the agreement between theory and experiment is good only after correction for the effect of thermally induced stress had been carried out. It should be stressed that the character of molecular motion giving rise to the dispersions remains unchanged, because the temperature position of the loss maxima is independent of the filler content. In the case of the γ dispersion the proportionality between the height of the loss maximum and the corresponding decrease in the modulus $\Delta G'_\gamma = G'_{cs}(-196°C) - G'_{cs}(-60°C)$ is preserved, so that the ratio $Q_\gamma = \Delta G''_\gamma / \Delta G'_\gamma$ practically does not vary with the filler content (Table 2).

The elastic modulus of a dry PHEMA network in the rubber-like state increases owing to the presence of spherical filler more than predicted by Kerner's theory. This theory describes adequately experimental data for the glassy state, but for the systems swollen in water the presence of a low concentration of glass beads reduces Young's relaxation modulus of the PHEMA network.

VI. REFERENCES

1. J. F. Clauser and W. G. Knaus, Trans. Soc. Rheol., 12, 143 (1968).
2. V. Vojta, in press.
3. S. Bernstein, Acta Mathematica, 52, 1 (1928).
4. M. Takayanagi, S. Minami and S. Uemura, J. Polym. Sci., C5, 113 (1964).
5. E. H. Kerner, Proc. Phys. Soc., B69, 808 (1956).
6. J. Kolarik, J. Svantner and J. Janacek, Chem. Listy, 70, 82 (1976).
7. J. D. Ferry, "Viscoelastic Properties of Polymers," 2nd ed., Interscience, New York 1970.
8. G. Kraus, R. W. Rollmann and J. T. Gruver, Macromolecules, 3, 92 (1970).
9. Y. T. Chen, J. Polym. Sci., Polym. Phys. Ed., 11, 2013 (1973).
10. Z. Hashin and S. Shtrikman, J. Mech. Phys. Solids, 10, 335, 343 (1962).
11. L. Nicolais, R. F. Landel and P. Giordano Orsini, Polymer J., 7, 259 (1975).
12. M. Ilavsky, J. Hasa and J. Janacek, Int. J. Polym. Mater., 1, 187 (1972).
13. L. E. Nielsen and T. B. Lewis, J. Polym. Sci., A2, 7, 1705 (1969).
14. T. B. Lewis and L. E. Nielsen, J. Appl. Polym. Sci., 14, 1449 (1970).
15. L. E. Nielsen and B. L. Lee, J. Composite Materials, 6, 136, (1972).
16. D. H. Ender, J. Macromol. Sci.-Phys. Ed., B4, 635 (1970).
17. L. E. Nielsen, Appl. Polym. Symposia, 12, 249 (1969).
18. T. Hirai and D. E. Kline, J. Composite Materials, 7, 160 (1973).
19. J. E. Ashton, J. C. Halpin and P. E. Petit, Primer on Composite Materials, Technomic Publ. Co., Stamford, 1969.
20. J. L. Kardos, W. L. McDonnell and J. Raisoni, J. Macromol. Sci.,-Phys. Ed., B6, 397 (1972).

PREDICTION OF THE STRUCTURE OF CROSSLINKED CONDENSATION POLYMERS*

H.E. Marsh, Jr., S.Y. Chung, G.C. Hsu,
and C.J. Wallace
Jet Propulsion Laboratory

Flory's branching coefficient, defined as "the probability that a given functional group of a branch unit leads via a chain of bifunctional units to another branch unit," is used as the basis for a set of relationships describing the structure of crosslinked condensation polymers. The relationships deal with distributions of branch units: (1) between sol and gel, and (2) according to function, i.e. whether branch points, chain extenders, or chain terminators. Truly crosslinking branch points are distinguished from all others by a set of expressions, based on a hierarchy of branching coefficients, which define successively higher orders of branch units and chains.

Network characteristics which can be calculated from these distributions are: sol and gel fractions, concentrations of effective chains and of crosslinking sites, average effective chain lengths, and the distribution of a hierarchy of pendent chains, varying in size and complexity. The parameters needed for these calculations are: composition, ingredient functionality distributions, and the extent of reaction.

Good agreement was obtained between calculated and measured values of gel fractions and of effective chain concentrations in simple polyesters. Calculated values of average length of effective chains correlated with extension-to-break measured at elevated temperature and slow extension rate.

I. INTRODUCTION

The basic theoretical concepts regarding the formation of three-dimensional polymer networks were established many years ago by Carothers (1), Flory (2), and Stockmayer (3). Both Flory's and Stockmayer's studies inspired considerable

*This paper presents the result of one phase of research carried out at the Jet Propulsion Laboratory, California Institute of Technology, under Contract No. NAS 7-100, sponsored by the National Aeronautics and Space Administration.

exploration of the correlations between theoretical and experimental gel points in various condensation polymer systems (2, 4-8). For this purpose, Stockmayer's general relationship was found to be easier to apply in those cases where equal reactivity of all functional groups of the same kind could be assumed, but it is limited to only the critical point, incipient gelation. The chief disadvantage of the Flory approach is the requirement for derivation of separate relationships for each set of functionality mixes (i.e., trifunctional, tetrafunctional, combinations of the two, etc.). On the other hand, this form of modelling has several advantages. Unequal reactivities can be accounted for. Each step in the mathematical development has an easily visualizable conceptual counterpart. For the purpose of this paper, the fact that the relationships derived following Flory's approach hold for all states of polymerization, especially after the gel point, is a necessity.

The gel point of a condensation polymer system is of interest because it is a critical point in the two models just discussed which corresponds to an observable critical condition. However, the post-gel state is much more important to the understanding of mechanical behavior of practical polymeric systems. Considerable attention has been given to the development of models describing post-gel structure (9-17). The aims of the present work are to base the models on some of Flory's concepts and retain easy visualization.

In this paper, a quantitative theory is described by which the post-gelation characteristics, crosslink density, sol and gel fractions, average length of effective chains, and the distribution of pendent chains, can be calculated for condensation polymers containing trifunctional branch units from a small number of predetermined parameters. Those parameters are the polymer composition, the functionality distributions of the ingredients, and the extent of reaction. The theory is verified experimentally by a set of esterified compositions of model compounds.

II. THEORY

The key parameter of this model is Flory's branching coefficient, α (2). Flory defines α as "the probability that a given functional group of a branch unit leads via a chain of bifunctional units to another branch unit."

Flory's assumptions that any two functional groups of the same type have an equal chance to react and that this equality is not altered by structural features are retained throughout the development of this model. We believe, however, that definable cases of unequal reactivity (6) can also be treated. We agree with Macosko and Miller (16) that the assumption of no intramolecular reaction cannot hold for post-gel networks.

A. Starting Parameters

This model was developed for calculating post-gel characteristics of specific systems. Its derivation and the significance of its application can best be demonstrated with a specific system. The diagram in Fig. 1 represents the most complex condensation polymer system we have tried. It has considerable practical importance, in binders for solid propellants for example. The elements in the diagram represent the ingredients that can be used to make such a polymer by causing the functional groups A and B to react to form primary bonds. In this case, the ingredients are: A-functional molecules, tri-, bi-, and monofunctional (A_3, A_2, and A_1), and B-functional molecules bi- and mono-functional (B_2 and B_1). In terms of a convenient shorthand which will appear later, this system is identified as a 3,2,1/2,1 system. The essential parameters are:

1. *Stoichiometric Ratio*

$$r = \Sigma\ B's/\Sigma\ A's \tag{1}$$

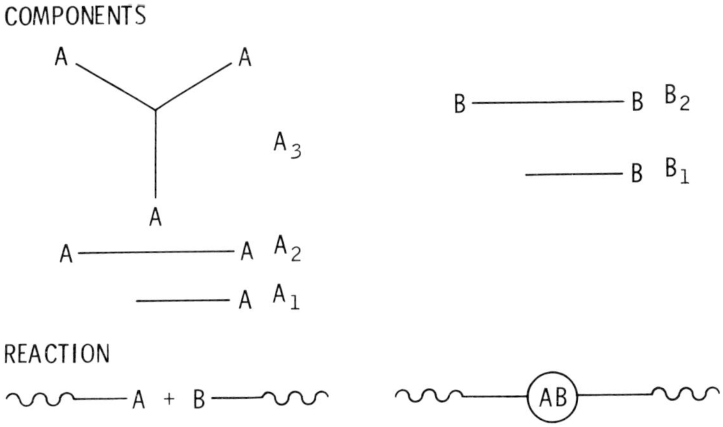

Fig. 1. Representation of the ingredients of a condensation polymer.

2. *A-Molecules*

a_3 = *mole fraction of A's on trifunctional A-molecules.*

a_2 = *mole fraction of A's on bifunctional A-molecules.*

a_1 = *mole fraction of A's on monofunctional A-molecules.*

Thus,

$$a_3 + a_2 + a_1 = 1 \tag{2}$$

3. *B-Molecules*

b_2 = *mole fraction of B's on bifunctional B-molecules.*

b_1 = *mole fraction of B's on monofunctional B-molecules.*

Likewise,

$$b_2 + b_1 = 1 \tag{3}$$

4. *Extent of Reaction*

p_A = *fraction of A's reacted.*

p_B = *fraction of B's reacted.*

Material balance is represented by

$$r = p_A/p_B \tag{4}$$

5. *Basis*

Throughout this development, one mole of the functional group, *A*, is the basis of all quantities. The relationship given in this and the next two sub-sections generate conversion factors needed to transform desired quantities to mass or volume bases. Let *W* represent the mass of polymer per mole of *A*. It can be calculated from

$$W = a_3E_{A_3} + a_2E_{A_2} + a_1E_{A_1} + rb_2E_{B_2} + rb_1E_{B_1} \tag{5}$$

where the E's represent the equivalent weights of the ingredients identified by subscripts.

6. *Elimination Product*

In the experimental part of this work, ester-cured polymers were made. To account for the loss in mass caused by evaporation of reaction-produced water, the conversion factor, W, is corrected as follows:

$$W_R = W - 18.016p_A \tag{6}$$

If there is no elimination product, $W_R = W$.

7. *Volume Basis*

$$V = W_R/d \tag{7}$$

where

d = density.

B. Calculation of α

For the system just described, and as shown in Fig. 1, the expression for calculating the degree of branching is as follows:

$$\alpha = \frac{p_A p_B b_2 a_3}{1 - p_A p_B b_2 a_2} = \frac{p_A^2 b_2 a_3}{r - p_A^2 b_2 a_2} \tag{8}$$

A description of methods for deriving expressions for α and some problems presented by more complex systems will appear in Section IV.

C. Distributions of Branch Units

Knowing the value of α for a polymer system in some given state of cure, one can calculate the distribution of four states of trifunctional branch units. The four states, shown in Fig. 2, are distinguished by whether none, only one, two, or all three of the branches are connected to other branch units. The relative probabilities, or concentrations in moles of branch units per mole of all A's in the polymer, are:

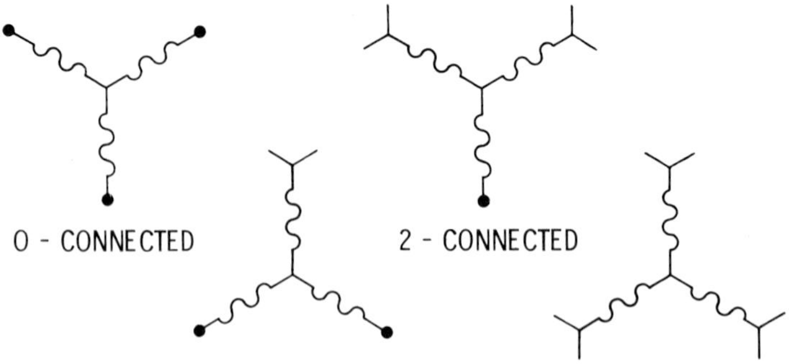

Fig. 2. Branch units identified with regard to how many arms are connected via chains of bifunctional units to other branch units.

$$\text{All:} \quad T = a_3/3 \tag{9}$$

$$\text{0-Connected:} \quad T_0 = T(1 - \alpha)^3 \tag{10}$$

$$\text{1-Connected:} \quad T_1 = 3T(1 - \alpha)^2 \alpha \tag{11}$$

$$\text{2-Connected:} \quad T_2 = 3T(1 - \alpha) \alpha^2 \tag{12}$$

$$\text{3-Connected:} \quad T_3 = T\alpha^3 \tag{13}$$

To get at the structure of the network, the only part of the polymer capable of truly elastic deformation, it is necessary to find the distribution of these four states of branch units in the gel fraction. Two key observations are used here. First, it is impossible for 0-connected branch units to be part of the network or gel. Therefore, letting the subscripts G,0 and S,0 represent 0-connected in gel and sol respectively,

$$T_{G,0} = 0; \; T_{S,0} = T_0 \tag{14}$$

Second, Flory provides a branching coefficient for those branch units which are in the sol fractions of trifunctional systems (18):

$$\alpha' = 1 - \alpha \tag{15}$$

This allows us to calculate the distribution of the four states in the sol:

$$T_{S,0} = T_S\alpha^3 \tag{16}$$

$$T_{S,1} = 3T_S\alpha^2(1 - \alpha) \tag{17}$$

$$T_{S,2} = 3T_S\alpha(1 - \alpha)^2 \tag{18}$$

$$T_{S,3} = T_S(1 - \alpha)^3 \tag{19}$$

The value of T_S needed in the above equations can be determined by combining equations 10, 14, and 16. Then the concentrations of branch units, distributed by state, in the gel fraction of the polymer are

$$T_{G,1} = T_1 - T_{S,1} \tag{20}$$

$$T_{G,2} = T_2 - T_{S,2} \tag{21}$$

and

$$T_{G,3} = T_3 - T_{S,3} \tag{22}$$

D. Sol and Gel Fractions

The other result of combining equations 10, 14, and 16 is

$$\frac{T_S}{T} = \frac{(1 - \alpha)^3}{\alpha^3} \tag{23}$$

which is the same as Flory's relationship for w_S, the weight fraction of sol in the trifunctional case (18). The gel fraction is

$$w_g = 1 - w_s = 1 - \frac{T_S}{T} \tag{24}$$

and the mass of gel per mole of *A* is

$$W_G = W_R\, w_g \tag{25}$$

E. Network Elements

Now that we have a means of counting the three kinds of branch unit in the network or gel, it is important to identify the minimum set of elements necessary to construct them. The network can be visualized as being made up of a set of two kinds of chains. One kind of chain is connected to a branch unit at each end. The other kind is connected to a branch unit at one end, but the other end is connected to a terminating moiety. The terminating moiety can be any of three different things, an unreacted A, an unreacted B, or a monofunctional ingredient. These two kinds of chains are illustrated in the first expression of Fig. 3 as consisting of a series of reacted bifunctional molecules. For the purposes of this paper, all chains in each class of chains are visualized as having the same, or average, length. In Fig. 3, the chains are shown to be divided in half. This is a convenience and is justified as a consequence of the original assumptions that , once a chain has started, it has the same probability as others of reaching some given length, regardless of the nature of the starting point. These half-chains are the smallest in this model and are classified as being zero-order (0-order) later on (referring still to the first set in Fig. 3).

It is possible to count the two kinds of half-chains in the gel fraction. If there are T_G moles of branch units in the gel, there are $3T_G$ moles of half-chains emanating from branch points. In addition, each 2-connected branch unit is connected through one of its branches to a terminating half-chain, and each 1-connected branch unit accounts similarly for two terminating half-chains. So, the total moles of half-chains in the gel are

$$HC_G = 3T_G + T_{G,2} + 2T_{G,1}$$

$$= 3T_{G,3} + 4T_{G,2} + 5T_{G,1} \tag{26}$$

The total number of moles of whole chains in the gel, then is $HC_G/2$.

One of the objectives of this model is the calculation of the lengths of effective chains and of pendent chains. As will be shown later, those lengths are multiples of the half-chains described here. The mass per average half-chain in the gel can be computed by dividing the mass of the gel by the number of half-chains,

$$W_0 = W_G/HC_G \tag{27}$$

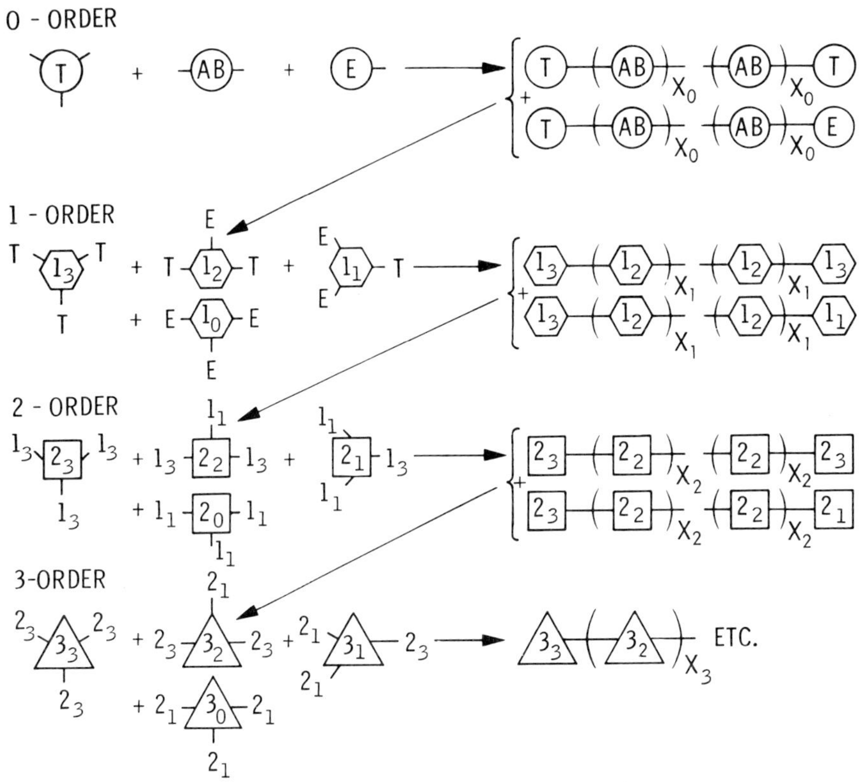

Fig. 3. The process of hierarchy formation. Only 3-connected branch units in one order form the basis for counting elements of the next higher order. In this figure, T, AB, and E respectively represent trifunctional ingredient, AB chemical linkage, and terminating element. Main numerals represent order in the hierarchy. Sub-numerals represent number of connected arms.

Let L_{sp} represent the specific length, in moles of chain-atoms per unit mass. (Chain-atoms are only those in the connecting chain; those atoms in pendent side chains native to the starting ingredients are not counted.) Then, the half-chain length, in moles of chain-atoms, is

$$L_0 = W_0 \, L_{sp} \tag{28}$$

In most cases, high precision in the calculation of L_{sp} is not important. If in a polymer system, such as the one shown in Fig. 1 for example, the A_3 molecules are not large enough to contribute much to chain length, a satisfactory estimate can be made by averaging over half of an A_2 and half of a B_2 plus the *AB* linkage between them.

F. Structural Functions of Branch Units

Consider the three states of branch units in the gel. Clearly, 2-connected branch units perform the function of chain extension; 1-connected branch units are terminals. In the network, the ultimate effect of a 1-connected branch unit is the neutralization of a 3-connected branch unit. It can do this directly, if it is connected to the unit in question. On the other hand, it can do so by converting a 2-connected branch unit to a pendent-chain terminal, which itself is connected to the unit in question by a series of 2-connected branch units. Each such neutralization removes the crosslinking capacity of the affected 3-connected branch unit, which then becomes a chain extender. Only those 3-connected branch units in the gel that are not neutralized by 1-connected branch units can be truly crosslinking. Thus, one of the ways to calculate the concentration of crosslink sites is based on this principle:

$$T_X = T_{G,3} - T_{G,1} \tag{29}$$

in moles per mole of *A*.

G. Hierarchy of Network Elements

The previous step in the development of this model used a set of principles which are at the heart of the rest of the development:

1) A crosslinked condensation polymer can be visualized, at its lowest level of complexity (0-order), as consisting of four elements: branch units, chain extenders, chain terminals, and inactive units. (These elements correspond respectively to trifunctional molecules, bifunctional molecules, monofunctional molecules and unreacted functional groups, and molecules which have not reacted or have no groups.)
2) Because of the structural effects of the chain terminals at the lowest level of complexity, some of the branch units lose their function at the next level of complexity (1-order in this case) and are visualized as a new set of chain extenders, chain

terminals and inactive units. (These elements and their functions are shown in the first expression of Fig. 3.)

Transformed to the general case, these principles guide a mental process which can be continued, stepping one at a time to higher levels of complexity, resulting in a hierarchy of network elements. The first three steps of the process are illustrated in Fig. 3.

The 0-order elements (starting ingredients) assemble themselves by the joining of half-chains to form 1-order elements (those shown in Fig. 2). This is the point which has been reached by the mathematical model so far. Two more steps in the development of the hierarchy are shown in Fig. 3, 1-order elements assembling to produce 2-order elements, which in turn produce 3-order elements. The product of the next step, a 3-order half-chain is illustrated in Fig. 4.

It is important to notice a consequence of the second principle: the elements of one order descend from only the 3-connected branch units of the next lower order.

The question is, how far does this process go? How big and complex do half-chains become? As the mathematics below will show, the building of complexity never stops theoretically, but it does practically. The coefficients, x_1, x_2, x_3, etc. (See Fig. 4.) become successively smaller until the contribution of the next one becomes insignificant in the computation of network characteristics.

H. Calculations of Hierarchic Parameters

It is now necessary to modify some of the previous notation to distinguish between orders of the hierarchy. To illustrate, two specific examples are: Equation 22 would be written

$$(T_{G,3})_1 = (T_3)_1 - (T_{S,3})_1$$

and the T in equations 9 through 13 would be written $(T)_1$ in the new notation.

1. *A Useful Parameter*

In trifunctional systems, algebraic convenience was effected by the use of a parameter,

$$R_1 = (1 - \alpha)/\alpha \tag{30}$$

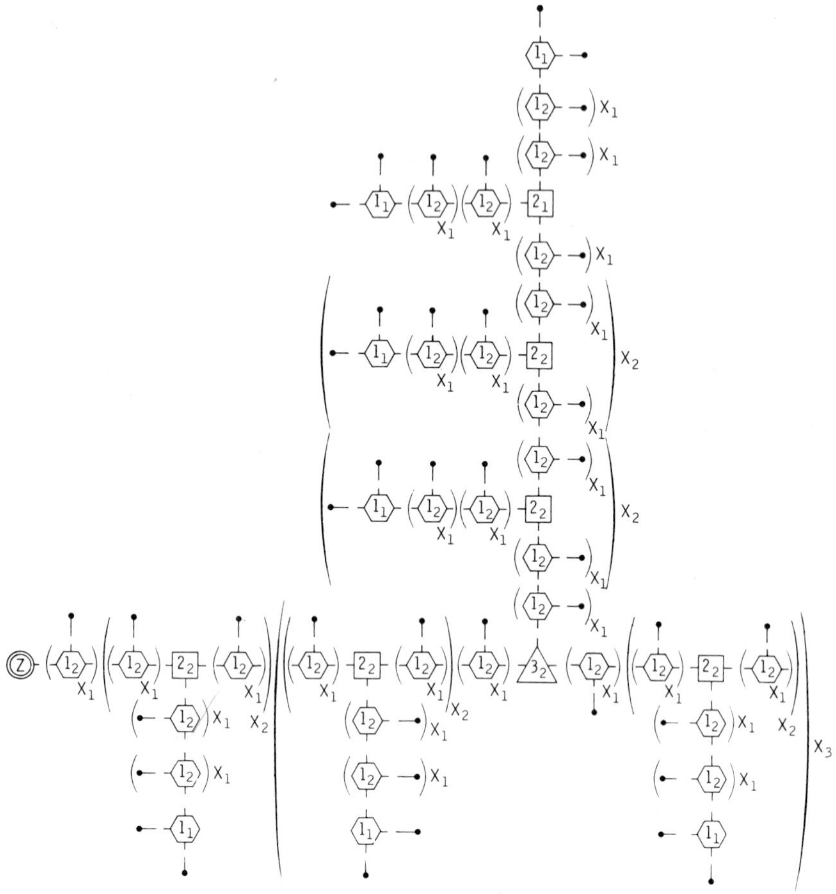

Fig. 4. Structure of a 3-order half-chain. (Notation is the same as in Fig. 3.) The branch unit represented by Z in the diagram can be either a 3_3 or a 3_1. Also it can be any type (4_3, 4_2, 4_1, 4_0) of the next higher orders.

Physically, this term is equivalent to the cube root of the sol fraction (see equation 23). It has one other physical significance. R_1 is the ratio of non-connected to connected branches at order number 1 in the hierarchy. Later, higher orders of this parameter, R_n, will be used.

2. *Higher Order Branching Coefficients*

The paraphrasing of Flory's definition of α with regard to a higher order of network elements is:

α_n is the probability that a given branch of an (n-1)-order 3-connected branch unit leads via a chain of (n-1)-order 2-connected branch units to another (n-1)-order 3-connected branch unit.

This definition, in conjunction with the principles set out for the hierarchic model, results in new sets of distributions of n-order branch units having the same forms as those in equations 10 through 13, 16 through 19, and 20 through 22. A key relationship, based on the principle that only the 3-connected branch units of one order are distributed in the next order, is

$$(T)_n = (T_3)_{n-1} \tag{31}$$

Application of the above definition, through visualization of the model as in Fig. 3, leads to the observation that the 2-order branching coefficient, α_2, is equal to the probability that a given branch of a 1-order branch unit has of connecting to another 1-order branch unit:

$$\alpha_2 = \frac{3(T_3)_1}{3(T_3)_1 + (T_1)_1} \tag{32}$$

For the general case, this is stated as

$$\alpha_n = \frac{3(T_3)_{n-1}}{3(T_3)_{n-1} + (T_1)_{n-1}} \tag{33}$$

Reduced to basic parameters, equation 33 is

$$\alpha_n = \frac{\alpha_{n-1}^2}{\alpha_{n-1}^2 + (1 - \alpha_{n-1})^2} = \frac{1}{R_{n-1}^2 + 1} \tag{34}$$

and higher orders of R are generated:

$$R_n = \frac{1 - \alpha_n}{\alpha_n} = (R_{n-1})^2 \tag{35}$$

Thus, we have the essential relationship for generating the whole hierarchy of distributions.

3. *Chain Extension Coefficients*

According to the view of the model shown in Figs. 3 and 4, the symbol, x_1, represents the number of 1-order 2-connected branch units in the average 1-order half-chain. The relationship is the same for higher orders. Thus, in the general case for the gel, these coefficients are

$$x_n = \frac{(T_{G,2})_n}{3(T_{G,3})_n + (T_{G,1})_n}$$

which is equivalent to

$$x_n = \frac{1}{R_n + 1/R_n} \tag{36}$$

I. Concentrations of Crosslink Sites and Effective Chains

A calculation of the concentration of crosslink sites was given earlier (equation 29). On the basis of the previous development, this relationship can be put in general terms, still in moles per mole of A,

$$T_x = (T_{G,3})_n - (T_{G,1})_n \tag{37}$$

Equation 37 gives the same value for any order, n (=1, 2, 3, . . .). As n increases, $(T_{G,1})_n$ decreases. At sufficiently high orders,

$$T_x = (T_{G,3})_n$$

Substitution of appropriate terms, from equations 20 and 22, etc., into equation 29 gives

$$T_x = \frac{a_3}{3}\left(\frac{2\alpha - 1}{\alpha}\right)^3 = \frac{a_3}{3}(1 - R_1)^3 \tag{38}$$

Notice the term $(1 - R_1)^3$, in the last expression; it is equivalent to

$$\left(1 - w_s^{1/3}\right)^3$$

where w_s is the sol fraction.

Effective chains are those chains in the gel which connect true crosslink sites with each other. They are the chief contributors to a polymer's ability to deform elastically under load, and the only contributors when the loading is done under equilibrium conditions (19). There are three effective half-chains connected at every crosslink site in systems based on trifunctional branch units. Thus, the concentration of effective chains in moles per mole of *A* is

$$\nu_{e,A} = 3T_x/2 \tag{39}$$

The conversion factor from equation 7 is used to convert $\nu_{e,A}$ to $\nu_{e,V}$, in the commonly reported dimensions of moles of effective chains per cubic centimeter.

J. Sorting Out Network Chains

A close examination of Figs. 3 and 4 reveals a regular pattern of construction for any order of half-chain and its associated pendent chains. This regularity allows the expression of desired parameters algebraically in terms of the chain extension coefficients, $x_1, x_2, x_3, \ldots, x_n$. Chain lengths (be they pendent or effective) become multiples of the average 0-order half-chain, whose unit length, L_0, is expressed in equation 28. Concentrations of pendent chains (whether they are connected directly to effective chains or as parasites on larger pendent chains) depend on their respective orders and the local concentrations of 2-connected branch units of corresponding order. Certain of these formulas for length and concentration will be given in the following sections.

K. Length of Effective Chains

By analysis of Fig. 4, one can find the length of a 3-order half-chain:

$$L_3 = L_0(1 + 2x_1)(1 + 2x_2)(1 + 2x_3) \tag{40}$$

The pattern is evident for any order. An average effective chain is composed of two half-chains of order, n, sufficiently high that the addition of the term, $(1 + 2x_{n+1})$ does not affect the value:

$$L_x = 2L_0(1 + 2x_1)(1 + 2x_2)\ldots(1 + 2x_n) \tag{41}$$

It is recognized that the original ingredients from which a polymer is made can include compounds or prepolymers which already have pendent side chains native to them (e.g., the methyl groups on poly(propylene oxide)). In our notation, these are arbitrarily labeled 0-order pendent chains. Their concentrations in the polymer can be calculated using the reasoning of equations 26 through 28.

Higher order pendent chains are generated in the formation of the polymer, and their concentrations and complexities depend inversely on α. The structure of 1-order pendent chains consists merely of two 0-order half-chains. Thus, their average length is $2L_0$. The only parasitic pendent chains they contain are native. The pattern of structure for all higher orders, *n*, of pendent chains can be seen to be two (n-1)-order half-chains capped by a (n-1)-order 1-connected branch unit terminated on its other two branches by (n-1)-order pendent chains. It seems reasonable to distinguish between these last two chains as to function: while one of them can contribute length (designated sub-E below), the other will be a pendent parasite (designated sub-P below). The average length of an n-order pendent chain can be calculated on the basis of this regular structure. Letting $L_{P,n}$ and $L_{E,n}$ be the lengths of n-order pendent and end chains,

$$L_{E,1} = L_{P,1} = 2L_0$$

and

$$L_{E,2} = L_{P,2} = 2L_1 + L_{E,1}$$

The general relationship of 2-order and higher is

$$L_{E,n} = L_{P,n} = 2L_{n-1} + L_{E,(n-1)} \tag{42}$$

A given pendent chain can be located at either of two kinds of structural regions in a polymer network. Some n-order pendent chains branch out from the backbone of effective chains. Others are parasites on (n+1)- or higher-order pendent chains. The pattern of concentrations of pendent chains on half-chains, from which the two distributions just cited can be calculated, is shown in the following set of expressions, in which $P_{m/n}$ represents the average number of m-order pendent chains on an n-order half-chain:

$$\left.\begin{aligned} P_{n/n} &= x_n \\ P_{(n-1)/n} &= x_{n-1}(1 + 2x_n) \\ &\text{-------------} \\ P_{1/n} &= x_1(1 + 2x_2)(1 + 2x_3)\ldots(1 + 2x_n) \end{aligned}\right\} \quad (43)$$

Equations 42 and 43 generate sets of discrete values which might be taken to imply that pendent chain lengths and concentrations are discontinuous functions, a situation which of course does not represent the true condition in the types of polymers for which this model was developed. These parameters should be thought of in the following way: A typical n-order half-chain has an average length of L_n moles of chain atoms; it contains $P_{m/n}$ pendent chains of length $L_{P,m}$ (for m = 1, 2, 3 ... n), where $P_{m/n}$ and $L_{P,m}$ are averages of continuous distributions.

III. EXPERIMENTAL TESTING OF THEORY

The previous section develops a set of relations which, for a 3,2,1/2,1 system and its subsystems, predicts sol and gel fractions, crosslink density (as volume concentration of effective chains), the average length of effective chains, and the distribution of pendent chains according to size and complexity. Ester-cured 3,2/2 polymers were prepared from small molecules. Measurements were made on cured samples to test the significance of these predictions. Both sol/gel fractions and effective chain concentration were measured directly, the first by extraction and the second by the measurement of equilibrium modulus in tension. These two properties are independent, direct measurements of corresponding predictions of the theory. With regard to effective chain length and pendent chain distribution, we do not know of properties which measure them directly. Since, however, the ultimate extensibility of a network polymer should be related to effective chain length, we decided to test this relationship and to evaluate pendent chain prediction by inference from the results of this test.

A. Experimental Techniques

1. *Polymer Preparation*

Polymer samples were prepared using the following compounds in various proportions: 1,3,5-pentane-tricarboxylic acid, sebacic acid, and decanediol. p-Toluene sulfonic acid was used as catalyst. Ingredients were melted together at 43°C in a high-speed mixer, an apparatus with viscosity monitoring capability used for measuring gel points (6). Mixing was continued until the viscosity indicated close approach to gelation in order to eliminate most of the water of reaction. The partially polymerized material was poured into preheated, flat, open molds to a depth of about 0.3 cm. The molds were placed in a vacuum oven set at 71°C; remaining gas bubbles were removed by careful application of vacuum. Samples were then held at 71°C for one week.

2. *Sol and Gel Fractions*

Sol and gel fractions were separated for weighing by 48-hour extractions in a Soxhlet apparatus, using benzene as the solvent.

3. *Effective Chain Concentration*

Equilibrium modulus was measured two ways. In both methods, the rate of load application was low. Rheologic effects were reduced in one method by solvent plasticization and in the other method by temperature elevation.

Dog-bone samples, preswelled and immersed in benzene, were stressed in tension in small increments to provide about ten increments over a total strain of 10% or less. A laboratory scale was adapted for use in the application of measured loading. Extension was measured by the sighting with a cathetometer of two fine-wire pins stuck into the two ends of the narrow section of the dog bone before swelling. Data were plotted as load versus extension, and the slope, *S*, of the straight line drawn through them was calculated. Effective chain concentration in moles per 10^6 cubic centimeters was calculated according to the following relationship (19):

$$\nu_{e,V} = \frac{10^6 h_0/A_0}{3RT} S \qquad (44)$$

where h_0 was the distance between pins in the unswollen, unstressed sample, and A_0 was the cross-sectional area at the same condition, T was the absolute temperature at which the test was made, and R was the universal gas constant in appropriate units.

The elevated-temperature tests were made in an Instron tensile test machine. Dog-bone specimens of 2.5 cm length were pulled at a crosshead speed of 2.5 cm/min at a temperature of 77°C. The data were reduced using equation 44. The representative slope was taken as the best straight line that could be drawn from a point just beyond start-up anomalies to 10-20% extension.

4. *Ultimate Extensibility*

This property was taken to be the elongation reached at break in the above-described Instron tests.

B. Results and Discussion

The results of the measurements described above are presented in the first three tables: gel fraction in Table 1, effective chain concentration in Table 2, and elongation at break in Table 3 (not all measurements were made on all samples). These and subsequent tables are arranged parametrically so as to illustrate graphically the functional relationships. The data in vertical columns are in order according to descending concentrations of trifunctional branch unit. The left-to-right sequence in horizontal rows is ascending levels of stoichiometric ratio. Thus, compositions in the upper left-hand corner of a table will have higher crosslink densities than those to the right and below, providing extents of reaction are comparable. Compositions in the lower right corner cannot gel. The gelation limit is expressed for the 3,2/2 system by equation 8 which reduces to $r = 1 + a_3$.

TABLE 1

Weight Fraction of Gel in Cured Compositions

r	a_3 = *Tri-COOH/COOH*							
OH/COOH	*0.9*	*0.8*	*0.7*	*0.6*	*0.5*	*0.4*	*0.3*	*0.2*
1.1				0.874	0.876	0.638	0.723	
1.14								
1.15				0.869	0.794	0.574	0.680	
1.2	0.882	0.876	0.796	0.767				
1.25								
1.3	0.825	0.779	0.657	0.649	0.440			
1.4								
1.45			0.519					
1.5			0.341					
1.55			0.303					
1.8	0.473							

TABLE 2

Concentration of Effective Chains[a]

r	a_3 = *Tri-COOH/COOH*							
OH/COOH	*0.9*	*0.8*	*0.7*	*0.6*	*0.5*	*0.4*	*0.3*	*0.2*
1.1				191[b]	160	65	59	
				-	251	-	54	
1.14								-
								34
1.15				173	82	17	14	
				-	-	-	-	
1.2	250	283	170	83			-	
	238	-	-	-			0.7	
1.25							-	
							0.8	
1.3	106	133	70	51	8.6	-		
	155	-	61	28	14	0.5		
1.4					-			
					5.2			
1.45			18		-			
			-		6.3			
1.5			11					
			-					
1.55			5.3					
			-					
1.8	39							
	55							

a. *Dimensions: moles/m*^{3}.

b. *Upper values from swollen specimen tests; lower values from high-temperature tests.*

1. *Accuracy*

On inspection of the data presented in Tables 1, 2, and 3, it is clear that the trends are all in the expected directions. A more quantitative analysis will be discussed later, but it is important now to address the question of precision. A closer inspection will reveal that not all of the trends are perfect. We believe this result was caused chiefly by a choice of emphasis on determining gross effects over obtaining

TABLE 3
Percent Extension at Break

r	a_3 = *Tri-COOH/COOH*							
OH/COOH	*0.9*	*0.8*	*0.7*	*0.6*	*0.5*	*0.4*	*0.3*	*0.2*
1.1					33		98	
1.14								103
1.15								
1.2	25						340	
1.25							591	
1.3	33		53	83	78	443		
1.4					150			
1.45					150			
1.5								
1.55								
1.8	51							

accuracy. The precision resulting from this choice shows up in replicate measurements. Of the 21 compositions tested for gel fraction, only one value was run in duplicate; its standard deviation was 28% of its mean. Of the 21 tests for effective chain concentration (swollen specimen technique), 3 were run in triplicate, and 9 were run in duplicate; the standard deviations of the replicates ranged from 1.6% to 39% of the respective means. Of the 14 high-temperature Instron tests, 8 were duplicates, and there was one triplicate and one quadruplicate. The corresponding ranges of percent standard deviation were 1.5% to 30% for effective chain concentration and 1.4% to 27% for extension. In the tables, the values are means.

In future work, the following items will be given special attention for the purpose of improving precision: control and/or measurement of environmental moisture during curing and storage, more accuracy in the preparation and measurement of tensile specimens, and the use of a better model for branching coefficient. The last item refers to the fact that not all three carboxyls on 1,3,5-pentane-tricarboxylic acid can be expected to be equally reactive. The effect of this circumstance on gelation was shown in an earlier paper (6).

The seven sets of data in which effective chain concentration was measured both ways were subjected to statistical analysis. The use of both of these measurements for the same property was justified by the result, a correlation coefficient of 0.92.

2. *Prediction of w_g and ν_e*

Because the extents of reaction, p_A, were neither controlled nor measured, it was not possible to test the model's predictions of gel fraction and effective chain concentration directly. However, since for each composition both measurements were made from samples cut from the same sheet, a comparison of branching coefficients calculated from the two different measurements should be a good test. In Table 4, α_g was calculated using equations 24 and 23; α_ν was calculated using equations 39, 38, and 7. A graphical comparison of these two sets of α is shown in Fig. 5. In this graph, a 45° line represents a perfect correlation. Visually, the fit appears to be satisfactory. The scatter of points is to be expected from the precision discussed above. Since both parameters were derived from measurements subject to error, the usual least-squares regression calculation is inappropriate. A somewhat more detailed calculation, which assumes equal variability, is more suitable. The conclusion of such a calculation is that a slope of one is within the 95% confidence limits. A further test of the model can be made by assessing the prediction of extent of reaction (see Table 5). These values were calculated from α_g and α_ν using equation 8. With the exception of the last pair ($p > 1$ is impossible), these values all fall within a range that seems reasonable for the conditions under which the polymerizations were carried out. What is more important, there is no statistical justification for saying the two sets, $p_{A,g}$ and $p_{A,\nu}$ came from different populations. Thus, the prediction by this model of sol/gel fractions and crosslink density in 3,2/2 systems is verified.

If all of the compositions had been made under the same conditions, a first assumption might be that the extents of reaction of carboxyl, p_A, would be the same. This is a reasonable assumption on statistical grounds, especially when considering the precision of the measurements. The mean for all of the values in Table 5 is 0.925, and the standard deviation of 0.139 is 15% of the mean. A closer look at Table 5, however, shows two trends in p_A. One of these trends (p_A varies inversely with a_3) is in accord with the comment made in Section B.1. about the effect of unequal reactivity of the three carboxyls on 1,3,5-pentane-tricarboxylic acid. The other trend relates to another comment made in Section B.1. In this

TABLE 4
Branching Coefficients Derived from Sol/Gel and Equilibrium Modulus Measurements

r	a_3 = *Tri-COOH/COOH*							
OH/COOH	*0.9*	*0.8*	*0.7*	*0.6*	*0.5*	*0.4*	*0.3*	*0.2*
1.1				0.666[a] 0.653	0.662 0.654	0.589 0.617	0.605 0.621	
1.14								
1.15				0.663 0.648	0.629 0.618	0.571 0.570	0.594 0.573	
1.2	0.671 0.644	0.667 0.661	0.629 0.638	0.619 0.610				
1.25								
1.3	0.641 0.603	0.623 0.619	0.588 0.580	0.586 0.592	0.548 0.551			
1.4								
1.45			0.561 0.540					
1.5			0.535 0.551					
1.55			0.530 0.539					
1.8	0.553 0.576							

a. *Upper values are derived from sol/gel data; Lower values from equilibrium modulus.*

case, p_A varies with *r*. It seems safe to assume this to be a result of mass action of varying levels of excess hydroxyl. The modeling for this, to be applied to future controlled-humidity experiments, would include equilibrium expressions for esterification.

3. *Significance of* L_x

Since the high-temperature measurement of effective chain concentration was found to be acceptable, α derived from these values was used for the calculation of effective chain length,

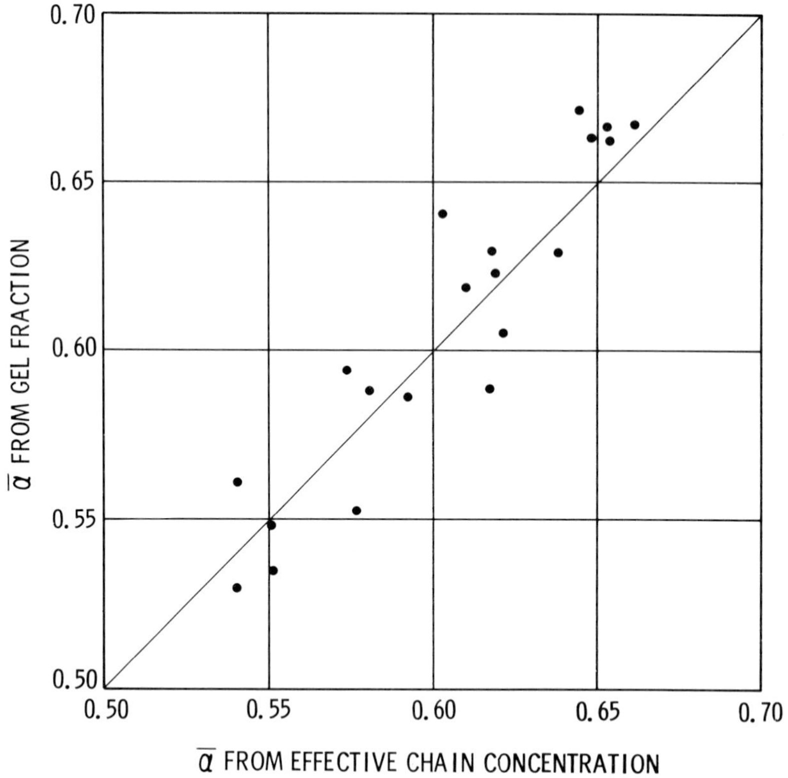

Fig. 5. Correlation of branching coefficients calculated from two measurements on polyester polymers: sol/gel fractionation and equilibrium modulus. The 45° line represents perfect correlation. Statistical analysis showed this slope to be within the 95% probable range.

L_x.* This allowed the data for L_x and extension at break, ε_b, to be taken from the same test. The correlation of these data

---

*The calculation of L_x from $\nu_{e,V}$ is tedious without a computer. In brief, it is as follows: One. Compute W by equation 5. Two. Iterate equations 6,7,8,38 and 39 with $\nu_{e,A} = \nu_{e,V}{}^{*}V$ for α. Three. Compute W_G by equations 23,24 and 25. Four. Compute HC_G using equations 9,11-13,17-23 and 26. Five. Compute L_0 by equations 27 and 28. Six. Compute X_1, X_2, ..., X_n by equations 35 and 36 until X_n becomes less than a desired limit. Seven. Compute L_x by equation 41. As expected, this set of relationships reduces to $L_x = L_{sp}/\nu_{e,V}$ for the perfect case in which all chains are effective chains ($a_1=0$, $b_1=0$, $r=1$, and $p_A=1$).

in Table 6 and Fig. 6 supports the assumption that extensibility is realted to effective chain length predicted by the model. Because the mathematical relationships leading to L_x lead also to the parameters describing the concentrations and sizes of pendent chains, these predictions are also supported by this result.

TABLE 5
Extents of Reaction Derived from Sol/Gel and Equilibrium Modulus Measurements

r	a_3 = *Tri-COOH/COOH*							
OH/COOH	*0.9*	*0.8*	*0.7*	*0.6*	*0.5*	*0.4*	*0.3*	*0.2*
1.1				0.920[a]	0.936	0.927	0.959	
				0.913	0.933	0.939	0.964	
1.14								
1.15				0.939	0.942	0.940	0.977	
				0.931	0.937	0.940	0.969	
1.2	0.912	0.926	0.922	0.936				
	0.895	0.922	0.927	0.931				
1.25								
1.3	0.930	0.936	0.934	0.956	0.959			
	0.903	0.933	0.940	0.959	0.961			
1.4								
1.45			0.968					
			0.967					
1.5			0.965					
			0.977					
1.55			0.978					
			0.985					
1.8	1.021							
	1.041							

a. *Upper values are derived from sol/gel data; Lower values from equilibrium modulus.*

TABLE 6
Correlation of Effective Chain Length[a] *with Extension at Break*[b]

r	a_3 = *Tri-COOH/COOH*							
OH/COOH	*0.9*	*0.8*	*0.7*	*0.6*	*0.5*	*0.4*	*0.3*	*0.2*
1.1					95[c] 33		254 98	
1.14								397 103
1.15								
1.2	69 25						1357 340	
1.25							1680 591	
1.3	86 33		150 53	228 83	339 78	1312 443		
1.4					504 150			
1.45					472 150			
1.5								
1.55								
1.8	150 51							

a. *Dimensions: chain atoms.*
b. *Dimensions: percent.*
c. *Upper values:* L_x*; Lower values:* ε_b.

IV. MODELING MORE COMPLEX SYSTEMS

The branching coefficient, which is the probability that any given branch leads to another branch, is the fundamental parameter in this post-gel model. This parameter must be calculated from a sub-model specifically derived for the system under consideration. This specificity applies also to the details of the overall model. The model described in this

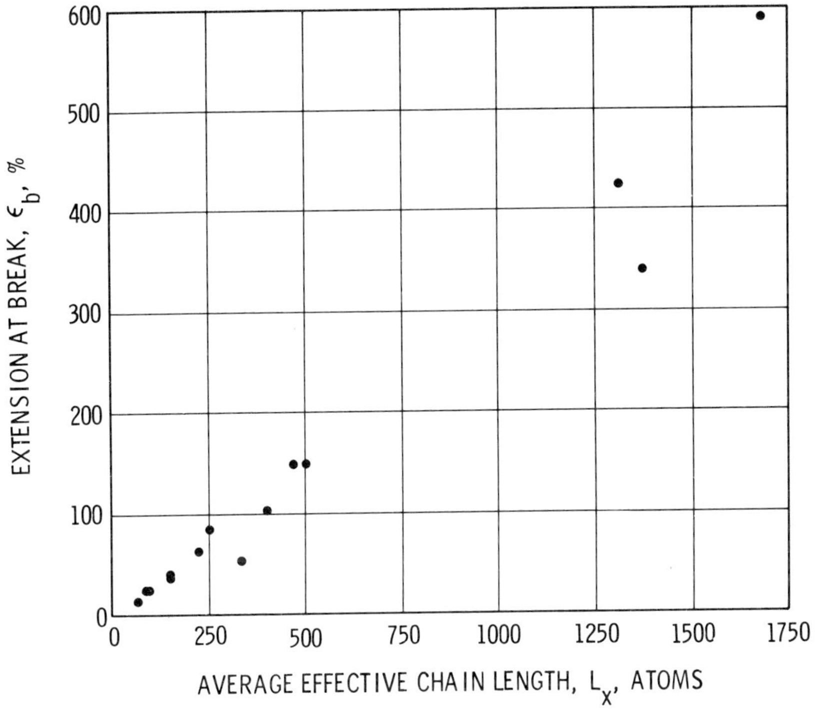

Fig. 6. Relationship between extensibility at 170°F of polyester polymers and calculated length of effective chains.

paper is specific for the 3,2,1/2,1 system. However, it is general in the sense that it applies to sub-systems (e.g., 3,2/2, 3,2/2,1, etc.). Although we haven't studied the question thoroughly, it seems probable that this generality can be advanced to more complex systems, as long as all of the branching components have the same chemical polarity. For example, branching coefficient for the 4,3,2,1/2,1 system is

$$\alpha = \frac{p_A p_B\ b_2(a_4 + a_3)}{1 - p_A p_B\ b_2\ a_2} \tag{45}$$

It is readily seen, by comparing equations 8 and 45 at the condition $a_4 = 0$, that the 3,2,1/2,1 system is a subsystem of 4,3,2,1/2 1.

In simple systems, 3,2,1/2,1 etc., the accounting for unequal reactivity appears to be manageable also (6).* In another case, an expression for calculating the branching coefficient for a 3,2/2,1 system in which the A-functional group is hydroxyl and the B group is isocyanate has been derived to account for the secondary reaction of isocyanate with active hydrogen on urethane groups to form allophanate (20). This secondary reaction produces additional cross-linking. In solid propellant formulations, in which catalytic effects not present in pure binders are to be expected, this model does not work with most hydrocarbon systems, but it does with polyether systems. (The distinction here refers to the structures of prepolymers, hydroxyl-terminated polybutadienes versus hydroxyl-terminated polypropylene oxide.)

The modeling of systems in which there are branch units of both chemical polarities is a more difficult problem.** This problem has been a stimulus to a search for improved approaches to the development of theoretical models for calculating branching coefficients. Guiding principles being used in this search and some of its results will be described briefly in the following paragraphs.

A universal model is the ideal goal; all systems of interest should be subsystems of the same general model. Thus one of the rules by which a candidate model is tested is that it must reduce to a known, simpler model when appropriate constituents are removed.

The critical point of network formation at which incipient gelation occurs is defined by Stockmayer's model. This model is universal for all subsystems of the general form, n ... 3,2,1/m ... 3,2,1. Any model for predicting branching coefficients, α, should yield a value of $\alpha = 1/(f - 1)$

---

*Equation (3) in Reference (6) was shown by Flory, in a private communication, to be incorrect. The correct equation is:

$$R = \frac{1}{1 - (1 - x)\,\rho/3} + \frac{x\rho}{(1 - (1 - x)\,\rho/3)^2}$$

Numerical values in the system studied were not affected significantly by the error.

**Even though the model for 3,2,1/3,2,1 systems presented in Reference (7) was supported by experimental data, it is not correct. In a private communication, Stockmayer showed its predictions to be theoretically impossible.

(where f is the functionality of the branch units (2)) at the critical conditions given by Stockmayer's relationship. We have found that the appropriate f in the case of mixed functionalities of one chemical polarity, such as in the 4,3,2,1/2,1 system, is the functional average functionality, $f_f = (4a_4 + 3a_3)/(a_4 + a_3)$.

The horizons of this search have been broadened by the post-gel modeling of Macosko and Miller (16). Using a recursive method involving the law of conditional probability, their model corresponds step-by-step with a readily visualized physical process. Instead of the branching coefficient, this model yields a parameter, $P(F_A^{out})$, which could be called the finite chain coefficient. It is defined as the probability that a given branch leads to a finite chain. From this parameter, they calculate sol/gel fractions and crosslink density. Like Stockmayer's model, Macosko and Miller's model is general for n ... 3,2,1/m ... 3,2,1, and they have extended it to account for unequal reactivity (17).

We have confirmed that in the case of 4,3,2,1/2,1 and 3,2,1/2,1 systems the Macosko-Miller model at incipient gelation $(P(F_A^{out}) = 1)$ reduces to the Stockmayer expression. We have also found that the Macosko-Miller parameter, $P(F_A^{out})$, is equivalent to R_1 of this paper in 4,2,1/2,1 and 3,2,1/2,1. Also, we were able to derive, for these two simpler cases, a simple relationship between the two network coefficients:

$$\alpha = \frac{1 - P\,F_A^{out}}{1 - \left(P\left(F_A^{out}\right)\right)^{f-1}} \tag{46}$$

for

$$f = 3 \text{ or } 4$$

The logical inference is that equation 46 applies generally to systems, f,2,1/2,1, in which f is any digit 3 or higher. The relationship between the two coefficients for the 4,3,2, 1/2,1 system is more complex. More cases will have to be tried before a general relationship can be identified.

Up to this point, two methods for calculating the branching coefficients for simple systems have been identified, adaptation of the Macosko-Miller model, just described, and the original method of Flory (2). For each of these methods, the generalization for m ...,3,2,1/2,1 systems appears possible. Several other methods are being considered and will be mentioned below.

One of the chief problems in attempts to model systems with branch units of both chemical polarities (e.g., the 3,2,1/3,2,1 system) is the proper identification of the chain ends that should be counted, along with appropriate expressions of their probability. One way to do this is to expand the Macosko-Miller relationship for a system under consideration at incipient gelation ($P(F_A^{out}) = 1$). The individual terms in the expanded expression are the probabilities of all possible 1-order ends. For example, this treatment of the 3,2,1/3,2,1 system showed the number was 16. The proper identification of the functions (chain terminating, chain extending, or branching) of some of these ends is still in question. Once this distribution has been identified, the expression for α can be set up in the same manner as equation 32, the sum of the branching probabilities divided by the sum of branching and terminating probabilities together.

It is conceivable that convenient algebraic relationships between the branching and finite chain coefficients cannot be found for some systems. There are some common parameters in the Macosko-Miller model and the model of this paper that can be arranged for numerical solution so as to yield α compatible with $P(F_A^{out})$. The efficacy of numerical solution was demonstrated for the 4,3,2,1/2,1 system by the use of a computer. This calculation yielded the same values of α as were computed other ways. Crosslink density prediction remained the same at higher orders, as would be expected from equation 37. Although it is not necessary to resort to numerical solution with the 3,2,1/2,1 system this simple system will be used to illustrate the general nature of parameter commonality. Using the finite chain coefficient, $P(F_A^{out})$, a new distribution of branch units is generated. The new distribution quantifies the concentrations of four states which are different from those based on the branching coefficient, α, illustrated in Fig. 2. Letting $P = P(F_A^{out})$ for convenience, $TP^3 = T_0$ (the number of branch units in the sol) and $T(1 - P)^3 = T_X$ (the number of crosslinking sites). These identifications are made in Reference (16). The other two combinations relate to characteristics of this paper's model in somewhat different ways. The term $3T(1 - P)P^2$ is the total number of 2-connected branch units in the effective chains only, but without reference to order. This term in this simple system could be used in the calculation of average effective chain length, obviating the necessity for determining α, except to obtain the distributions of pendent chains. The term $3T(1 - P)^2P$ is the total number of branch units in pendent chains.

One more method of modeling for the branching coefficient is being studied. Using the logic of Macosko and Miller, the relationships for $\alpha = P(Br_A^{out})$ are derived. For all the simple cases described above (those with branch units of one chemical polarity only), the expected expressions resulted. Two non-equivalent branching coefficients occur in the 3,2,1/3,2,1 system. This problem is still being studied.

In summary, the status of modeling for branching coefficients of complex systems is as follows. In addition to the traditional method of Flory (2), several methods have been generated based on or employing the method of Macosko and Miller (16). Models have been derived for the 4,3,2,1/2,1 system and its subsystems, and the applicability generally to n ... 3,2,1/2,1 systems appears likely. A satisfactory model for the 3,2,1/3,2,1 system, or the more general case, n ... 3,2,1/m ... 3,2,1, has not been developed.

V. CONCLUSIONS

A mathematical model, based on Flory's branching coefficient, has been developed for the post-gelation state of crosslinked condensation polymers containing trifunctional branch units. Each step in the derivation of the equations of this model is accompanied by an easily visualized conceptual image. At the heart of the model is a hierarchy of branching coefficients, and derived functions, based on the observation that chain-terminating structural elements negate the crosslinking function of branch units and transform their function, one for one, into chain extension.

Given the starting composition of a polymer, including the functionality distributions of the ingredients, and a measure of extent of reaction, this model predicts sol and gel fractions, crosslink density (effective chain concentration), average length of effective chains, and the distribution of pendent chains according to size/complexity.

The predictions of sol/gel fractions and effective chain concentration have been verified experimentally by data from a set of compositions polymerized by esterification. Good correlation was found between effective chain length calculated for these polymers and their extensibility in the amorphous state (heated to 77°C).

In this set of experiments, initial moduli of 77°C tensile tests (100% per minute extension rate) were found to be equivalent to equilibrium moduli measured by the slow extension of solvent-swollen specimens at room temperature for effective chain concentration determination.

REFERENCES

1. W.H. Carothers, Trans. Faraday Soc., 32, 39 (1936).
2. P.J. Flory, J. Am. Chem. Soc., 63, 3083 (1941).
3. W.H. Stockmayer, J. Poly. Sci., 9, 69 (1952).
4. A.H. Strecker and D.M. French, Poly. Preprints, ACS, 7 (2), 952 (1966).
5. D.H. Solomon and J.J. Hopwood, J. Appl. Poly. Sci., 10, 1893 (1966).
6. J.H. Hodgkin, F.J. Martinelli, J. Heller, and H.E. Marsh, Jr., Poly. Preprints, ACS, 12 (1), 593 (1971).
7. H.E. Marsh, Jr., J. Heller, J.H. Hodgkin, and F.J. Martinelli, Poly. Preprints, ACS, 12 (1), 598 (1971).
8. J.H. Hodgkin and F.J. Martinelli, J. Macromol. Sci. A6 (4), 789 (1972).
9. L.C. Case, J. Poly. Sci., 45, 397 (1960).
10. L.C. Case and R.V. Wargin, Die Makromolekulare Chemie, 77, 172 (1964).
11. M. Gordon, et al., Proc. Roy. Soc. (London), A295, 29 (1966).
12. G.R. Dobson and M. Gordon, J. Chem. Phys., 43, 705 (1965).
13. M. Gordon and T.G. Parker, Proc. Roy. Soc., Edin. (A) 69, 13 (1970/71).
14. M. Gordon, W.C. Ward, and R.S. Whitney in "Polymer Networks" (eds. A.J. Chompff and S. Newman) Plenum Press, N.Y., 1971.
15. D.M. French, J. Macromol. Sci. A5 (6), 1123 (1971).
16. D.R. Miller and C.W. Macosko, Macromolecules, 9 (1976).
17. C.W. Macosko, Organic Coatings and Plastics Chemistry Preprints, ACS, 35 (2), 38 (1975).
18. P.J. Flory, "Principles of Polymer Chemistry", Cornell University Press, page 376 (1953).
19. K. Tsuge, R.J. Arenz, and R.F. Landel, "Mechanical Behavior of Materials" (Proceedings of the 1971 International Conference on Mechanical Behavior of Materials, Kyoto, Japan), 3, 443 (1972).
20. H.E. Marsh, Jr., AIAA Preprint No. 76-193 (1976).

NOTATION

A	functional group A
A_3, A_2, A_1	tri-, bi- and monofunctional A-molecules, respectively
A_0	cross-sectional area of tensile sample in unswollen state
B	functional group B

B_2, B_3	bi- and monofunctional B-molecules respectively
E_{A_i}, E_{B_j}	equivalent weights of ingredients
HC_G	moles of 0-order half-chains in gel
$L_0, L_1, L_2, \ldots, L_n$	lengths of n-order half chains in chain-atoms, for $n=0,1,2,\ldots,n$
L_{sp}	specific chain length, in moles of chain-atoms per unit mass
L_x	average length of effective chains, in chain atoms
$L_{E,n}, L_{P,n}$	average length of n-order ending and pendent chains
$P_{m/n}$	average number of m-order parasitic pendent chains on an n-order half-chain, for $m \leq n$
$P(F_A^{out})$	finite chain coefficient (Macosko and Miller)
$P(Br_A^{out})$	$= \alpha$
R	universal gas constant
$R_1, R_2, \ldots, R_n$	functions of α, as defined by equations 30 and 35
S	slope of load versus extension in equilibrium tensile test
T	absolute temperature (equation 44 only)
T	concentration of branch units, in moles per mole of A
T_S, T_G	moles of branch units in sol and gel respectively, per mole of A
$T_{S,i}, T_{G,i}$	moles of i-connected branch units in sol and gel respectively, per mole of A, for $i=0,1,2$, or 3
$(T_i)_j, (T_{S,i})_j, (T_{G,i})_j$	moles of j-order, i-connected branch units in the whole polymer, the sol and the gel, respectively, per mole of A, for $i=0,1,2$, or 3 and $j=1,2,\ldots,n$
V	volume of polymer per mole of A
W	mass of polymer per mole of A
W_R	mass of polymer per mole of A, corrected for loss due to evaporation of reaction product-water
W_G	mass of gel per mole of A
W_0	mass per average 0-order half-chain in gel
a_3, a_2, a_1	mole fraction of A's on tri-, bi and mono-functional A-molecules, respectively
b_2, b_1	mole fraction of B's on bi-and monofunctional B-molecules, respectively
d	density

h_0	distance between pin placements in an unswollen tensile test sample
p_A	fraction of *A's* reacted
p_B	fraction of *B's* reacted
r	stoichiometric ratio; ratio of *B's* to *A's* initially present
w_S	weight fraction of sol
w_G	weight fraction of gel
$x_1, x_2, \ldots, x_n$	chain extension coefficients for orders 1,2,...,n
α	branching coefficient (Flory)
$\alpha_1, \alpha_2, \ldots, \alpha_n$	branching coefficients for orders 1,2,...,n
α_g	branching coefficient determined by sol/gel fractionation measurement
α_ν	branching coefficient determined by effective chain concentration measurement
α'	branching coefficient for the sol fraction
ε_b	extension at break
$\nu_{e,A}, \nu_{e,V}$	concentration of effective chains, in moles per mole of *A* and per unit volume, respectively

CHARACTERIZATION OF POLYMER NETWORKS BY ELASTICITY MEASUREMENTS

A. J. Chompff
Department of Chemical Engineering
University of Southern California

Crosslinking of linear polymers is commonly thought to occur homogeneously throughout the reacting material, yielding networks of chains which are considered to be in the unperturbed state. This hypothesis forms one of the bases for the classical theory of rubber-elasticity from Gaussian chain statistics. A review is given of Gaussian and non-Gaussian network models leading to constitutive equations for rubbery behavior. It is shown that current knowledge of rubber elasticity has been insufficient to characterize polymer networks. Therefore, a new theory has been developed, based on excluded volume and molecular anisotropy considerations, to describe rubbery response in extension as well as in compression. This treatment can be used to characterize polymeric networks adequately.

I. INTRODUCTION

Due to the complex chemical nature of network formation most investigators attempt to describe the process as well as the product in terms of more general physico-chemical parameters. Thus, one is confronted with structural parameters such as the concentration as well as the functionality of crosslink points, wasted loops, possible chain entanglements which are trapped by crosslinking and polymeric molecules which are still unattached to the network.

Of course, in every practical application of crosslinked polymers one needs to obtain guidelines by characterizing the product, preferably not in terms of the primary molecules present before crosslinking, but rather in terms of the network structure. The present paper contains a review of this characterization by measurement of the rubber elasticity of the network. If the network is not rubbery it can be made rubbery by swelling in suitable solvents or plasticizers. Only the overall structure of the network will be considered in this paper. Other papers in this symposium will focus on the wasted loops, entanglements and soluble fractions. We will further limit the present treatment to mechanical characterization at small to moderate strains.

The most pressing problem in network characterization is the determination of the "crosslink density", or in other words the "concentration" of elastically effective network chains, ν^*. The statistical thermodynamic theory of rubber-elasticity provides an absolute method to characterize this quantity, provided the network consists of "ideal" polymer chains which are randomly coiling between their crosslink points. In the next section the basic premises and results of this theory will be reviewed and its deficiencies indicated. In the following sections various theoretical explanations of non-ideal rubbery behavior will be reviewed and a new mechanism is suggested. It should be noted, that network defects, such as crosslink density inhomogeneities lead to additional complications thus far not accounted for in traditional treatments of rubber elasticity.

II. NETWORKS OF GAUSSIAN CHAINS (1-4)

Free linear polymer molecules are commonly represented by infinitesimally thin very long randomly coiling chains, whose end-to-end distance is given by a Gaussian distribution function. Thus, if one chain end is placed at the origin of a cartesian coordinate system the probability of finding the other chain end in a volume element (dx dy dz) located at a distance $\underline{r}$ from the origin at the point (x, y, z) is given by

$$P\,(\underline{r})\,d\,\underline{r} = P\,(x,\,y,\,z)\,dx\,dy\,dz,$$

where

$$P\,(x,\,y,\,z) = \left(\frac{\beta}{\sqrt{\pi}}\right)^3 \exp\left\{-\beta^2\,(x^2 + y^2 + z^2)\right\}, \qquad (1)$$

which is the Gaussian error function. The proportionality constant to the third power is a normalization factor and β is given by

$$\beta = \left(\frac{3}{2\,\langle r_o^2\rangle}\right)^{\frac{1}{2}}, \qquad (2)$$

where $\langle r_o^2\rangle$ is the mean square end to end distance of the free linear molecules.

The meaning of the function P(x, y, z) is illustrated in Fig 1 for the one-dimensional case, P(x). Analogous relations hold for P(y) and P(z). Since P(x) is maximal at x = 0, and since P(x, y, z) = P(x) P(y) P(z) it is clear that the probability for finding a certain end-to-end distance is greatest when the distance is zero. This is physically impossible. Traditionally, one argues around this deficiency of the model by stating that the treatments will be limited to very long, thin and flexible macromolecules. In addition, if the volume element is expanded into a spherical shell the resulting (scalar) distribution function becomes insensitive to whatever happens at small r. Unfortunately, networks become anisotropic as soon as they are stressed and thus the scalar distribution function cannot be applied. In our opinion, if the probability of finding an end-to-end distance near r = 0 happens to be large - becoming larger as the chains become shorter, according to Eqs. (1) and (2) - then a very large fraction of the chains will have an r near zero and the response of these chains to stress will depend a great deal on how exactly their distribution near r = 0 occurs. This point, however, is deliberately ignored in the traditional kinetic theory of rubber elasticity of Gaussian chains. Thus, excluded volume effects are neglected in the Gaussian chain model.

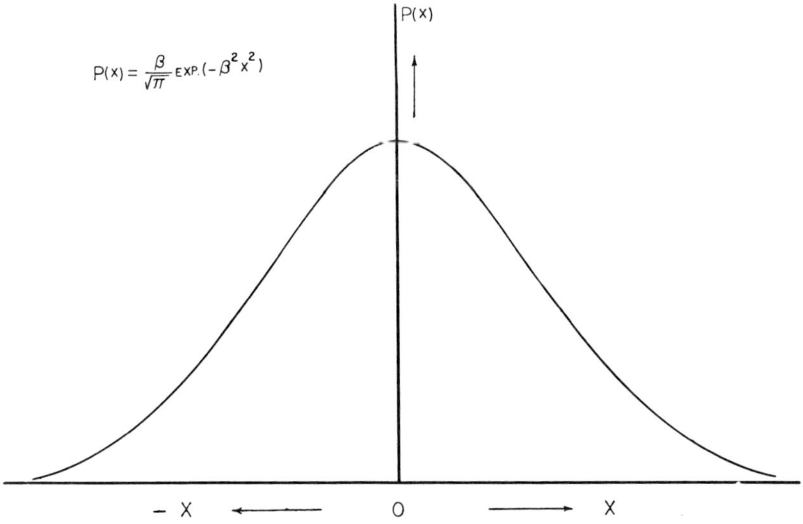

Fig. 1. Gaussian end-to-end distribution projected on the x-coordinate for a linear, freely jointed, randomly coiling macromolecule.

It is generally assumed that during network formation momentarily the network chains possess and end-to-end distance distribution identical to that whereby all the chains would exist as free linear molecules of the same contour length (5-9). Then the unperturbed mean square end to end distance between crosslinks is given by $\langle r_o^2 \rangle$. The fraction of network chains having one end at the origin of their private coordinate system and their other end in the volume element (dx, dy, dz) located at (x, y, z) is proportional to P(x, y, z). Each of these chains can assume a number of configurations that is also proportional to P(x, y, z). Upon deformation, the chain end-to-end vectors are assumed to transform in an affine way.

Using this model, the network partition function can be specified and the free energy change, ΔF_{el}, during elastic deformation can be calculated. Performing this operation using the method of Hermans, Flory and Wall (HFW) we find for the elastic free energy change (6,8,10,11)

$$\Delta F_{el} = \tfrac{1}{2} kT\nu \left[\frac{\langle r_i^2 \rangle}{\langle r_o^2 \rangle} A \; (\Lambda_x^2 + \Lambda_y^2 + \Lambda_z^2 - 3) - 2\,B \ln (\Lambda_x \Lambda_y \Lambda_z) \right], \qquad (3)$$

where k is Boltzmann's constant, T is the absolute temperature, ν is the number of elastically effective network chains in the system, $\langle r_i^2 \rangle$ is the mean square end to end distance of network chains in the undeformed isotropic state, $\langle r_o^2 \rangle$ is the mean square end to end distance of network chains in the unperturbed reference state, Λ_x, Λ_y and Λ_z are the deformation ratios with respect to the undeformed isotropic state and A and B are factors which depend on the molecular theory being used.

At present, a considerable amount of theoretical and experimental evidence (4,9,11,13-18) indicates that the factor B has the value predicted by Flory and Wall (11,15)

$$B = 2/f \,, \qquad (4)$$

where f is the functionality of the crosslinks. Using a variety of theoretical approaches one also may conclude (4,9, 19-23) that

$$A = (1 - \frac{2}{f}) \,, \qquad (5)$$

or ½ for four-functional crosslinks. Due to uncertainties in the interpretation of non-ideal rubbery behavior of real networks (see following sections) the factor A has not been evaluated unambiguously.

The meaning of the ratio $\langle r_i^2\rangle/\langle r_o^2\rangle$, also called "Tobolsky's (5,7) front factor", is illustrated in Fig 2, where the hypothesis of crosslinking in the unperturbed state is maintained (13). In Fig 2A molecules are being crosslinked while in solution, resulting in end-to-end distances which are distributed identically to that in the unperturbed state. Upon deswelling this network a "super-coiled" state is obtained, illustrated in Fig 2B, where $\langle r_i^2\rangle$ is now much smaller than $\langle r_o^2\rangle$. On the other hand, if the network would have been crosslinked to the same cross-link density in the absence of diluent the network shown in Fig 2C would have been obtained, where the end to end distances are again the same as in Fig 2A. It is also shown that the network chains "leap-frog" over other crosslink points, indicating that "composite networks" may be formed in this case. Upon swelling the network of Fig 2C a (still isotropic) expanded network is obtained where $\langle r_i^2\rangle$ is now much greater than $\langle r_o^2\rangle$. Thus "Tobolsky's front factor" takes into account the compressed or stretched perturbed state of the chains in the isotropic network just prior to testing.

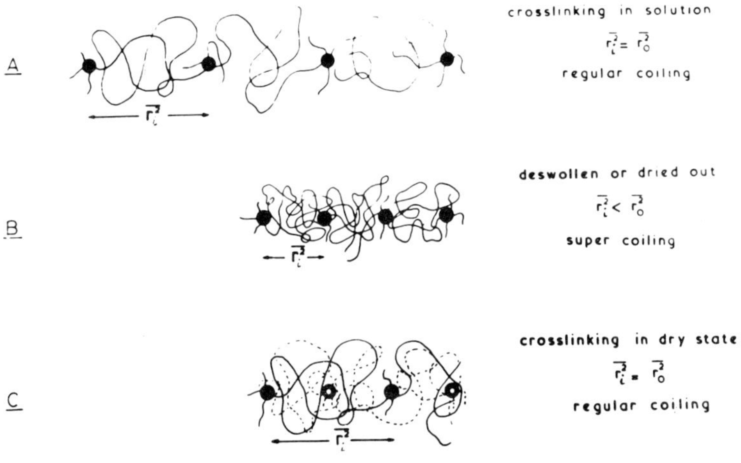

Fig. 2. Crosslinking in solution versus in bulk. In A as well as in C chain end-to-end distances are assumed identical to those in the unperturbed state. Crosslink densities in B and in C are the same, but in B there are fewer connectivity restrictions than in C. In C chains "leap frog" over crosslinks (From ref. (13)).

Similarly, the stretch ratios with respect to the isotropic network prior to testing are indicated by Λ, which are related to the stretch ratios with respect to the unperturbed reference state, indicated by λ, through the relationship

$$\lambda_x^2 = \frac{\langle r_i^2 \rangle}{\langle r_o^2 \rangle} \Lambda_x^2 , \qquad (6)$$

and analogous relations apply for the y and z direction.

The relation between elastically stored free energy and deformation, as given by Eq (3), may now be used to calculate the mechanical response of a network. For simple tension or unidirectional compression one obtains (14)

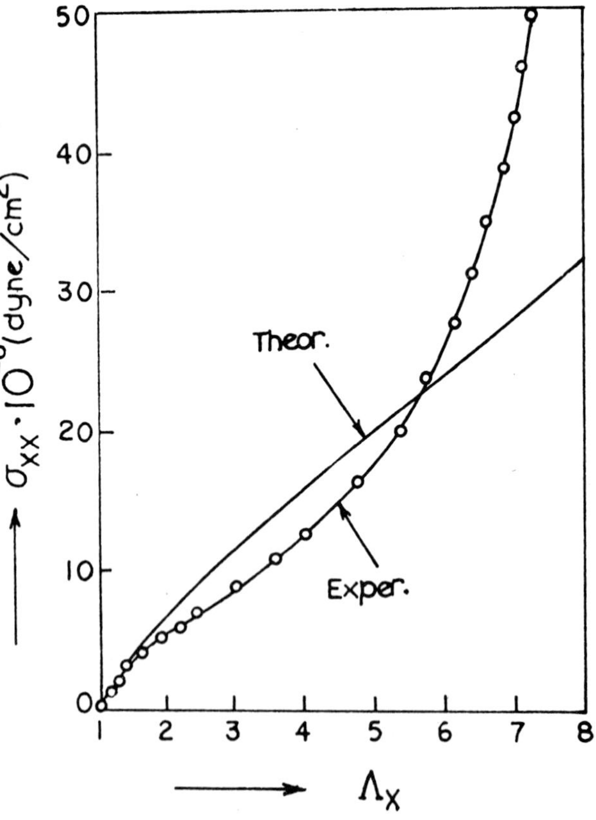

Fig. 3. Unidirectional extension curves for natural rubber. (From ref. (2)) The theoretical curve is calculated using Eq (7).

$$\sigma_{xx} = kT\nu^* A \frac{\langle r_i^2 \rangle}{\langle r_o^2 \rangle}\left[\Lambda_x - \frac{V}{V_i \Lambda_x^2}\right], \qquad (7)$$

where σ_{xx} is the tensile force per unit unstrained cross-section, Λ_x is the stretch ratio in the direction of tension, ν^* is the number of network chains per unit dry polymer volume, V_i is the volume in the undeformed isotropic state and V is the volume in the stretched state.

The result shown in Eq (7) can now be tested experimentally. A typical test is shown in Fig 3 for a crosslinked natural rubber, where both curves possess identical slopes at the origin (2). The correlation is generally fair to poor. Very few dry elastomers (24,25) obey the stress strain relationship of Eq (7) which is based on Gaussian chain statistics. Most elastomers follow an empirical relationship known as the Mooney-Rivlin equation (26-28) given by

$$\sigma_{xx} = C_1 \,(\Lambda_x - \Lambda_x^{-2}) + \frac{C_2}{\Lambda_x}\,(\Lambda_x - \Lambda_x^{-2}) , \qquad (8)$$

where C_1 and C_2 are independent of strain but still depend on temperature.

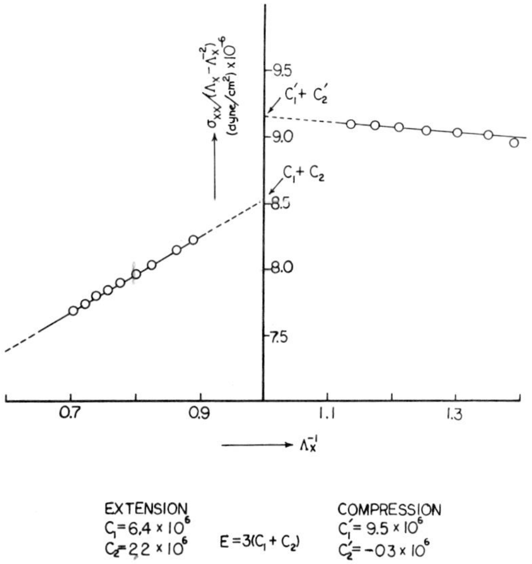

Fig. 4. Mooney-Rivlin plot of unidirectional extension and compression for a crosslinked polyurethane elastomer at 30°C. The values of C_1 and C_2 appear to be different in tension or compression (From ref. (29).)

This behavior is illustrated in Fig 4 for both extension and compression measurements on a polyurethane elastomer (29). It should be noted that the behavior of an ideal rubber, given by Eq (7), would yield in this plot a horizontal line given by

$$\sigma_{xx} / (\Lambda_x - \Lambda_x^{-2}) = C. \tag{9}$$

Thus, the tensile modulus, E, according to Eq (9) should be

$$E = 3\ C\ , \tag{10}$$

whereas Eq (8) would have yielded

$$E = 3\ (C_1 + C_2)\ . \tag{11}$$

Thus, the determination of the number of elastically effective network chains is in jeopardy.

From this comparison, it is clear that the "second term" in the Mooney-Rivlin equation does not represent a second term in a series expansion, such as to increase the accuracy at large elongations. Figs 3 and 4 clearly show that the "second term" is effective at very small strains. Eqs (10) and (11) clearly show that the stress/strain relations (7) and (8) are two completely independent constitutive equations for the rubbery state and that one may not relate C and C_1. This is again illustrated in Fig 5 for the same data as in Fig 4. Until now, no molecular theories have yet been developed which explain this non-ideal behavior adequately (30,31). Surprisingly, however, the mechanical response of swollen networks usually follows the Gaussian prediction (32-42).

In the following section various molecular theories attempting to explain non-ideal rubbery behavior will be reviewed. The effects of swelling, however, will not be treated in this paper.

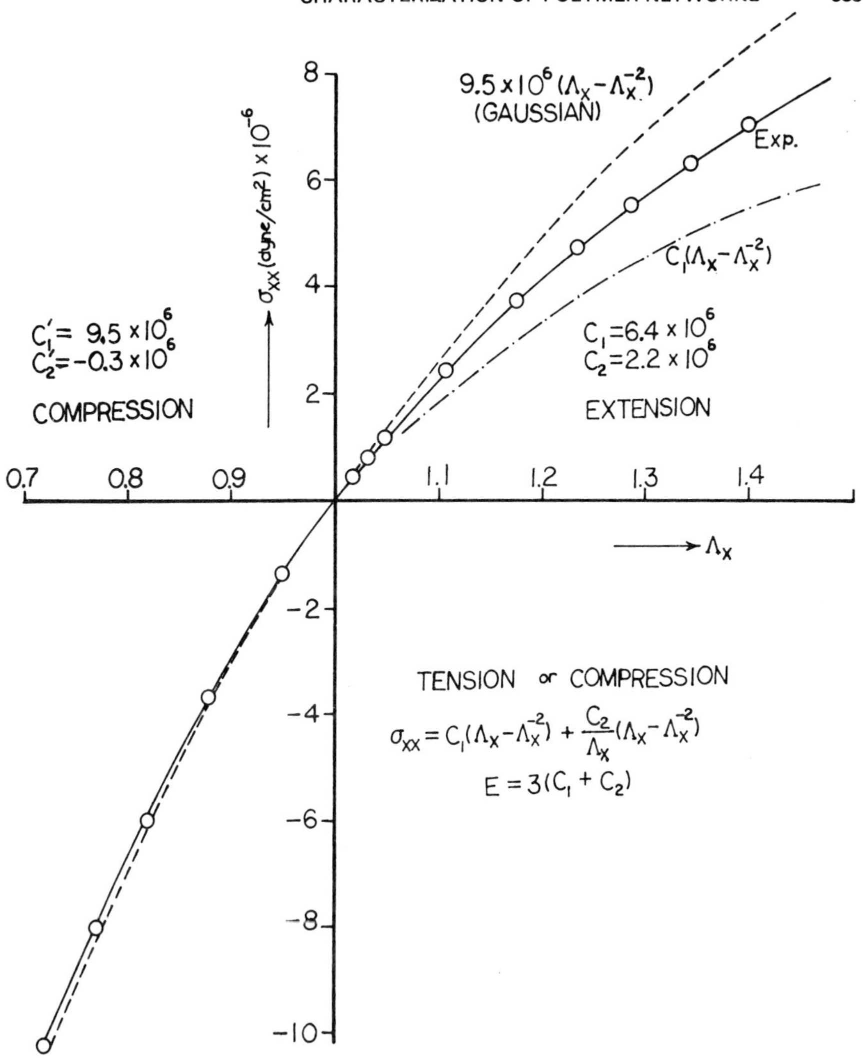

Fig. 5. The same data as in Fig 4 plotted conventionally. The first Mooney-Rivlin term lies considerably below the Gaussian curve (From ref. (29).)

III. NON-IDEAL NETWORKS

A disturbing characteristic of the Mooney-Rivlin equation is that different equations apply for extension or compression as shown in Figs 4 and 5. Even more disturbing is that extrapolation of the straight lines shown in Fig 4 leads often to different moduli for extension or compression. From this one may conclude that the Mooney-Rivlin equation is only a convenient way of representing a set of experimental data, but not all the data. Conversely, a theoretical derivation leading to an exact Mooney-Rivlin like response must be wrong, since it cannot account for all the data. Instead, the behavior at various modes of deformation must be dealt with in the same theory coherently.

Several authors (13) have tried to analyze the non-ideal behavior through a molecular mechanism. Intuitively, one may distinguish between models considering intra-chain interactions and those considering inter-chain interactions. The results of those analyses are briefly summarized in Tables I and II, which contain only a fraction of the works considering this problem. A selection had to be made to limit the length of this review. In addition, only small to moderate strains will be discussed and relaxations will be ignored

Table I

INTRA-CHAIN INTERACTIONS

Mechanism	Authors	Year	t_2	Notes
Short Chains	Treloar	1946	Negl.	N<6
Excl. Volume	Gee/Edwards	1966	Negl.	
	Prins	1964	$t_2 = 0$	
Int. Energy	Krigbaum/ Kaneko	1962	Negl.	
	Guth/Wang	1966	$+ t_2$	M.R.
Non-Affine Def.	Gordon/Dobson	1964	$- t_2$, Negl.	?

since they can be neutralized experimentally. In the penultimate column of Tables I and II the result of the theory is expressed in terms of its alteration of the expression for the Gaussian network. This modification may be accomplished through a negative term, $-t_2$, which lowers the Gaussian result for extension (see Fig 5), or it may be achieved through a positive term, $+ t_2$, such as in the

Mooney-Rivlin form.

A. INTRA-CHAIN INTERACTIONS (see Table I)

The effect of short chain lengths has been investigated by Treloar (43), who calculated the exact end-to-end distribution for a chain of N random links. For small N Treloar finds a small positive correction, + t_2, which becomes negligible when N exceeds 6. In normally crosslinked elastomers N is usually much larger than 6. One may then conclude that deviations from Gaussian behavior at moderate extensions cannot be caused by short chains only.

The effects of excluded volume on single chain statistics have been derived by Edwards (44). The resulting non-Gaussian distributions have been applied by Gee (45) in calculations of the stress/strain response of non-Gaussian networks. Gee found that at moderate extensions ($\lambda = 1$ to $\lambda = 2$) the networks behave in an ideal manner and concludes that the correction, t_2, should not be due to excluded volume effects. A more disturbing result, however, was that non-affine deformations may play a role when non-Gaussian chains are used. This would complicate matters enormously.

Excluded volume effects have been considered by Prins(13) in a different context. Although Prins did not derive a t_2 term, his treatment is reviewed here for its simplicity and it will clarify some of the following paragraphs. Mukherji and Prins (12) have suggested that the value of the front factor A might be connected with deviations from Gaussian statistics due to topological complexities. As noted in the previous section, a maximum probability for finding a chain end-to-end distance equal to zero is a physical impossibility, especially if the chain ends also drag six other chains along. Based on Schatzki's (46) self avoiding random walk results Mukherji and Prins (12,13) postulated an end-to-end distribution function in one dimension as shown in Fig 6. If similar expressions are written for the y and z direction and the end-to-end distribution in three dimensions can be given by P(x) P(y) P(z) the result is

$$P(x, y, z) = C^3 |x\ y\ z|^n \exp\{-\beta^2(x^2 + y^2 + z^2)\}, \quad (12)$$

where C and n are constants and n represents a chain expansion parameter independent of chain length or deformation. Following the HFW treatment one finds

$$\Delta F_{el} = \tfrac{1}{2} A(n + 1)\ \nu kT\ (\lambda_x^2 + \lambda_y^2 + \lambda_z^2 - 3) - (n + \tfrac{2}{f})\ \nu kT\ \ln\ (\lambda_x\ \lambda_y\ \lambda_z)\ , \quad (13)$$

where the λ symbol has been used to simplify the treatment. For unidirectional tension or compression one obtains from Eq (13)

$$\sigma_{xx} = A\ (n + 1)\ \nu^*\ kT\ (\lambda_x - \frac{1}{\lambda_x^2})\ . \qquad (14)$$

Typical n values for networks crosslinked in solution range from zero to one.

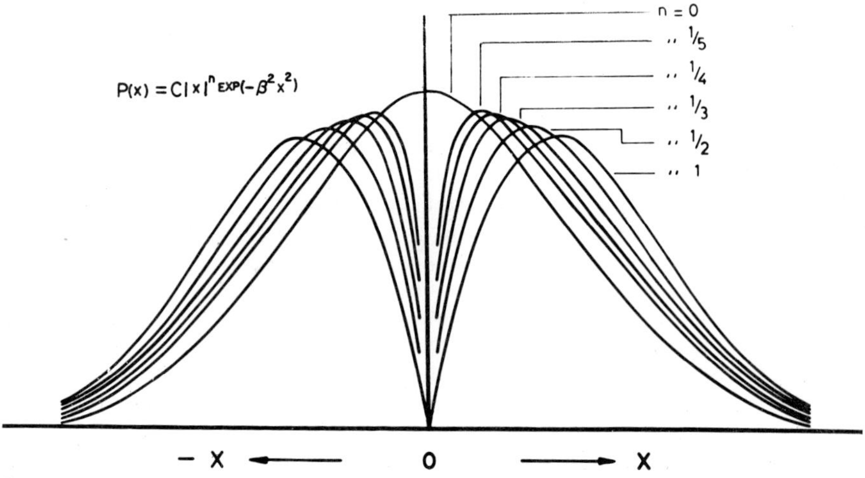

Fig. 6. Non-Gaussian end-to-end distribution projected on the x - coordinate according to Mukherji and Prins (12).

In our opinion, a serious deficiency of Prins' model is that P(x, y, z) becomes zero when either x, or y, or z is zero. Thus, in two dimensions P(x, y) has the form as illustrated in Fig 7, where equal end-to-end probabilities are drawn in the xy plane. Thus, in three dimensions P(x, y, z) will consist of eight lobes; a very unlikely physical model. Instead, one should expect a spherically symmetric distribution function where P(x, y, z) should vanish when the end-to-end vector, $\underline{r}$, becomes zero. This example illustrates that construction of P(x, y, z) from multiplication of P(x),

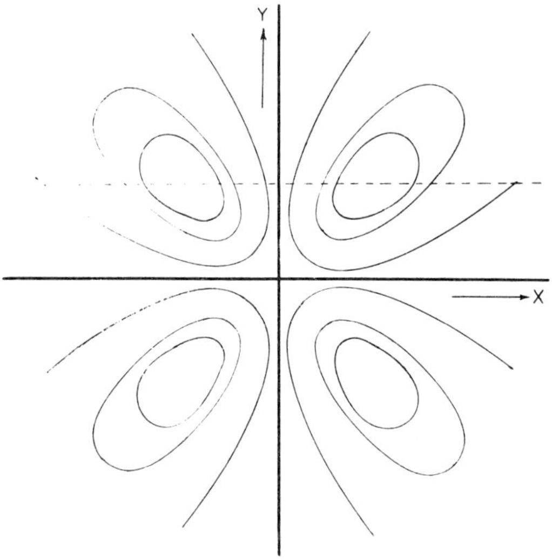

Fig. 7. Non-Gaussian end-to-end distribution according to Mukherji and Prins in two dimensions. The curves represent equal probabilities. A cross-section at the dotted line will reproduce the curve of Fig 6.

P(y) and P(z) is not always permitted.

A different intra-chain interaction, the effect of internal energy contributions, has been studied by Krigbaum & Kaneko (47) and by Wang and Guth (48). The first two authors developed a logical random walk model in N steps on a cubic lattice where the energy associated with each step is directionally sensitive, representing the rotational isomeric character of a real chain. Unfortunately, the results do not fit experimental data: a) if N = 100 the stresses calculated are always a little higher than that of the Gaussian curve contrary to experiment (see Fig 5), and b) the model is directly tied to an energy effect whereas it is known that C_2/C_1 ratios cannot be correlated with internal energy contributions to the macroscopic stress. Moreover, from calculations using large N values it can be concluded that intramolecular energy effects contribute negligible corrections to the ideal elastic theory.

Wang & Guth (48) and later Guth (49,50) have postulated that internal energy interactions can be treated analogous to a theory of ferromagnetism. Without giving many details Guth puts forward a stress/strain relation which is exactly the form of the Mooney-Rivlin equation. From the discussion in the beginning of this section we may conclude that this result must be wrong since only part of the data can be fit.

Finally, Dobson & Gordon (51) and later Gordon et. al. (52) draw attention to possible non-affine deformation of very short chains in the network, as indicated earlier by Kuhn and Grün (53). Their calculations yield a correction term which is negative. Unfortunately, their derivation is suspect. From the calculations of Roe and Krigbaum (54) one can conclude that the orientation of statistical elements is very small compared with the orientation of end-to-end vectors. For this reason a correction based on segment orientation is anticipated to be very small indeed. This last result has also been found by Blokland (29) after reconsidering Dobson and Gordon's calculations. Moreover, if non-affine deformations were found to be the main cause of non-ideal behavior all rules thus far developed would cease to exist and the problem becomes essentially insoluble.

In summary, (see Table I) it may be concluded that all intra-chain interactions discussed here lead to negligible corrections of the ideal elastic behavior. A more successful approach can be expected from inter-chain interactive effects which are more complex in nature.

B. INTER-CHAIN INTERACTIONS (see Table II):

Table II

INTER-CHAIN INTERACTIONS

Mechanism	Authors	Year	t_2	Notes
Entanglements	Priss	1957-1975	$+ t_2$	?
Packing (Excl. Vol.)	DiMarzio	1962	Negl.	
	Jackson et al	1968	$- t_2$	?
Micro-Anisotropy	Volkenstein	1959	$+ t_2$	
	Blokland	1969	$- t_2$	
Non-Gaussian netw.	Chompff	1976	$+ t_2$	

The effects of entanglements obstructing chain reorganization during deformation has been studied by Priss. (55,56). Essentially, Priss suggests a non-affine deformation mechanism. The physical premises, however, are not very convincing. His model of a polymer chain is a rather static model and his averaging procedures remain obscure. In our opinion, if a network chain happens to be severely obstructed by one or n entanglements we probably should not consider it as one elastically effective network chain but as two chains or (n + 1) individual chains respectively.

The effects of excluded volume type obstruction due to packing has been considered in great detail by Di Marzio (57) and by Jackson et al. (58,59). Both treatments involve calculation of the entropy of packing chains in a cubic lattice in addition to the conformational entropy of the isolated chains. Di Marzio's results yield rather small negative corrections to the Gaussian force which are insufficient to explain the non-ideal behavior. Jackson et al arrive at a much larger negative correction. Jackson's result can be summarized as follows

$$\sigma_{xx} = A\nu^{*}kT\left(\lambda_x - \frac{1}{\lambda_x^2}\right)\left[1 - \frac{f(2\lambda_x^2 + \lambda_x^{-1})}{3N(1-f)}\right], \tag{15}$$

where N is the number of steps on the cubic lattice and f is the fraction of space occupied by polymeric chains. This treatment, however, when fit to experimental data, yield free volume fractions, 1-f, ranging from 15% to 25% (29). It seems likely, therefore, that Jackson et al overestimate the effect of excluded volume obstruction and that Di Marzio's treatment is more nearly correct. This fact has been verified by Gaylord and Smith (60), who recalculated Jackson's approach using a more consistent non-Gaussian model.

The existence of microstructural anisotropy and its effect on rubber elasticity has been postulated by several authors. Volkenstein et al (61), elaborating on the calculations by Kuhn and Grün (62), assume that the network chains pass through elongated ordered regions, "bundles", which orient during deformation. Since this mechanism resembles that of orientation of short rigid chains, Volkenstein's result, except for the sign, greatly resembles that of Dobson and Gordon (51) and also implies non-affine deformation. When fit to experimental data, Volkenstein's theory predicts a number of "bundles" almost as large as the number of network chains; an impossible result. It can be shown from analyses of light scattering data on networks that the number of bundles, if present, must be at least four orders of magnitude smaller (13,29). If Volkenstein's model (see Fig 8) applies, a network of two chains should be mechanically equivalent to a matrix of a four chain network reinforced by a rigid rod. It is known, however, that the mechanical response of elastomers cannot be simulated by such a composite.

Blokland and Prins, (29,63) inspired by rheo-optical evidence of microstructural anisotropy (64,65), postulated an "obstructed random walk" model, as illustrated in Fig 8. Each network chain passes through an "extended chain region" occupying about 10 to 15% of the chain's contour length. Thus, a network chain starting at A performs a random walk in space until it arrives at the obstructed region, where it performs a number of steps in one direction.

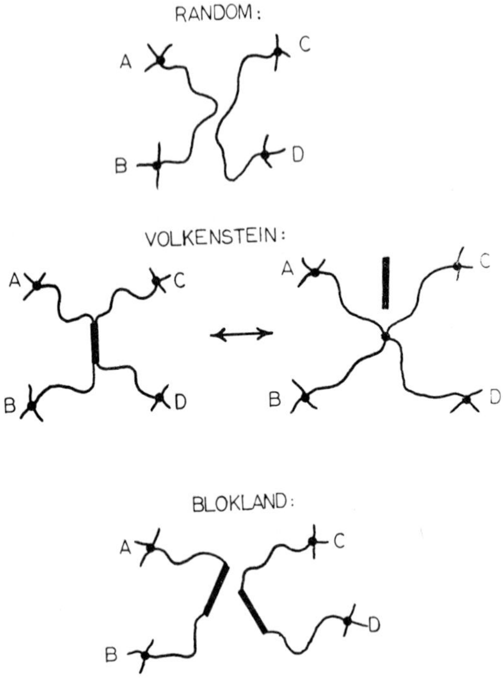

Fig. 8. Comparison of the random network model with that of Volkenstein et al (61) and of Blokland (29). Volkenstein's model of two network chains behaves as four chains plus a whisker-like rod. Blokland's model of two chains remains to behave as two independent chains, each passing through their own "extended chain region".

Upon exitting this obstructed region the chain continues a random walk until it arrives at B. The obstructed regions of different chains are uncorrelated in Blokland's model, as opposed to correlated in Volkenstein's model. This implies that the obstructed region must be very mobile, probably as much as the random sections. For this model Blokland derives an end-to-end distribution which in the one dimensional case has the form

$$P(x) = K \exp\left\{-\frac{3x^2}{2(N - 3m_x)\, A_x^2}\right\}\cosh \phi_x \ , \tag{16}$$

$$\phi_x = \frac{3xm_x}{(N - 3m_x)\, A_x^2} \ , \tag{17}$$

where N is the total number of steps from A to B, A_x is the step length and m_x is (a new parameter) the number of obstructed steps in the x direction which are given in the undeformed state by

$$m_{xo} = m_o/3 \ , \tag{18}$$

and in the deformed state by

$$m_x = \left(\frac{1}{3} - \frac{\lambda_x^2 - \lambda_x^{-1}}{3N}\right)m_o \ , \tag{19}$$

in agreement with Di Marzio (57).
Analogous relations apply to the y and z direction and P(x, y, z) is constructed by multiplying P(x), P(y) and P(z). Instead of using the HFW method, the method of James and Guth (49,66) is used to derive the elastically stored free energy. The final result obtained is

$$\sigma_{xx} = C\ (\lambda_x - \lambda_x^{-2}) - C\sum_{i=x,y,z}\tanh\ \phi_i \left(\frac{\partial\phi_i}{\partial\lambda_x}\right) . \tag{20}$$

To fit Eq (20) to experimental data Blokland introduces an additional "extra orientation" parameter (29).

Aside from the uncomfortable situation that two additional parameters are introduced, Blokland's model containing uncorrelated ordered regions of high mobility seems rather extravagant. Even if the "extra orientation" parameter is omitted it seems that the resulting (sizeable) corrections to the ideal elasticity theory are a consequence of a rather fortuitous mathematical choice of the probability distribution function, Eqs (16) through (19).

In summary, (see Table II) one may conclude that presently described inter-chain interaction mechanisms do not satisfactorily describe non-ideal elastic behavior. The models from DiMarzio and Jackson et al do not yield large enough correction terms. The models containing micro-anisotropy are not generally applicable since the degree of microstructural order is not a constant. Moreover, Flory (67) has commented that the magnitude of the observed optical anistropies are comparable to the correlative effects normally expected in liquids and are insufficient to be reconciled with the degree of order postulated.

IV. A NEW NON-GAUSSIAN CHAIN MODEL

In retrospect, most of the models discussed above exhibit a common feature: a non-Gaussian chain end-to-end distribution with probabilities $P(\underline{r})$ which at large r are greater than those for the Gaussian coil. For example, in Volkenstein's and Blokland's model the extended chain section serves to stretch the whole chain without placing unduly stress at the ends. In DiMarzio's and Jackson's model it is emphasized that large end-to-end distances, particularly in the stressed state, have greater probability than Gaussian theory predicts. In Krigbaum's model, and perhaps in Guth's model also, trans conformations are given a greater probability than gauche. The opposite effect may be expected for networks crosslinked in solution and stretched in the dry state. Indeed, such networks tend to behave more ideal elastic than conventional elastomers (68-74). The effects of excluded volume on zero end-to-end distances have been considered by a number of authors for many years(44,75-77). Monte Carlo techniques for non-intersecting random walks have been developed just for this purpose. The results, however, have seldom been expressed or approximated in closed form as in Prins' approach. Our concern for the elastic response of these non-Gaussian chain distributions has already been expressed in the previous section on Gaussian chains.

More clarity on these effects have been provided by the analytical treatments of Reiss and Yamakawa. Reiss (78) derived that the end-to-end distribution of a random flight chain, if excluded volume is taken into account, is

$$P(\underline{r}) = C \exp\left(- Br^{2} - Ar^{-1} \right) , \tag{21}$$

where A, B and C are constants. Yamakawa (79) indicates some deficiencies in Riess' calculation and arrives at

$$P(\underline{r}) = C \exp\left(- Br^{2} - Ar^{-3}\right) . \tag{22}$$

These results apply to self avoiding random walks for free molecules, where one chain end is at the origin and the location of the other end is found by chance. For a network chain, however, both chain ends have (on the average) predetermined locations thereby placing an additional requirement on the random walk process. The closed form expression, P(r), for such a chain is presently not known.

In this context another non-Gaussian phenomenon should be highlighted: the anisotropic radial segment distribution of a network chain. Presently, only radial segment distributions of free molecules have been calculated. Many years ago, Kuhn (80) drew attention to the strong asymmetry of the random flight chain, following from consideration of the average loci of several special segments in the chain relative to its end-to-end vector. More recently Šolc (81), Stockmayer (82) and Kranbuel (83) et al have reconsidered this problem and have confirmed their results by Monte Carlo studies. They find that the radial segment distribution of a random flight chain is quite anisotropic, which in our opinion implies that even in the unstressed state end-to-end distances of network chains must be considerably larger than would follow from the Gaussian model.

These considerations and the results shown in Eqs (21) and (23) led us to postulate a non-Gaussian chain model, which would intrinsically possess the characteristics of a chain expanded by excluded volume effects (remember Fig 6) and by restrictions due to packing.

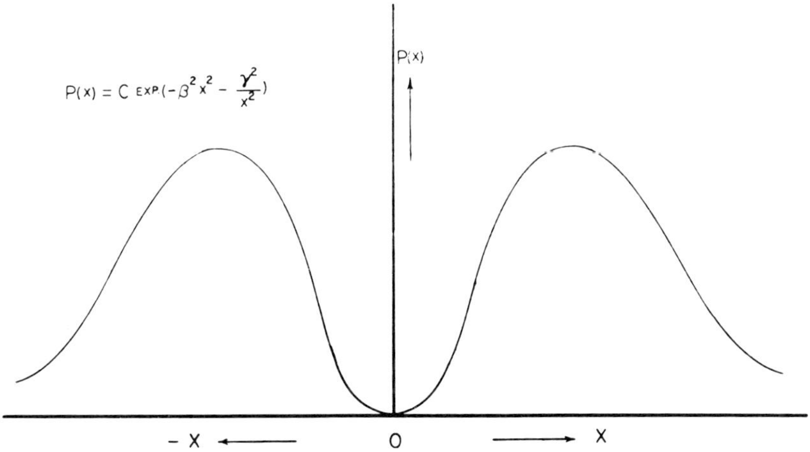

Fig. 9. End-to-end distribution of a new model of a non-Gaussian network chain. The parameter γ is a semi-empirical chain expansion parameter.

A model whose one dimensional end-to-end distribution is shown in Fig 9 is suggested, where the probability along the X- coordinate is given by

$$P(x) = C \exp\left(-\beta^2 x^2 - \frac{\gamma^2}{x^2}\right), \tag{23}$$

and where γ presently is introduced as a semi-empirical "chain expansion parameter".

An interesting result follows if we now would make the same mistake made by Mukherji and Prins (12) by writing

$$P(x, y, z) = C^3 \exp\left\{-\beta^2 r^2 - \gamma^2\left(\frac{1}{x^2} + \frac{1}{y^2} + \frac{1}{z^2}\right)\right\}. \tag{24}$$

Using the method of James and Guth we obtain from this

$$\sigma_{xx} = kT\nu^* (1 + 2\beta\gamma)(\lambda_x - \lambda_x^{-2})$$
$$+ 2kT\nu^* \beta\gamma(1 - \lambda_x^{-3}), \tag{25}$$

which is a Mooney-Rivlin equation. This answer must be wrong because equation (24) is suspect, since it would possess characteristics as shown in Fig 7. Equation (25) shows that the correction term, t_2, will be a positive term and illustrates that a Mooney-Rivlin type result cannot be trusted.

A correct consequence of Eq (23) should be written as

$$P(x, y, z) = C^3 \exp\left\{-\beta^2 r^2 - \frac{\gamma^2}{x^2 + y^2 + z^2}\right\}. \tag{26}$$

We now calculate the elastically stored free energy using the method of James and Guth. Fortunately, a large part of the labor involved in solving this problem has already been performed several years ago by Thomas (84). In his treatment, however, no molecular model or qualitative mechanism was suggested. The result for unidirectional extension is

$$\sigma_{xx} = \frac{1}{3} kT\nu^* (1 + 2\beta\gamma)(\lambda_x - \lambda_x^{-2}) \tag{27}$$
$$+ \frac{kT\nu^* \beta^2\gamma^2}{(1 + 2\beta\gamma)Q}\left[\frac{(\lambda_x^3 + 2)\tan^{-1} Q^{.5}}{Q^{.5}} - 3\right],$$

where

$$Q = \lambda_x^3 - 1. \tag{28}$$

This result has already been tested by Thomas and is shown in Fig 10 as a Mooney-Rivlin plot for the data of Rivlin and Saunders (85) for natural rubber. The fit to the experimental data is excellent and the apparently different response of networks to extension or compression can now be explained. Further studies are in progress to better understand the physical meaning of the chain extension parameter γ for a variety of networks (86).

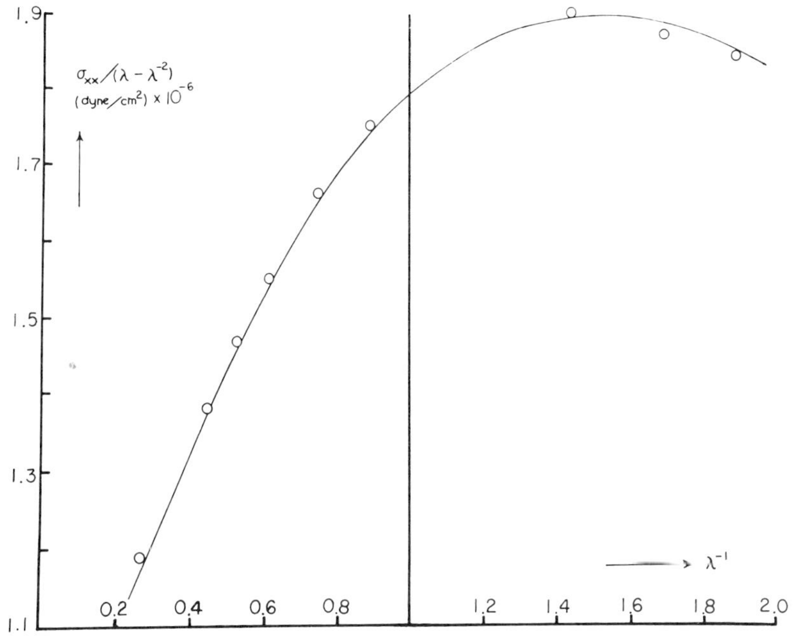

Fig. 10. Comparison between theory and experiments. Tension and compression data from Rivlin and Saunders (85) on crosslinked natural rubber.

In our opinion, this new model is preferrable over existing models discussed in the previous sections. The non-ideal elastic behavior of elastomers is hereby explained in a natural way. If one accepts this model, other particular effects such as inhomogeneities and entanglements can be evaluated individually.

V. CONCLUDING REMARKS

The previous sections clearly show that the new molecular model outlined in the last section is superior to other mechanisms which describe non-ideal rubber elasticity. This model is based on recent findings of the effect of excluded volume on closed form expressions for non-Gaussian chain end-to-end distributions.

In experiments and calculations on free molecules the population of end-to-end distances near $\underline{r} = 0$ is generally masked, since the volume element $(dx\ dy\ \overline{dz})$ is generally expanded to $4\pi r^2 dr$. In the theory of rubber elasticity, however, the anisotropic notation is preserved. This implies that the population near $r = 0$ will affect the mechanical response of network chains enormously. In Gaussian chains, expecially those with short contour lengths, the population near $r = 0$ is very high. In the present non-Gaussian model the end to end distribution near $r = 0$ vanishes.

In principle, equation (27) can now be used to characterize the overall structure of polymer networks, which was the objective of this paper. It should be noted, however, that such interpretations of experimental data should not be applied indiscriminatory. A great deal of theoretical and experimental evidence exists (see other papers in this symposium) that most networks are not formed in a homogeneous state (14,87-89). A discussion on this topic exceeds the scope of the present paper. It is clear, however, that a careful selection of experiments is required to further develop and verify the suggested network model.

VI. ACKNOWLEDGEMENTS

The author wishes to thank Drs. R. Salovey and W. V. Chang for stimulating discussions and Mr. Mukesh C. Gandhi for his assistance in many of these calculations.

VII. REFERENCES

1. P. J. Flory, "Principles of Polymer Chemistry", Cornell University Press, Ithaca, N.Y. (1953).
2. L. R. G. Treloar, "The Physics of Rubber Elasticity", Oxford University Press (1958).
3. F. Bueche, "Physical Properties of Polymers", Intersci-ence Publ., N.Y. (1962).
4. A. J. Staverman, in "Encyclopedia of Physics", S. Flügge, Ed., 13, 432ff, Springer Verlag, Berlin (1962).
5. A. V. Tobolsky, Ph.D. Thesis, Princeton U. (1944).

6. J. J. Hermans, Trans. Faraday Soc. 43, 591 (1947).
7. A. V. Tobolsky, D. W. Carlson and N. Indictor, J. Polymer Sci. 54, 175 (1961).
8. P. J. Flory, Trans. Faraday Soc. 57, 829 (1961).
9. J. A. Duiser and A. J. Staverman, in "Physics of Non-Crystalline Solids", J. A. Prins, Ed., pp. 376, North Holland (1965).
10. F. T. Wall, J. Chem. Phys. 11, 527 (1943).
11. F. T. Wall and P. J. Flory, J. Chem. Phys. 19, 1435 (1951).
12. B. Mukherji and W. Prins, J. Polymer Sci., A,2, 4367 (1964).
13. W. Prins, in "Physics of Non-Crystalline Solids", J. A. Prins, Ed., pp.360, North Holland (1965).
14. K. Dusek and W. Prins, Advanc. Polymer Sci. 6, 1 (1969).
15. P. J. Flory, J. Chem. Phys. 18, 108 (1950).
16. J. Van Dam, Ph.D. Thesis, Delft (1967).
17. W. Borchard, Ph.D. Thesis, Aachen (1966).
18. E. J. Van de Kraats, M. A. M. Winkeler, J. M. Potters and W. Prins, Rec. Trav. Chim. Pays-Bas 88, 449 (1969).
19. H. M. James and E. Guth, J. Chem. Phys. 15, 669 (1947).
20. A. J. Chompff, Ph.D. Thesis, Delft (1965).
21. A. J. Chompff and J. A. Duiser, J. Chem. Phys. 45, 1505 (1966).
22. S. Imai and M. Gordon, J. Chem. Phys. 50, 3889 (1969).
23. S. F. Edwards, in "Polymer Networks", A. J. Chompff and S. Newman, Eds., Plenum Press, N.Y. (1971).
24. G. Kraus and G. A. Moczvgemba, J. Polymer Sci. A,2, 277 (1964).
25. R. F. Landel, in "Polymer Networks", A. J. Chompff and S. Newman, Eds., Plenum Press, N.Y. (1971).
26. M. Mooney, J. Appl. Phys. 11, 582 (1940).
27. R. S. Rivlin, Philos. Trans. Roy. Soc. A, 241, 379 (1948).
28. B. M. E. Van der Hoff and E. J. Buckler, J. Macromol. Sci. A1, 747 (1967).
29. R. Blokland, Ph.D. Thesis, Delft (1968).
30. K. J. Smith and R. J. Gaylord, A.C.S. Polymer Preprints 14, 708 (1973).
31. J. E. Mark, Rubber Chem. Tech. 48, 495 (1975).
32. G. Gee, Trans, Faraday Soc. 42, 585 (1946).
33. S. M.Gumbrell, L. Mullins and R. S. Rivlin, Trans. Faraday Soc. 49, 1495 (1953).
34. L. Mullins, J. Appl. Pol. Sci. 2, 257 (1959).
35. A. Ciferri and P. J. Flory, J. Appl. Phys. 30, 1498 (1959).
36. K. J. Smith, A. Greene and A. Ciferri, Kolloid-Z. Z. Polym. 194, 49 (1964).

37. J. E. Mark and P. J. Flory, J. Appl. Phys. 37, 4635 (1966).
38. G. Allen, M. C. Kirkham, J. Padget and C. Price, Trans. Faraday Soc. 67, 1278 (1971).
39. F. de Candia and L. Amelino, J. Polym. Sci., A2, 10, 715 (1972).
40. F. de Candia, Macromolecules, 5, 102 (1972).
41. C. U. Yu and J. E. Mark, Macromolecules 7, 229 (1974).
42. P. J. Flory and Y. Tatara, J. Polym. Sci., Polym. Phys. Ed. 13, 683 (1975).
43. L. R. G. Treloar, Trans. Faraday Soc. 42, 77 (1946).
44. S. F. Edwards, Proc. Phys. Soc., Lond. 85, 613 (1965).
45. G. Gee, Polymer 7, 373 (1966).
46. T. F. Schatzki, J. Polymer Sci. 57, 337 (1962).
47. W. R. Krigbaum and M. Kaneko, J. Chem. Phys. 36, 99 (1962).
48. M. C. Wang and E. Guth, J. Chem. Phys. 20, 1144 (1952).
49. E. Guth, J. Polymer Sci, C, 12, 89 (1966).
50. E. Guth, J. Polymer Sci, C, 31, 267 (1970).
51. G. R. Dobson and M. Gordon, Trans. Inst. Rubber Ind. 40, T 261 (1964).
52. M. Gordon, J. A. Love and D. Pugh, J. Chem. Phys. 49, 4680 (1968).
53. W. Kuhn and F. Grün, Kolloid-Z. 101, 248 (1942).
54. R. J. Roe and W. R. Krigbaum, J. Appl. Phys. 35, 153 (1964).
55. L. S. Priss, Dokl. Acad. Nauk SSSR, 116, 225 (1957).
56. L. S. Priss, J. Polymer Sci., C, 53, 195 (1975).
57. E. A. DiMarzio, J. Chem. Phys. 36, 1563 (1962).
58. J. L. Jackson, M. C. Shen and D. A. McQuarrie, J. Chem. Phys. 44, 2388 (1966).
59. M. Shen, W. F. Hall and R. E. DeWames, J. Macromol. Sci.-Revs. Macromol. Chem., C2, 183 (1968).
60. R. J. Gaylord and K. J. Smith, Jr., in preparation.
61. M. V. Volkenstein, Iu. Ya. Gotlib and O. B. Ptitsyn, Vysokomolekul. Soedin. 1, 1056 (1959).
62. W. Kuhn and F. Grün, Helv. Chim. Acta 29, 1615 (1946).
63. R. Blokland and W. Prins, J. Polymer Sci. A2, 7, 1595 (1969).
64. M. C. A. Donkersloot, J. H. Gouda, J. J. Van Aartsen and W. Prins, Rec. Trav. Chim. Pays-Bas 86, 321 (1967).
65. J. H. Gouda, Ph.D. Thesis, Delft (1969).
66. H. M. James and E. Guth, J. Chem. Phys. 21, 1039 (1953).
67. P. J. Flory, Macromol. Chem. 8, 1 (1973).
68. J. Hasa and J. Janáček, J. Polymer Sci., C, 16, 317 (1967).
69. J. E. Mark, J. Am. Chem. Soc. 92, 7252 (1970).
70. C. Price, G. Allen, F. de Candia, M. C. Kirkham and A. Subramaniam, Polymer 11, 486 (1970).

71. M. C. Kirkham, J. Appl. Polym. Sci. 15, 1099 (1971).
72. F. de Candia, L. Amelino and C. Price, J. Polym. Sci., A2, 10, 975 (1972).
73. R. M. Johnson and J. E. Mark, Macromolecules 5, 41 (1972).
74. C. S. M. Ong and R. S. Stein, J. Polymer Sci., Polym. Phys.Ed., 12, 1599 (1974).
75. J. J. Hermans, M. S. Klamkin and R. Ullman, J. Chem. Phys. 20, 1360 (1952).
76. M. Kumbar and S. Windwer, J. Chem. Phys. 49, 4057 (1968).
77. C. Domb. J. Chem. Phys. 38, 2957 (1963).
78. H. Reiss, J. Chem. Phys. 47, 186 (1967).
79. H. Yamakawa, J. Chem. Phys. 48, 3845 (1968).
80. W. Kuhn, Kolloid Z. 68, 2 (1934).
81. K. Šolc, J. Chem. Phys. 55, 335 (1971).
82. K. Šolc and W. H. Stockmayer, J. Chem. Phys. 54, 2756 (1971).
83. D. Kranbuehl, P. H. Verdier and J. Spencer, J. Chem. Phys. 59, 3861 (1973).
84. A. G. Thomas, Trans. Faraday Soc. 51, 569 (1955).
85. R. S. Rivlin and D. W. Saunders, Phil. Trans. Royal Soc. A 243, 251 (1951).
86. in preparation.
87. A. J. Chompff and S. Newman, Eds., "Polymer Networks", Plenum Press, N.Y. (1971).
88. K. Dušek, Coll. Czech. Chem. Comm. 33, 1100 (1968).
89. J. Janáček and V. Vojta, J. Polymer Sci. C, 53, 291 (1975).

THE EFFECT OF NETWORK STRUCTURE IN THE EQUATION OF RUBBER ELASTICITY. II. FURTHER RESULTS

E. M. Valles* and C. W. Macosko
Department of Chemical Engineering and Materials Science
University of Minnesota, Minneapolis, 55455

Though the stress, strain and temperature dependence for an ideal rubber is fairly well established, the relation between network structural features like crosslinks, dangling ends and entanglements and mechanical response is still uncertain. Miller and Macosko have recently derived some modulus structure relations for several types of networks. These relations are tested here with a model system: the hydrosilation crosslinking of vinyl terminated polydimethylsiloxane chains with tetra- and tri-functional silane. Results of shear modulus versus extent of reaction and versus stoichiometric imbalance are in good agreement with the theory.

I. INTRODUCTION

The statistical theory of rubber elasticity is one of the simplest and most successful theories in polymer science. It correctly predicts that modulus increases with temperature and does reasonably well in fitting stress-strain data for real elastomers (see, for instance, Flory (1), Treloar (2)).

The theory also predicts a simple relation between shear modulus, G, and network structure

$$G = \phi \nu RT , \tag{1}$$

where R is the gas constant, T the absolute temperature, and ν the number of elastically effective network chains per unit volume, while ϕ is the ratio of the mean square end-to-end distance of the polymer chains in the undeformed network to that of random coils of the same length. For networks formed in bulk, with long flexible chains between junction points and

* Permanent address: Universidad del Sur, Bahia Blanca, Rep. Argentina.

without orientation, ϕ is expected to be close to unity.

Thus the key structural parameter is ν. Despite the widespread acceptance of the rubber elasticity theory, the relation between network structure and mechanical response has not been verified quantitatively (1-5).

Recently Miller and Macosko (6) have presented theoretical relations for ν for several types of networks. Qualitatively their approach breaks ν down into a contribution from chemical crosslinks or junctions, ν_c, and one from trapped physical entanglements, ν_e:

$$\nu = \nu_c + \nu_e \tag{2}$$

$$\nu_c = [A_f]_o [\sum_{i=3}^{f} P_i (i/2)(i - 2)/i] \tag{3}$$

$$\nu_e = \epsilon T_e \, , \tag{4}$$

where $[A_f]_o$ is the initial concentration of f-functional groups in the system; P_i the fraction of junctions in the system which have i infinite strands emanating from them; ϵ the concentration of potential entanglements; and T_e the fraction of trapped entanglements.

Calculation of the terms that make up ν_c can be illustrated by considering network formation from f-functional molecules of type A polymerizing with bifunctional B's. If the reaction goes to completion with stoichiometric amounts of A and B groups, the concentration of chemical junctions will be just $[A_f]_o$. For each A_f there will be f/2 chains. However, if the reaction is not complete or if stoichiometry of the reactants is unbalanced, not all chains attached to a random A_f will lead to the infinite network; some will be dangling. In this case, the concentration of effective chemical junctions in the system is given by the contribution of the junctions which have at least three strands leading to the infinite network structure (7). Assuming ideal network formation (equal reactivity and no loop formation). Miller and Macosko (6) show how to calculate the fraction of junctions with i infinite strands in the system as a function of the extent of the crosslinking reaction and the initial stoichiometric imbalance of the reactants.

The last term in Equation (3), (i-2)/i, follows from the theoretical arguments of Duiser and Staverman (8) and Graessley (9) that, as the functionality of the junction point increases, the junction becomes more mechanically effective. Thus, a chain ending in trifunctional junctions will be 1/3 as effective as one ending in immobile junctions, one with an infinite number of chains to the network.

It has long been postulated that entanglements also can contribute to the equilibrium modulus of chemically crosslinked networks (1). When long, linear polymer chains are tested dynamic mechanically, over a certain time scale they behave like crosslinked rubbers with an average molecular weight between crosslinks of M_e (see, for instance, Ferry (10)). Thus a concentration of mechanically effective entanglements can be defined; $\epsilon_o = d_o/2M_e$, where d_o is the polymer density. The value of ϵ_o should only depend on the type of polymer.

In a truly crosslinked system, Langley (11) argues that, if an entanglement is trapped (that is, if all four ends of the two chains involved in the entanglement lead to the infinite network), then it will contribute to the equilibrium modulus through a concentration ϵ. This ϵ should be related to ϵ_o. The product of ϵ and the fraction of trapped entanglement, T_e, in the rubber gives the total contribution of entanglements, ν_e, to G. T_e has been derived for a number of cases (6,11).

Miller and Macosko derive complete equations for ν for a number of systems. For example, for the case of A_4 polymerizing with B_2,

$$\nu = [A_4]_o[\frac{3}{2} - 1/rp^2 + (1/rp^2 - \frac{3}{4})^{\frac{1}{2}}][\frac{3}{2} - (1/rp^2 - \frac{3}{4})^{\frac{1}{2}}]^2 + \epsilon\{rp - (rp/8)[(4/rp^2 - 3)^{\frac{1}{2}} - 1]^3\}^4 , \quad (5)$$

And for A_3 polymerizing with B_2,

$$\nu = [A_3]_o \frac{1}{2}(\frac{2rp^2 - 1}{rp^2})^3 + \epsilon(\frac{2rp^2 - 1}{rp^3})^4 \quad (6)$$

where p is the extent of reaction of A groups, $([A]_o - [A])/[A]_o$, $r = [A]_o/[B]_o$, and thus rp is the extent of reaction of B groups.

Quantitative testing of Equation (1) requires independent determination of the equilibrium modulus and ν. Note that determination of ν from Equation (5) and (6) requires the average size or concentration of the starting species and the extent of reaction, p. Measuring the latter is not easy. Concentration measurements in a solid network down to 1 mol/m^3 are required. Thus, there are few results available in the literature to test the theory.

This led us to seek a model network system. The typical rubber vulcanization, random crosslinking of polymer chains, does not seem suitable since it is difficult to accurately determine the crosslink concentration and the functionality of the crosslinking points. The process also yields a wide distribution of chain lengths. Rempp and coworkers (12) have discussed some of the problems in selecting model networks. End linking of fairly long molecules with a simple reaction which can be followed accurately seems to provide the best means for testing network structure relations. Below we describe some preliminary results with such a silicone rubber system.

II. EXPERIMENTAL

An important silicone-network forming reaction is the coupling of polyfunctional hydrosilanes with substituted polydimethylsiloxane (PDMS). The reaction of tetra(dimethylsiloxy) silane with vinyl-terminated PDMS, which we used, is

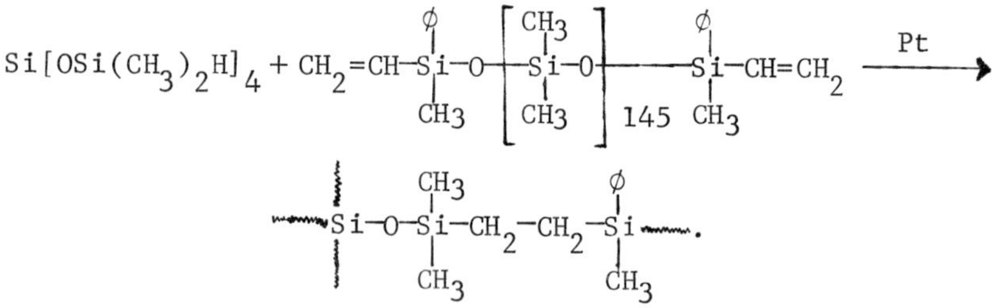

(7)

We also report in this paper some preliminary results with some PDMS system and a trifunctional silane, tris (dimethyl hydrosiloxy) silane $(HSi(CH_3)_2O)_3Si\phi$. Both silanes were found to be better than 99% pure by liquid chromatography. For the vinyl-PDMS Mn = 10400 and Mw/Mn = 2.21 by GPC and Mn = 11040 by titration of the vinyl groups with iodine monochloride. The reactants were used as received from Dow Corning.

A platinum catalyst is essential for the reaction. Cis-dichlorobis (diethyl sulfide) platinum (II) crystals were prepared following the procedure described in ref. (13). A 0.15% Pt by weight solution of the catalyst in low molecular weight PDMS was used.

The reaction of Equation (7) should come very close to fulfilling the ideal network polymerization assumptions. For monofunctional compounds, Chalk and Harrod report essentially complete conversion with no side reactions, byproducts or isomerization (14). The reacting groups are sufficiently far apart to reduce the substitution effects, although the size of the proposed Pt complex (14) may cause deviations due to steric hindrance particularly at high conversions. The length of the vinyl-PDMS and the use of bulk reaction greatly reduces the probability of loop formation. The system is also convenient: the reactants are low viscosity liquids, easily mixed; they react at room temperature at a rate essentially controlled by Pt level. PDMS networks are close to ideal rubbers.

To determine G the dynamic shear modulus was followed continuously with time at 43°C by polymerizing the networks between eccentric rotating disks in the Rheometric Mechanical Spectrometer (15). The disks were rotated at 1 rad/sec. The loss component of the dynamic modulus was found to be less than 2% of the elastic one when G' is greater than 0.5×10^5 N/m^2. Thus the dynamic modulus is expected to be equivalent to the equilibrium modulus G (10). This was also verified experimentally by studying the frequency dependence of the modulus as it is shown in Figure 1. G' remains constant within the experimental error with a variation in frequency over five decades and coincides with equilibrium shear modulus, G determined with the eccentric disks without rotation.

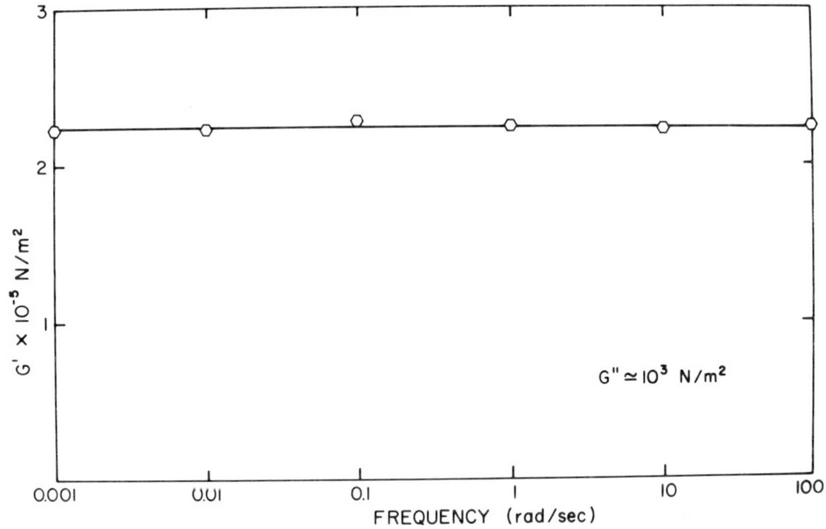

Fig. 1. Frequency dependence of the elastic modulus G'. The viscous modulus $G'' \simeq 10^3 N/m^2$. Measurements done at $p \simeq 0.93$, r=1 .

To convert the modulus vs. time data to modulus vs. extent of reaction p , Equation (5-6), accurate kinetic data at the same reaction conditions as that used in the Mechanical Spectrometer are required. Decrease of the SiH peak at 2134 cm^{-1} was followed with a Perkin Elmer 283 infrared spectrophotometer. NaCl plates with 0.2 mm spacers were kept at 43° ± 0.2° in a water jacketed cell holder. Linearity between absorbance and concentration, Beer's law, was verified for [SiH] from 180 to 4 $mole/m^3$ by known mixtures of the reactants without catalyst.

III. RESULTS AND DISCUSSION

A plot of the infrared conversion results for the stoichiometric balanced sample of the $A_4 + B_2$ system is shown in Figure 2 together with the kinetic expression, the solid line, used to fit the data.

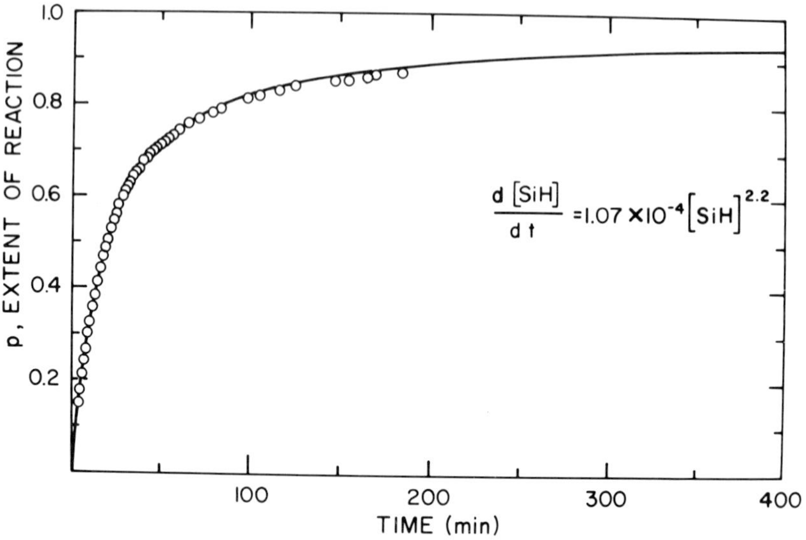

Fig. 2. Kinetic data for the [SiH] disappearance for $[SiH]_0 = [-CH=CH_2]_0$ and 10 ppm Pt at 43°C. Full line corresponds to kinetic expression shown where (d[SiH]/dt)(moles/m^3 min). Points are experimental infrared data.

Figures 3 and 4 show good agreement between experiments and theory. It was assumed that in Equation (1), $\phi = 1$, the expected value for an ideal network reacted in bulk and that the concentration of entanglements in Equations (5) and (6) is constant and equal to $\epsilon = \epsilon_0 = 62$ moles/m^3. This value is the one reported by Langley and Ferry for linear PDMS (16) and is very close to the value reported for radiation crosslinked silicone rubber by Langley and Polmanteer (17).

The results shown here extend our previous work (18). A new catalyst was used at a lower Pt concentration. This increased the gel time which improved accuracy considerably in both the G(t) and p(t) measurements. Furthermore, the infrared measurements were improved significantly by isolating the SiH peak using pure PDMS in the reference beam and by automatic peak picking feature of the Perkin Elmer 283.

The amount of soluble material in the network prepared with $r = 1.56$ was measured after complete reaction with a Soxhlet extractor refluxing n-hexane. Each sample was placed in an extractor thimble and refluxed for a week. The gel

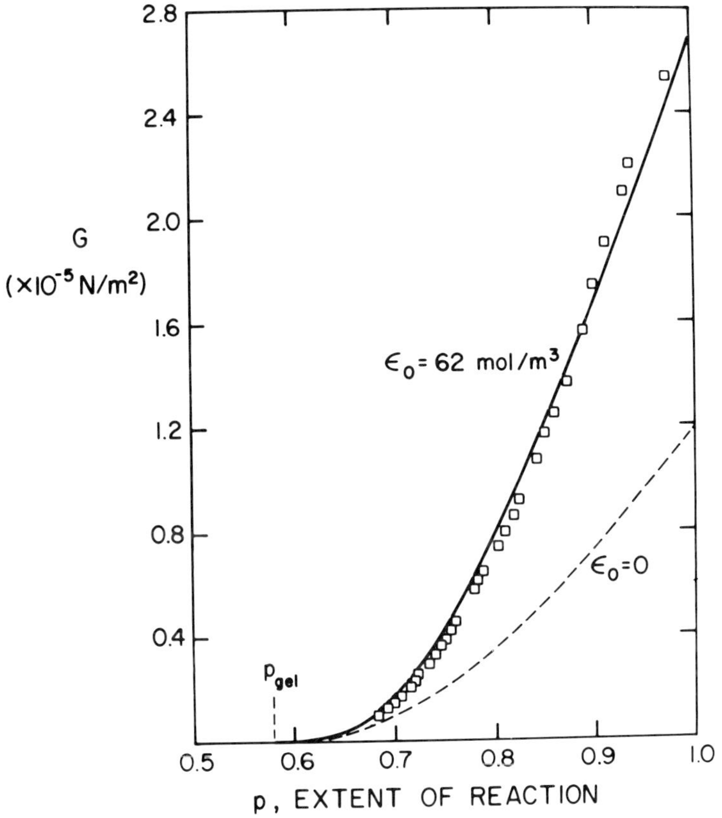

Fig. 3. Modulus for $A_4 + B_2$ system with r=1 and p changing with reaction time. Points experimental from dynamic shear measurements. Solid line from Equations (1) and (5) with $\phi = 1$ and $\epsilon = \epsilon_0 = 62$ mole/m^3. Dashed line $\epsilon = 0$.

fraction was calculated by comparison with the initial weight. Two runs gave $w_s = .0071$ and .0076 which from Equation (39) in ref. (6) gives an average $p_A = 0.635$. This agrees with the infrared measurements ($p_A = 0.63$) within the experimental error.

Figure 5 shows some preliminary data on the $A_3 + B_2$ system. Agreement with theory is also good except for a slight deviation in the region $0.90 \leq p \leq 0.99$. This may be due to inaccuracy in the infrared measurements for the $A_3 + B_2$ system.

Agreement between theory and experiment for the last data point (p=1) obtained after curing several samples for 24 hrs. is remarkably good. Further work is in progress to study the reason for the deviation in the $0.90 \leq p \leq 0.99$ region and to investigate the influence of varying the molecular weight

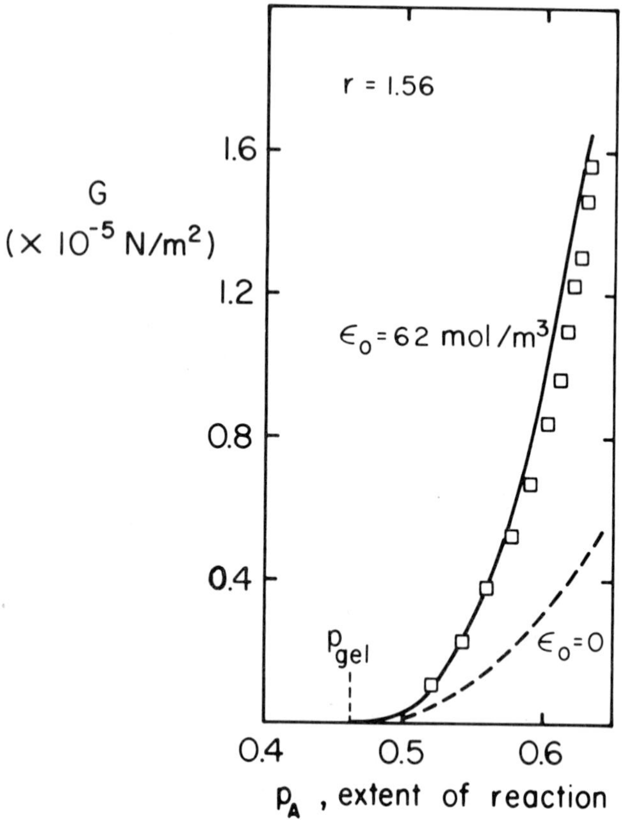

Fig. 4. Modulus for $A_4 + B_2$ system with stoichiometric imbalance $r = 1.56$ and p changing with reaction time. Points experimental from dynamic shear measurements, solid line from Equations (1) and (5) with $\phi = 1$ and $\epsilon = \epsilon_0 = 62$ moles/m^3. Dashed line $\epsilon = 0$.

between crosslinking points on the properties of the system.

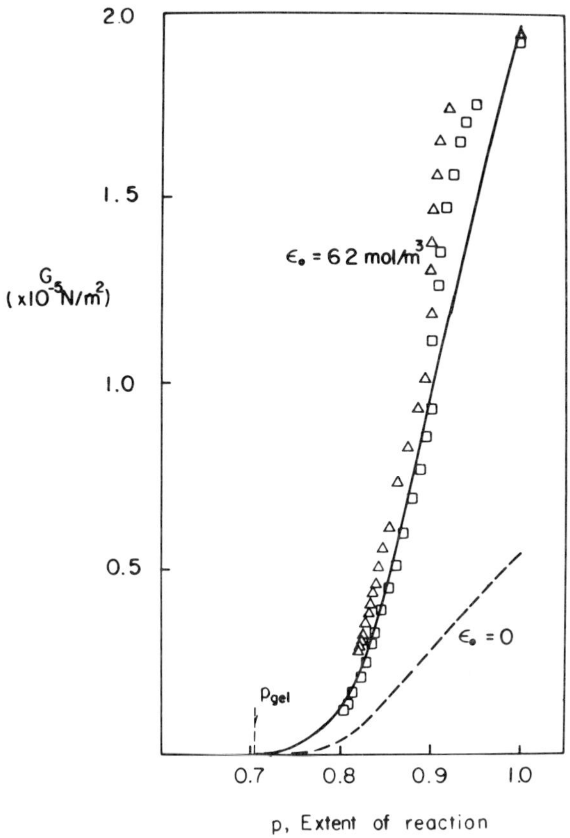

Fig. 5. Modulus for $A_3 + B_2$ system with r=1 and p changing with reaction time. Points experimental from dynamic shear measurements, solid line from Equations (1) and (6) with $\phi=1$ and $\epsilon = \epsilon_o = 62$ mole/m^3 . Triangles and squares correspond to two different runs to show repeatability.

IV. ACKNOWLEDGEMENTS

We appreciate helpful discussions with Drs. N. R. Langley, C. L. Lee, and K. E. Polmanteer, all of Dow Corning Corp., which also provided materials and financial support for this work. The work was also supported by the U.S. Army Research Office and through a research fellowship to E. M. V. from the National Research Council of Argentina (CONICET).

V. REFERENCES

1. P. J. Flory, "Principles of Polymer Chemistry," Cornell University Press, Ithaca, 1953.
2. L. R. G. Treloar, "The Physics of Rubber Elasticity," Oxford University Press, Oxford 1953.
3. L. Mullins, J. Appl. Polym. Sci., 2, 1 (1959).
4. D. Katz and A. Tobolsky, J. Polym. Sci., Part A 2, 1595 (1964).
5. M. Gordon, T. C. Ward, and R. S. Witney, in "Polymer Networks," A. J. Chompff and S. Newman, Eds., Plenum Press, New York, 1971.
6. D. R. Miller and C. W. Macosko, Macromolecules 9, 206 (1976); Rubber Chem. Technol. 49, 0000 (1976).
7. J. Scanlan, J. Polymer Sci. 43, 501 (1960).
8. J. A. Duiser and A. J. Staverman, in "Physics of Non-Crystalline Solids," J. A. Prins, Ed., North-Holland Publ., Amsterdam, p. 376.
9. W. W. Graessley, Macromolecules 8, 186 (1975); Rubber Chem. Technol. 48, 1008 (1975).
10. J. D. Ferry, "Viscoelastic Properties of Polymers," 2nd ed., Wiley, New York, 1970, ch. 13.
11. N. R. Langley, Macromolecules 1, 348 (1968).
12. G. Beinert, A. Belkevir-Mrani, J. Herz, G. Hild, and P. Rempp, Faraday Discuss. Chem. Soc. 57, 27 (1974).
13. G. B. Kauffman, D. O. Cowan, Inorg. Syn. V. 6, 214 Ed. E. G. Rochow, McGraw Hill (1960).
14. A. J. Chalk and J. F. Harrod, J. Am. Chem. Soc. 87, 16 (1965).
15. C. W. Macosko and W. M. Davis, Rheol. Acta. 13, 814 (1974).
16. N. R. Langley and J. D. Ferry, Macromolecules 1, 353 (1968).
17. N. R. Langley and K. E. Polmanteer, J. Polymer. Sci. Physics 12, 1023 (1974).
18. E. M. Valles and C. W. Macosko, Rubber Chem. Technol. 49, 0000, (1976).

RUBBER NETWORKS CONTAINING UNATTACHED POLYMER MOLECULES

Ole Kramer
University of Copenhagen

and

John D. Ferry
University of Wisconsin

The presence of molecularly dispersed unattached polymer molecules in a rubber network causes additional losses in the rubbery plateau zone. The viscoelastic contribution from the unattached polymer molecules has a weighting factor of roughly $1-v_2^2$*, where* v_2 *is the volume fraction of network component. The location of the loss peak on the frequency scale depends on molecular weight of the unattached component; the time for the stress-contribution of unattached polymer molecules to relax to half the plateau value is roughly proportional to molecular weight to the 3.5 power, and roughly independent of concentration. Two different systems have been studied: Butyl-rubber networks containing 25 and 50% polyisobutylene (unattached) - linear viscoelastic properties were measured in shear creep for periods up to* $5x10^5$ *sec at* 25^oC *and oscillating shear deformations from 0.1 to 3 Hz, at temperatures from 2 to* 63^oC*; and ethylene-propylene terpolymer networks containing 25 and 50% ethylene-propylene copolymer (unattached) - stress relaxation in simple elongations and dynamic Young's moduli at frequencies from 3.5 to 110 Hz were measured at temperatures from 10 to* 50^oC*.*

I. INTRODUCTION

A. Polymer Blends

An enormous number of different polymer blends has been made by the polymer industry in an attempt to improve processing and end product properties as reviewed by Corish and Powell (1). Notable examples are blends of ethylene-propylene terpolymer (EPDM) with diene rubbers (2) for improved ozone resistance in tire sidewalls, and blends of polystyrene with a minor proportion of polybutadiene (3) for improved impact resistance. The former type is made by simple mechanical mixing while the latter is made by polymerization of styrene onto particles of polybutadiene. A more recent example is the socalled interpenetrating polymer networks studied by Frisch and coworkers (4,5) and by Sperling and coworkers (6,7).

However, it is a well-known fact that chemically different polymers nearly always are found to be immiscible (micro-heterogeneous), the reason being that the entropy of mixing for polymers is too small to overcome an even very small but positive enthalpy of mixing (8). Interpenetrating networks, prepared by polymerization of a chemically different monomer in a rubbery network swollen by the monomer, are also found to be microheterogeneous (7).

The networks of the present study are different in the sense that it is a requirement that the unattached polymer molecules are molecularly dispersed in the network. The kinds of blends which can be made are therefore limited practically to polymers of nearly identical chemical composition.

B. Rubber Networks Containing Unattached Polymer Molecules

The more straight forward candidates for making such networks are homopolymers containing no unsaturation (unattached component) and the corresponding copolymer with a few per cent diene to make it sulfur curable but without changing the overall chemical composition appreciably. One such pair is polyisobutylene (unattached) and butylrubber (network-forming) which is a copolymer of isobutylene and isoprene. Another similar pair is ethylene-propylene copolymer (EPM, unattached) and ethylene-propylene terpolymer (EPDM, network-forming). In this case the ethylene-propylene ratios in EPM and EPDM should be matched. Blends of EPM and EPDM have been studied by Imoto and coworkers (9), who measured the usual physical properties (not viscoelastic) of blends cured with sulfur, dicumyl peroxide, and brominated alkylphenol resin.

1. *Aim of this Study*

Rubber networks containing molecularly dispersed unattached polymer molecules provide information about the motions of polymer molecules around obstacles such as network junctions and network strands (which cannot be crossed by the unattached polymer molecules). In Fig. 1 is shown what is thought to happen to a linear, unattached polymer molecule in a stress-relaxation experiment. Before stretching at time $t = t_o$, the unattached molecules assume their random configurations. The stretching operation is assumed to be fast enough to assure essentially affine deformation of the polymer molecules ($t = t_o + \delta t$). However, since the polymer molecules are unattached, they will eventually revert back to their random configurations ($t = t_\infty$) thereby relaxing the stress associated with the untrapped entanglements in which they took part.

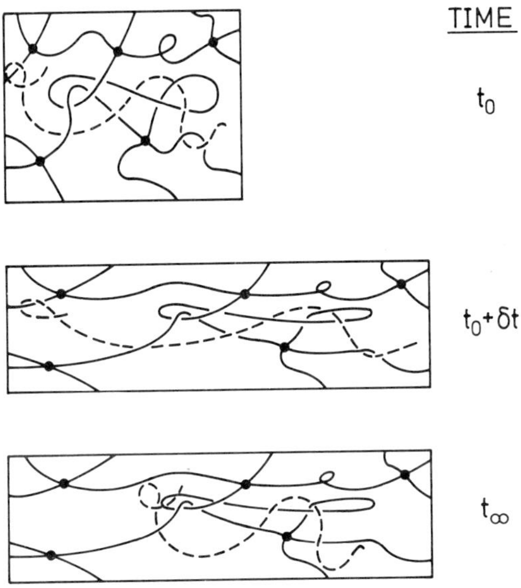

Fig. 1. Hypothetical stress relaxation experiment for rubber networks containing unattached polymer molecules. Only one unattached molecule is shown, dashed.

The rate and amount of the relaxation as a function of molecular weight, structure (linear, branched), and concentration can be studied by this method.

Although the obstacles are of a more permanent nature in a rubber network than in an uncross-linked polymer, the situation may not be all that different. The study of rubber networks containing unattached molecules may therefore provide valuable information on the molecular motions which take place upon deformation and during flow in 'polymer melts'.

Lightly crosslinked rubbery polymers exhibit very slow relaxation mechanisms (10) which are attributed to entanglement coupling. It has been proposed that the entanglements responsible for the slow relaxation processes are untrapped entanglements (11,12) on dangling chain ends some of which may have complicated branched structures. However, studies by Cohen and Tschoegl (13) on block copolymers indicate that entanglements trapped between permanent junctions may also contribute to slow relaxation mechanisms.

The proportion of untrapped entanglements in lightly crosslinked rubbers may be varied by changing the degree of crosslinking, and it may be predicted from statistical calculations (11,14). However, since the untrapped entanglements are present on chain ends of not only different lengths but also various degrees of branching, a direct interpretation of stress-relaxation measurements in terms of possible molecular motions will be extremely difficult. In rubber networks containing unattached polymer molecules, the proportion of untrapped entanglements can be varied from zero to nearly one by changing the concentration of unattached polymer molecules. And, prior to incorporation, the unattached molecules can be well characterized with respect to molecular weight, molecular weight distribution, and molecular structure (branching).

Finally, it should be pointed out that the unattached molecules are free to diffuse through the network structure of these materials, as they are in uncross-linked rubbery materials. Rubber networks with unattached polymer molecules therefore combine the adhesive and energy dissipative properties of an uncross-linked elastomer and the mechanical strength and stability of a crosslinked material.

II. EXPERIMENTAL

Two systems have been studied so far, namely butylrubber (sulfur crosslinkable) with polyisobutylene (non-crosslinkable) (15), and EPDM (sulfur crosslinkable) with EPM (non-crosslinkable) (16,17).

The butylrubber/polyisobutylene samples were prepared by mixing butylrubber (Polysar 600) with polyisobutylene (Vistanex L-140 or LMMS), see Table 1. The mixtures with L-140

TABLE 1
Composition of Butylrubber/Polyisobutylene Sample Mixtures

Code	Polyisobutylene		
	Type	$\bar{M}_v \times 10^{-3}$	Content, %
0	-	-	0
25 L	LMMS	55	25
50 L	LMMS	55	50
25 H	L-140	2300	25
50 H	L-140	2300	50
100 H[a]	L-140	2300	100

[a]Also mixed with vulcanizing ingredients and subjected to vulcanizing treatment.

(higher molecular weight) were made by dissolving the polymers at a total concentration of about 5% in n-heptane and subsequently evaporating the solvent at 50°C and atmospheric pressure to constant weight; the other mixtures were made by milling. Also present in each mixture were (per 100 parts total polymer): 1.0 part stearic acid, 3.0 zinc oxide, 1.75 sulfur, and 1.0 tetramethylthiuram disulfide. The samples were vulcanized at 150°C for 40 min.

The EPDM/EPM samples were prepared by mixing on the mill an experimental B.F. Goodrich EPDM (Code no. 1134-71-397-4, 39 wt-% propylene, 3.3 wt-% ethylidene norbornene, $\bar{M}_w$ = 17 x 10^4, and $\bar{M}_w/\bar{M}_n$ = 2.5) with ethylene-propylene copolymers of three different molecular weights, see Table 2.

TABLE 2
Composition of EPDM/EPM Sample Mixtures

Polymer composition			Copolymer characterization			
Sample code	EPDM	EPM copolymer	$\bar{M}_w \times 10^{-4}$	$\bar{M}_w/\bar{M}_n$	Wt-% P	% Extr.
0	100	0	-	-	-	1
25 L	75	25	3.6	2.5	42	20
50 L	50	50	3.6	2.5	42	45
25 M	75	25	17	2.4	42	14
50 M	50	50	17	2.4	42	39
25 H	75	25	45	2.4	49	9
50 H	50	50	45	2.4	49	31

The curing ingredients were added on the mill: 1.0 part tetramethylthiuram disulfide (TMTD), 0.5 parts mercaptobenzothiazyl disulfide (MBTS), and 1.5 parts sulfur for sample 0 (100% EPDM), proportionate amounts for lower EPDM contents. In addition all samples contained 3.0 parts zinc oxide and 1.0 part stearic acid per 100 rubber. All samples were cured for 35 min at 160°C.

For the butylrubber/polyisobutylene samples, the Plazek torsion pendulum (18) was used for measurements of dynamic storage and loss shear compliances, J' and J", in the frequency range from 0.11 to 3 Hz at temperatures from 2 to 63°C. The same apparatus was used for measurements of shear compliance, J(t), for time periods up to 5×10^5 sec near 25°C. For the EPDM/EPM samples measurements of stress relaxation in simple elongations were made at 10°, 30°, and 50°C, over time periods up to 10^5 sec. Strips of about 0.1 cm x 0.4 cm cross section were cut from the vulcanized sheets. A separate strip was used for each experiment. A few measurements of storage and loss Young's moduli were made with a Rheovibron model DDV-II at frequencies of 3.5, 11, and 110 Hz and temperatures of 30 and 50°C. The data were corrected for apparatus compliance as recommended by Massa (19).

III RESULTS

A. Butylrubber/Polyisobutylene Blends

The data were reduced to 25°C by shift factors a_T calculated from the WLF equation (20) with c_1 = 9.03 and c_2 = 201.6. The compliances were multiplied by $T\rho/T_o\rho_o$, where T and ρ are the absolute temperature of measurement and the density at that temperature, and T_o and ρ_o refer to the reference temperature. The volumetric thermal expansion coefficient was taken as 5.8×10^{-4} K^{-1}; the density was taken

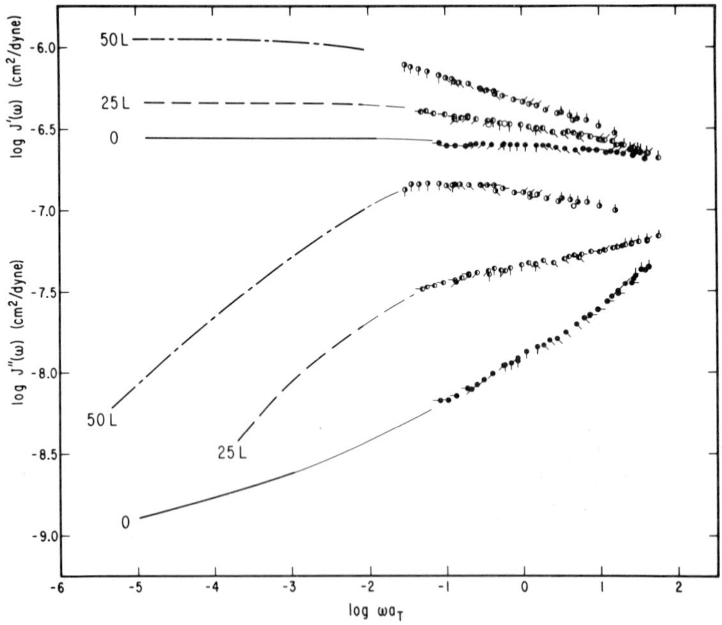

Fig. 2. Storage and loss compliances of the L samples of butylrubber/polyisobutylene blends (Table 1) plotted logarithmically against radian frequency, reduced to 25°. Pips denote individual temperatues of measurement. Heavy curves are converted from creep data; light curves are interpolated.

as 0.94 g cm^{-3}.

Figures 2 and 3 show storage and loss compliances, sample codes are identified in Table 1. By comparison to pure butyl-rubber (sample 0), the presence of unattached molecules in the network gives rise to an additional loss peak in the rubbery plateau region. The location of the loss peak is shifted to lower frequencies with increasing molecular weight. The intensity of the loss peak increases with increasing concentration of unattached molecules.

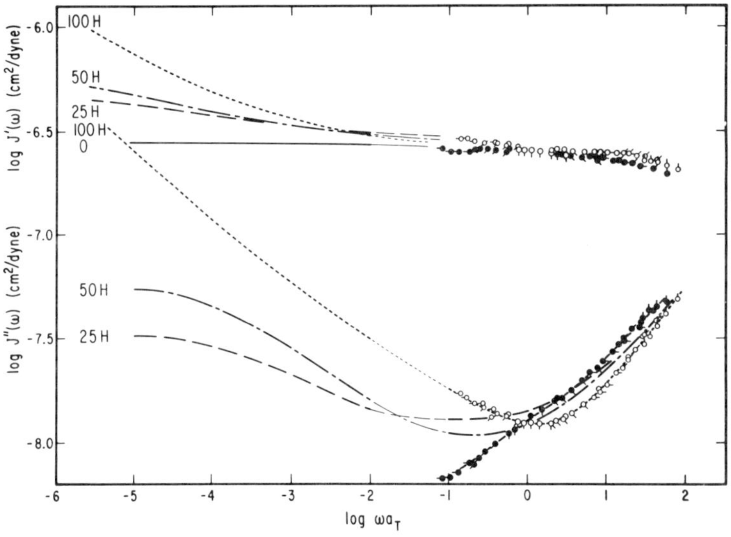

Fig. 3. Storage and loss compliances of the H samples of butylrubber/polyisobutylene blends (Table 1) reduced and plotted as in Fig. 2.

B. <u>Ethylene-Propylene Terpolymer/Ethylene Propylene Copolymer Blends</u>

The data were reduced to 50°C by shift factors a_T calculated from the WLF equation (20) with c_1 = 3.61 and c_2 = 147.7. The volumetric thermal expansion coefficient was taken as 6.6×10^{-4} K^{-1}; the density as 0.894 g cm^{-3} at 25°C.

1. Stress Relaxation Moduli

Stress relaxation data for small simple extensions ($\lambda \simeq 1.15$) are shown in Fig. 4 for samples containing 25% EPM.

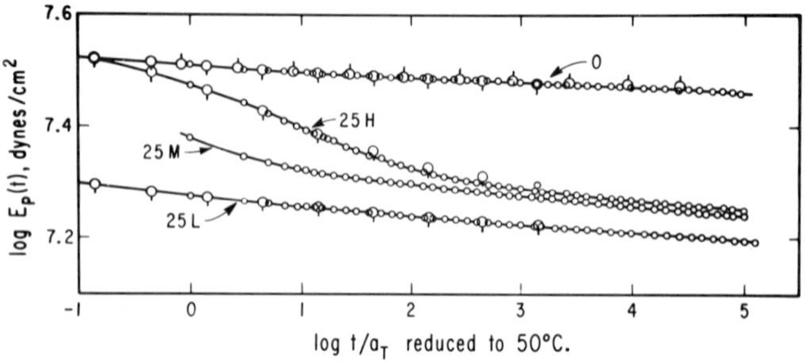

Fig. 4. Relaxation modulus in simple extension plotted logarithmically against time in seconds reduced to 50°C for EPDM/EPM samples. Sample 0 contains no unattached species, the other three samples contain 25% EPM of different molecular weights (Table 2).

For sample 0, very little relaxation occurs. For the other three samples a substantial proportion of the modulus relaxes, corresponding to the unattached polymer molecules recovering their random configurations. In case of the lowest

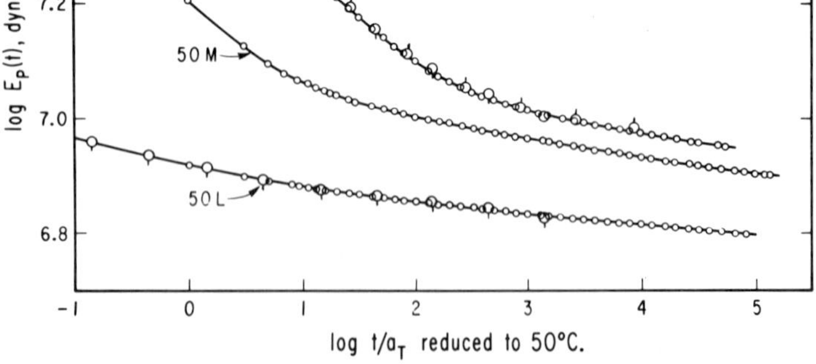

Fig. 5. Relaxation moduli of EPDM/EPM samples plotted as in Fig. 4 for sample 0 (reproduced from Fig. 4) and three samples containing 50% unattached polymer molecules of different molecular weights (Table 2).

molecular weight of the unattached polymer molecules, sample 25 L, the relaxation appears to be almost complete before the first experimental point, but the process shifts rapidly to longer times with increasing molecular weight of the unattached species. The relaxation associated with the unattached polymer molecules at a concentration of 25% is of the order of 40% of the modulus of sample 0.

In Fig. 5, the relaxation moduli for samples containing 50% EPM are shown. The results are very similar to those of Fig. 4, except that the magnitudes of the modulus changes are greater (of the order of 75% compared to 40% in Fig. 4). Even for the highest molecular weight, the relaxation associated with the unattached polymer molecules appears to be complete before the experiment is terminated. This is a distinct advantage of the EPDM/EPM system over the butylrubber/polyisobutylene system for which the frictional coefficient is very high even at temperatures close to 100°C.

2. *Dynamic Moduli*

To combine the stress relaxation and Rheovibron data, the former were first converted to storage and loss dynamic Young's moduli by the approximation method of Schwarzl (21). The loss moduli reduced to 50°C are plotted logarithmically against radian frequency in Fig. 6. The unattached polymer molecules make large contributions to the loss modulus with the loss peaks shifting to higher frequencies with decreasing molecular weight.

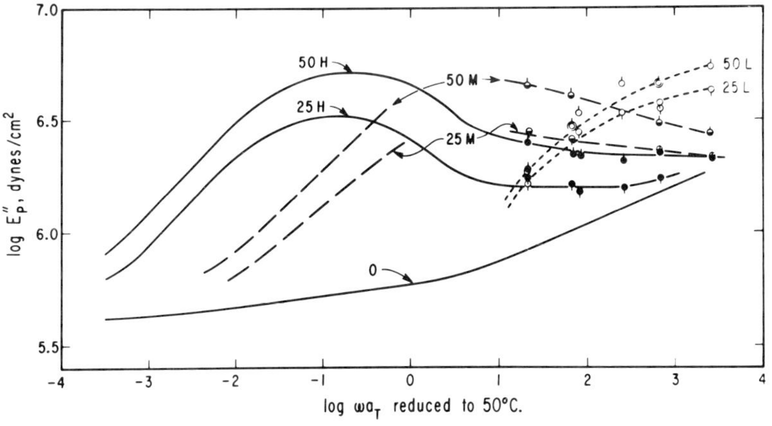

Fig. 6. Loss Moduli of EPDM/EPM samples plotted logarithmically against radian frequency reduced to 50°C for 0, H, and L samples (Table 2). For log ωa_T<1, derived from stress relaxation; for log ωa_T>1, measured on Rheovibron.

3. *Extracted Samples*

Samples were immersed in cyclohexane at room temperature for 4½ months in an attempt to extract the unattached polymer molecules. The percentage extracted is shown in the last column of Table 2. For samples containing EPM of low molecular weight, nearly all of the EPM can be extracted. With increasing molecular weight of the EPM, decreasing proportions are extracted.

Stress relaxation measurements were also performed on the extracted samples in extension at 50°C. The results are shown in Fig. 7, where $3f(t)/A_o\ (\lambda-\lambda^{-2})$ for $\lambda\rightarrow 1$ is Young's

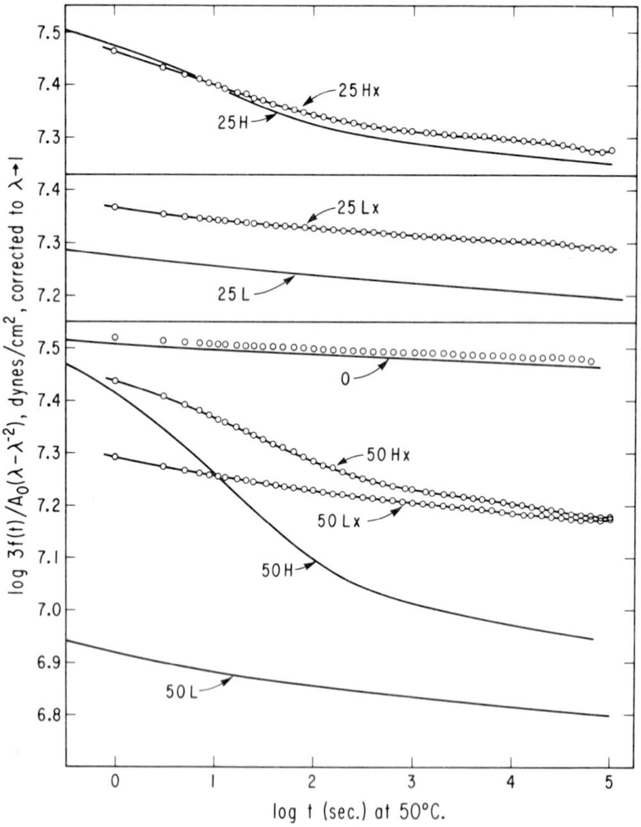

Fig. 7. Relaxation modulus in extension plotted logarithmically against time in seconds at 50°C, for samples of Table 2, before extraction (solid curves reproduced from Figures 4 and 5) and after extraction (curves with points, designated with x).

relaxation modulus.

Extraction does not change sample 0 appreciably; a small increase of about 2% is probably due to removal of low molecular weight vulcanization byproducts. Removal of the unattached species of the L samples results in a uniform increase in the relaxation modulus over the whole time scale. This is not unexpected since the unattached molecules of the L samples have relaxed completely before the first experimental point (see Figure 6). For samples 25 H and 50 H, extraction does not affect the modulus at short times but increases it at long times. This is also to be expected since the unattached molecules of high molecular weight relax within the time scale of the experiment.

Measurements of non-linear stress relaxation of EPDM/EPM were also made (17) but will not be discussed in the present paper.

IV DISCUSSION

A. Extraction of Unattached Polymer Molecules

Ideally, complete extraction of the unattached polymer molecules should be possible. However, the amount extracted from EPDM/EPM blends was less than the proportion of EPM in the blends, especially for EPM of high molecular weight, as can be seen from the last column of Table 2 (the same effect was found in butylrubber/polyisobutylene blends (15)). Whether the incomplete extraction is due to the extraction process being so slow that several months of extraction is insufficient, or whether some of the supposedly unattached molecules are permanently attached to the network, cannot be said at this time.

Both EPM (22) and polyisobutylene (23) may contain a terminal double bond which potentially could cause a permanent linkage to the network. That there should be less than one crosslink per polyisobutylene molecule on a weight average basis (24) was indicated by sample 100 H (100% Vistanex L-140, $\bar{M}_v = 2.3\times10^6$, Table 1). This sample was completely soluble in n-heptane although it contained the same vulcanizing ingredients and had been subjected to the same vulcanizing treatment as the other samples of Table 1.

If a polymer molecule were connected to the network by a single (terminal) crosslink, the fraction of untrapped entanglements would be unchanged. However, the relaxation time should be expected to be different, probably longer (25).

B. Viscoelastic Contributions from Unattached Polymer Molecules

The presence of unattached polymer molecules in rubber networks gives rise to additional losses, as can be seen in Figures 2, 3, and 6. The location of the additional loss peak depends on molecular weight, and the strength depends on concentration of the unattached polymer molecules.

1. *Blending Law Analysis*

Figures 3 and 6 indicate that the viscoeleastic contributions from the network and the unattached species might simply be additive. A simple blending law which has had some success in mixtures of linear polymers with different molecular weights, expressed in terms of the storage modulus, is (26)

$$G'_{bl}(\omega) = V_{11}\, G'_{11}(\omega\lambda_{11}) + V_{22}\, G'_{22}(\omega\lambda_{22}) \qquad (1)$$

where the subscripts bl, 11, and 22 will refer in our system to the complete system, the unattached polymer from which the blend was made, and a rubber network of similar character to that present in the complete system in the absence of reptating species. The time shift factors λ_{11} and λ_{22} are the ratios of relaxation times of species 1 and 2 in the complete system to those in the isolated components. The weighting factors V_{11} and V_{22} are functions of the volume fractions v_1 and v_2 but not necessarily equal to them. A similar equation holds for G".

A detailed analysis is possible for butylrubber networks containing high molecular weight polyisobutylene, Figure 3. At frequencies below log ω = -1, the pure network, sample 0, has very little loss compared with the blends, and its storage compliance is close to the equilibrium value. If we assume that the same is true for the butylrubber networks in the blends, the storage and loss moduli of the system will be

$$G'_{bl}(\omega) = V_{11}\, G'_{11}(\omega\lambda_{11}) + G_e \qquad (2)$$

$$G''_{bl}(\omega) = V_{11}\, G''_{11}(\omega\lambda_{11}) \qquad (3)$$

where G_e is the low-frequency limiting value of $V_{22}\, G'_{22}$ and also of G'_{bl}, since at sufficiently low frequencies the unattached molecules make no contribution to G'. Equations 2 and 3 permit a comparison of sample 100 H (pure polyisobutylene) with samples 25 H and 50 H. Sample 100 H gives G'_{11} and G''_{11}. Since data do not extend to low enough frequencies to determine G_e directly, it was determined from eq 2 with V_{11} determined from eq 3. The values of G_e for 25 H and 50 H in Table 3 were obtained in this manner.

TABLE 3
Parameters from Blending Law Analysis for the Butylrubber/Polyisobutylene System

Sample code	λ_{11}	V_{11}	$1-v_2^2$	log G_e	log $t_{1/2}$
25 H	1.00	0.44	0.44	6.26	4.08
50 H	1.00	0.60	0.75	6.13	4.08
100 H	1.00	1.00		-	4.08
25 L				6.31	-0.81
50 L				5.94	-0.59

Quite good agreement with equations 2 and 3 is obtained for both 25 H and 50 H, as shown in Figure 8, with the values of

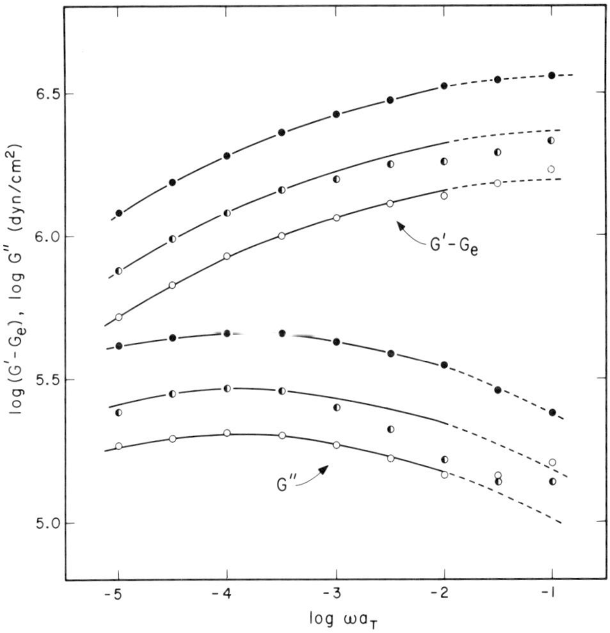

Fig. 8. Log ($G'-G_e$) and Log G'' plotted against log ω reduced to 25°C, for samples 25 H (open circles), 50 H (half black), and 100 H (black) of Table 1. Curves drawn as V_{11} G'_{11} and V_{11} G''_{11} with λ_{11}=1 and values of V_{11} shown in Table 3. Dashed portions are from interpolated region of Figure 3 and hence less reliable.

λ_{11} and V_{11} given in Table 3. The shift factors λ_{11} are found to be close to unity: The relaxation times for polyisobutylene molecules of high molecular weight present in a network are approximately the same as when surrounded by their own kind alone. For sample 25 H, the weighting factor $V_{11} = 0.44$ which is equal to $1 - v_2^2$; the fraction of entanglement loci involving at least one polyisobutylene partner and hence capable of relaxation. The agreement is not as good for sample 50 H but blending law analysis for the EPDM/EPM system (16) also indicates a weighting factor of $1 - v_2^2$.

2. *Relaxation Times of Unattached Polymer Molecules*

The contribution to relaxation modulus from the unattached species, $V_{11}E_{11}(t)$, may be calculated from an equation analogous to equations 1-3

$$E(t) = V_{11} E_{11}(t) + E_2(t) \tag{4}$$

where E(t) is Young's relaxation modulus of the blend, and $E_2(t)$ is the contribution of the network as present in the blend, with a single subscript because it is not referred to a hypothetical equivalent network without the copolymer component. The network contribution in the blend is assumed to have the same time dependence as E(t) for sample 0, which is given by d log E(t)/d log t = 0.0067. The results are shown in Figure 9 for EPDM/EPM blends and in Figure 10 for butylrubber/polyisobutylene blends. In the latter case results are given in terms of shear moduli; the quantity $G_e + v_2\, \Delta G_o$ is equal to $G_2(t)$.

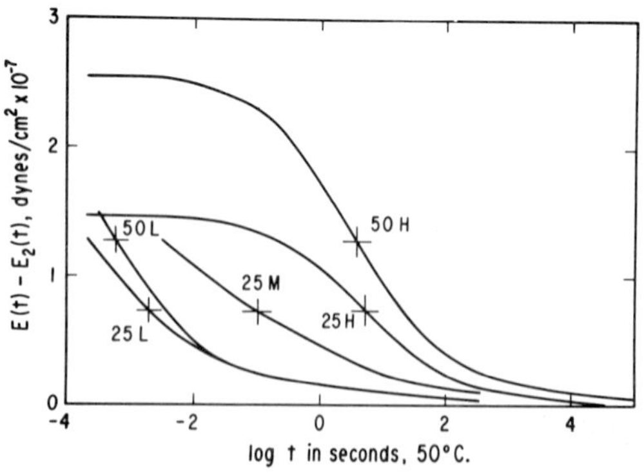

Fig. 9. Contribution of unattached polymer molecules to Young's relaxation modulus for EPDM/EPM blends (Table 2), E(t) - E_2(t) plotted against log t. Crosses denote times where ordinate has fallen to half its initial value.

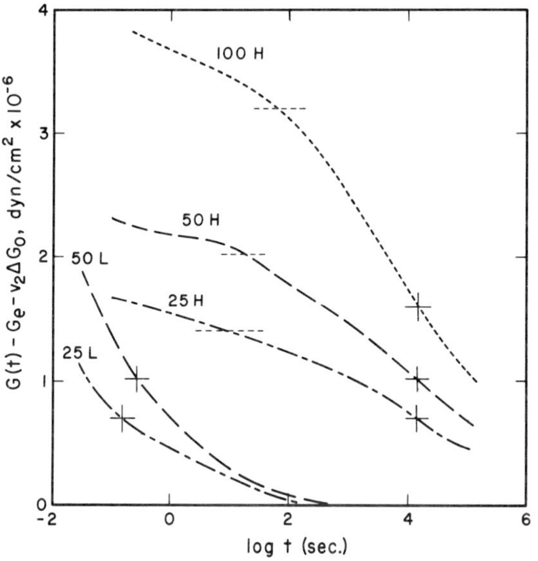

Fig. 10. Contribution of unattached polymer molecules to the shear relaxation modulus for samples of Table 1, $G(t) - G_e - v_2\ \Delta G_o$ plotted against log t. Dashed horizontal lines denote $V_{11}\ G^o_{eN}$; crosses, $V_{11}\ G^o_{eN}/2$.

The initial value is best determined for the H samples and is assumed to be the same for the others. As a measure of the relaxation time, the time $t_{\frac{1}{2}}$ at which the ordinate has fallen to half its initial value, is used. These times are also given in Tables 1 and 2, $t_{\frac{1}{2}}$ increases rapidly with molecular weight but is roughly independent of concentration of unattached polymer molecules. The dependence of $t_{\frac{1}{2}}$ on molecular weight corresponds approximately to a power of 3.5 for EPDM/EPM blends and a power of 3 for butylrubber/polyisobutylene blends (based on two molecular weights, only). The molecular weight distributions of both EPM and polyisobutylene are quite broad, and a more precisely specified dependence of relaxation time on molecular weight can therefore not be given at present. Similar measurements with unattached polymer molecules of very narrow molecular weight distribution are required.

Both the dependence on molecular weight and the dependence on concentration of unattached polymer molecules are in qualitative agreement with Graessley's theory of viscoelasticity of entangling polymers (26), specifying the network component as one of infinite molecular weight. However, the experimentally observed relaxation is much more gradual than predicted from Graessley's theory, as expected for unattached polymer molecules with a relatively broad molecular weight distribution.

It is reassuring that the EPDM/EPM system and the butylrubber/polyisobutylene system behave so similarly except for a large shift on the time scale, reflecting the difference in monomeric friction coefficient. It means that the additional loss peak due to the presence of unattached polymer molecules can be tuned in frequency by choice of molecular weight as well as chemical nature.

3. *Comparison with Lightly Crosslinked Networks*

Lightly crosslinked rubbers exhibit very slow relaxation mechanisms which have been attributed to untrapped entanglements on dangling chain ends (12). In Figure 11, the present results on butylrubber/polyisobutylene blends are compared to results obtained by Sanders and Ferry (27) on lightly crosslinked butylrubber. Sample 0 is a fairly tightly crosslinked butylrubber while sample 3-140 is a very lightly crosslinked butylrubber. The latter shows large low-frequency losses of

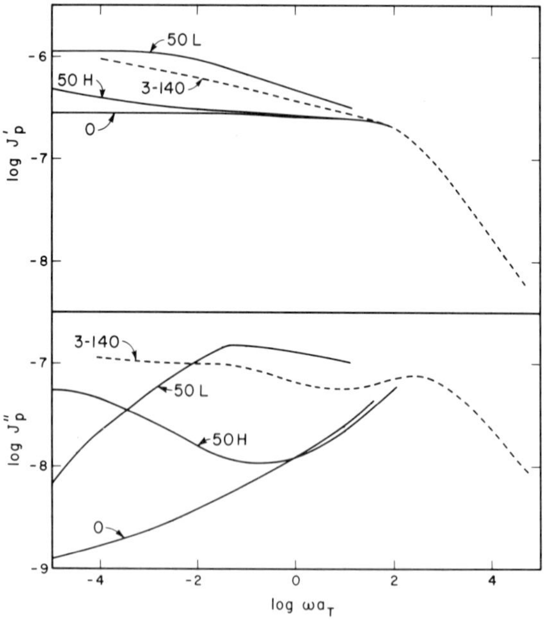

Fig. 11. Logarithmic plots of J' and J" for butylrubber /polyisobutylene samples 0, 50 L, 50 H of Table 1, compared with sample 3-140 of reference 27 (a very lightly crosslinked butylrubber).

similar magnitude as for the butylrubber networks with unattached polymer molecules. This is quite reasonable since the magnitude of the losses (expressed in terms of G") should depend primarily on the concentration of untrapped entanglements. However, the dispersion region for sample 3-140 is much broader than for samples 50 L or 50 H.

Even though the primary molecular weight of sample 3-140 is only about 1.7×10^5 (27), compared to a molecular weight of about 2.3×10^6 for the unattached polyisobutylene in sample 50 H, the presence of long dangling chain ends with branched structures would be expected to add some extremely long relaxation times as observed for sample 3-140.

C. Theoretical Models

The motions of unattached polymer molecules in the presence of fixed obstacles have been discussed theoretically on the basis of various models (25, 28-32). de Gennes proposes (28) that a linear molecule in the presence of fixed obstacles,e.g. the junctions and strands of a rubber network, will be restricted in its motions as though constrained in a narrow tube along the contour of the polymer molecule. The primary motion should be a snake-like motion ("reptation") of the whole molecule sliding back and forth inside the tube with the molecular ends choosing new routes. The time for complete rearrangement of its configurations should be proportional to M^3, in reasonably good agreement with the present experiments, i.e.,the stress relaxation time, $t_{\frac{1}{2}}$, being proportional to molecular weight to a power of 3 to 3.5. It is interesting to note that the exact nature of the obstacles does not appear explicitly in the de Gennes theory. This is consistent with the experimental observation that the relaxation times are the same in polyisobutylene and in the butylrubber networks.

The sliding motion of the whole molecule, back and forth inside the tube, should be very restricted for star shaped molecules (25). Complete renewal of configurations should now take place by a different process, in which the ends of the molecule must find their way back to the branch point, and then generate a new tube (25). This process is very slow for polymers of high molecular weight. A comparison of networks containing linear polymer molecules with networks containing star shaped polymer molecules should therefore give valuable information on the exact nature of the molecular motions involved. Such experiments are in progress.

V. ACKNOWLEDGMENTS

The work reviewed here was supported in part by grants from the National Science Foundation and the NATO Research Grants Programme, and by the Research Committee of the Graduate School of the University of Wisconsin with funds from the Wisconsin Alumni Research Foundation. We are indebted to John Wiley and Sons, Inc., for permission to publish the figures, which appeared in the Journal of Polymer Science.

VI. REFERENCES

1. P.J. Corish and B.D.W. Powell, Rubber Chem. Technol. 47, 481 (1974).
2. Z.T. Ossefort and E.W. Bergstrom, Rubber Age 101 (9), 4 (1969)
3. B.W. Bander, J. Appl. Polym. Sci. 9, 2887 (1965).
4. H.L. Frisch, D. Klempner, and K.C. Frisch, J. Polym. Sci. B7, 775 (1969).
5. D.Klempner, H.L. Frisch and K.C. Frisch, J. Elastoplastics 3, 2 (1971).
6. L.H. Sperling and D.W. Friedman, J. Polym. Sci. Part A-2 7, 425 (1969).
7. V. Huelck, D.A. Thomas and L.H. Sperling, Macromolecules 5, 340 and 348 (1972).
8. P.J. Flory, "Principles of Polymer Chemistry," p. 555, Cornell University Press, Ithaca, 1953.
9. M. Imoto and coworkers, Nippon Gomu Kyokaishi 43, 439 (1969).
10. J.D. Ferry, "Viscoelastic Properties of Polymers" 2nd ed. Chapter 14, Wiley, New York, 1970.
11. N.R. Langley, Macromolecules 1, 348 (1968).
12. N.R. Langley and J.D. Ferry, Macromolecules 1, 353 (1968).
13. R.E. Cohen and N.W. Tschoegl, Intern. J. Polym. Mater. 2, 49 (1972).
14. N.R. Langley and K.E. Polmanteer, J. Polym. Sci., Polym. Phys. Ed. 12, 1023 (1974).
15. O. Kramer, R. Greco, R.A. Neira, and J.D. Ferry, J. Polym. Sci., Polym. Phys. Ed. 12, 2361 (1974).
16. O. Kramer, R. Greco, J.D. Ferry, and E.T. McDonel, J. Polym. Sci., Polym. Phys. Ed. 13, 1675 (1975).
17. R. Greco, C.R. Taylor, O. Kramer, and J.D. Ferry, J. Polym. Sci., Polym. Phys. Ed. 13, 1687 (1975).
18. D.J. Plazek, M.N. Vrancken, and J.W. Berge, Trans. Soc. Rheol. 2, 39 (1958).
19. D.J. Massa, J. Appl. Phys. 44, 2595 (1973).
20. M.L. Williams, R.F. Landel, and J.D. Ferry, J. Amer. Chem. Soc. 77, 3701 (1955).

21. F. Schwarzl, Rheol. Acta 8, 6 (1969); Rheol. Acta 10, 165 (1971).
22. F.P. Baldwin and G. Ver Strate, Rubber Chem. Technol. 45, 709 (1972).
23. F.S. Dainton and G.B.B.M. Sutherland, J. Polym. Sci. 4, 37 (1949).
24. Ref. 8, p. 359.
25. P.G. de Gennes, "Reptation of Stars", to appear in J. Phys. (Paris).
26. W.W. Graessley, J. Chem. Phys. 54, 5143 (1971).
27. J.F. Sanders and J.D. Ferry, Macromolecules 7, 681 (1974).
28. P.G. de Gennes, J. Chem. Phys. 55, 572 (1971).
29. S.F. Edwards and J.W. Grant, J. Phys. A6, 1169 and 1186 (1973).
30. M. Doi, Polym. J. (Japan) 5, 288 (1973).
31. M. Doi, Chem. Phys. Lett. 26, 269 (1974).
32. M. Doi, J. Phys. A8, 417 (1975).

A NEW MEASURE OF STRAIN TO DESCRIBE THE MECHANICAL RESPONSE OF ELASTOMER NETWORKS

W. V. Chang
Department of Chemical Engineering
University of Southern California

R. Bloch and N. W. Tschoegl
Division of Chemistry and Chemical Engineering
California Institute of Technology

The elastic behavior of a real network deviates frequently from the ideal behavior predicted by the Gaussian statistical theory. Often this non-ideal behavior is further complicated by the viscoelastic nature of the network. We propose a consistent scheme to separate the time and strain-dependent responses. This allows us to extend our study of the non-ideal strain dependent behavior to wider ranges of temperature and crosslink density. We further introduce a special measure of strain to quantify this non-ideal behavior. A possible molecular origin of the deviation from Gaussian theory is discussed in the light of experimental results.

I. INTRODUCTION

Probably one of the most successful applications of statistical mechanics may be found in the development of the Gaussian theory of rubber elasticity, which quantitatively predicts the relationship between stress and strain for a deformed network at constant temperature, as well as the swelling behavior and the thermoelastic behavior of polymer networks. However, numerous experiments indicate that the theory does not apply quantitatively. For example, deviations from the prediction become appreciable if the strain is higher than about 20% in simple tension experiments for most polymer networks. Extensive research has been conducted to describe the mechanic behavior of rubberlike materials. These efforts can be classified into two approaches: one consists in modifying the Gaussian statistical theory by removing some of the assumptions on which it is based, the other is the phenomenological approach which rests on continuum mechanics without recourse to molecular considerations. At present, the second approach appears to offer greater possibilities for success.

In this paper, we first introduce a phenomenological model which describes successfully both the time-dependent and equilibrium mechanical properties of elastomeric networks. In the model we define a strain parameter to measure the deviation of the behavior of real networks from the ideal behavior predicted by the Gaussian statistical theory. We then apply the model to composite networks, and comment on the possible molecular origin of the deviation.

II. A GENERALIZED STRAIN MEASURE IN A SINGLE-INTEGRAL CONSTITUTIVE EQUATION

The constitutive theory of an incompressible elastic body is based on the concept of the strain energy density function, W. Many representations of W have been proposed. Among these the Mooney-Rivlin equation has probably received most attention. The equation has the form:

$$W = C_1 (\lambda_1^2 + \lambda_2^2 + \lambda_1^{-2} \lambda_2^{-2} - 3) + C_2 (\lambda_1^{-2} + \lambda_2^{-2} + \lambda_1^2 \lambda_2^2 - 3) \qquad (1)$$

which reduces to the equation furnished by the statistical theory for $C_2 = 0$. The ratio between the two parameters, C_2/C_1, can serve as a measure of the deviation from ideal rubber elasticity. Indeed, a large body of research has attempted to assess the significance of C_2. Literature data indicate that C_2 depends on the following variables (1,2): (A) type and extent of deformation; (B) time scale of experiment; (C) temperature; (D) degree of swelling and nature of solvent; (E) degree of crosslinking; (F) molecular weight and molecular weight distribution of the gum stock; (G) chemical nature of the polymer and of the crosslinkage; and (H) chain orientation during crosslinking. Theoretical attempts to describe C_2 have met with very limited success (2).

The fundamental objection to this approach is that the Mooney-Rivlin equation is not a constitutive representation for most elastomers. Mooney-Rivlin constants obtained from uniaxial tension experiment do not agree with those determined in other modes of deformation (3,4). Typically, C_2 obtained from uniaxial compression data is much smaller than that from uniaxial tension data. The inadequacy of the Mooney-Rivlin equation can also be demonstrated by an experiment on the torsion of a right circular cylinder. Using eq. (1), the distribution of the normal traction, Z, on the two ends, is given (5) by

$$Z = - \{\psi^2 (C_1 - 2C_2)(R^2 - r^2) + 2R^2 C_2\} \quad (2)$$

where ψ is the torsion angle per unit height, R is the radius of the cylinder, and r is the radial distance from the axis. Eq. (2) predicts that the magnitude of Z decreases with decreasing r if $C_1 < 2C_2$. This prediction is not borne out by experiment, although it is not uncommon that $2C_2$ exceeds C_1 in simple tension experiments. We believe that it is illogical to try to attribute molecular meaning to C_2, if the equation on which C_2 is based is not a constitutive equation.

Recent work by Blatz, Sharda and Tschoegl (6,7) on unfilled elastomers provides a simple but realistic constitutive equation. If the maximum stretch ratio of the deformation is less than about three (we call this a "moderately large deformation"), the strain energy density function takes the form

$$W = (2G/n)(\lambda_1^n + \lambda_2^n + \lambda_3^n - 3)/n \quad (3)$$

where n is a material constant, and G is the shear modulus.

With the incompressibility assumption,

$$\lambda_1 \lambda_2 \lambda_3 = 1 \quad (4)$$

eq.(3) gives the stress-stretch ratio relation as

$$\bar{\sigma}_i = -p + (2G/n)\lambda_i^n \quad (5)$$

where $\bar{\sigma}_i$ is the principal Cauchy stress in the i direction and p is an unspecified hydrostatic pressure. As the Mooney-Rivlin equation, eq. (5) requires only two material constants, G and n. It was shown (6,7) that eq. (5) correctly describes the equilibrium mechanical behavior of natural rubber (NR) and styrene-butadiene rubber (SBR) in different modes of deformation, both for homogeneous and inhomogeneous deformations. Therefore, it appears more appropriate to study the dependence of n and G on the experimental variables, and employ n as a measure of the deviation from the Gaussian statistical theory (for which n = 2), than to use C_2 or C_2/C_1 for this purpose.

The above development assumes that the material is a purely elastic body. However, like all polymers, rubberlike materials are viscoelastic. Therefore, the measurements must be conducted at elastic equilibrium, i.e. in the completely ralaxed state. In practice, equilibrium can be approached only asymptotically, either by increasing the experimental time scale, or by increasing the experimental time scale, or by increasing the temperature. The statistical theory is commonly employed to describe even the rheological properties of polymer melts and concentrated polymer solutions (8,9), i.e. of systems in which elastic equilibrium does not exist. It is desirable to examine whether the statistical theory is applicable to both crosslinked and uncrosslinked polymers over wide time and temperature ranges. For such a task a constitutive equation representing the visco-elastic behavior of the system is indispensable.

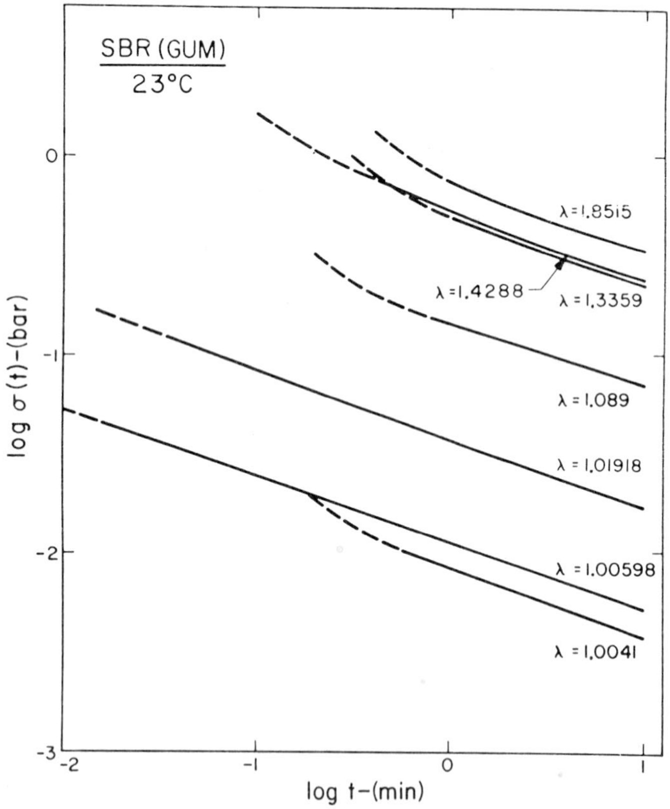

Fig. 1. Engineering stress, σ(t), as function of time t in logarithmic coordinates. Step response of uncrosslinked SBR at 23°C to strain at various stretch ratios.

Soft polymeric materials usually show a unique feature in a stress relaxation experiments: the ratio of stress at time t to that at an arbitrary reference time t_o is independent of strain. A typical example is given in Fig. 1 which presents data from 1.004 to 1.852. The broken lines in Fig. 1 indicate the response to the ramp (constant extension rate) excitation which proceeds the constant strain in a stress relaxation experiment. Ramp transient behavior had effectively decayed away for times longer than 10 times the time required to impose the final strain. Note that the solid curves are all parallel. This observation is generally true for both cross-linked and uncrosslinked rubberlike materials, in both homogeneous and heterogeneous deformation fields, at different temperatures over relatively long times (10-12).

These observations seem to imply that the nonlinear mechanical response of soft polymeric materials results from strain nonlinearity while time-shift invariance is essentially preserved (i.e. the relaxation spectrum remains unchanged) at least in moderately large deformations. We therefore proposed (13) a single integral constitutive equation by incorporating a non-linear strain measure into the Boltzmann superposition Integral. In pure deformation, the model takes the form

$$\bar{\sigma}_i(t) = -p + (2/3n)\int_0^t E(t-u)\, d\lambda_i^{\,n}(u) \qquad (6)$$

where $\bar{\sigma}_i$ and p are defined before, t is the present time, u is the past time, and E(t) is the tensile relaxation modulus in small deformation, which is 3G(t) for soft (incompressible) polymeric materials. The only material information needed to apply eq. (6) is knowledge of the time function, E(t), and the strain parameter, n. The relaxation function can be constructed, utilizing the time-temperature superposition principle, by conducting stress relaxation tests at different temperature in small deformations. The strain measure n, which is independent of time at any particular temperature, can be determined from similar tests at longer stretch ratios (11). According to eq. (6), elimination of p yields the stress in uniaxial tension as

$$\bar{\sigma}(t) = (2/3n)\,(\lambda^n - \lambda^{-n/2})\,E(t) \qquad (7)$$

The exponent n can therefore be determined, using nonlinear least squares fitting, from isochronal stress-strain relaxations crossplotted from Fig. 1. Eq. (6) can then be applied to other strain histories. As an example, we show the application to constant extension rate experiments in Fig. 2. The agreement between the theoretical prediction and the experimental data are remarkable. Similar good agreement was found for numerous literature data as well as our own. These studies will be published elsewhere (10,12).

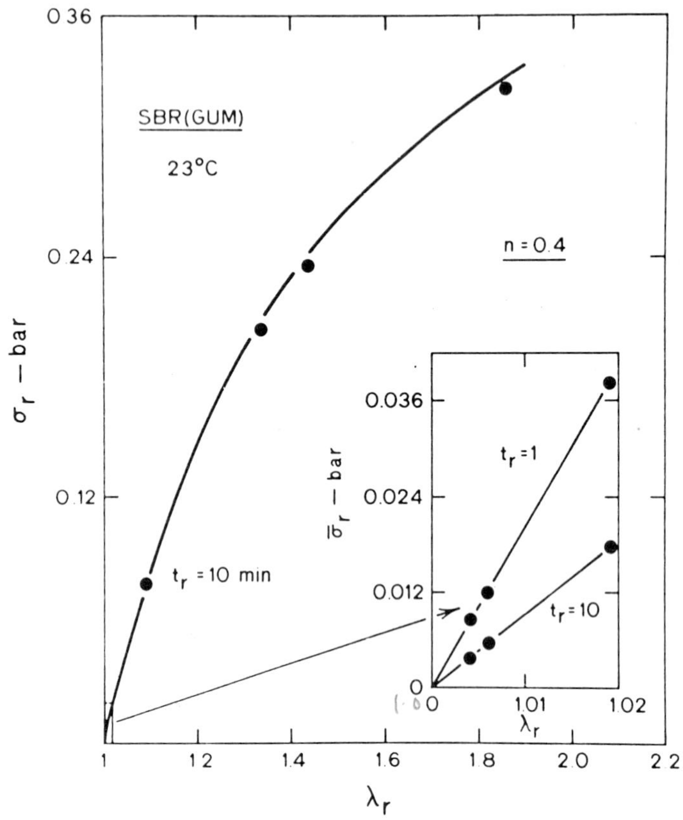

Fig. 2. Engineering stress as function of stretch ratio at the isochronal time t_r = 10 min. Uncrosslinked SBR at 23°C.

When applicable (i.e. in "moderately large deformations"), eq.(7) provides a rational scheme to separate time-dependent effects from equilibrium properties. Hence, we can characterize a material by n and study the dependence of this parameter on temperature as well as on other experimental variables unencumbered by possible complications from relaxation effects. A phenomenological theory is basically a bookkeeping method of representing data. Therefore, it is not necessary that there exist a simple relation between n and molecular parameters.

The statistical theory in its current form offers only limited enlightenment on the organization of the network in elastomers. Future refinement will probably result from the incorporation of the most important structure factors into the theory. The scheme proposed here may offer a consistent way to analyze experimental results, infer the molecular origins of the deviation from the statistical theory and, hence, point the way towards improving the theory.

III. THE DEPENDENCE OF n ON EXPERIMENTAL VARIABLES

We now proceed to discuss the dependence of n on degree of crosslinking, temperature, molecular weight of gum stock, degree of swelling, and presence of diluent during crosslinking. We will mainly summarize conclusions without elaborating details. More complete information will be published elsewhere (10,12).

Values of n for uncrosslinked SBR and polyisobutylene (PIB) were determined from our own (10) as well as literature data (14,15,16). It was found (10) that n is about 0.5 for both materials, and it seems to be independent of temperature, at least in the region from -50°C to 25°C. We infer from Noordermeer and Ferry's data (17) on 1,2- polybutadiene that n is about 0.2 for this material. In the temperature range and on the time scale studied, the mechanical behavior of the above mentioned materials is dominated by molecular motions manifesting themselves in the lower transition region and in the entanglement plateau of a relaxation modulus curve. Therefore, it appears that entangled networks show similar stress-strain behavior in spite of their different chain structures. Moreover, their behavior deviates from the prediction of the Gaussian theory, as shown by their low n-values. It should be interesting to ascertain if this conclusion could be extended to the terminal (flow) region, and to polymer melts whose molecular weights are less than M_e, the average molecular weight between entanglement coupling points.

Arenz, Landel and Tsuge (18) presented relaxation data in uniaxial and bi-axial tension on a series of SBRs crosslinked to different degrees with sulfur. We calculated n from their data and plotted the values against their values for ν_e, the number of effective chains in the network per undeformed volume, in Fig. 3. The figure shows that n increases with the crosslink density, except at the highest values of ν_e. We have no explanation at present for the decrease in n at the latter values.

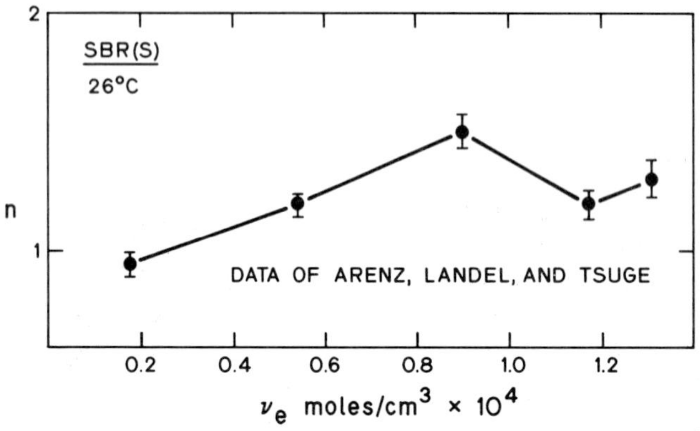

Fig. 3. The parameter of n as a function of crosslink density for SBR at 26°C. Data of Arenz et al. (18)

The dependence of the Mooney-Rivlin constants C_1 and C_2 on the degree of crosslinking has been studied on natural rubber (19,20), cis-1,4-polyisoprene (20), polyethylene (21), and polyurethane (22). Our parameter n can be estimated from the C_2/C_1 ratio determined from uniaxial tension and/or compression experiments. Excepting polyurethane, where n is insensitive to the degree of crosslinking, the other materials show that n increases and approaches two as the crosslink density increases.

The dependence of n on temperature for a crosslinked SBR is shown in Fig. 4. The parameter n increases sigmoidally with temperature. (12) The error bars represent $\pm$ 1 standard deviation as obtained from the least square estimation of n. No error bar is shown at − 45°C because this value was estimated from two stretch rations only. Similar temperature dependencies were also found on butyl rubber (14,23). Furthermore, at sufficiently low temperatures, crosslinked polymers seem to show the same low value of n as do uncrosslinked (i.e. entanglement) networks.

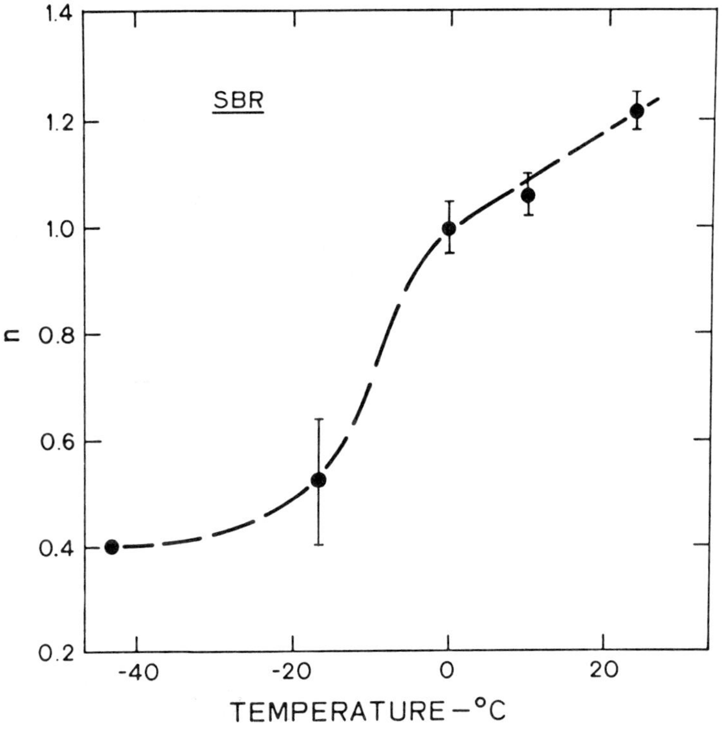

Fig. 4. The parameter n as a function of temperature for SBR .

The number of entanglement crosslinks introduced in a random crosslinking process is, to some extent, controlled by the primary molecular weight. The higher the molecular weight the higher the ratio of effective chains from entanglements to those from crosslinks (24). An extensive study of the effect of molecular weight on C_1 and C_2 was conducted by Kraus and Moczygemba (25) on narrow distribution poybutadiene (PBD) samples cured by different amounts of sulfur. The n-value of the cured specimens can be estimated from their C_1 and C_2 values (10). The swelling in n-heptane (υ_r). From cross-ploting the 10 hr. data of Kraus and Maczygemba, we obtain n as function of primary molecular weight at different υ_r (Fig. 5). The small hump in the curve for υ_r - 0.38 may be due to scattering of the data. It is clear that the parameter n decreases with increasing primary molecular weight. The figure also indicates that n is independent of υ_r if the primary molecular weight is low enough. At a molecular weight of 5500, which is below the entanglement spacing, N = 2. The latter sample was prepared by crosslinking carboxy terminated polybutadiene chains through a coupling agent (25).

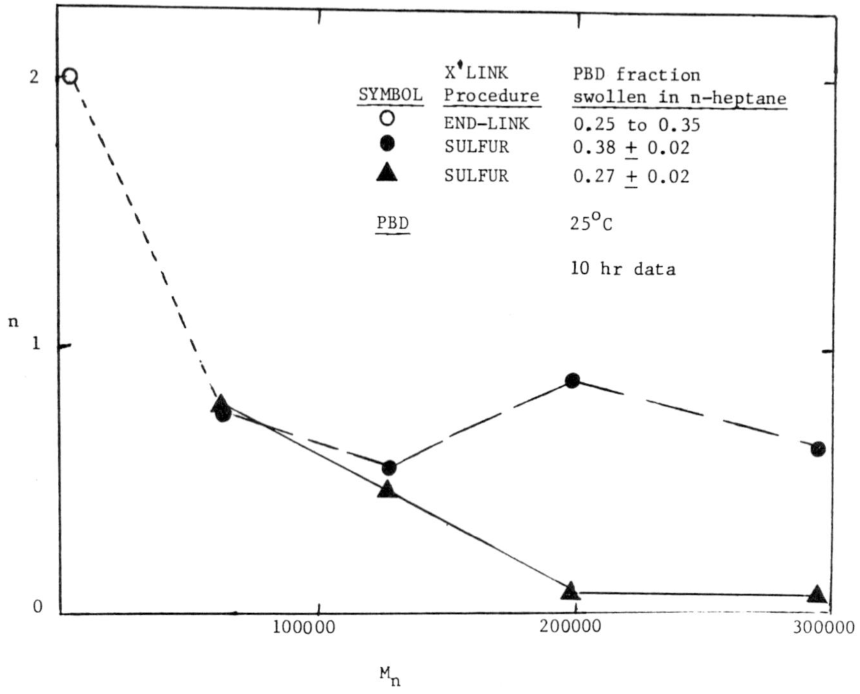

Fig. 5. The parameter n as a function of primary molecular weight for PBD at 25°C. Data of Kraus and Moczygemba(25).

The relative concentration of entanglement chains in a network can also be reduced by crosslinking in solution. Literature data (2,26,27) suggest that the network formed in solution, after solvent removal, has an n value much closer to two than the corresponding network formed in bulk. Swelling of a polymer network by a diluent has a very pronounced effect on its n-value (2). Data of Gumbrell et al. (19) suggest that n increases and approaches to two as υ_r decreases.

We conclude that the n-value for an entanglement network is quite different from that for a network which contains only chemical crosslinks. The n-value for the former is close to 0.5, that for the latter is close to 2. An elastomeric network generally contains both chemical crosslinks and physical entanglements, and n-value for the network will be determined by the relative numbers and importance of these two kinds of interchain points.

IV. COMPOSITE NETWORKS

The mechanical behavior of crosslinked networks also dedends on the state of strain during the crosslinking process. Natural rubber (28,29) and polyethylene (30) crosslinked in the unidimensionally oriented state and thereafter disoriented without rearranging the crosslinks, usually exhibit C_2-value close to zero when stretched in the direction of orientation. C_2 is close to zero also in biological polymers (31,32), where the crosslinking process occurs naturally in the fibrous state. These findings were considered as confirmation of the essential correctness of Flory's theory of elasticity for a system of macromolecules crosslinked in a paralleled array (33). However, since an oriented synthetic polymer is not formed by packing together rodlike molecules but rather by stretching an initially unoriented entanglement network, both natural rubber and polyethylene may be considered more appropriate as two-state composite networks. In fact, the experimental data quoted above are also supported by the two state composite network theory of Berry, Scalan and Watson (34). A two-state composite network is a network whose crosslinks (physical or chemical) are introduced in two deformational states. A general composite network usually contain several sets of physical and/or chemical crosslinks introduced at different states of strain.

More recent work of Greene et al. (35,36) indicates that two-state composite networks of natural rubber show aniosotropic behavior in the swelling, optical and mechanical experiments. Due to their use of the Gaussian approximation, both the theory of Flory (33) and the theory of Berry et al. (34) do not predict the observed anisotropy. Therefore, several theories of composite networks, based on non-Gaussian statistics, were proposed (37,38). These theories still need improvement.

Greene et al. (36) also analyzed the anisotropy phenomenologically, i.e. without recourse to a statistical theory. They assumed that networks formed at different states of strain could be represented by the Mooney-Rivlin equation with different sets of material constants and derived the constitutive equation for the composite network. They attributed the anisotropy to the C_2 - term.

We attempt to modify the theory of Greene et al by replacing the Mooney-Rivlin equation by eq. (3). Following Berry, Scanlan and Watson (34), we assume that the networks formed in the different states behave independently. We further assume that the strain energy density function of the network formed in the strained state could, in the absence of the first network (unstrained state), also be represented by eq. (3). We therefore write the strain energy density function of a two-state composite network as

$$W = (2G_1/n_1^2)\ (\lambda_x^{n_1} + \lambda_y^{n_1} + \lambda_z^{n_1} - 3)$$
$$+ \ (2G_2/n_2^2)\ [(\lambda_x/\lambda_{xo})^{n_2} + (\lambda_y/\lambda_{yo})^{n_2} + (\lambda_z/\lambda_{zo})^{n_2} - 3] \tag{8}$$

where λ_x, and λ_y, and λ_z are the principal stretch ratios referred to the rest lengths of the first network and λ_{xo}, λ_{yo} and λ_{zo} are the principal stretch ratios at which the second stage crosslinks are introduced. On the release of the stress the network will return to a deformation state defined by the principal stretch ratios λ_{xs}, λ_{ys}, and λ_{zs}. Equation (8) and the incompressibility condition, eq. (4), are sufficient to define the equilibrium deformation behavior of the composite network. It can be shown that in the degenerate case $n_1 = n_2$, the model predicts isotropic behavior.

We will illustrate the application of the model by considering the special case in which the second crosslinks are introduced in a uniaxially stretched state defined by

$$\lambda_{xo} = \lambda_o \tag{9a}$$

and

$$\lambda_{yo} = \lambda_{zo} = \lambda_o^{-0.5} \tag{9b}$$

Following the same procedure as used by Greene et al. (36), we determine the apparent Young's modulus and the stress-deformation relation along the direction parallel to the oriented axis as

$$E_{/\!/} = 2G_1(1 - n_2/n_1)\{(\lambda_{xs})^{n_1} + 0.5(\lambda_{xs})^{-0.5n_1}\}$$
$$+ \ 1.5\ \chi n_2 \tag{10}$$

and

$$\bar{\sigma}_{/\!/} = \{2G_1[(\lambda_x)^{n_1} - (\lambda_{xs})^{n_1}(\lambda_x/\lambda_{xs})^{n_2} - (\lambda_x)^{-0.5n_1}$$
$$+ \ (\lambda_x)^{-0.5n_2}\ (\lambda_{xs})^{-0.5(n_1-n_2)}]\ /\ n_1\}$$
$$+ \ \chi[(\lambda_x/\lambda_{xs})^{n_2} - (\lambda_x/\lambda_{xs})^{-0.5n_2}] \tag{11}$$

where

$$\chi = [2G_1(\lambda_{xs})^{n_1}] / n_1 + [2G_2(\lambda_{xs}/\lambda_o)^{n_2}] / n_2 \tag{12}$$

and the stretch ratio λ_{xs} is defined by

$$\{2G_1[(\lambda_{xs})^{n_1} - (\lambda_{xs})^{-0.5n_1}]\} / n_1 + \{2G_2[(\lambda_{xs}/\lambda_o)^{n_2} - (\lambda_{xs}/\lambda_o)^{-0.5n_2}]\} / n_2 = 0 \tag{13}$$

The apparent Young's modulus of the composite network along the y-axis (perpendicular to the oriented axis), $E_\perp$, can also be determined. The relative Young's modulus, which is defined by $E_\perp/E_{/\!/}$ and serves as a measure of the degree of anisotropy, is then obtained as

$$E_{rel} = 2[2G_1(1 - n_2/n_1)(\lambda_{xs})^{-0.5n_1} + \chi n_2] / [2G_1(1 - n_2/n_1)[(\lambda_{xs})^{n_1} + (\lambda_{xs})^{-0.5n_1}] + 2\chi n_2 \tag{14}$$

The stress-deformation relation along the direction perpendicular to the oriented axis is governed by

$$\bar{\sigma}_\perp = \{2G_1[(\lambda_y)^{n_1} - (\lambda_y)^{n_2}(\lambda_{xs})^{0.5(n_2-n_1)} - (\lambda_x)^{n_1} - (\lambda_x)^{n_2}(\lambda_{xs})^{(n_1-n_2)}]\} / n_1 + \chi[(\lambda_y)^{n_2}(\lambda_{xs})^{0.5n_2} - (\lambda_x/\lambda_{xs})^{n_2}] \tag{15}$$

where λ_y is a known quantity which depends on the strain imposed during the experiments, and λ_x is defined by

$$\{2G_1[(\lambda_x\lambda_y)^{-n_1} + (\lambda_{xs})^{n_1}(\lambda_x/\lambda_{xs})^{n_2} - (\lambda_x)^{n_1} - (\lambda_x\lambda_y)^{-n_2}(\lambda_{xs})^{0.5(n_2-n_1)}]\} / n_1 + \chi\{[(\lambda_{xs})^{0.5} / (\lambda_x\lambda_y)]^{n_2} - (\lambda_x/\lambda_{xs})^{n_2}\} = 0 \tag{16}$$

Eq. (14) indicates that E_{rel} is larger, equal or smaller than one if n_2 is correspondingly larger, equal or smaller than n_1. Recently the elastic behavior of composite networks of 1,2-polybutadiene was reported by Kramer et al. (39,40). These networks were crosslinked in states of strain just above the glass transition temperature with entanglements serving as first stage crosslinks. The mechanical data and swelling data indicate that $E_{rel} > 1$. Therefore, these data are in qualitative agreement with the prediction of our model, if n_1 (entanglement) is less than n_2 (crosslinked network) as we expect to be.

Since the G_i and n_i are functions of chemical crosslinks as well as physical entanglements, the anisotropy, as it is measured by E_{rel}, would depend on crosslink densities in both states. The exact dependence will not be known until sufficient information about the effect of crosslinks on G_i and n_i is available. However, qualitative features could be deduced based on the assumption that the individual network in the absence of the other network, behaves isotropically. Let us adopt G_2/G_1 as a measure of the relative crosslink densities between two states. The parameter G_2/G_1 is equal to zero (or infinity) if there exist no first crosslinks (or second crosslinks). From the discussion in the previous section we expect n_2 to be larger than n_1 if G_2 is much larger than G_1. This implies $E_{rel} > 1$ when $G_2 >> G_1$. Therefore we expect at least one maximum in a plot of E_{rel} vs G_2/G_1.

Literature data on elastic behavior are frequently reported in terms of the Mooney-Rivlin constants along both directions perpendicular and parallel to the oriented axis. These constants may be calculated from eqs (11), (12), (13), (15) and (16). For a given λ_o, computer calculations indicate that $(C_2/C_1)_{\perp} \gtrless (C_2/C_1)_{\parallel}$ if $n_1 \lessgtr n_2$. Greene et al. studied the elastic behavior of composite networks of NR and found that $(C_2/C_1)_{\perp}$ was always smaller than $(C_2/C_1)_{\parallel}$, indicating that $n_1 \geq n_2$. Their composite networks were prepared by radiation crosslinking with the first stage crosslinks ranging from purely physical entanglements to crosslinks produced by high radiation dosages.

Since we expect n_2 to be larger than n_1, the data of Greene et al., at least for the systems in which the first crosslinks consist only of physical entanglements, seem to conflict with our model. There are four possible explanations for this. First, the prestretch ratios, λo, at which the second crosslinks are introduced, might be too large for eq. (3) to be applicable. Secondly, as suggested by Greene et al. (35), the oriented networks may contain regions of inhomogeneity (possible paracrystalline phase) which are rendered permanent by the second stage crosslinks. Literature data on the uniaxial tensile properties of polyurethane systems, which contain small domains of hard segments, show negative C_2-values (10,41). Recent work by Jánaček (42, 43) indicates that negative parameters can be expected for polymer networks prepared in the presence of high concentrations of a diluent. They attributed the phenomenon to the inhomogeneous deformation of supermolecular domains resulting from network heterogoneity. We note that a negative C_2-value implies that $n>2$. If the systems investigated by Greene et al. contain regions of inhomogenity, the network formed by the first crosslinks may require an n higher than that formed by the second crosslinks. Thirdly, our model, as most other composite network models, assumes that the elastical behavior of the crosslinks introduced in the strained state can be represented by an isotropic strain energy density function. No a priori judgment can be made concerning this assumption. Fourthly, the model assumes that the two crosslinks introduced in different strained states are independent of one another. This implies that the values of n_1 and G_1, which could be determined before the introduction of the second set of crosslinks, will not be changed by the second crosslinking process. Smith and Gaylord (38) have shown that the independent network hypothesis is not valid for non-Gaussian systems. However, published data are not sufficient for a crucial check of this hypothesis.

We conclude that there is no compelling experimental evidence against the application of our model for two-state composite networks to elastomeric networks which contain physical entanglements in addition to chemical crosslinks. Clearly, much further experimental work is needed, however, before the two-state theory can be applied successfully.

V. THE MOLECULAR ORIGIN OF n.

We have shown that the Gaussian theory fails to describe the behavior of the real network. An obvious follow up question is the molecular causes of this failure. Before we attempt to answer this question, let us first list the assumptions underlying the Gaussian statistical theory: 1. The rubber is incompressible, 2. all deformations are purely elastic, i.e. no relaxation occurs, 3. all the network chains can be described as Gaussian chains in the range of deformation we are interested ($\lambda \leq 3$), 4. all chains have the same molecular weight, 5. all chains are elastically active, 6. energy changes accompanying deformation are purely intra-molecular conformation effects, 7. the crosslink deforms the same way as the continuum (affine deformation), 8. the network is crosslinked in the unstrained state.

Many attempts have been directed to account for the non-ideal elastic behavior by removing either one or several of the above assumptions. Several extensive reviews of the proposed molecular models are available (see, for example, references 22 and 44). A recent account is given by Chompff in this symposium. We will briefly examine all the assumptions in order to explore the molecular origins of this non-ideal behavior.

If the relative small volumetric changes accompanying uniaxial deformation of the elastomer are accounted for through refining the reference state as suggested by Flory (45), the nonideal behavior is still not predicted. Thus, assumption 1 is not the weakness of the theory. The assumption of purely elastic behavior should not be the source of the deviation based on argument presented in section II. That is, the time dependent effect may be removed and yet the equilibrium behavior still fails to follow the Gaussian theory. Assumption 3 will be valid if a network chain can be considered isolated and is free from the interaction of other chains. For an isolated chain, the stress-strain behavior should be represented by a Gaussian statistics theory in the deformation region we are interested ($\lambda \leq 3$) (4). Assumption 4 is perfectly legitimate for a Gaussian chain, since the average energy stored in such chain is independent of its molecular weight. Assumption 5 will not be valid for a real network because of interchain crosslinking, the presence of dangling chains, entanglements, etc. The quantitative effect of these entanglements is not yet known. Assumption 6 is often considered as the possible source of non-Gaussian behavior. Several molecular models of bundle structures and "meander" arrays have been proposed to account for the effect of internal energy changes due to interchain interactions. However, as Flory (46) pointed out, thermoelastic studies on both swollen and unswollen networks discount the existence of any kind of order. Our observation of the insensitivity of n in uncrosslinked systems to the local chemical structure and temperature supports Flory's view. Assumption 7 which requires affine deformation of the crosslink is often cited as being another major cause of the nonideal network behavior. This nonaffine deformation results from the non-Gaussian behavior of chains in the network (4). Assumption 8 can not be the main cause in light of our observation that the uncrosslinked network behaves even more nonideal than the crosslinked network.

The previous discussions suggest that the nonideal behavior is a direct consequence of the non Gaussian network (as opposed to the non-Gaussian isolated chain) which is, in turn, due to the interaction between chains. This interaction cannot be attributed to any internal energy change due to the orderly structure. We support the idea that these interchain interactions result from chain entanglements. In the Gaussian statistical theory, the network chains are assumed to be free to choose configurations without considering the configurations of neighboring chains. In real networks the chain cannot pass through one another's backbone contours. Thus, the configuration available to any chain depends on the topological relationship with neighboring chains. Under deformation or swelling, this obstruction effect will cause a change in entropy of the network differing from that for a network of independent chains. The importance of the obstruction effect depends on the relative concentration of physical entanglements versus that of chemical crosslinks. Experimental data of the dependence of n on crosslink density generally agree with this concept.

A rigorous treatment of entanglement is an extremely

difficult statistical mechanical problem. Although some efforts have been directed along this line (47,48), no quantitative conclusions can be drawn about the deviation from the Gaussian statistical theory. However, qualitatively, it is found that there is no reason to expect the Gaussian theory to be valid (49). An alternative approach calculates the free energy of deformation of a simplified molecular model, assuming the model to keep the most essential characteristics of a real network.

Recently, Priss (50) proposed a simple model to treat the effect of steric obstructions. Assuming that the end-to-end distance of a network chain after deformation changes affinely, but, due to the obstruction effect imposed by the neighboring chain, the change of transversal chain dimensions follow a different law. The entropy of a single chain is assumed to be determined by its end-to-end distance and location of its middle point, the displacement of which represents the change of transversal chain dimensions. This model predicts a strain energy density of the following form

$$W = C_1 (\lambda_1^2 + \lambda_2^2 + \lambda_3^2 - 3) + KF(\lambda_1, \lambda_2, \lambda_3) \qquad (17)$$

where F characterizes the additional free energy change due to the obstruction effect, C_1 and K are material constants. The exact form of F can be obtained from Priss's article (50).

Priss claimed that eq. (17), along with eq. (4), successfully represents Treloar's data (51) on natural rubber for different homogeneous deformations. Indeed, for this material we could not determine relative merits between his model and eq. (3). We, therefore, decided to compare F with the second term of eq. (1), which corresponds to n = -2 of eq. (3), on a Mooney-Rivlin Plot. As shown in Fig. 6, both equations give similar predictions for simple tension; however, F does predict a lower compression stress than that predicted by the second term of Moony-Rivlin equation. This demonstrates why eq. (17) represents data better than eq. (1). In the same figure, we also plot the predictions of eq. (3) with n = 0 and n = 2 (the first term of eq. (1) and eq. (17)). Noting that the ratio of stresses predicted by setting n = 0 and n = 2, relative to that for n = 0 and n = -2, has different values for both tension and compression regions, there are no combinations of C_1 and K in eq. (17) which can offer the same prediction as that of eq. (3) with n = 0. Since we know that the tensile stress-stretch ratio of uncrosslinked polymers can be described by an n close to zero, isochronal stress-stretch ratio data for different modes of deformation on these materials should allow us to distinguish eq. (3) and eq. (17) from each other.

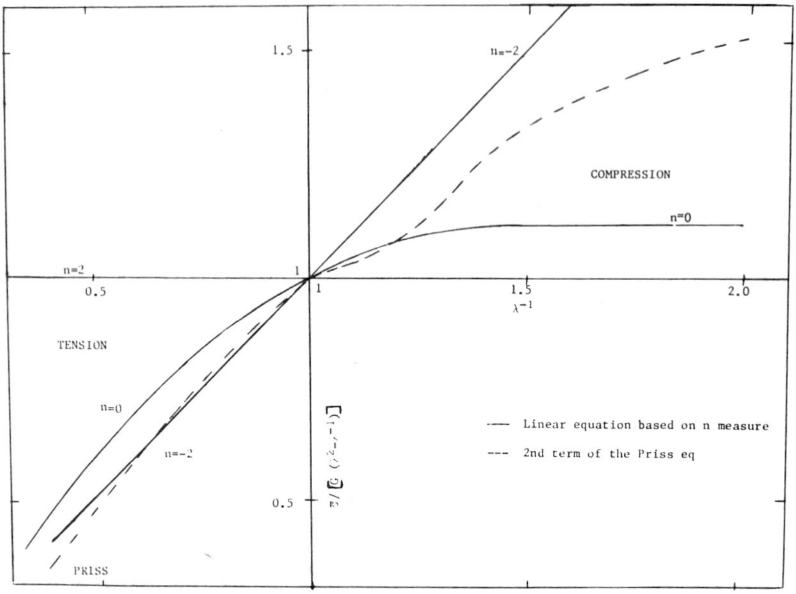

Fig. 6. A Mooney-Rivlin Plot of stresses predicted both by the second term of Priss's equation (50) and by the n-measure of strain for n = -2, 0, and 2.

Another approach to represent the obstruction effects on the configurations of a network chain is to consider a chain confined in a tube formed by its neighboring chains. The available configurations to the confined chain has been discussed by Edwards (52). It is believed that stress-strain behavior depends on the ratio $\langle r^2\rangle o/L_o^2$, where $\langle r^2\rangle o$ is the mean square end-to-end distance of free chain and Lo^2 characterizes the dimension of the tube. For a crosslinked network, Lo and the temperature dependence of Lo should be related to the dimension and the thermal expansivity of the specimen, respectively. The temperature dependence of Lo is expected to be different from that of $\langle r^2\rangle o$ for a crosslinked polymer. We speculate that the dependence of n on temperature for crosslinked systems might be related to the change of $\langle r^2\rangle o/Lo^2$ with temperature. We expect that an uncrosslinked polymer has a weaker temperature dependence of $\langle r^2\rangle o^2$. However, more experiments are needed to clarify the issue. A similar tube model has been adopted successfully by Gennes (53) in describing the relaxation behavior of crosslinked polymeric gel. We believe that more effort should be directed along this line.

VI. ACKNOWLEDGMENTS

The authors are grateful for a National Science Foundation grant which supported one of them (R.B.) as a post-doctoral research fellow. The authors are indebted to Drs. R. Salovey, A. J. Chompff and R. W. Fillers for critical readings of the manuscript.

VII. REFERENCES

1. A. Ciferri, Rheol. Acta 12, 276 (1973)
2. J. E. Mark, Rubber Chem. Technol. 48, 495 (1975)
3. N. W. Tschoegl, J. Polymer Sci. A-1, 9, 1959 (1971)
4. L. R. G. Treloar, Reports on Progress in Physics 36, 755 (1973); Reprinted in Rubber Chem. Technol. 47, 625 (1974)
5. R. S. Rivlin, in "Rheology, Theory and Applications" (F. R. Erich, Ed.) Vol. 1, p. 351, Academic Press, N.Y., 1956.
6. P. J. Blatz, S. C. Sharda, and N. W. Tschoegl, Trans. Soc. Rheol. 18, 145 (1974)
7. S. C. Sharda, P. J. Blatz, and N. W. Tschoegl, Letters Applied Eng. Sci. 2, 53 (1974)
8. A. S. Lodge, "Elastic Liquids", Chapter 6, Academic Press, N.Y., 1964
9. A. S. Lodge, Proc. 5th Intern Cong. Rheology 4, 169 (1970)
10. W. V. Chang, R. Bloch, and N. W. Tschoegl, submitted to J. Polymer Sci.
11. W. V. Chang, R. Bloch, and N. W. Tschoegl, Proc. Natl. Acad. Sci. USA, 73, 981 (1976).
12. R. Bloch, W. V. Chang and N. W. Tschoegl, submitted to Trans. Soc. Rheol.
13. W. V. Chang, R. Bloch and N. W. Tschoegl, Rheol. Acta 15, 367 (1976).
14. B. Bernstein, E. A. Kearsley and L. J. Zapas, Trans. Soc. Rheol. 7, 391 (1963).
15. L. J. Zapas and T. Craft, J. Res. Natl. Bur. Stand. 69A, 541 (1965).
16. W. Goldberg, B. Bernstein and G. Lianis, Int. J. Nonlinear Mech. 4, 277 (1969).
17. J. W. M. Noordermeer and J. D. Ferry, J. Polymer Sci: Polymer Phys. 14, 549 (1976).
18. R. J. Arenz, R. F. Landel and K. Tsuge, in "Mechanical Behavior of Materials", Vol. III, p. 443, The Society of Materials Science (Japan), Kyoto, 1972; Private Communication.
19. S. M Gumbrell, L. Mullins and R. S. Rivlin, Trans. Faraday Soc. 49, 1495 (1953).
20. G. M. Bristow, J. Applied Polymer Sci. 9, 1571 (1965)
21. A. N. Gent and V. V. Vickroy, Jr., J. Polymer Sci. A2, 5,

47 (1967).

22. R. Blokland, Ph.D. Thesis, Delft (1968)
23. T. L. Smith, J. Polymer Sci. 16, 841 (1967)
24. N. R. Langley and K. E. Palmanteer, J. Polymer Sci.: Polymer Phys. 12, 1023 (1974).
25. G. Kraus and G. A. Moczygemba, J. Polymer Sci.: Part A, 2, 277 (1964).
26. B. Meissner, I. Klier and S. Kuchařík, J. Polymer Sci.: Part C, 16, 793 (1967).
27. C. S. M. Ong and R. Stein, J. Polymer Sci: Polymer Phys. 12, 1599 (1974)
28. D. E. Roberts and L. Mandelkern, J. Amer. Chem. Soc., 80, 1289 (1958).
29. J. F. M. Oth and P. J. Flory, J. Amer. Chem. Soc., 80, 1295 (1958).
30. L. Mandelkern, D. E. Roberts, A. F. Diorio, and A. S. Posner, J. Amer. Chem. Soc. 81, 4148 (1959).
31. J. F. M. Oth, Kolloid - Z. 171, 1 (1960).
32. P. T. Speakman, Trans. Faraday Soc. 57, 518 (1961)
33. P. J. Flory, J. Amer. Chem. Soc. 78, 5222 (1956)
34. J. P. Bery, J. Scanlan and W. F. Watson, Trans. Faraday Soc., 52, 1137 (1956).
35. A. Greene and A. Ciferri, Kolloid - Z. 186, 1 (1962).
36. A. Greene, K. J. Smith, Jr. and A. Ciferri, Trans. Faraday Soc. 61, 2772 (1965).
37. K. J. Smith, Jr., A. Ciferri, and J. J. Hermans, J. Polymer Sci. A, 2, 1025 (1964).
38. K. J. Smith, Jr. and R. J. Gaylord, J. Polymer Sci. A-2, 10, 283 (1972).
39. O. Kramer, R. L. Carpenter, V. Ty, and J. D. Ferry, Macromolecules 7, 79 (1974).
40. O. Kramer and J. D. Ferry, Macromolecules, 8, 87 (1975).
41. Y. Yamaguchi, N. Yoshitake, T. Yokoyama and T. Tanaka, Chem. High Polymers (Japan) 26, 651 (1969).
42. J. Janáček, J. Macromol. Sci. - Revs. Macromol. Chem., C9, 1 (1973).
43. J. Janacek and V. Vojta, J. Polymer Sci. Polymer Symp. 53, 291 (1975).
44. K. Dusek and W. Prins, Advance Polymer Sci:, 6, 1, 43 (1969).
45. P. J. Flory, J. Am. Chem. Soc., 78, 5222 (1956).
46. P. J. Flory, Macromolecular Chemistry 8, 1 (1973).
47. S. F. Edwards, Proc. Phys. Soc. 91, 513 (1967).
48. S. F. Edwards, In "Polymer Networks" (A. J. Chompff and S. Newman, Eds.), p. 83, Plenum, New York, 1975.
49. W. W. Graessley, Adv. Polym. Sci. 16, 1 (1974).
50. L. S. Priss, J. Polym. Sci. Polym Symp. 53, 195 (1975).
51. L. R. G. Treloar, Trans. Faraday Soc. 40, 59 (1944)
52. S. F. Edwards and K. F. Freed, J. Phys. A. Gen Phys.

2, 151 (1969).
53. P. G. de Gennes, J. Chem. Phys. 55, 572 (1971).

CREEP BEHAVIOR OF NETWORKS UNDERGOING SCISSION REACTIONS

Wu-Nan Huang and J.J. Aklonis
University of Southern California

We have carried out a set of experiments to test the accuracy of two procedures, one suggested by Curro and Salazar and the other by Moacanin, Aklonis, and Landel, in predicting the behavior of polymer networks which are simultaneously chemically reacting and physically relaxing. The necessary input data to support the calculations were measured directly on the experimental samples in the absence of chemical reactions. The chemical reaction utilized was a photo-induced scission of disulfide linkages which had been incorporated into the network; thus the reaction could be turned on and off at will. Our results show that the behavior predicted by the MAL technique is in good agreement with that observed experimentally.

I. INTRODUCTION

The behavior of polymers which simultaneously physically relax and chemically react is an area of polymer science which has not been extensively studied in the past. This fact is strange when we realize that relaxation and reaction occur simultaneously in virtually all long service applications of stressed polymers in hostile environments; and, for most polymers, simple exposure to weathering conditions constitutes a hostile environment. Clearly, it would be helpful to understand the behavior of such systems.

The lack of attention paid to this area by researchers is quite understandable. For example, several years ago it was possible to measure the creep behavior of a polymer which was undergoing crosslinking reactions but it was not possible to analyze such data. No generally applicable interpretation of the experimental results which would separate the effects of the chemistry from the physical relaxation could be made. In fact, we are aware of only one piece of data on reacting-relaxing systems reported in the pre-1970 literature,[1] and this information was included merely as an unanalyzable curiosity which should be avoided.

In the early 1970's, several papers[2-5] were published which treated relaxing-reacting systems. These fall into two categories: those developed by Curro and Salazar (CS)[2] and those of Moacanin, Aklonis, and Landel (MAL).[3,4,5] The fundamental difference between these two treatments can be understood by referring to Figures 1 and 2. Here we plot schematically the length of two samples of different cross-link densities ($\nu_1 > \nu_2$) during a creep experiment where the sample sizes and stresses are identical in each case.

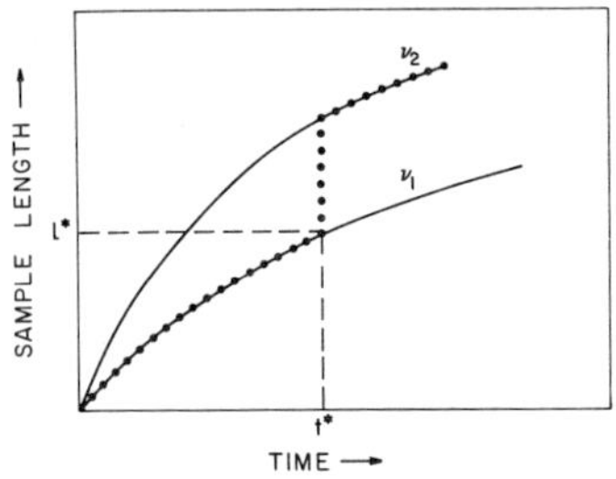

Fig. 1. Schematic representation of the predicted behavior of a simultaneously relaxing reacting network according to Curro and Salazar.[2]

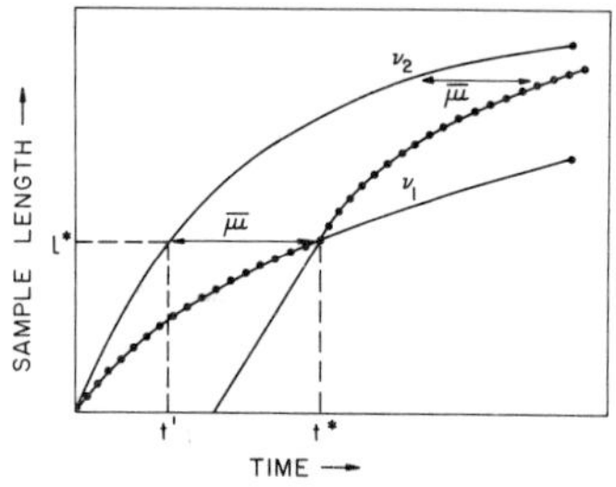

Fig. 2. Schematic representation of the predicted behavior of a simultaneously relaxing reacting network according to Moacanin, Aklonis, and Landel.[3,4,5]

Consider, now, an experiment started with sample ν_1, which would be carried out to the time t^* indicated on the figures. Further, suppose that at t^* an instantaneous transformation from crosslink density ν_1 to ν_2 were performed. How does the length of the sample behave at times greater than t^*? The answer to this question is different in the two treatments we are considering. Fundamentally the CS treatment assumes a vertical jump directly to the ν_2 curve at time t^*. This jump and the subsequent creep behavior are indicated by dots in Figure 1.

MAL, on the other hand, assume that the length of the sample will remain constant in spite of the scission; and that the sample's subsequent behavior will start from the point indicated on the ν_2 curve which is shifted by a time adjustment factor defined as $\bar{\mu}$. Their prediction is shown in Figure 2 as the dotted path.

Both groups have shown that their assumptions lead to mathematical formulations which can be used to treat relaxing-reacting systems. CS, in fact, have analyzed some experimental data on EPR and butyl rubber[2] and purport to have been able to measure the rate of a chemical reaction occurring in the polymer network by using this technique. In their analysis, they have assumed that the vertical excursion shown in Figure 1 is appropriate; but as yet, we have no experimental evidence to substantiate this assumption.

The only way to determine whether either the CS or the MAL prediction is actually correct is by experimentation, and we have just completed the initial stage of such an investigation.

As a first step, we decided to limit our investigation to a system where only scission and no crosslinking occurred. In this way, complications associated with multiple networks in different strain states can be avoided. Furthermore, we decided to seek a system where the scission reaction was not continuous, but could be turned on and off at will. The first system we investigated which potentially satisfies these requirements employs a crosslinked polyurethane based on a polyether prepolymer. A small concentration of disulfide linkages was incorporated into the network during the synthesis. It is known that under U.V. irradiation of the appropriate wavelength, disulfide linkages cleave;[(6)] and photoinduced cleavage, we hoped, would cause the controlled change in crosslink density necessary to check to theoretical predictions.

The results of the experiments carried out with this system are presented and discussed below.

II. POLYMER SYNTHESIS AND CHARACTERIZATION

Our samples were prepared by the addition of poly(oxypropylene-1,2)glycol (PPG 1025), to 4,4'-diisocyanate dicyclohexylmethane (SMDI) with 2-ethyl-2-hydroxymethyl-1,3 propanediol (TMP) used as the trifunctional crosslink forming agent. In addition, some dithiodiglycol was added to the preparation to introduce photo labile disulfide linkages into the network. A detailed account of the exact scheme used to prepare the samples is presented elsewhere.[(7)]

The characteristics of several samples prepared according to this method are listed in Table 1. The number average molecular weight between crosslink values were calculated using the modified Flory-Rehner equation[(8)] with a X_1 value of 0.40.[(9)]

TABLE 1
Sample Characteristics

Sample	*Sol (%)*	*Density (g/cm^3)*	M_c	*Free Dithiodiglycol Added, Wt. %*
94070302	29.	1.132	11,000	0.0
B	5.8	1.082	5,800	9.2
C	5.8	1.082	5,800	23.2

III. EXPERIMENTAL

A particularly simple creep extensometer which has been described elsewhere[(10)] was used in this study. It employs a Schaevitz Linear Variable Differential Transformer No. 503XS-A which has a precision of ± 0.0003 cm; to perform experiments at such high degrees of precision a special procedure was followed.

After attaching the sample to the clamps of the extensometer in the usual fashion, temperature equilibrium was established for a period of approximately one hour. (The thermostated chamber surrounding the extensometer kept the temperature constant to ± 0.1°C for periods of several hours). Next, a creep experiment of perhaps one hour's duration was performed, after which the sample would be allowed to relax under zero load for approximately twenty-four hours. Repeated experiments were carried out in this way to determine the creep response of the starting polymer sample and also to determine the reproducibility of the measurement. Next, another creep experiment was started; but after some amount of time (usually 2 to 10 minutes) radiation from a high pressure mercury lamp (PEK, BH-6-1-B) was focused on the sample for several minutes. The sample's extension was carefully monitored during this period and after the lamp was extinguished. Once again a long recovery period was allowed; and the creep behavior of the sample at the new lower crosslink density was subsequently measured as many times as necessary to obtain accurate creep behavior. Since the single sample was never removed from the extensometer during this entire procedure, the usual small errors associated with characterization and property measurement of different samples were completely avoided. In fact, we often carried out subsequent irradiation and creep experiments at even lower crosslink densities on the same sample. With such a procedure, even if the absolute accuracy of our results were limited for some unknown reason, the accuracy with which experimental results can be compared is still very high. In this fashion, we feel that we have been successful in exploiting this high precision yet extremely simple apparatus.

IV. RESULTS AND DISCUSSION

Typical results for the first type of experiment carried out on reacting-relaxing systems are shown in Figure 3. Here a single sample was irradiated for different amounts of time starting at different periods after the initial stress application (various periods after the creep experiment began). The particular conditions for these experiments are given in Table 2. The results indicate that the sample's behavior is viscoelastic since the change in sample length upon irradiation depends rather markedly on the time when irradiation was initiated. Curves 1 and 3, for example, represent identical experiments, except that in experiment 1 the light was turned on 6.25 minutes after the stress application, while for experiment 3 the irradiation was started 40 minutes after the stress application. Good reproducibility is indicated by the fact that the short-time response is the same for experiments 1 and 5 which differ significantly in the duration of illumination but only slightly in the time of onset. The reaction rate law is essentially zero order which is to be expected since only a small fraction of the disulfide linkages incorporated in the network are cleaved under our experimental conditions.

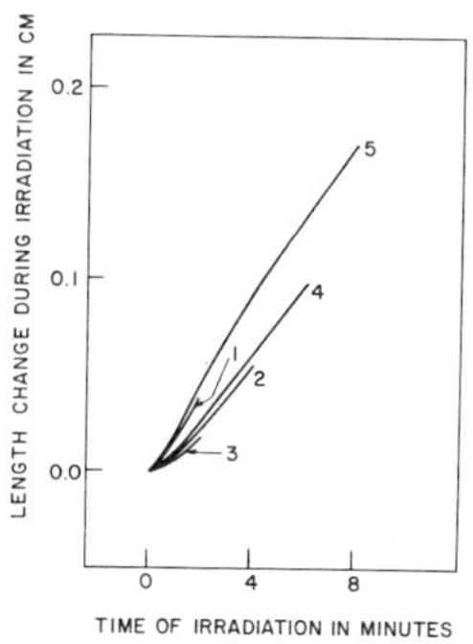

Fig. 3. Creep behavior of Sample 94070302 during irradiation. Particular experimental conditions are given in Table 2.

TABLE 2
Behavior During Irradiation - Sample 94070302

Experiment	*Temperature*	*Time of onset of irradiation (t^*) in minutes*	*Duration of irradiation in minutes*
1	25.0	6.3	2.0
2	25.2	18.0	4.0
3	25.5	40.0	2.0
4	25.3	10.0	6.0
5	25.4	6.0	8.0

These results are encouraging since they indicate that response to scission does, indeed, depend on the state of relaxation of the system, an observation which is in accord with both CS and MAL predictions but which had never before been demonstrated experimentally. Although it seemed clear from these results, additional experiments were performed which proved that scission of network chains was indeed taking place during irradiation. "Equilibrium" (long-time, apparently constant) compliance values have been measured[10] for several samples at many crosslink densities and they clearly show the effectiveness of irradiation in chain scission.

The results of the first experiments thus demonstrated that our system was well suited for use in the study of relaxing-reacting networks.

The ideal method for carrying out the evaluation of the CS and MAL treatments would use the scheme depicted in Figures 1 and 2. We would measure the creep of a sample several times to insure reproducible results. We would next measure the behavior of a sample whose crosslink density was photolytically decreased during a creep experiment, and finally determine the creep of the sample at the new, lower crosslink density. Then these data would be analyzed to ascertain if either CS or MAL were accurate in treating the behavior of polymer networks during and immediately after photolysis.

In actually carrying out experiments on real systems, however, three significant complications were encountered. All of them have been circumvented in one way or another but modifications in the "ideal" approach were necessary to allow our comparison between theory and experiment. First we were unable to change the crosslink density of our sample "instantaneously" or very quickly as had been assumed in Figures 1 and 2. This is partly due to lack of suitable light sources, but mainly resulted from our attempt to carry out the scission part of the experiment isothermally. Low intensities result in little sample heating but necessitate longer exposure periods (four minutes in our standard experiments). This is not a major difficulty, since both the CS and MAL treatments have been applied to situations where continuous scission occurs, as is the situation during irradiation; these formulations were then used during the illumination period. With this modification, no additional information is necessary for our calculations except for a knowledge of the shapes of the creep curves at crosslink densities between ν_1 and ν_2. Since the extent of scission was quite small, reasonable representations of these creep curves were available.(10)

The second problem became clear while we were trying to evaluate reproducibility of behavior during illumination. Here the response of a single sample to several illumination periods was observed. Careful experimental length measurements indicated that appreciable permanent set sometimes occurred. Permanent set (permanent elongation of the sample after some chemical transformation) results from a dissociation of the disulfides into radicals which separate from one another through diffusional type motions of the polymer chains and later recombine with other radicals in the system to form a new network of chains. It is known that such a newly formed network is unstrained, in spite of the fact that the pre-existing network was strained.(11) Upon removal of the applied stress, the newly formed network becomes strained, resulting in permanent elongation or permanent set in the polymer. In such a situation, an unambiguous analysis of the data would be difficult if not impossible.

On further experimentation we found that irradiation of creeping samples for periods of less than about four minutes usually resulted in no permanent set. Although the reasons for this behavior were not clear, and much longer periods of illumination could sometimes be sustained before permanent set resulted, we presently feel that low levels of impurities of some sort (perhaps catalyst residues) were present in some of the samples, and these impurities efficiently quenched the sulfur radicals formed during the initial stages of the reaction. Although we could have proceeded at this point by limiting irradiation of each sample to four minutes or less, we attempted to find a material which could be added to our network to act as a radical scavenger but which would not complicate any other aspects of the experiments. One of our initial candidates for such a compound, dithiodiglycol, turned out to be very effective in this role. Dithiodiglycol was the component used to introduce the photo-labile group into the network through condensation with a diisocyanate. The additional material which was intended to act as a scavenger was added as a plastizier. The procedure involved swelling the sample films (without sol extraction) in pure dithiodiglycol for several days. The swollen samples were then evacuated at low pressure ($\sim$ 1 mm Hg) and at moderate temperature (60-90^{0}C) for suitable periods of time to obtain the desired amount of free dithiodiglycol in each sample. The two plasticized samples reported on here, B and C, had 9.2 and 23.2 weight percent concentrations of free dithiodiglycol respectively. Sample weight was carefully monitored to insure that the plasticizer concentration remained fixed throughout our experimental procedure. With such levels of plastizier, no permanent set was detected even upon extended periods of irradiation.

The final complication involved sample heating during scission. Even though we had chosen materials which were transparent in the spectral range of the incident irradiation (e.g., SMDI rather than TDI) except for dithiodiglycol, we still found that during irradiation some heating resulted which was potentially significant in analysis of the results. After several attempts to limit temperature increases during irradiation, we concluded that some heating would result irrespective of what was done. With such intense irradiation some sample heating was inevitable.

Faced with this situation, we found that the work of McCrum and Morris[12] could be used to good advantage. These workers have carefully studied the effects of temperature jumps on the viscoelastic behavior of polymers and have shown, for example, how temperature variation during creep can be treated. We have used their technique to treat the temperature variations in our own experiments as will be explained later.

Still it was necessary to measure the actual variation of temperature with time due to irradiation. We used a small thermocouple which was shielded from direct illumination by the source and imbedded in the sample. Temperature variations during and after irradiation are shown for several samples for four minute irradiation periods in Figure 4.

In Figure 5, we show actual data obtained using sample B, whose characteristics are described in Table 1. The lower curve represents the creep behavior of the sample before irradiation (ν_1). This curve is actually a combination of several creep curves, all measured on the identical sample. The upper curve shows the creep behavior of the sample after irradiation (ν_2). Here, too, the results of several experiments were combined to yield the curve. The intermediate curve shows the sample's behavior before (t < 4 min) during (4 min < t < 8 min) and after irradiation (t > 8 min). With such data we can now determine if either the CS or MAL treatments are accurate.

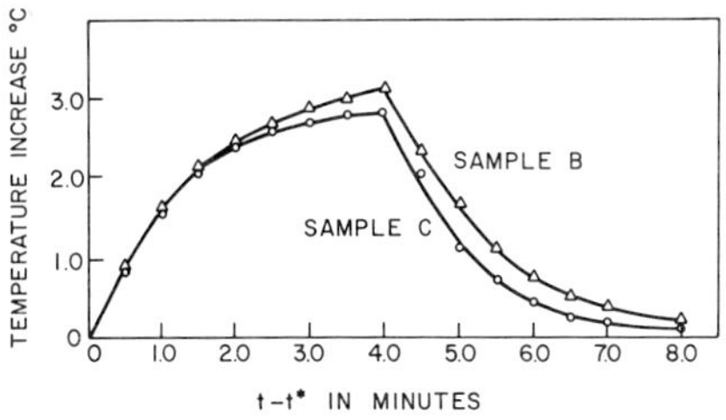

Fig. 4. Measured temperature increases in experimental samples during and immediately after irradiation. In each case, the lamp was turned on at time t^* and extinguished at $t^* + 4$ min.

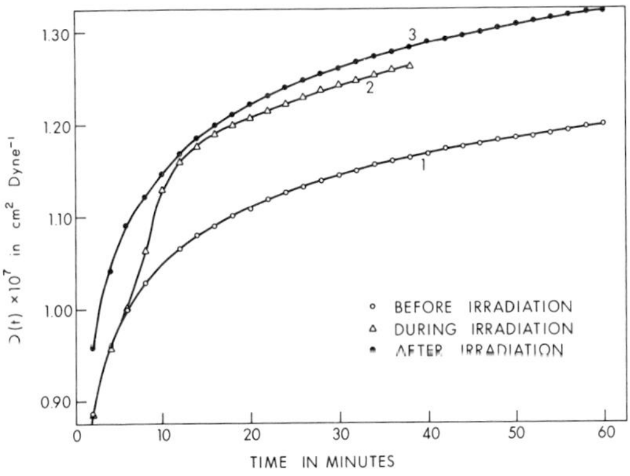

Fig. 5. Creep behavior of Sample B. Curve 1 depicts creep before irradiation and Curve 3 depicts creep after irradiation; the two curves are composites of many experimental runs. The sample was irradiated for the period between 6 and 10 minutes after creep started and the observed behavior during this experiment is shown as Curve 2.

Since the temperature varied during irradiation, the temperature dependence of the viscoelastic behavior of our networks was important; and, although the extent of heating was small (less than 3^0C), this factor turned out to be quite significant in our final analysis. Here our procedure was to actually measure the creep response of the networks at several different temperatures, as shown in Figure 6. The experimental behavior was found to be in accord with time-temperature correspondence.[13] In our case, however, the temperature change was so small that the usual vertical shift associated with changes in equilibrium properties with temperature could be ignored. In addition, rather than attempting to fit a WLF-curve[13] through the data points on a log shift factor versus temperature plot, a simple straight line was used, as shown in the figure. This, too, could be done with no loss of accuracy, since the temperature variation we are concerned with here is very small and the curvation of the WLF equation on such a small scale is negligible.

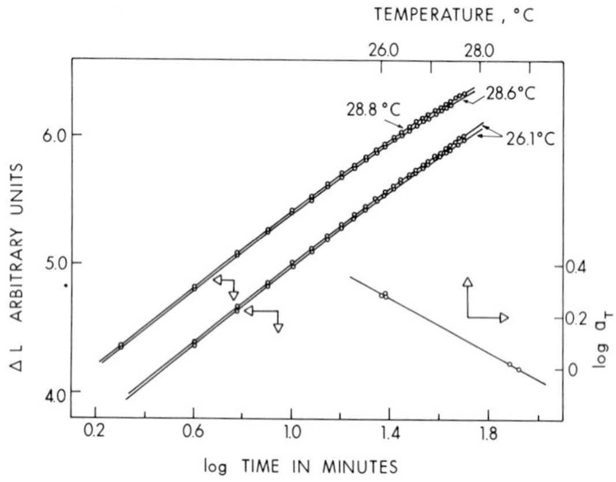

Fig. 6. Creep at various temperatures for Sample B and a "WLF" plot for this data.

Since instantaneous of very rapid changes in crosslink density were not possible experimentally, we were forced to use formulations of the two predictive techniques which are suitable for continuous chemical scission. Input to such a calculation in this instance is the creep behavior of the sample at all crosslink densities between ν_1 and ν_2; clearly an analytical expression which accurately represents the creep of sample B at different crosslink densities would be very helpful.

In a previous paper[10] we have shown that the well-known expression

$$D(t) = \frac{D_e(\nu)}{1 + (\frac{t}{\tau})^{-m}} \qquad (1)$$

where D(t) and $D_e(\nu)$ are tensile creep compliances at time t and at equilibrium respectively, and τ and m are adjustable parameters, was very successful in representing our experimental data; see Figure 7. In that work, it was shown that $D_e(\nu)$ values could either be measured experimentally by employing very long duration creep experiments (6 days in one case); or values could be determined by a best-fit procedure. A similar fitting procedure was previously used by Dickie and Ferry.[14] In addition we found that time-crosslink density correspondence, as first observed by Plazek,[15] was applicable to our networks. Since the two lines in Figure 7 are parallel they have the same value of m in equation (1), even though the sample crosslink density varies from one line to the other. This means that changes in crosslink density or chain length merely cause a multiplicative shift in the time scale of a sample's response (linear shift on a log time scale) after account has been made for changes in equilibrium compliance values associated with the crosslink density changes. Thus the shape of the retardation spectrum is unaffected by changes in crosslink density, but the entire spectrum moves intact along the log τ axis as crosslink density is varied. The applicability of time-crosslink density reduction is a great simplification in this study since now the behavior of a sample at <u>any</u> intermediate crosslink density between ν_1 and ν_2 can be determined simply from a knowledge of the creep behavior of sample B at the two crosslink densities ν_1 and ν_2 alone. These ideas are more fully presented elsewhere.[10]

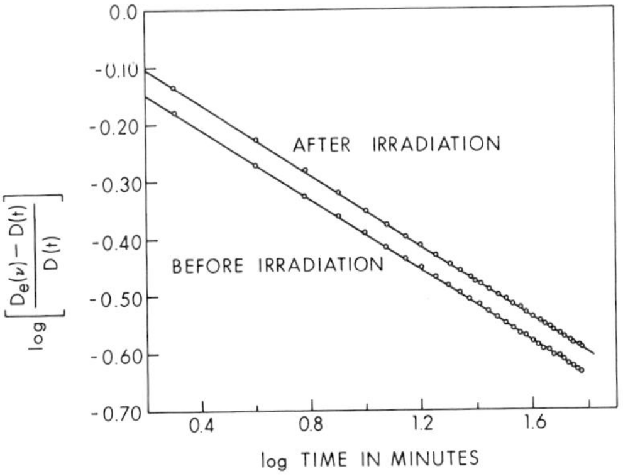

Fig. 7. Analysis of creep data for Sample B according to equation (1).

To carry out the comparison between theory and experiment we viewed both the CS and MAL treatments as predicting distinct responses to incremental amounts of scission. Thus, the four minute irradiation during which scission occurred was approximated as some number of discrete events happening during the irradiation period which, when added together, acounted for the actual change in crosslink density. Reference to Figure 8 will make this idea and the subsequent calculation clearer. Here the curves labelled ν_1 and ν_2 are creep curves which were actually measured on the non-reacting system. These are segments of the curves ν_1 and ν_2 in Figure 5, except that ν_2 has been shifted along the log time scale so that it represents behavior at a slightly higher temperature than the ν_1 curve. This temperature increase is that given in the temperature profile shown in Figure 4 and is appropriate for the point after a four minute irradiation. This method of treating the temperature variation is consistent with that given by McCrum and Morris.[12]

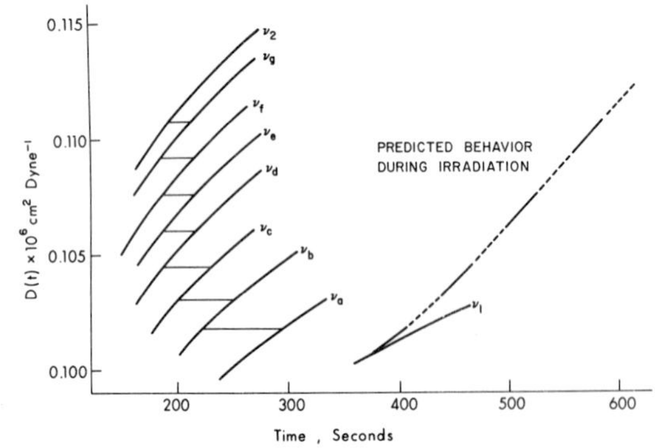

Fig. 8. Graphic calculations of predicted behavior during irradiation; continuous scission process approximated by several discrete steps.

In the particular example presented in Figure 8, the continuous scission was approximated by eight discrete steps, each taking place at 30-second intervals. The necessary input is the manifold of creep curves shown in the figure and was calculated using the time-crosslink density reduction method described earlier and in other publications.[10,15] In addition, each of the individual curves in the manifold is presented at the temperature consistent with the temperature variation shown in Figure 4. It then becomes a simple matter to construct the creep behavior predicted by CS and MAL. This is done merely by connecting the appropriate segments of the intermediate curves, as shown on the right hand portion of Figure 8 for the MAL formalism.

At this point, we could not be certain that approximating the continuous scission process by eight discrete steps will result in a prediction of behavior which is mathematically consistent with the CS and MAL treatments. To check the accuracy of our approximations, we employed various numbers of increments of scission (between 8 and 480 for a four minute irradiation period); and we have found that the predicted behaviors are the same for anything over sixteen increments. Clearly, the calculations with more than eight increments would be overly tedious if attempted graphically using the procedure depicted in Figure 8. Instead, the calculations were carried out on an IBM 370 computer employing simple programs to arithmetically perform the graphically represented operations.

The results for sample B irradiated for four minutes are shown in Figure 9. The solid curve is the experimentally observed creep behavior of this sample during and shortly after irradiation. The circles and squares represent predicted behavior calculated according to the MAL formalism; and the triangles show predicted behavior calculated according to the CS formalism. In this figure it is clear that the horizontal shifting procedure which involves the time adjustment parameter μ suggested by MAL is more appropriate than the vertical jump technique and in all of our experiments we have come to the same conclusion.

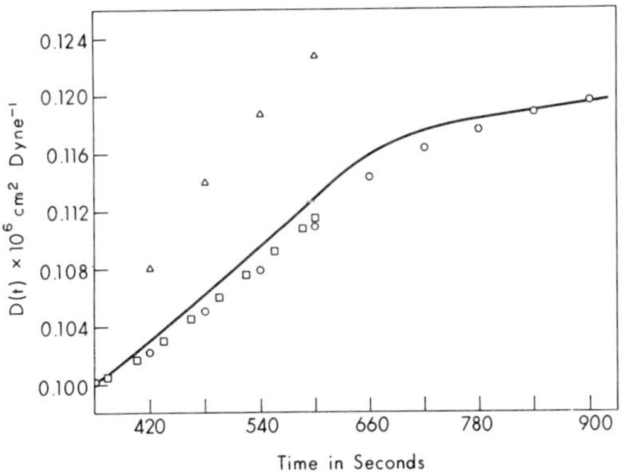

Fig. 9. Creep of Sample B during and after irradiation. The solid line is experimental data; triangles are predicted using the CS technique; circles are predicted using the MAL technique with 240 incremental steps during reactions; squares are predicted using the MAL technique with eight incremental steps during scission.

It should be pointed out, however, that as viscous effects become less important, making elastic behavior dominant, both the CS and MAL techniques yield identical predictions. Since the previous work of Curro and Salazar(2) was in a region where the component of relaxation is small, we think that the analysis of their results based on the vertical jump method is essentially correct in this limited situation.

To be sure, there is still a small discrepancy between the experimentally determined sample behavior and that predicted by the MAL formalism. In our opinion, however, this discrepancy is very small and is close to the limits of certainty of our experiments.

Finally, in Figure 10 we show experimental and predicted creep curves using the MAL formalism for sample C at eight different crosslink densities. A four minute irradiation was used to change crosslink density in each instance. Creep curves for the non-reacting network were measured as usual and analyzed as above. The agreement between experiment and prediction is obvious. Such agreement is indicative of the results we have obtained on other similar samples under comparable conditions and is clear evidence that creep behavior predicted by the MAL formalism is in good agreement with experiment.

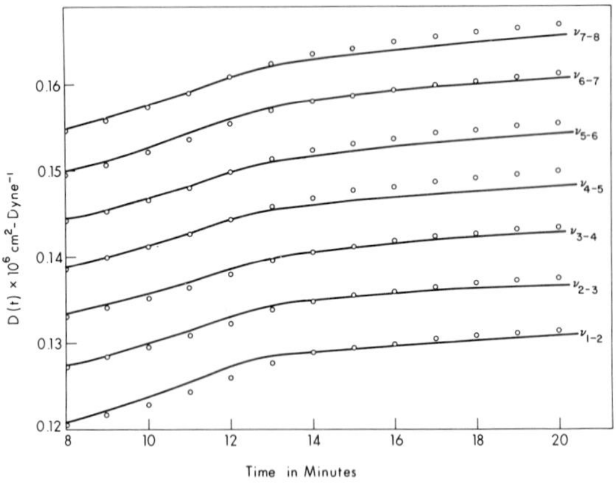

Fig. 10. Experimental (solid lines) and predicted (circles) behavior of Sample C during and after seven separate irradiation periods each of four minute duration during the eight to twelve minute creep period.

V. CONCLUSIONS

We have carried out a set of experiments to test the success of two procedures, one proposed by Curro and Salazar[2] and the other by Moacanin, Aklonis, and Landel,[3,4,5] in predicting the behavior of polymer networks which are simultaneously chemically reacting and physically relaxing. The necessary input data to support the calculation in each case were measured directly on the experimental sample under conditions where chemical reactions did not occur. All parameters were then determined from this data. In view of the fact that there are no independently adjustable parameters involved, we feel that the agreement between experimentally observed behavior during and immediately after chemical scission and that predicted according to the MAL technique as described above is convincing evidence of the applicability of that method.

VI. ACKNOWLEDGEMENT

This work was supported by the Army Research Office under grant number DAAG29-76-C-0194 and contract number DAAG29-76-C-0004.

VII. REFERENCES

1. P. Thirion and R. Chasset, Rubber Chem. and Tech., 37, 617 (1964).
2. J.G. Curro and E.A. Salazar, J. Appl. Polymer Sci., 19, 2571 (1975).
3. J. Moacanin, J.J. Aklonis and R.F. Landel, J. Macromol. Sci., B11, 41 (1975).
4. J. Moacanin, J.J. Aklonis and R.F. Landel, J. Chem. Phys., 64, 430 (1976).
5. J. Moacanin and J.J. Aklonis, J. Polymer Sci., C35, 71 (1971).
6. J.G. Calvert and J.N. Pitts, Photochemistry, John Wiley & Sons, New York, 1967, page 401.
7. Wu-Nan Huang and J.J. Aklonis, Polymer Preprints, 16, No. 2, 88 (1975).
8. P.J. Flory, "Principles of Polymer Chemistry," Cornell Univ. Press, Ithaca, N.Y., 1953, p. 580.
9. T.L. Smith and A.B. Magnusson, J. Polymer Sci., 42, 391 (1960); J.H. Saunders and K.C. Frisch, High Polymers, Vol. XVI, Part 1, 1962, p. 304.
10. Wu-Nan Huang and J.J. Aklonis, submitted to J. Macromol. Sci.

11. A.V. Tobolsky, "Properties and Structure of Polymers," John Wiley & Sons, N.Y., 1960, pp. 242-247.
12. N.G. McCrum and E.L. Morris, Phil. Mag., 7, 2115 (1962).
13. J.D. Ferry, "Viscoelastic Properties of Polymers," 2nd ed., John Wiley & Sons, New York, 1970, Chapter 11.
14. R.A. Dickie and J.D. Ferry, J. Phys. Chem., 70, 2594 (1966).
15. D. Plazek, J. Polymer Sci., A-2, 4, 745 (1966).

KINETICS OF THE CRYSTALLIZATION OF CROSSLINKED POLY(VINYL ALCOHOL) FILMS BY SLOW EVAPORATION OF HYDROGELS

Nikolaos A. Peppas
Purdue University

The kinetics of crystallization of polymer-diluent mixtures with the restraint of polymeric chains with finite molecular weight, are of particular interest in the case of dehydration of swollen polymeric networks. The scope of this communication is to study the nucleation and crystal growth of plasticized crosslinked polymeric systems in terms of drying theories and to predict the behavior of structurally defined polymeric networks under well monitored drying conditions. Crosslinked hydrogels prepared by electron beam irradiation of aqueous PVA solutions were dehydrated at 25 ± 1°C under drying conditions of varying relative humidity of the environment. The degree of crystallinity was a function of crosslinking density, water (or polymer) weight fraction and evaporation rate. For low evaporation rates, the degree of crystallinity and the crystallization rate were affected by the average distance between crosslinks in the network and by the difference in initial polymer weight fraction of the material. At higher evaporation rates these effects were significantly minimized. Depending on the drying conditions, nucleation started at induction times varying between 15-115 hours and always at polymer weight content above 75%. A kinetic model of the results is presented and discussed.

I. INTRODUCTION

The kinetics of crystallization of polymeric chains in polymer-diluent mixtures have been of particular interest in the last few years (1, 2). Systems such as polyethylene and polyoxymethylene in different solvents have been studied by different investigators (3-6).

Crystallization of many polar polymers is associated with strong kinetic hindrances, on account of which the production of a microscopic crystalline phase in the form of spherulites or single crystals is practically impossible. The usual method of crystallization of difficult to solubilize polymers, consists of crystallizing them in the presence of a plasticizer, which is a poor solvent for the given polymer (7). The kinetics of this phenomenon are affected by the low molecular weight diluent in accord with the thermodynamic principles governing two-phase equilibria (8).

Poly(vinyl alcohol)-diluent systems can be used in many commercial applications for the production of films or coatings upon evaporation from concentrated solutions. Poly(vinyl alcohol) or PVA is difficult to solubilize in water; the solubility depends on the degree of hydrolysis and 99.5% hydrolyzed PVA can be dissolved in water only at temperatures above 80°C (9).

When PVA films or fibers are subjected to heat treatment crystallites are formed that normally do not dissolve in water. PVA acquires rather compact conformations in water, which do not promote the formation of extended critical nuclei of crystallization and yet, only such crystalline bundles can form crystals; in the best case, microcrystalline formations may arise. The crystallites are much shorter than the polymer molecules and a single molecule may pass through several crystallites separated by amorphous regions.

The state of an unoriented semicrystalline polymer is usually defined by the degree of crystallinity w_x and the average dimension of the crystallite (10).

The crystallization process of plasticized PVA systems either with water (1, 2) or with ethylene glycol (11) or with mixtures of them (12) have been recently studied under well characterized dehydration conditions.

Here we examine the kinetics of nucleation and crystal growth of these systems, with the additional restrain of a finite polymeric chain, which is imposed by the chemical or radiation-induced crosslinking of the polymer in a solution state. The case of a crosslinked PVA-water system, and more specifically a PVA hydrogel, is taken as a representative experimental system with particular commercial applications (13).

In the present study, aqueous PVA solutions were subjected to controlled electron beam irradiation leading to the formation of well characterized swollen PVA networks. The effects of slow dehydration of these hydrogels on the formation of crystallites were studied with the purpose of developing a kinetic model of nucleation through macroscopic studies. Specifically, the dependence of degree of crystallinity, and polymer weight fraction of the swollen networks were studied as functions of independent variables such as physicochemical properties of the gels (crosslinking density) and dehydration conditions (humidity, temperature, evaporation rate).

II. EXPERIMENTAL PART

A. Crosslinking of Aqueous PVA Solutions

The poly(vinyl alcohol) used in this study was Elvanol, grade 73-125 G (DuPont de Nemours) with the highest commercially available molecular weight of $\bar{M}_w$ = 184,800 and $\bar{M}_n$ = 88,800 as calculated by gel-permeation chromatography. Elvanol contains less than 1% head-to-head units, less than 0.1% carbonyl groups and it has a degree of hydrolysis of 99.4%; stereoregular analysis showed that it is mostly atactic (>70%).

Aqueous solutions of 10% by weight in PVA were prepared in 50 x 15 mm Petri dishes under nitrogen atmosphere by dissolving PVA in degassed distilled water and heating the mixture up to 90°C for 6 hours to dissolve the polymer. They were covered by a 0.25 mil Mylar film and irradiated under nitrogen with electron beams from a Van de Graaff accelerator delivering electrons at a dose rate of 90-150 x 10^3 rads/sec. The total dose delivered was 5-10 Mrads and the irradiations took place at 30°C in a glycerol-water bath preheated by heating coils (14, 15).

Parameters characterizing the extent of crosslinking are the crosslinking density ρ (moles/cm^3) and the number average molecular weight between crosslinks $\bar{M}_c$.

The crosslinking density ρ is defined as in equation (1).

$$\rho = \frac{1}{\bar{\upsilon}\bar{M}_c} \qquad (1)$$

Determination of $\bar{M}_c$ was done by allowing the samples to swell in water at 30 ± 0.5 °C until thermodynamic equilibrium. Equation (2) developed by Bray and Merrill (16), was used to calculate $\bar{M}_c$.

$$\frac{1}{\bar{M}_c} = \frac{2}{\bar{M}_n} - \frac{\frac{\bar{\upsilon}}{V_1}\left[\ln(1-\upsilon_{2,s}) + \upsilon_{2,s} + \chi_1 \upsilon_{2,s}^2\right]}{\upsilon_{2,r}\left[\left(\frac{\upsilon_{2,s}}{\upsilon_{2,r}}\right)^{1/3} - \frac{1}{2}\left(\frac{\upsilon_{2,s}}{\upsilon_{2,r}}\right)\right]} \qquad (2)$$

Here $\bar{M}_n$ is the number average molecular weight of the initial PVA = 88,800.

$\bar{\upsilon}$ is the specific volume of PVA in the amorphous state = 0.788 cm^3/gr

V_1 is the molar volume of water = 18 cm^3/mole

$\upsilon_{2,r}$ and $\upsilon_{2,r}$ are the polymer volume fractions before and after swelling respectively, and

χ_1 is the Flory PVA-water interaction parameter = 0.494

at 30°C and $\upsilon_{2,s}$ between 0 and 0.15 (15).

B. Dehydration and Nucleation

Using equation (2) it was found that the samples prepared for and used in this study had $\bar{M}_c$ varying between 1395 and 5830 as reported in Table I. The various polymer weight fractions w_{po} of these networks after swelling were also calculated.

After irradiation, 1mm thick hydrogels were cut in 1 x 1 cm^2 squares, transferred to a dust-free temperature-controlled chamber and dried by slow dehydration at 25 ± 1°C under controlled humidity agents such as SiO_2 (RH=5%) and $Ca(NO_3)_2 \cdot 4H_2O$ (RH=51%), where RH is the relative humidity in the chamber. At various intervals during the dehydration the samples were weighed and the weight was compared to the dry PVA weight after vigorous dehydration at 80°C for 48 hours. Thus, the polymer weight fraction w_p at any time was calculated.

Evaluation of the degree of crystallinity w_x of the films was done via density measurements from the following relation.

$$\frac{1}{\rho_h} = w_p \left[\frac{w_x}{\rho_c} + \frac{1-w_x}{\rho_a}\right] + \frac{1-w_p}{\rho_w} \quad (3)$$

where ρ_h is the density of the PVA hydrogels at any time during the experiment,

ρ_a and ρ_c are the densities of 100% amorphous and 100% crystalline PVA respectively, i.e., 1.269 and 1.345 gr/cm^3 (14), as calculated by x-ray analysis and

ρ_w is the density of water at 30°C (=0.996 gr/cm^3).

The rate of dehydration of the polymer r_d and the rate of increase of PVA concentration can be defined and expressed as:

$$r_p = -r_d = dw_p/dt \qquad (hr^{-1}) \quad (4)$$

Finally the rate of crystallization r_c can be expressed as:

$$r_c = dw_x/dt \qquad (hr^{-1}) \quad (5)$$

III. RESULTS AND DISCUSSION

A. Effect of Dehydration Conditions

The degree of crystallinity w_x as a function of time t and polymer weight fraction w_p is shown in Figures 1 & 2.

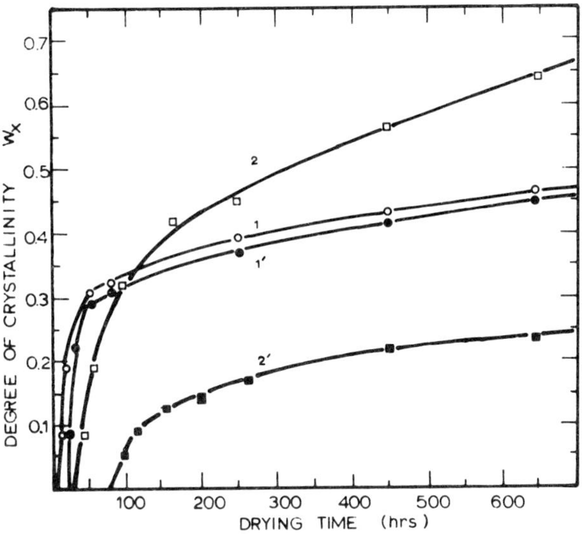

Fig. 1. Variation of degree of crystallinity with drying time. Crosslinked PVA films of molecular weight between crosslinks M_c=5830 (1, 2) and M_c=4770 (1', 2') dried under SiO_2 (1, 1') and $Ca(NO_3)_2$ (2, 2') at 25 ± 1°C.

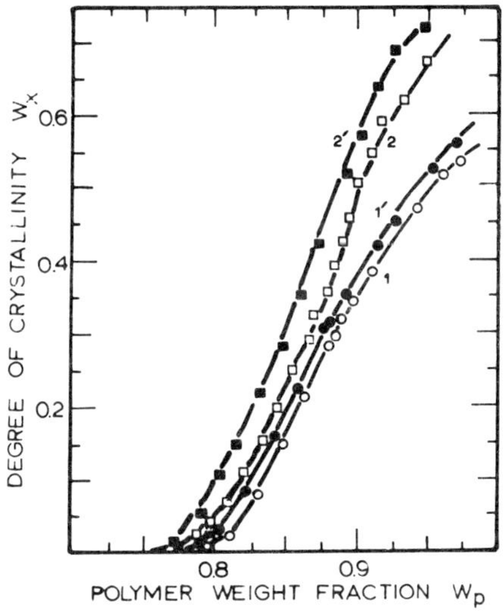

Fig. 2. Dependence of degree of crystallinity on the polymer weight fraction during drying. Crosslinked PVA films of molecular weight between crosslinks M_c=5830 (1, 2) and M_c= 4770 (1', 2') dried under SiO_2 (1, 1') and $Ca(NO_3)_2$ (2, 2') at 25 ± 1°C.

From Figure 2 the polymer weight fraction w_p can be expressed as:

$$w_p = w_{p_o} + k\ [1-\exp(-r_{p_o} t]\qquad (6)$$

and for low dehydration times as:

$$w_p = w_{p_o} + k\ [\exp(r_{p_o} t)]\qquad (7)$$

where w_{p_o} is the initial polymer weight fraction
r_{p_o} is the initial dehydration rate and
k is a constant (=0.25 for these curves).

The crystal growth rate r_c as calculated from equation (5) and from the results of Figure 1 can be plotted as a function of polymer weight fraction w_p as in Figure 3. It is evident that there is a certain induction period $\bar{t}$ below which no crystallites can be formed. This induction time is a function of the crosslinking density ρ and the evaporation-dehydration conditions as shown in Tables I and II.

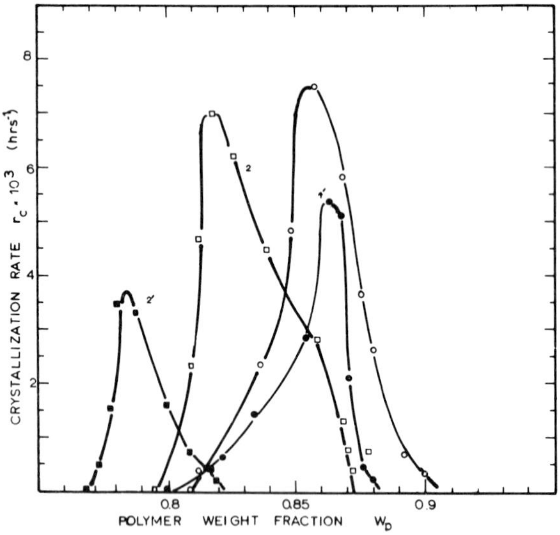

Fig. 3. Effect of polymer weight fraction during drying on the crystallization rate of crosslinked PVA films of M_c = *5830 (1, 2) and* M_c=*4770 (1', 2') dried under* SiO_2 *(1, 1') and* $Ca(NO_3)_2$ *(2, 2') at 25 ± 1°C.*

TABLE I

Characteristics of Crosslinked PVA Hydrogels Before Dehydration

Sample Number	Drying Agent	$\bar{M}_c$	Crosslinking Density $\rho*10^4$ (moles/cm^3)	Initial polymer wt fraction w_{p_o}	Initial Evaporation Rate r_{p_o} (hr^{-1})
D-1	SiO_2	5830	2.18	0.085	0.080
D-2		4770	2.66	0.091	0.073
D-3		2050	6.19	0.132	0.065
D-4		1395	9.10	0.164	0.063
D-11	$Ca(NO_3)_2$	5830	2.18	0.085	0.0112
D-12		4770	2.66	0.091	0.0095
D-13		2050	6.19	0.132	0.0078
D-14		1395	9.10	0.164	0.0072

TABLE II

Crystallization of Crosslinked PVA Hydrogels by Dehydration at 25 ± 1°C

Sample Number	Drying Agent	Induction Time $\bar{t}$ (hrs)	Polymer wt Fraction at Induction Time w_p	Maximum Polymer wt Fraction $w_{p,max}$	Maximum Crystallization Rate $r_{c,max}$ (hr^{-1})
D-1	SiO_2	14	0.810	0.940	0.0075
D-2		23	0.803	0.922	0.0054
D-3		31	0.796	0.914	0.0047
D-4		36	0.793	0.909	0.0039
D-11	$Ca(NO_3)_2$	41	0.795	0.917	0.0071
D-12		79	0.770	0.832	0.0036
D-13		101	0.753	0.817	0.0028
D-14		112	0.741	0.806	0.0024

The experimental results of Figure 3 can be expressed by parabolic relations of the general equation (8).

$$r_c = 4r_{c,max} P(1-P) \tag{8}$$

with

$$P = (w_p - \bar{w}_p)/2(w_{p,max} - \bar{w}_p) \tag{9}$$

where w_p is the polymer weight fraction at any time during dehydration,
$\bar{w}_p$ is the polymer weight fraction at crystal growth induction time $\bar{t}$ and
$\bar{w}_{p,max}$ is the maximum polymer weight fraction attained during these experiments.

From equations (6) and (9) the following relationship can be obtained.

$$P = \frac{[1-\exp(-r_{p_o} t)]}{2[\exp(-r_{p_o} t) - \exp(r_{p_o} t_{max})]} = P(t) \tag{10}$$

Using this expression, the degree of crystallinity w_x can be calculated as following:

$$\frac{dw_x/dt}{dw_p/dt} = \frac{r_c}{r_p} = \frac{4r_{c,max}}{r_p} \cdot P(t)[1-P(t)] \tag{11}$$

or finally

$$w_x = \frac{r_{c,max}}{r_p} \cdot [2P^2(t) - 1.33P^3(t)] \tag{12}$$

Thus, the degree of crystallinity w_x is a function of time and the rate of dehydration r_p. The rate of dehydration is affected by the drying conditions of the hydrogels, i.e. temperature, relative humidity and water content of the samples (17). This rate can be easily determined from the curves of Figure 4, which show the polymer weight fraction w_p as a function of drying time. The rate of dehydration in all cases decreased with decrease in the solvent activity and the vapor pressure. The initial dehydration rate depends on the relative humidity of the evaporation chamber and there is a ten-fold increase for drying in SiO_2 versus $Ca(NO_3)_2$ hydrate. A recent theoretical analysis of the drying process of gels (17) has shown the importance of such parameters on the mechanical properties of these materials. Due to the concentration and temperature gradients across the samples, care has been taken in this study to use materials with thickness lower than 1 mm.

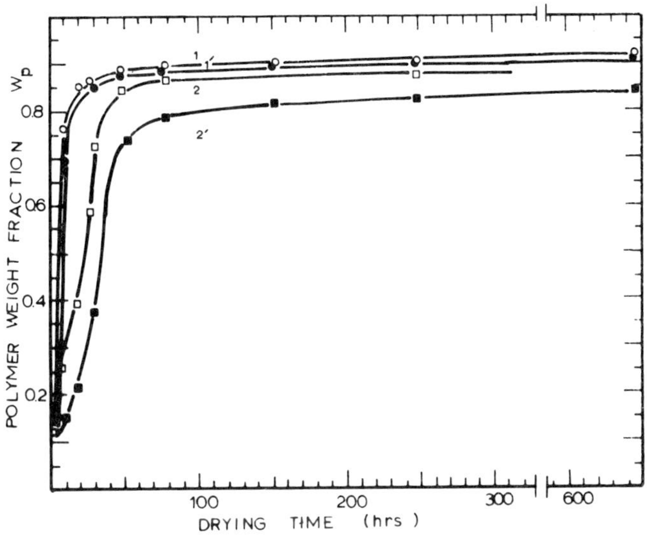

Fig. 4. Variation of polymer weight fraction during dehydration with drying time for crosslinked PVA films of M_c*=5830 (1, 2) and* M_c*=4770 (1', 2') dried under* SiO_2 *(1, 1') and* $Ca(NO_3)_2$ *(2, 2') at 25 ± 1°C.*

B. Effect of Crosslinking Density

Recently we have proven that the degree of crystallinity is affected by the crosslinking density as well (18). This phenomenon has been used for the production of controlled PVA hydrogels for biomedical applications (19).

It has been previously reported (1, 2) that a necessary condition for the crystallization of uncrosslinked PVA at room temperature is the formation of a gel. Upon evaporation of an aqueous solution of PVA, the system is for a short period at the stage of high supersaturation. Crystallization cannot proceed sufficiently because of rapid evaporation of water, which brings the PVA to the glass state and reduces the crystallization rate almost to zero. As a result, a film of very low degree of crystallinity is formed. However, at elevated temperatures the viscosity falls rapidly and crystallization becomes possible even in the absence of water. The crystallinity of PVA is expected to increase even more rapidly at temperatures around the melting point. As the molecular weight of PVA increases the size of the crystallites increases too. Despite the wide variation in the crystallite sizes and the relation to the extended chain length, the character and appearance of the crystallites remain essentially unaltered over a wide molecular weight range.

However, in crosslinked polymeric networks where the molecular weight between crosslinks is finite the formation of the crystallites in crosslinked polymers depends on the crosslinking density and very densely crosslinked polymers do not crystallize under any conditions. Thus an internal relation between the minimum crystallite length and the length between two crosslinks controls the formation of crystallites in a network that is heat treated.

The heat-treatment introducing crystallinity can be either mild or vigorous and depending on the conditions of drying, the degree of crystallinity and length of crystallites are expected to be different. In the case of crosslinked polymeric networks with a diluent, a slow drying rate process has the purpose of increasing the percentage of the polymer in the drying system. At the last stage of this process crystallization can start. A fast drying rate process, usually an annealing process can lead to rapid formation of crystallites.

The effect of the crosslinking density is significant for drying conditions under which the evaporation rate is low and the relative humidity in the drying chamber is very high (case of $Ca(NO_3)_2$). However, in the case of SiO_2 where the relative humidity is low, the variations due to the crosslinking density are not so important. The crosslinking density can affect the drying process in two ways. A direct effect can be expected because, in order for a crystallite to be formed, a minimum critical length of polymeric chain between crosslinks is necessary. Thus very low $\bar{M}_c$ does not favor the crystallization. An indirect effect can be expected because polymeric networks with different $\bar{M}_c$ show different swelling behavior (20) i.e. different initial polymer weight fraction w_{po} as shown in Table I.

Consequently, the crystallization rate and the final degree of crystallinity of a highly crosslinked network (low $\bar{M}_c$), are lower than those of a network with a higher $\bar{M}_c$.

IV. REFERENCES

1. A. Packter and M.S. Nerurkar, Coll. and Polym. Sci. 253, 916 (1975).
2. A. Packter and M.S. Nerurkar, Eur. Polym. J. 4, 685 (1968).
3. C. Devoy, L. Mandelkern and L. Bourland, J. Polym. Sci. 8, 869 (1970).
4. E. Ergoz, and L. Mandelkern, J. Polym. Sci., Polym. Lett. Ed. 11, 73 (1973).
5. A. Nakajima, F. Hamada, S. Hayashi and T. Sumida, Kolloid Zeit. 222, 10 (1968).

6. T. Korenaga, F. Hamada, and A. Nakajima, Polym. J. 3, 21 (1972).
7. V. N. Lebedeva, G. I. Distler, and Ye. I. Korkutova, Vysokom. Soyed. A9, 2076 (1967).
8. J. G. Patou, E. Riande, and R. G. Valdecasas, J. Appl. Polym. Sci. 13, 2103 (1975).
9. N. A. Peppas, and E. W. Merrill, J. Appl. Polym. Sci. 20, 1457 (1976).
10. M. I. Bessonov, and A. P. Rudakov, Fiz. Tverd. Tela. 6, 1333 (1964).
11. V. G. Baranov, T. I. Volkov, and S. Yo. Frenkel, Dokl. Akad. Nauk SSSR 172, 849 (1967).
12. E. N. Gubenkova, L. N. Verkhotina, G. F. Mikul'skii, and S. A. Glikman, Vysokomol. Soyed. B9, 550 (1967).
13. N. A. Peppas, Eur. Polym. J. 12, 575 (1976).
14. N. A. Peppas, and E. W. Merrill, J. Polym. Sci. 14, 441 (1976).
15. N. A. Peppas, and E. W. Merrill, J. Polym. Sci. 14, 459 (1976).
16. J. C. Bray, and E. W. Merrill, J. Appl. Polym. Sci. 17, 3779 (1973).
17. Y. T. Shah, and J. H. Porter, J. Appl. Polym. Sci. 17, 605 (1973).
18. N. A. Peppas, Techn. Chron. 44, 443 (1975).
19. N. A. Peppas, and E. W. Merrill, J. Biomed. Mater. Res. (in press).
20. N. A. Peppas, and E. W. Merrill, J. Appl. Polym. Sci. (in press).

THEORIES OF THE STRESS-INDUCED CRYSTALLIZATION OF CROSSLINKED POLYMERS

Richard J. Gaylord
Department of Metallurgy and Mining Engineering
University of Illinois at Urbana-Champaign

A review of theories dealing with the stress-induced crystallization of crosslinked polymers is presented. The areas which are considered include: the orientation of crystals formed during stress-induced crystallization, the melting temperature of the deformed, semicrystalline network, kinetic (nucleation) and thermodynamic (non-nucleation) models of stress-induced crystallization. The basic models and underlying physical assumptions of the various theories are stated, the mathematical development of the theories are followed and, where possible, a comparison with experiment is made. Critical evaluations are made of all the theories discussed.

I. INTRODUCTION

The understanding of the phenomenon of stress-induced crystallization in polymers is of great practical importance. The ability to correlate stress level with crystallization has the potential of enabling us to produce semicrystalline polymeric materials with specific properties. In this paper, we will review and evaluate various theoretical explanations which have been put forth for different aspects of stress-induced crystallization. Unless otherwise stated, Gaussian chain statistics are used in these theories and the network deformation is taken to be simple extension. The notation, which is different in the various papers, has been standardized herein.

II. CRYSTAL ORIENTATION

No theory of stress-induced crystallization is possible without specifying the orientation of the crystals which are formed. While several of the theories which will be discussed later have simply assumed some specific orientation, others have attempted to calculate the crystal orientation directly.

Krigbaum and Roe (1,2) view the nucleation process at the start of crystallization as completely determining the crystal orientation. Assuming that the critical nucleus consists of ν consecutive chain segments, they calculate the mean square cosine of the angle χ between the c axis of an extended-chain crystal and the stretching direction, using the probability of a segment having orientation χ, raised to the νth power. This probability, which they calculate (2) to the order N^{-1} using a series of Legendre polynomials and which can also be derived directly, using Kuhn-Grün chain statistics, is dependent on the extension ratio, α, and the number of segments in a chain, N. In order to check the theory, Krigbaum and Roe used a value of N=60 and values of ν were chosen to fit the theoretical value of $\langle\cos^2\chi\rangle$ to experimental data for crosslinked polychloroprene at different extensions. It was found that ν increased with decreasing α and for $\alpha<4$, exceeded the total number of segments in the chain. However, they did demonstrate that the crystal orientation is much sharper than that of a chain segment prior to crystallization. We note that the Krigbaum and Roe model is also applicable to a folded-chain crystal of thickness ν, if the first traverse through the crystal determines its orientation.

Baranov et al. (3) have considered the orientation of a folded-chain crystal, assuming that the crystal grows by folding back and forth with a fixed crystal thickness, ζ. They take the arithmetic average of the entropy change occurring in the uncrystallized section (the amorphous subchain) of the semicrystalline chain for odd- and even-folded crystals and maximize this average entropy with respect to the angle θ, between the crystal c axis and the end-to-end chain vector $\tilde{r}_N$. They obtain a value of tan θ which is independent of $\tilde{r}_N$ and related to the number of traverses through the crystal, which, in turn, is taken to be proportional to the degree of crystallinity. The proportionality constant is given as the ratio of the volume occupied by the chain in the amorphous state to the volume occupied by a single crystal fold. However, the crystal orientation with respect to the stretch direction is not calculated and the relation of their single chain calculation to a crystal consisting of many chains is not given. The number of chain segments in the crystal folds is also ignored in this model.

Yamamoto and White (4) have calculated the average orientation between an extended-chain crystal and the chain vector, using the chain distribution function for the amorphous subchain as the probability in the averaging. They find that the crystal lies essentially along the chain vector. We note that this can also be found by maximizing the entropy of the subchain with respect to the orientation between the crystal and the chain vector. Taking the result of Yamamoto and White and calculating the orientation of chain vectors with respect to the stretching direction as a function of extension using Kuhn-Grün statistics, it can be shown that the predicted increase in crystal c axis orientation with respect to the stretching direction with increasing extension is faster than that of a chain segment in an amorphous network but still far less rapid than experimental data indicate. A possible source for this discrepancy may lie in the fact that the theory is a single chain model which does not acknowledge that a crystal with a given orientation consists of many chains having different orientations of their chain vectors.

The most recent theory of crystal orientation as a function of network extension, by Gaylord, (5) calculates the orientation of the vector $\underset{\sim}{\ell}$ (the crystal vector) running from one end of the crystal to the start of the amorphous subchain, with respect to the network deformation, which maximizes the entropy of the amorphous subchain. It is assumed that the components of the crystal vector and the chain vector lie in the same direction (i.e., the vectors lie in the same octant). Averaging over the network chains in the crystal and then considering the case of extended-chain crystals and simple extension, a very good agreement with experiment is obtained.

We should note that there is some experimental evidence indicating a change in crystal orientation with temperature and crystallinity, as well as extension which the above theories do not consider.

III. MELTING TEMPERATURES

The melting temperature, as it pertains to stress-induced crystallization, is defined and calculated differently by various workers. Flory (6) has calculated what he denotes as T_{inc}, the "incipient melting temperature". Starting with a model of perfectly oriented, extended-chain crystal growth, Flory writes the total free energy of crystallization as the sum of the free energy of crystallization of n chain segments in the absence of any constraints and the free energy change arising from the conformational changes which occur in the remaining (N-n) segments of the amorphous subchain relative to the same subchain in a completely amorphous, unstretched chain with N segments. The equilibrium degree of crystallinity

ω_{eq}, which is found by minimizing the total free energy of crystallization with respect to ω, is a function of extension and T, the temperature at which crystallization occurs. Letting ω_{eq} go to zero, Flory obtains the temperature, T_{inc}, at which the network will no longer crystallize at a given extension. The Flory equation has been experimentally tested many times and has been found to give good agreement except at low extensions where the assumption of perfect crystal orientation with respect to the stretch direction is known to be incorrect.

Krigbaum and Roe (1) have calculated what they call the "melting point," T_m. Their calculation is somewhat complex and is based on the same principles as the simpler "equilibrium melting point" calculation of Ziabicki (7). The "melting point" or "equilibrium melting point," T_m, is defined as the temperature at which the free energy of the crystalline phase, F_c, equals that of the amorphous phase, F_a. It follows that $1/T_m = \Delta S/\Delta H$ where ΔH is the enthalpy of fusion, which is assumed to be independent of extension and is taken as equal to $N\Delta H\mu$ where ΔH is the enthalpy of fusion per segment for an N segment chain. Thus, the crystalline phase refers to a completely crystalline chain and the amorphous phase refers to a completely amorphous chain. The difference between the inverse of the melting temperature in an extended network, $1/T_m$, and an unstrained network, $1/T_m{}^{\circ}$, is therefore $[S_a(\alpha)-S_c(\alpha)]-[S_a(\alpha=1)-S_c(\alpha=1)]/N\Delta H\mu$. The entropy of a completely crystalline chain is independent of the extension and the entropy difference between a completely amorphous chain in the stretched and unstretched state is given by the theory of elasticity as $[S_a(\alpha)-S_a(\alpha=1)] = -\frac{1}{2}k(\alpha^2+(2/\alpha)-3)$. This yields the same expression for $1/T_m$ as calculated by Krigbaum and Roe (1) and Ziabicki (7) and others and based on the same principles. The calculation of T_m has a major difficulty, however. The assumption of a completely crystalline polymer chain is unrealistic, especially in a network structure where chains must terminate at points of crosslinkage. Furthermore, the assumption of a system with two distinct phases may not be justified.[1] A comparison of the "equilibrium

---

[1]An early treatment of the melting of crystalline polymers was given by Frith and Tuckett (8) using a lattice model. The two phase model, consisting of completely crystalline and completely amorphous chains was compared with the composite phase model, consisting of partially crystalline and amorphous chains in a fringed micelle arrangement. A very crude estimate was also made of the effect of extension on melting behavior. The authors concluded that under any circumstance, the two phase model will predict a sharp melting point and

melting point" as a function of extension with experiment is not at all satisfactory. This is not surprising in view of the fact that the experimental procedure is such that what is actually being measured is, in fact, the "incipient melting point."

Yamamoto and White (4) have obtained an expression for the "incipient crystallization temperature" which they define as that temperature at which the free energy of a semicrystalline chain equals that of a completely amorphous chain. This expression is necessarily dependent on the degree of crystallinity. It is not clear what is the significance of this quantity or how it might be experimentally measured.

IV. KINETIC (NUCLEATION) APPROACHES

Several attempts have been made to incorporate a nucleation mechanism into the process of stress-induced crystallization. These calculations are very badly flawed; nonetheless, it is of interest to examine them.

The first attempt to develop a nucleation theory of stress-induced crystallization appears to have been made by Dunning (9). Using the Flory lattice model of crystalline polymers in which chain ends are excluded from the extended-chain crystal, the free energy of crystallization is first written as the sum of the free energy change due to crystallization as given by the Flory model and surface free energy terms arising from the crystal boundaries. From this is subtracted the change in free energy due to stretching the completely amorphous chains prior to crystallization. The free energy of the critical sized nucleus is then calculated and the rate of nucleation is given. The authors note that extension should decrease the surface free energies between the crystal and the amorphous phase. The chief difficulties in the theory arise from the use of a lattice model and from

---

phase transition (because the Gibbs free energy of the two phase model is a linear function of the fraction of amorphous material) while the composite phase model (which predicts a nonlinear relation between the Gibbs free energy and the fraction of amorphous material) will give an unsharp melting point. In view of the experimental evidence that crystalline and amorphous material coexist in polymers over a range of temperatures, the authors rejected the two phase model in favor of the composite phase model. We note that Frith and Tuckett predict the same functional dependence of the equilibrium melting point on extension, using the two phase model, as do Krigbaum and Roe (1) and Ziabicki (7).

neglecting the effect of the state of deformation on the part of the chain which does not crystallize (the amorphous subchain).

Kobayashi and Nagasawa (10) begin with expressions for the crystal thickness, nucleation rate, nuclei growth rate and crystal volume growth rate, which are taken from the Lauritzen and Hoffman model of polymer crystallization. We can best understand their theory by looking at their calculation of crystal thickness, ζ. Starting with $\zeta = 4\sigma_e T_m^\circ/\Delta H(T_m^\circ - T) = 4\sigma_e/[\Delta H - \Delta H \cdot T/T_m^\circ]$, the authors write $\Delta H/T_m^\circ = \Delta S$ and $\Delta H - T\Delta S = \Delta f$, where ΔS represents the entropy change which occurs when a chain enters a crystal. However, if crystallization occurs in a deformed network, the chain has already lost some entropy, ΔS_o, due to the prior extension of the chain. Hence, the effect of prior molecular orientation is to reduce the entropy loss suffered by a chain crystallizing by the amount $\Delta S_o = -\frac{1}{2}k(\alpha^2 + (2/\alpha) - 3)$ from the elasticity theory. Therefore, $\Delta f = \Delta H - T(\Delta S - \Delta S_o)$ and $\zeta = 4\sigma_e/[\Delta H - T(\Delta H/T_m^\circ - \Delta S_o)]$. This same procedure is carried out for the other expressions. While the use of the Lauritzen and Hoffman equation necessarily requires that the chain crystallize completely, it is nonetheless an unphysical assumption as we have previously stated.

Baranov et al. (11) have written a general expression for the free energy of crystallization, incorporating terms for the surface energy and the free energy of fusion as well as a term for the conformational entropy change ϕ, in the chain entering the crystal. The free energy of fusion is written, as in the Kobayashi and Nagasawa theory, $\Delta f = \Delta H - T(\Delta S - \Delta S_o)$. The creation of a crystal with crystal vector $\underset{\sim}{\ell}$ reduces the chain vector $\underset{\sim}{r}_N$ to ($\underset{\sim}{r}_N$ to ($\underset{\sim}{r}_N - \underset{\sim}{\ell}$), which is the vector for the amorphous subchain. Therefore, ϕ is written as $[3k(\underset{\sim}{r}_N - \ell)^2/2Nb^2 - 3k\ r_N^2/2Nb^2] = 3k(\ell^2 - 2r_N\ell\cos\theta)/2Nb^2$, where θ is the angle between $\underset{\sim}{\ell}$ and $\underset{\sim}{r}_N$. Using these general terms, Baranov et al. calculate the critical free energy of nucleus formation as a function of ΔS_o. The calculation ends at this point and no results are obtained which can be compared with experimental data. One difficulty in their approach, however, lies in their expression for ϕ. If reference is being made to entropy of the amorphous subchain, then in the first term of the expression for ϕ, the number of links is not N, but rather N minus the number of links in the crystal section of the chain. The second term in ϕ represents the entropy of the completely amorphous, stretched chain. However, if the first term refers to the amorphous subchain, then the second term should refer to that part of a completely amorphous chain which forms the amorphous subchain. Additionally, if ϕ does refer to the amorphous subchain, then ΔS_o should not refer to the completely amorphous chain. On the other hand, if ϕ does not refer to the amorphous subchain, then it appears to have no meaning.

We should point out that the above approaches (9-11) are quite different from the Flory model (6) in that they treat the stretched, amorphous network as the reference state from which to calculate changes in free energy during crystallization while Flory uses the undeformed, amorphous network as the reference state.

Zurabian et al. (12) have continued the calculation of Baranov et al. (11). They write the total free energy of folded-chain crystallization for a single chain using the same terms, including ϕ. The only difference at this point is that they consider odd- and even-folded crystals separately and rewrite the crystal vector, $\tilde{\ell}$, in terms of the crystal dimensions. They then calculate the critical free energy of each and take the arithmetic average. This quantity represents the critical free energy of secondary, monomolecular nucleation. Next, the authors calculate the critical free energy of primary, multimolecular nucleation, for a number of chains forming an extended-chain nucleus. The final expressions for both the multi- and monomolecular nucleation critical free energies contain the orientation between the crystal c axis and the chain vector. Taking this angle at both 0 and $\pi/2$ and comparing the ΔF^* values as a function of r_N/Nb, it is concluded that for large values of the end-to-end chain vector $\tilde{r}_N$, a secondary, monomolecular, folded-chain nucleus is favored over a primary, multimolecular, extended-chain nucleus until $\tilde{r}_N$ reaches a critical value and then the situation is reversed. Again, as in the work of Baranov et al. (11), the theory stops short and precludes a more detailed analysis. There are, however, two points which cast some doubt on the approach. One is the validity of taking an arithmetic average of the critical free energies of forming single chain, even- and odd-folded secondary nuclei. The other is comparing that calculation with the critical free energy of forming a multichain, extended-chain, primary nucleus. Also, the same problem in the calculation of ϕ is encountered as in the papers of Baranov et al. (11) and the orientation of the crystal with respect to the stretch direction is not considered.

Thus, the nucleation approach to stress-induced crystallization is still very tentative. More work on this approach is highly desirable.

V. THERMODYNAMIC THEORIES

Non-nucleation theories of stress-induced crystallization are well developed to date, in the sense that they are worked out to a point where detailed experimental comparisons can be made with theoretical predictions. The first thermodynamic theory of stress-induced crystallization was put forth by Flory (6). As previously stated, the model consists of extended-chain crystal growth in the stretching direction. The total free energy of crystallization is the sum of the free energy of crystallization of n chain segments in the absence of any constraints and the free energy change in the (N-n) segment, amorphous subchain as a result of being attached to an n segment crystal rather than to an n segment amorphous subchain in the undeformed state. The theory predicts continued stress decay with increasing crystallization, even to negative stress values. Smith (13) has calculated the birefringence of the Flory model and the predicted behavior of both the stress and birefringence has been found to agree fairly well with experimental data on rubber at extensions greater than three. We have already stated that the incipient melting temperature as calculated from this theory has been confirmed many times at moderate and high extensions. The major shortcomings in this theory are that all crystallization is assumed to start in all the chains simultaneously, only extended-chain crystal growth is considered, and perfect crystal orientation in the stretch direction is assumed.

Smith (14) has modified the Flory theory by allowing for the possibility that a chain, rather than crystallizing in a direction which will reduce the stress on the chain, might crystallize in the opposite direction if some number of chain segments, σ, were to become trapped on the crystal. Smith calculates the free energy of crystallization for both occurrences and then takes their average, using the probability that σ consecutive segments have the same orientation, which is essentially the same as that used by Krigbaum and Roe (1,2). Considering $\alpha>3$ and perfect crystal orientation, Smith calculates various quantities which are in fairly good agreement with experiment. One shortcoming of the model is that, assuming perfect crystal orientation, it would seem very desirable for a chain which ran through the crystal antiparallel to the stretch direction to immediately fold back on itself and reenter the crystal. This possibility is not considered in the single pass crystallization model of Smith.

Yamamoto and White (4) have considered a lattice model for the stress-induced crystallization of extended-chain crystals oriented along their end-to-end chain vectors. They take into account the distribution of the trans and gauche bond conformations and the effect on lattice vacancies as chain ordering and crystallization occurs. The calculation is extremely involved and no comparison with experiment is made. However, the authors note that the theory does not predict negative stresses. This is, in fact, a flaw in the theory since polyethylene when crystallized at low extensions does give rise to negative stresses. Furthermore, stress rises have been observed at the latter stages of crystallization which are not predicted by any of the theories of stress-induced crystallization which have been discussed so far.

Gaylord (15) has developed a non-Gaussian theory which takes into account the free energy of fusion, crystal surface energies and entropic changes in the amorphous subchain. It is assumed that the crystal vector lies in the direction of stretch, irrespective of crystal morphology. For the case of extended-chain crystallization, the free energy of fusion and the amorphous subchain terms are the non-Gaussian equivalent of the Flory theory (6). The free energies of crystallization of chains with crystals having different numbers of folds are calculated for polyethylene and assuming that the network assumes the crystal morphology which minimizes the network free energy at a given degree of crystallinity, it is predicted that the initial mechanism of crystal growth is extended-chain, switching to a one- (two-) fold crystal having perpendicular (nearly parallel) orientation with respect to the stretching direction at low (high) extension. The stress decays initially and then rises as the morphological switch occurs. This switch is delayed by additional crosslinking and eventually becomes suppressed. The dependence of the stress behavior on the extent of crosslinking is calculated. At all extensions, the initial crystallization is extended-chain and the effect of deformation, crosslinking and temperature on the initial rate of crystallization is calculated using irreversible thermodynamics. The calculated value of T_{inc} is the non-Gaussian equivalent of Flory's expression, which it matches over most extensions. Changes in birefringence during crystallization are calculated for polyethylene and a continued rise in positive birefringence is predicted at high extension, while at low extension the initially positive birefringence first rises and then decays to negative values. All of these predictions are in qualitative agreement with experiment. The theory can also be applied to other polymers if the appropriate material constants are known. As in the other thermodynamic theories, simultaneous crystallization in all the chains of the monodisperse network is assumed.

VI. CONCLUSION

The above sections indicate that a great deal of effort has gone into the theoretical understanding of stress-induced crystallization. All of the theories, regardless of their individual merit, have raised points which need to be considered in order to reach a full understanding of this important phenomenon. Much more experimental and theoretical work is still needed in this area of polymer physics.

VII. REFERENCES

1. W. R. Krigbaum and R. J. Roe, J. Polymer Sci., Pt. A-2 2, 4391 (1964).
2. R. J. Roe and W. R. Krigbaum, J. Appl. Phys. 35, 2215 (1964).
3. V. G. Baranov, R. S. Zurabian, I. K. Atachodjev and S. Ya Frenkel, Polymer Mechanics 6, 963 (1970).
4. M. Yamamoto and J. L. White, J. Polymer Sci., Pt. A-2 9, 1399 (1971).
5. R. J. Gaylord, J. Polymer Sci., Polymer Letters Ed. 13, 337 (1975).
6. P. J. Flory, J. Chem. Phys. 15, 397 (1947).
7. A. Ziabicki, Int'l Polymer Sci. and Techn. 1, 20 (1974).
8. E. M. Frith and R. F. Tuckett, Trans. Faraday Soc. 40, 251 (1944).
9. W. J. Dunning, Trans. Faraday Soc. 50, 1115 (1954).
10. K. Kobayashi and T. Nagasawa, Macromolecular Sci., Phys. B4, 331 (1970).
11. V. G. Baranov, S. Ya Frenkel, V. I. Gromov, T. I. Volkov and R. S. Zurabian, J. Polymer Sci., Pt. C 38, 61 (1972).
12. R. S. Zurabian, V. G. Baranov and S. Frenkel, J. Polymer Sci., Symp. 44, 163 (1974).
13. K. J. Smith, Jr., J. Polymer Sci., Pt. A-2 6, 1723 (1968).
14. K. J. Smith, Jr., Polymer Eng. and Sci. 16, 168 (1976).
15. R. J. Gaylord, in press, J. Polymer Sci., Polymer Phys. Ed.

VIII. ACKNOWLEDGEMENTS

Support for portions of this work was provided by National Science Foundation Grant No. NSF-DMR 75-10284.

CHARACTERIZATION OF THERMOSETTING EPOXY SYSTEMS USING A TORSIONAL PENDULUM

J. K. Gillham and C. A. Glandt
Princeton University

and

C. A. McPherson
Western Electric Company, Inc.

An automated torsional pendulum has been used to investigate epoxy systems with respect to the effects of cure, transitions, morphology and active environments (water vapor and organic liquid). The findings include: 1) the thermosetting process is characterized by two transition temperatures (T_{gg} and $T_{g\infty}$), 2) thermomechanical and optical data correlate through a phase inversion in a rubber-modified system, 3) gelation time can be used to control development of morphology, 4) a reversible low temperature transition [T_{H_2O} ca. -70°C (1.6 Hz)] is induced by exposure to water vapor, 5) the glass transition temperature is lowered in the presence of water vapor, and 6) thermomechanical spectra of partially plasticized specimens display the transition of two phases (unplasticized and plasticized) superimposed.

I. INTRODUCTION

The first part of this communication generalizes earlier studies on consequences of quenching chemical conversion by vitrification. The second part illustrates correlation of thermomechanical and optical studies through a phase inversion in a rubber-modified system, and also controlled arresting of the development of morphology by varying the time to gelation. The third part reports results on a low temperature ($<T_g$) water-induced transition, and lowering of the glass transition by water vapor and organic liquid.

An automated torsional pendulum was employed which permits monitoring of the changes which occur throughout cure and of the transitions which occur in the cured material with change of temperature and environment (1).

II. EXPERIMENTAL

A. Torsional Pendulum

A torsional pendulum has been used to investigate unsupported and supported samples. Specimens for the present work included unsupported cured epoxy films, a cured epoxy/glass cloth composite, composite films formed by curing epoxies on polyimide film, and glass fiber braids impregnated with solutions of reactive epoxies for studying the curing process.

After mounting, the specimen is intermittently set into torsional oscillation to generate a series of freely damped waves. The frequency of oscillation is about 1 Hz. The character of these waves provides a monitor of changes. Two mechanical functions, rigidity and damping, are obtained from the frequency and decay constants which characterize each wave. A schematic diagram of the pendulum is shown in Fig. 1; photographs appear in Fig. 2. This adaptation of the torsional pendulum approach for characterizing small quantities of polymer has been developed under the name "torsional braid analysis (TBA)" (1).

The experiment provides plots of relative rigidity ($1/P^2$, where P is the period in seconds) and logarithmic decrement ($\Delta = \ln A_i/A_{i+1}$, where A_i is the amplitude of the ith oscillation) vs. temperature or time. The relative rigidity is directly proportional to the in-phase shear modulus (G'); the logarithmic decrement is directly proportional to the ratio of the out-of-phase shear modulus (G") to G'. G' and G" are material parameters of the specimen which characterize the storage and loss of mechanical energy on cyclic deformation.

Non-isothermal experiments were programmed, generally at ± 1.5°C/minute.

Specimens were exposed to various levels (parts per million by volume) of water vapor in a flowing stream of helium formed by mixing dry and saturated streams of helium in various proportions. After conditioning at a definite temperature for a measured period of time thermomechanical TBA data were obtained, in the conditioning atmosphere, on cooling to -190°C and subsequent heating.

III. RESULTS AND DISCUSSION

A. Cure

The generalized results of this section stem from examinations of several epoxy systems (2, 3, 4, 5).

The experimental results for the cure of an epoxy system at a series of constant temperatures can be used to obtain the

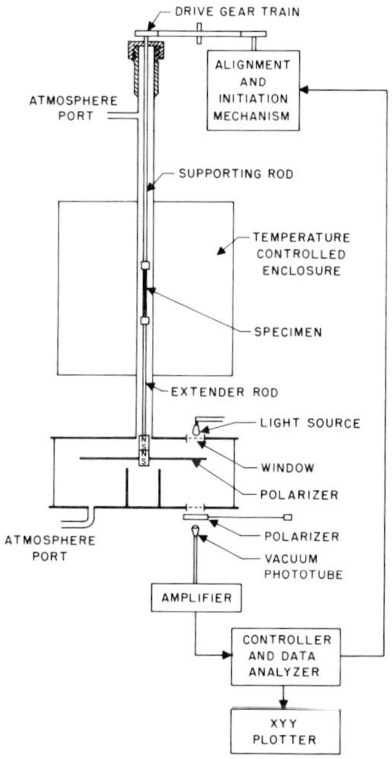

Fig. 1. Automated TBA torsional pendulum. An electrical signal is obtained using a light beam passing through a pair of polarizers, one of which oscillates with the specimen. The pendulum is aligned and oscillations are initiated by a dedicated analog computer which also processes the damped sine waves to provide the mechanical rigidity and mechanical damping data which are plotted in immediate time on an XYY plotter (1).

Fig. 2. TBA Torsional Pendulum. Plastics Analysis Consultants, P. O. Box 408, Princeton, New Jersey 08540.

gelation time and the vitrification time vs. cure temperature. These transformation times correspond to peaks in the mechanical damping curves; they also correspond to points of inflection in the rigidity curves (see Fig. 3). Schematic results for isothermal cure of a typical system relating the time to gelation and the time to vitrification to the temperature of cure are summarized in Fig. 4.

It is apparent from Fig. 4 that there are three types of behavior depending on the temperature of cure (2). At high temperatures the liquid gels but does not vitrify. At low temperatures the liquid vitrifies and need not gel -- if reactions are quenched at low degrees of reaction by vitrification. At intermediate temperatures the liquid first gels and later vitrifies (Figs. 3 and 4). The time to gelation decreases exponentially with temperature since the degree of reaction at the point of gelation is constant. [It follows that a plot of log (time to gelation) vs. 1/T (°K) provides an activation energy which can be used for obtaining gel times at experimentally inaccessible temperatures.] On the other hand, it is noted that the time to vitrify passes through a minimum which occurs at intermediate temperatures of cure (3, 4). This reflects competition between the increased rate constants for reaction and the increased degree of crosslinking (and therefore of reaction) required for vitrification at higher temperatures. The temperature at which gelation and vitrification occur together is defined as T_{gg} (Fig. 4) (2). Vitrification can occur before gelation ($T_{cure} < T_{gg}$) simply by an increase of molecular weight. Gelation occurs without vitrification when cure is performed above the maximum softening point of the system, $T_{g\infty}$ (Fig. 4). It is also apparent that if reactions cease at vitrification, the softening temperature (glass transition temperature, T_g) of the system after cure will equal the temperature of cure. The vitrification curve therefore gives the time to reach the softening temperature which the system can achieve by curing at T_{cure}. In particular, T_{gg} is the glass transition temperature of the reactive system at its point of gelation (2). A diagram such as Fig. 4 summarizes much of the behavior of the thermosetting process and in particular shows that it is characterized by two temperatures, T_{gg} and $T_{g\infty}$. In contrast, thermoplastic materials are characterized only by $T_{g\infty}$ since gelation does not occur in their formation. The temperatures T_{gg} and $T_{g\infty}$ are critical parameters which will vary from system to system.

From the practical point of view the diagram (Fig. 4) explains a number of practices in the field of thermosets. Examples follow.

• Finite vs. infinite shelf-life: if the storage temperature is below T_{gg}, a reactive material will convert to a

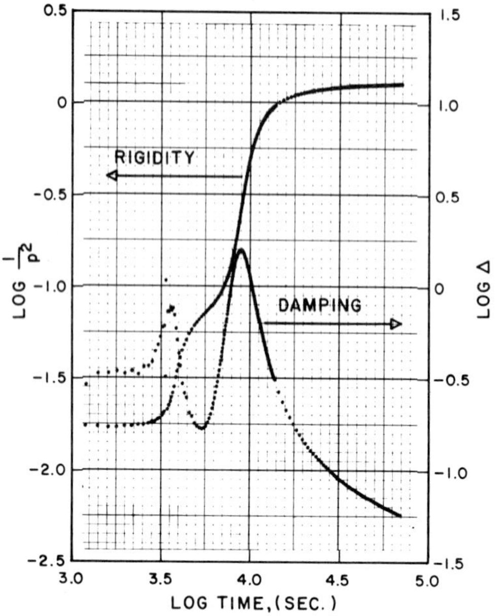

Fig. 3. TBA. Mechanical rigidity and mechanical damping vs. time during cure of an epoxy system at a constant temperature ($T_{gg}<T_{cure}<T_{g\infty}$). The first peak in the damping curve represents gelation, the second vitrification.

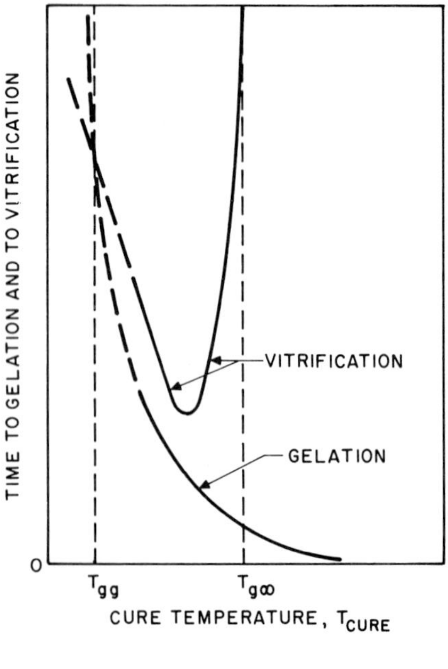

Fig. 4. Time to gel and time to vitrify vs. isothermal cure temperature for an epoxy system. (The dashed sections of the curves represent extrapolation of experimental data.) Note the two critical temperatures, T_{gg} and $T_{g\infty}$.

vitrified solid which is stable and can be later "melted" and processed; above T_{gg} the material will have a finite shelf-life since gelation will occur before vitrification. (A gelled material does not flow.) This concept lies at the basis of a widespread technology which includes thermosetting molding compounds and "prepregs" with latent reactivity.

• Post-cure: if $T_{cure} < T_{g\infty}$ a reactive material will vitrify and full chemical conversion may be prevented; the material will then need to be post-cured above $T_{g\infty}$ for development of optimum properties. As an example, Fig. 5 presents the thermomechanical data after isothermal reaction at an arbitrary temperature for a finite period of time and also after heating the same specimen to well above $T_{g\infty}$ (5). Using the transitions as a measure of material properties (see Fig. 5), it is apparent that the extent of cure affects not only the value of the glass transition but also properties at temperatures well below it. For the manufacture of objects of large size, it is usually necessary to go through a two-step process because of the exothermic nature of the reactions.

• Influence of reactants: the inherent reactivity of the functional groups together with the geometry and polarity of the growing chain segments will determine the transition temperatures (T_{gg}, T_g, $T_{g\infty}$) of each particular system and therefore the types of behavior which will be experienced during cure and after cure. For example, for highly crosslinked or rigid-chain polymeric structures $T_{g\infty}$ can be above the limits of thermal stability. In these cases the thermoset materials need not have measurable glass transition temperatures. In contrast, if $T_{g\infty}$ is below room temperature, the polymer systems will be used as elastomers.

B. Rubber-Modified Systems

1. *Effect of Rubber Concentration*

Epoxy/rubber systems exhibit two extreme morphologies, rubber distributed as domains in an epoxy matrix and vice versa. The present section demonstrates correlation between thermomechanical torsional pendulum data and optical micrographs through a phase inversion as the content of rubber is increased.

The formulation included a carboxy-terminated butadiene-acrylonitrile copolymer (CTBNX8, B. F. Goodrich) which was prereacted with an epoxy resin (Epon 1002, Shell Chemical) in the weight ratio of 40 to 60 to form an adduct. This was mixed with additional epoxy resin (Epon 1002) to provide formulations with a range of rubber content (5-40 percent by weight). The curing agent, a substituted dicyandiamide

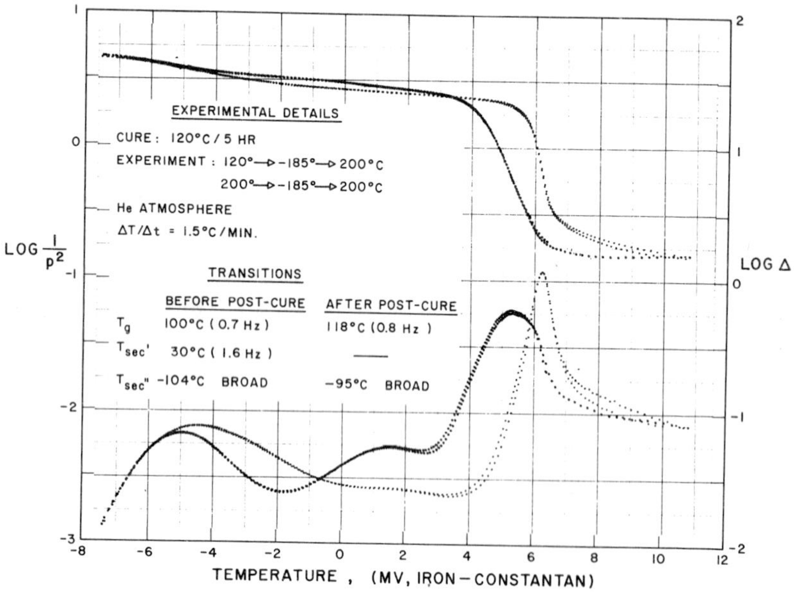

Fig. 5. Epoxy system: effect of cure on transitions.

(2,6-xylenylbiguanidine ,Ciba-Geigy), was used in stoichiometric amounts based on the epoxy equivalent weight of the rubber-epoxy mixture. An accelerator, benzyldimethylamine, was used in amount based on the quantity of curing agent. Dimethylformamide and 2-methoxyethanol were the solvents for the formulations.

Composite specimens of rubber-modified-epoxy coatings on films of polyimide (Kapton, duPont) were formed by polymerization of the formulations (at 170°C/30 minutes in air). This type of supported specimen permitted torsional pendulum data to be obtained above loading-limiting transitions and was suitable for sectioning of specimens (having low modulus) for examination by a transmission electron microscope (not shown here).

Comparison of the thermomechanical plots (Figs. 6 and 7A to 7E), which include a plot of the uncoated polyimide film (Fig. 6), shows that the glass transition temperatures of the rubber ($_{Rubber}T_g$) and epoxy ($_{Epoxy}T_g$) occur in regions where the polyimide contribution is minimal. The influence of increasing rubber content on the glass transition temperatures of the epoxy and the rubber is shown graphically in Figs. 8 and 9. The main conclusion is apparent from the intensity of the $_{Rubber}T_g$ increasing drastically above 20 percent rubber content (Fig. 9) which suggests the onset of a phase inversion. The *increase* of the rubber transition temperature with increasing rubber content (Fig. 9) to the value for the rubber itself (CTBNX8, T_g ca. -45°C) is noteworthy but not understood. The decrease in value of the epoxy glass transition with increasing rubber content (Fig. 8) could be a consequence of dissolution of rubber in the epoxy phase; however, the formulations themselves have epoxide equivalent weights which increase with increasing rubber content. [The latter factor alone will lead to lower crosslinking densities, and to lower glass transition temperatures, for the fully cured systems. Investigation of an analogous series of unsupported films containing different amounts of rubber in epoxy having a constant epoxy equivalent weight, resulted in the glass transition temperature of the epoxy in the series decreasing with increasing rubber content (6). This provides better evidence for the effect of solubilization of the rubber.] It is also especially noteworthy that the glass transition of the epoxy is not discernible at 40 percent rubber content (Fig. 7E).

Optical micrographs (X130) of the rubber-modified-epoxy films (after staining with OsO_4) are shown in Figs. 10A to 10E. The mean maximum size of the dispersed rubber aggregates increases from about 1 micron for 5 percent rubber (Fig. 10A) to about 10-20 microns for 20 percent rubber (Fig. 10C). At the 30 percent level of rubber (Fig. 10D), the rubber forms the continuous phase in which epoxy domains are immersed. The

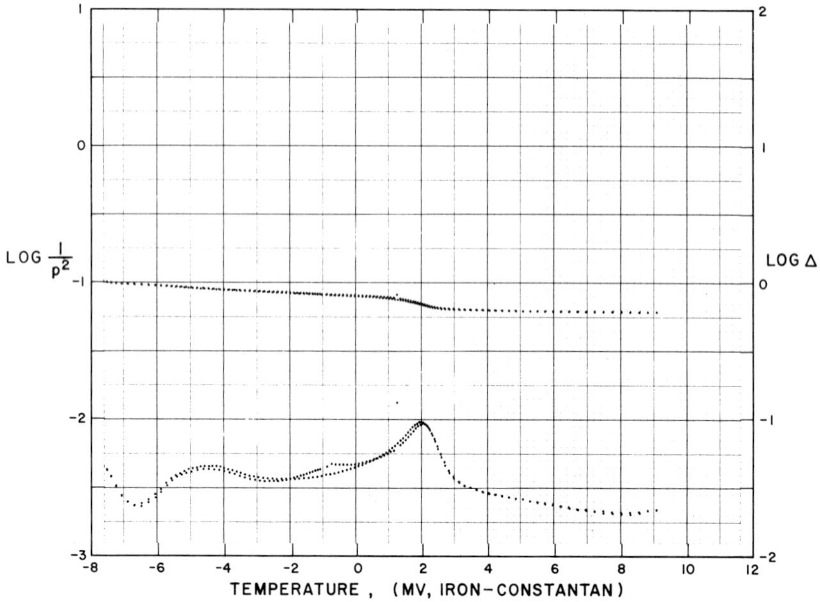

Fig. 6. Polyimide film (Kapton, du Pont). Plot: 170°C → -190°C → 170°C.

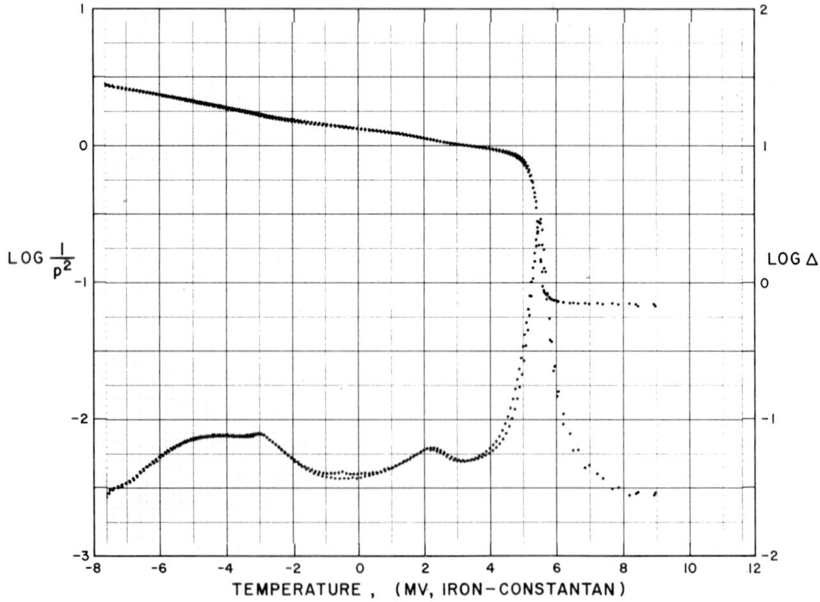

Fig. 7A. Epoxy/5 percent rubber. Cured coating on polyimide film. Plot: 170°C → -190°C → 170°C.

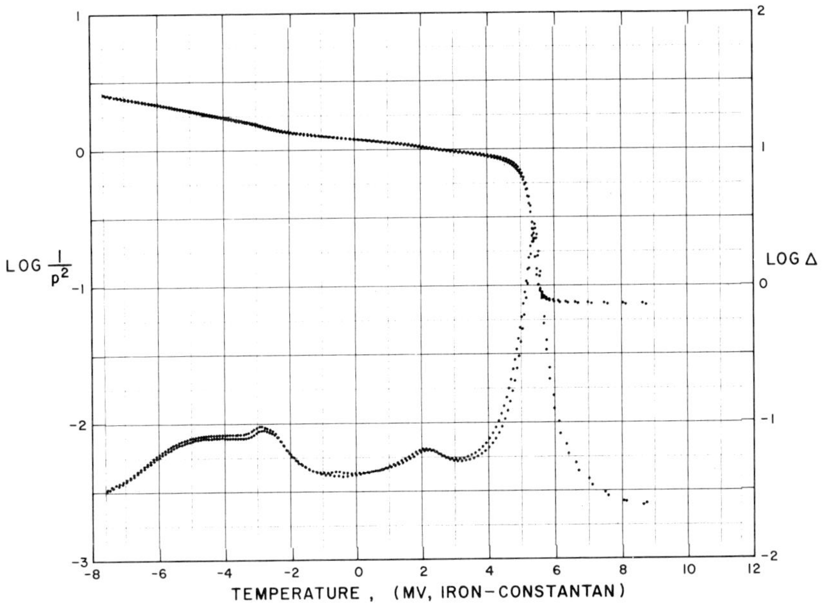

Fig. 7B. 10 percent rubber.

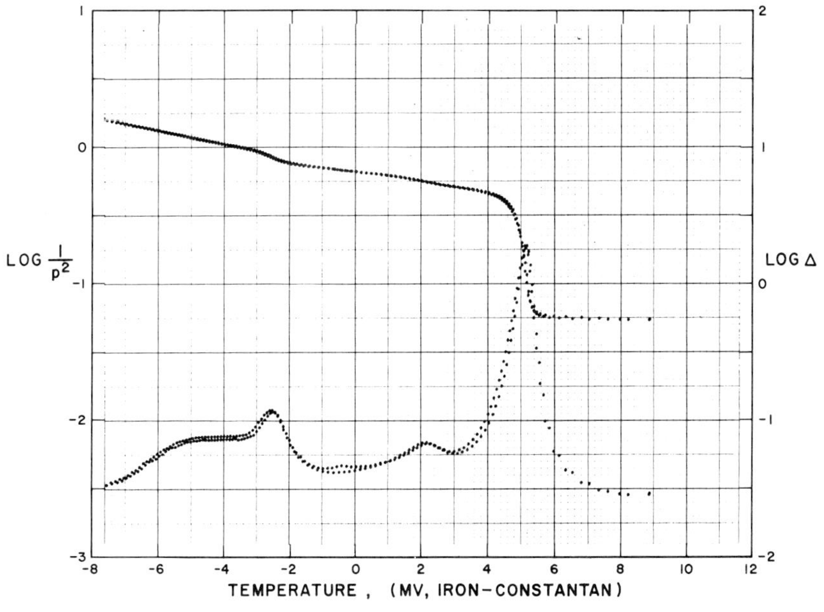

Fig. 7C. 20 percent rubber.

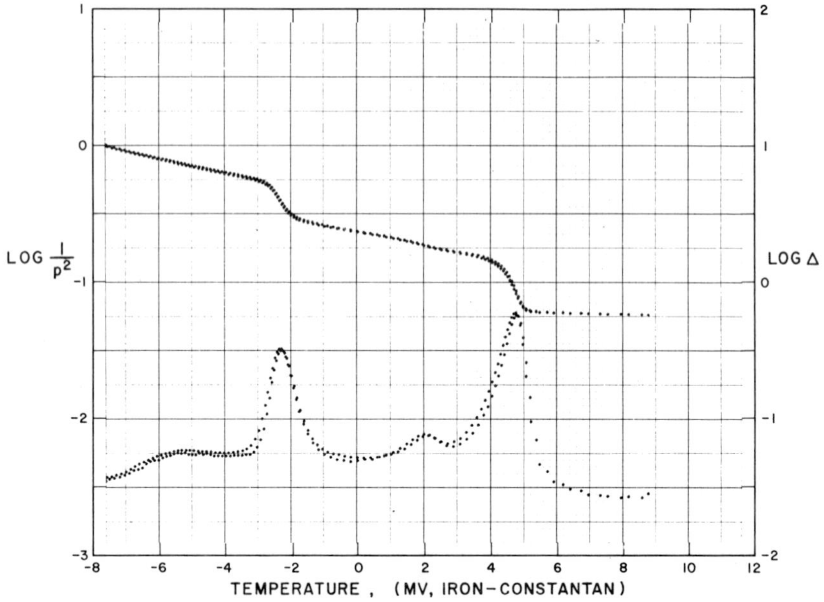

Fig. 7D. 30 percent rubber.

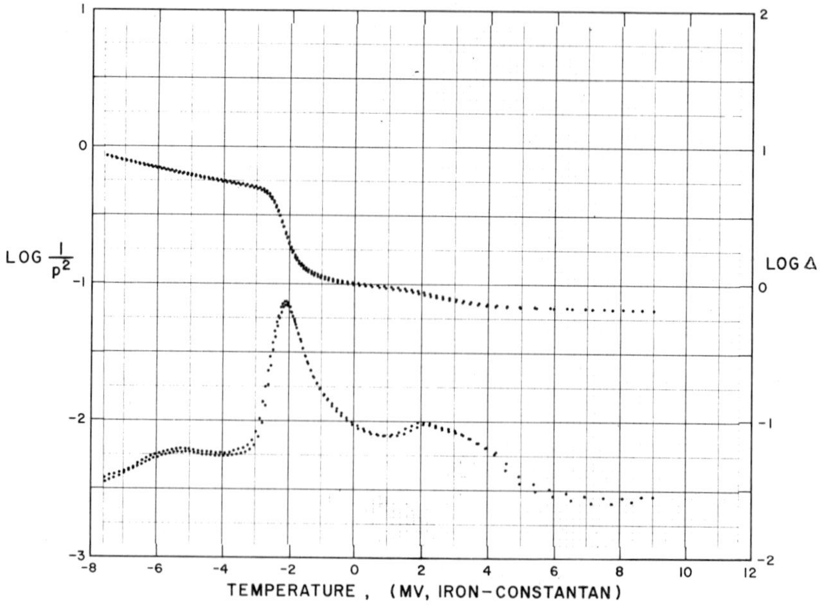

Fig. 7E. 40 percent rubber.

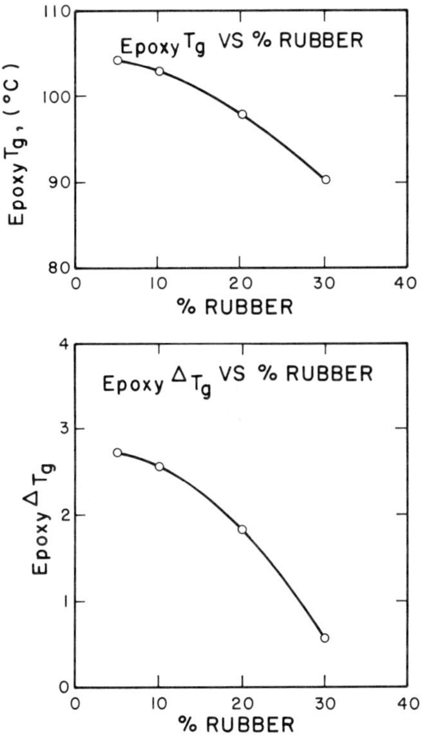

Fig. 8. Temperature and intensity of the glass transition of the epoxy phase vs. rubber content.

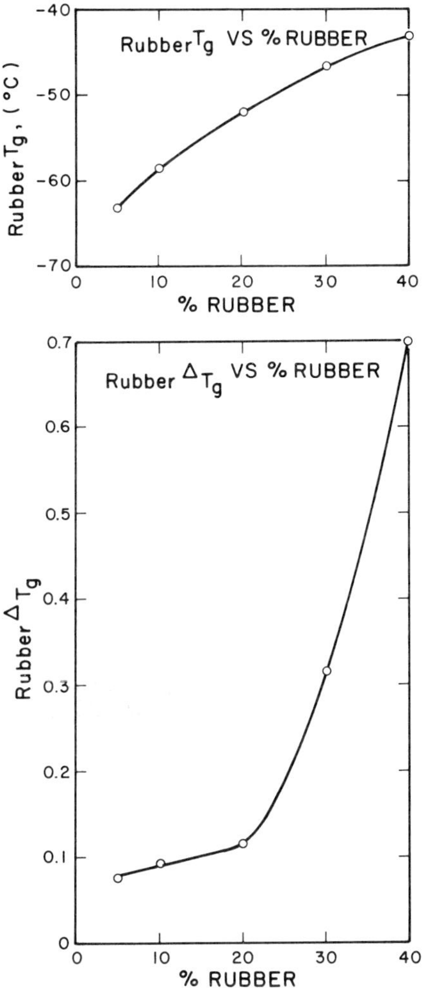

Fig. 9. Temperature and intensity of the glass transition of the rubber phase vs. rubber content.

Fig. 10A. Optical micrograph (X130) [Bausch and Lomb binocular microscope with Polaroid camera]. Epoxy/5 percent rubber. Cured coating on polyimide film stained for 20 minutes in 1 percent OsO_4 solution (1:1 H_2O/tetrahydrofuran).

Fig. 10B. 10 percent rubber.

Fig. 10C. 20 percent rubber.

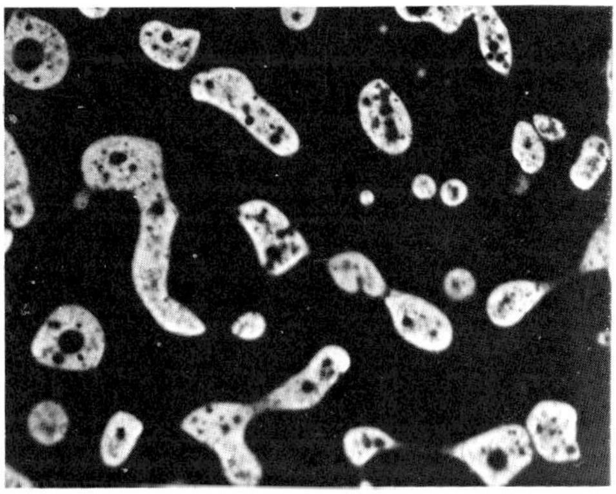

Fig. 10D. 30 percent rubber.

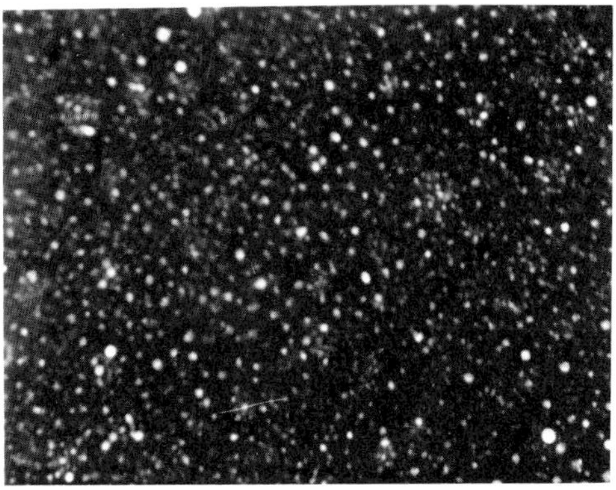

Fig. 10E. 40 percent rubber.

size of these glassy domains decreases with the presence of more rubber (Fig. 10E, 40 percent level).

The optical micrographs and torsional pendulum data therefore support the interpretation of a phase inversion occurring with increasing rubber in the system.

2. *Effect of Gel Time*

The curing of rubber-modified-epoxy systems often involves change from an initially homogeneous solution to a heterogeneous multiphase morphology. Evidence is presented here to show that the process of gelation arrests the development of morphology, and therefore that the time to gelation can be used to control mechanical properties. The gelation time can be varied by catalysts and temperature.

The effect of catalyst level on thermomechanical plots obtained after "complete" cure (170°C/100 min.) of a rubber-modified system on glass braid supports is made evident by comparison of Figs. 11A to 11D. The rubber glass transition is most dominant in the sample cured without catalyst (Fig. 11A). Curing without catalyst at a lower temperature (120°C/16 hr) also leads to a dominant rubber glass transition but, on the basis of the lower glass transition temperature of the epoxy, to inadequate cure (cf. Fig. 12 with Fig. 11A). Curing at a lower temperature (120°C/16 hr.) with catalyst can give rise to a marked rubber glass transition and yet a cured system (cf. Figs. 13 and 11C). These results suggest that the intensity of the rubber transition depends on the time available for the development of morphology, which is limited by the process of gelation. The higher glass transition temperature of the epoxy for the fully cured sample cured with long gelation time (cf. Fig. 11A with Figs. 11B, 11C and 11D) suggests more complete separation of the two phases -- which concurs with the proposition. It is noted that although reaction at lower temperatures will lengthen the time to gel, the increased viscosity at lower temperatures can retard the development of morphology. The effect of temperature on solubility is another complicating factor, increase of which *per se* would inhibit phase separation.

Optical studies on samples used for the thermomechanical work support the above conclusions. Curing without catalyst led to distinctly larger sized domains of dispersed rubber (Fig. 14A) than cure with catalyst (Figs. 14B, 14C and 14D). Similarly, the lower the temperature of cure, the larger the size of the rubber domains (cf. Figs. 15A, 15B and 15C). It is noteworthy that the thermomechanical behavior of a sample having a continuous rubber phase is similar to that of one having large domains of dispersed rubber (cf. Figs. 7D and 11A).

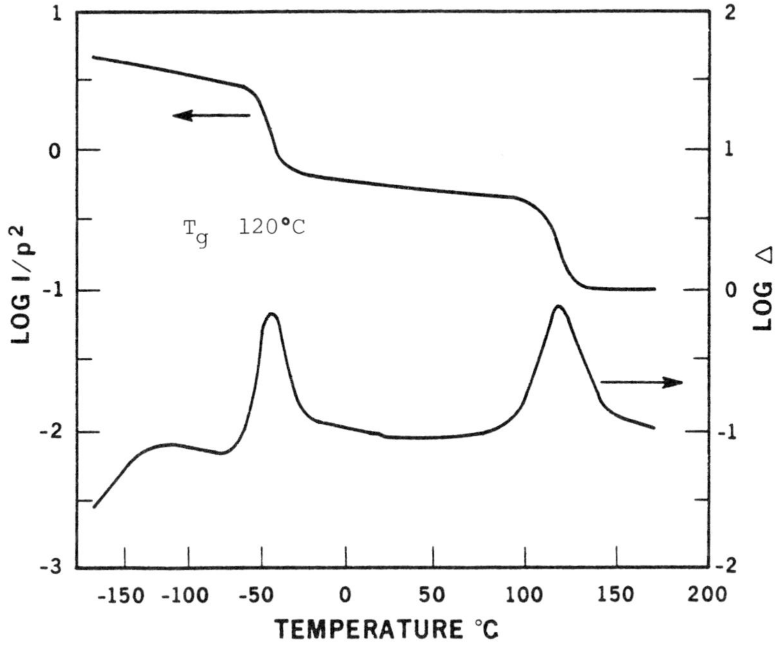

Fig. 11A. Epoxy/rubber system. 0 phr catalyst (benzyldimethylamine). Cured 170°C/100 min. Plot: 170°C → -190°C.

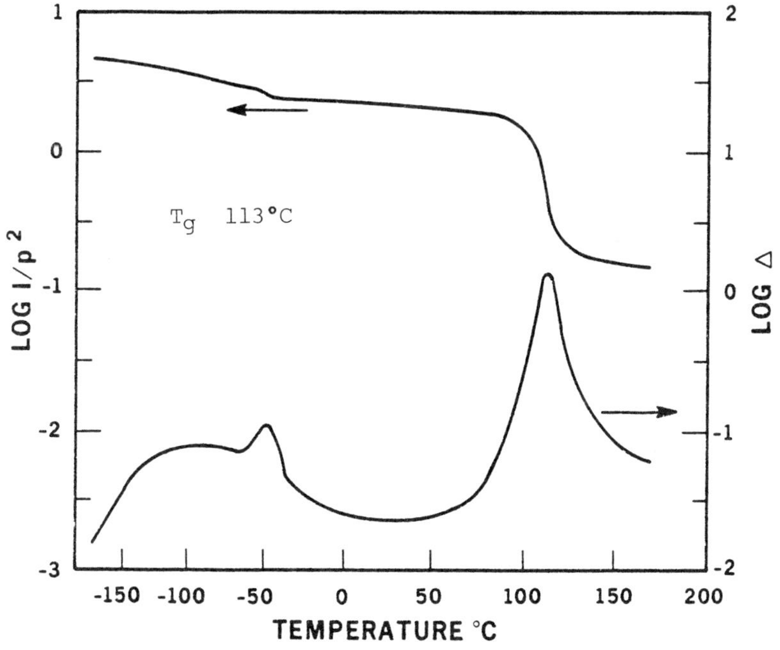

Fig. 11B. 0.5 phr catalyst.

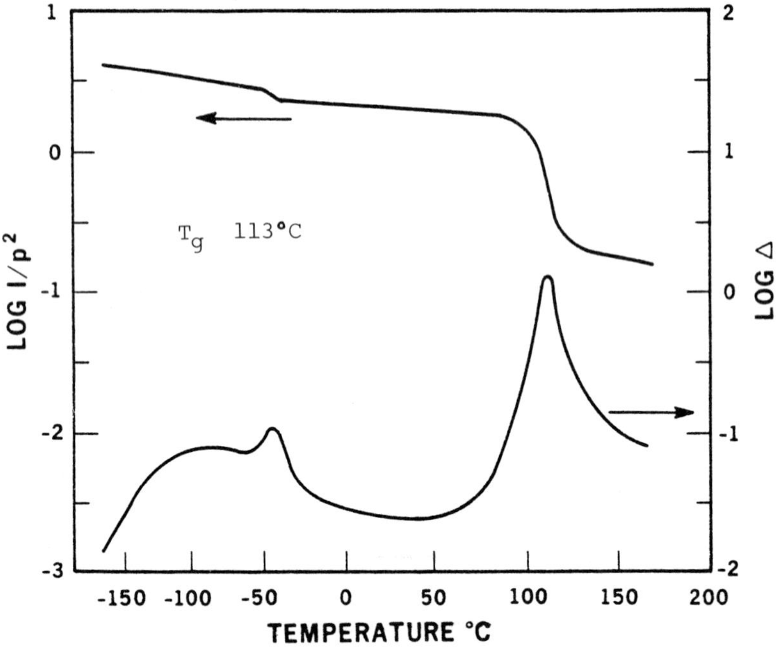

Fig. 11C. 1 phr catalyst.

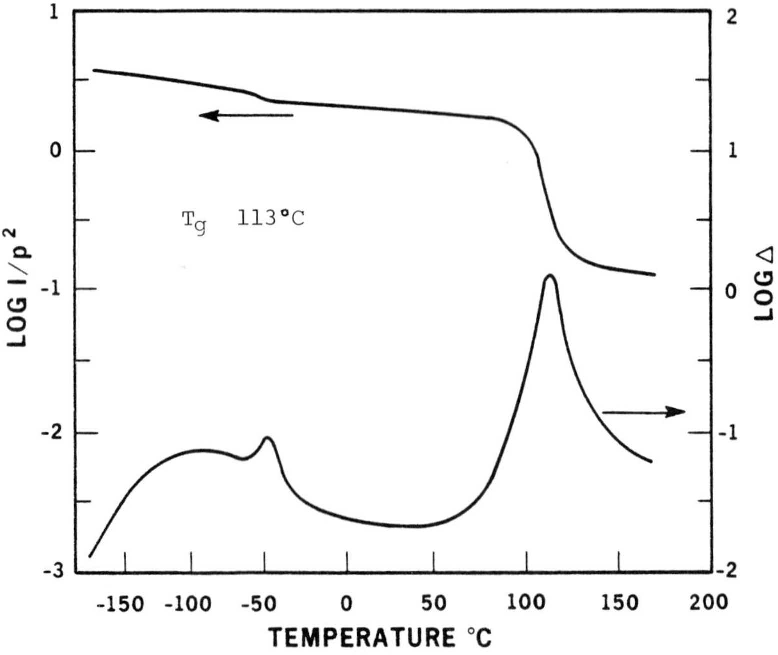

Fig. 11D. 2 phr catalyst.

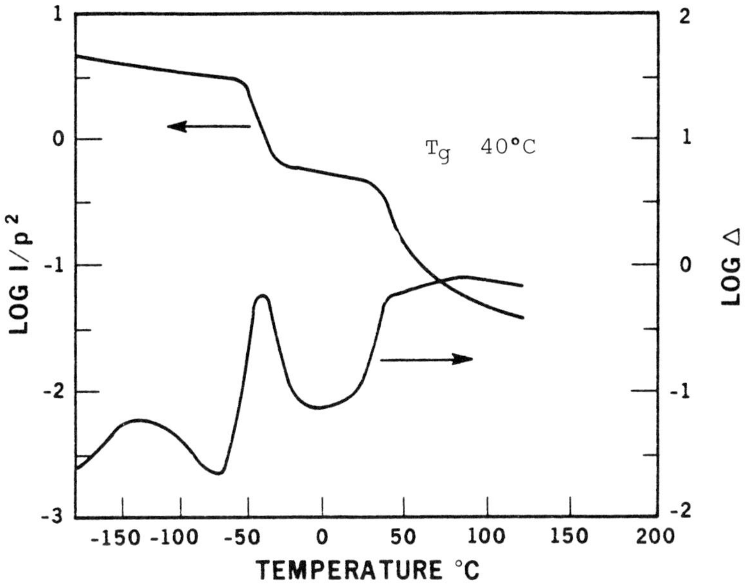

Fig. 12. Epoxy/rubber system. 0 phr catalyst. Cured 120°C/16 hr. Plot: 120°C → -190°C.

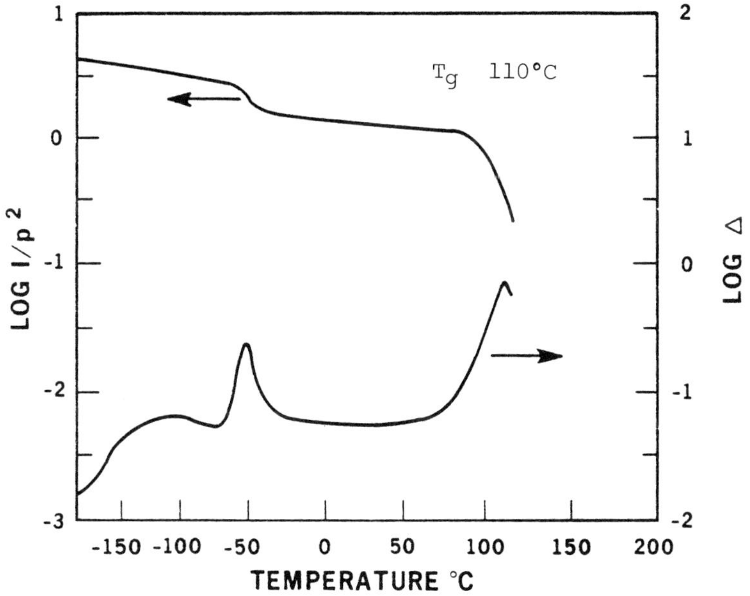

Fig. 13. Epoxy/rubber system. 1 phr catalyst. Cured 120°C/16 hr. Plot: 120°C → -190°C.

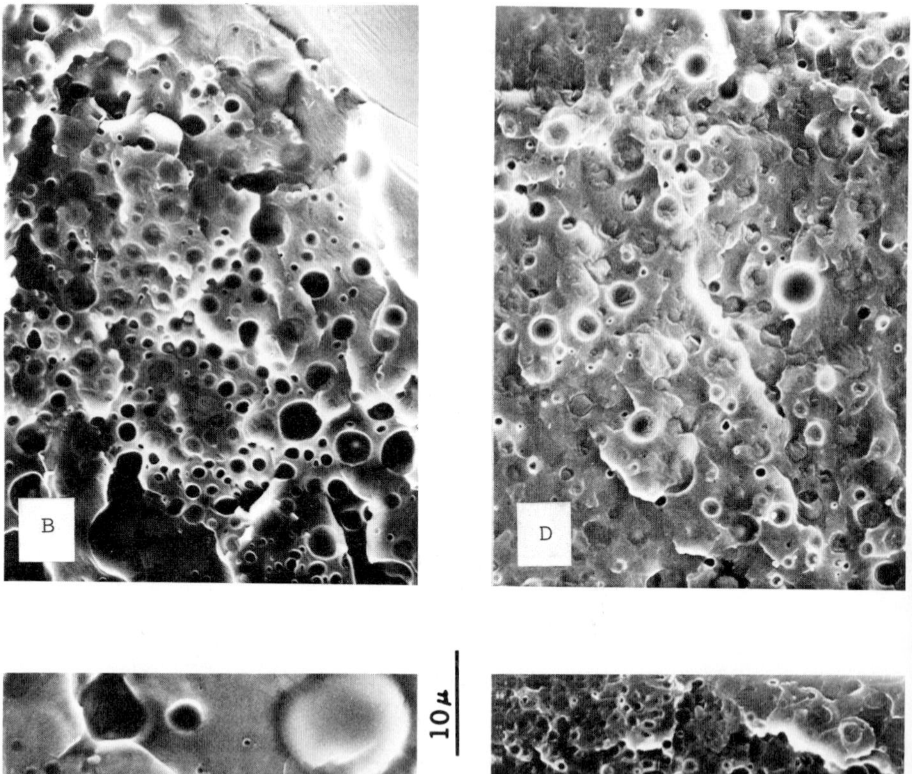

Fig. 14. Electron micrographs of stained fracture surfaces. Epoxy/rubber system. Effect of level of catalyst (benzyldimethylamine). Cured 170°C/100 min. A: 0 phr catalyst; B: 0.5 phr catalyst; C: 1 phr catalyst; D: 2 phr catalyst.

Fig. 15. Optical micrographs (X130). Epoxy/rubber system. Effect of temperature of cure. 1 phr catalyst.

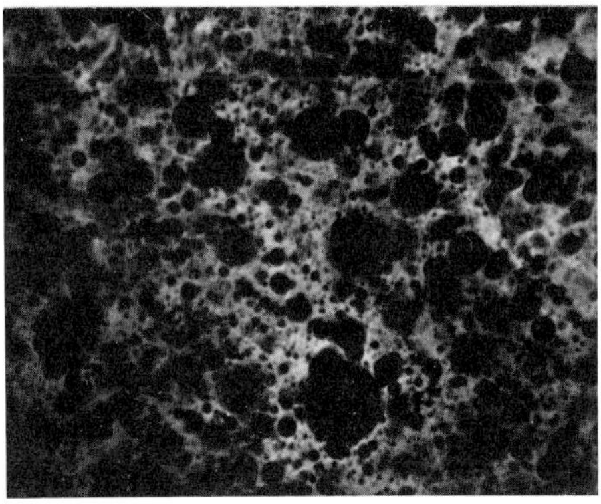

A. Cured 120°C/16 hr.

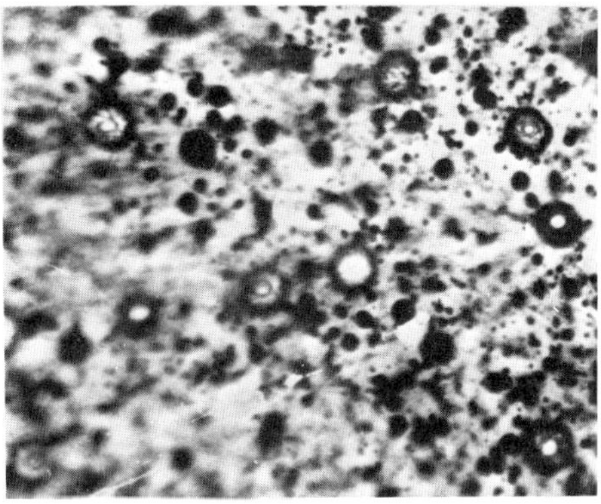

B. Cured 170°C/100 min.

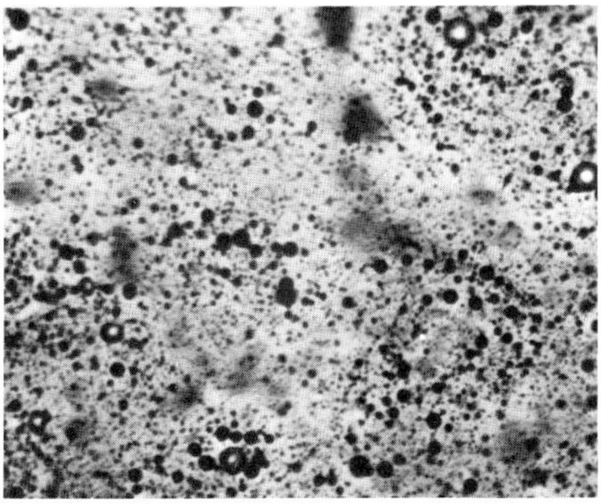

C. Cured 220°C/15 min.

C. Effect of Active Environments

This section illustrates application of the torsional pendulum to the study of environmental effects; in particular it deals with a water-induced transition (< T_g), and plasticization of the epoxy T_g by water and by an organic liquid.

1. *The T_{H_2O} (< T_g) Transition*

Investigations of the effect of water vapor on the T_{H2O} (< T_g) transition were performed on a single specimen of epoxy film. The specimen was preheated at 170°C ($T_{g\infty}$ ca. 132°C) for 20 hours in a dry atmosphere in an attempt to fully cure the material prior to exposure to water vapor. Exposures were made at different levels of water vapor (ppm_v H_2O/He) in the atmosphere at two temperatures (30°C and 150°C) prior to obtaining the thermomechanical plots ($\Delta T/\Delta t = \pm$ 1.5°C/minute). The atmosphere of the isothermal conditioning was not purposely changed in the subsequent thermomechanical experiment, the apparatus serving as a trap below 0°C. The experimental sequence is summarized:

170°C/20 hours/dry atmosphere	→	cure
170°C → -190°C → 170°C	→	thermomechanical plot of cured, dry material
170°C → 30°C		
30°C/8 hours/X ppm H_2O	→	conditioning at 30°C
30°C → -190°C → 170°C	→	thermomechanical plot after conditioning
170°C/5 hours/Xppm H_2O	→	removal of excess water which may have been absorbed on cooling to -190°C and then heating to 170°C
170°C → 30°C		
30°C/8 hours/Y(> X)ppm H_2O	→	conditioning at 30°C
etc. (e.g. Z > Y)		
170°C/>8 hours/< 20 ppm H_2O	→	dry material
170°C → -190°C → 170°C	→	thermomechanical plot of dry material

The procedure was then repeated conditioning at 150°C in place of 30°C.

The thermomechanical behavior of the cured and dried material (Fig. 16) reveals two transitions, T_g at 132°C (0.2 Hz) and a broad glassy-state transition T_{sec} centered at about -90°C (0.7 Hz). Exposure to water vapor induced a low-temperature "T_{H_2O}" transition which was accompanied by a decrease in intensity of the lower T_{sec} transition (Fig. 17). The intensity of the loss peak of the water transition increased with concentration of water and with decreasing temperature (30°C vs. 150°C) of the conditioning atmosphere, reaching a plateau level which was higher at the lower temperature (Fig. 18). [Since the level of the plateau after conditioning at 150°C was lower than when the subsequent thermomechanical spectrum was obtained at a more rapid cooling rate (data not shown) from 150°C (5°C/min vs. 1.5°C/min), the kinetics of water absorption-desorption on cooling prevented a reliable estimate being made of the pick-up of water by the specimen at 150°C. Nevertheless, the numerical value will be less than that measured (from the intensity of the T_{H_2O} peak).] The temperature (T_{H_2O}) of the maximum in the mechanical loss decreased correspondingly with increasing water level in the conditioning atmosphere (Fig. 19). Heating at 170°C in a dry atmosphere at the end of each isothermal set of levels of exposure resulted in thermomechanical plots (e.g. Fig. 20) which were similar to that of the pre-conditioned specimen (Fig. 16), demonstrating that the curing reactions had been completed prior to exposure to water vapor and that the T_{H_2O} transition was reversible. [Differences between the thermomechanical plots (Figs. 20 and 16) are attributed solely to changes in geometry which occurred over the long period of time of the experiments on the one specimen.] These results parallel those obtained with other epoxy systems (7,8).

Using the intensity of the loss peak as an index of the quantity of water absorbed, exposure at 30°C resulted in greater pick-up of water than exposure at 150°C at the same conditioning water level. If the loss peak is a linear measure of the amount of water in the specimen, it follows from Fig. 18 that the number of sites is limited. The *decrease* in water absorption with increasing conditioning temperature also suggests that a complex forms between water and specific chemical sites in the epoxy. The concomitant decrease in intensity of the low temperature secondary transition of the epoxy which accompanies the increase in intensity of the H_2O transition suggests further that the two relaxations are coupled. Addition of H_2O to a localized flexible segment (e.g.

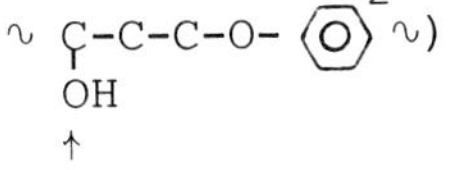

increases its size and restricts its motion until higher temperatures.

Results from similar experiments have been obtained with a polyimide (9); in this material a water-induced transition at -120°C occurs in a region which is free from other glassy-state transitions.

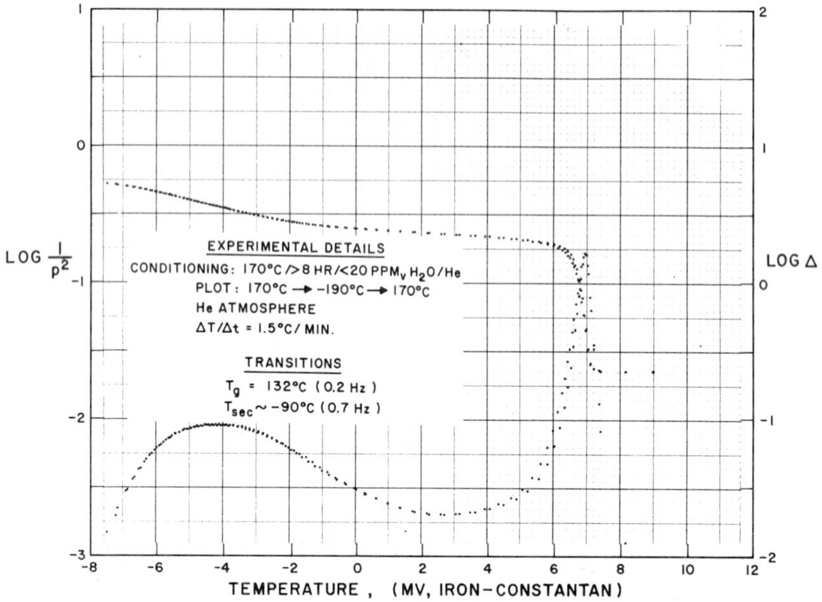

Fig. 16. Plot of dry cured epoxy system.

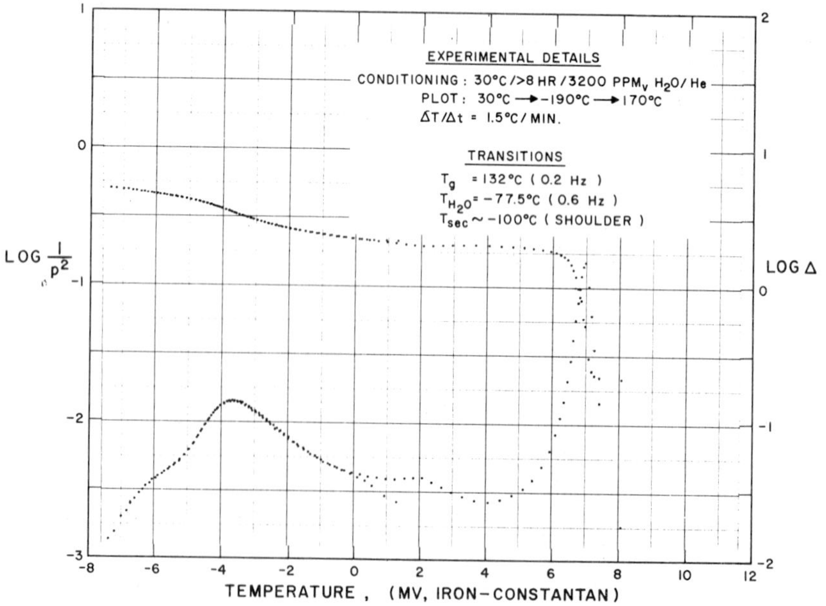

Fig. 17. Plot of epoxy system after conditioning in a humid atmosphere.

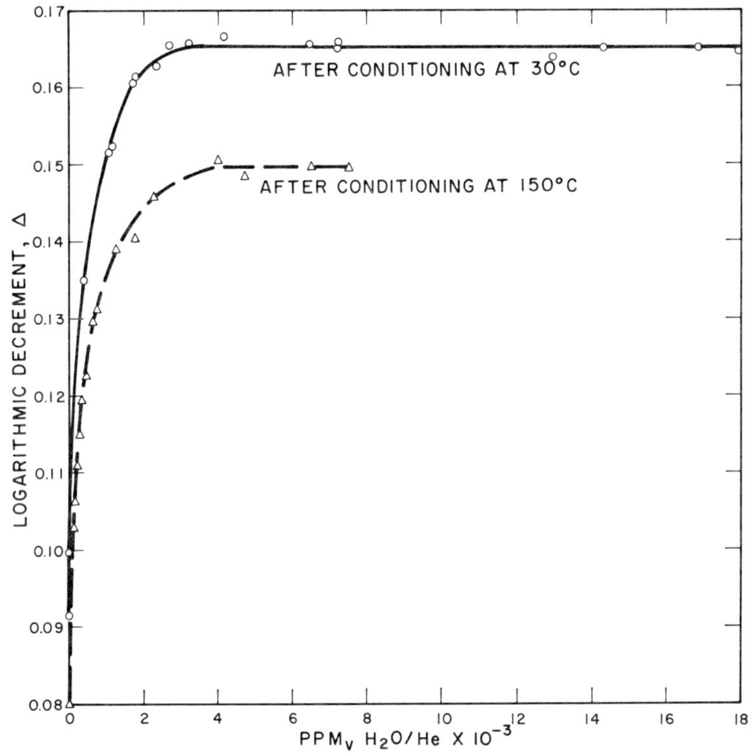

Fig. 18. Intensity of T_{H_2O} transition damping peak vs. ppm. H_2O in conditioning atmosphere.

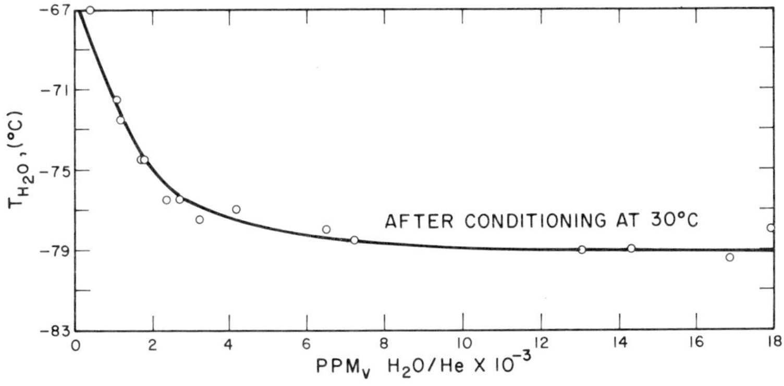

Fig. 19. Temperature of T_{H_2O} transition damping peak vs. ppm H_2O in conditioning atmosphere.

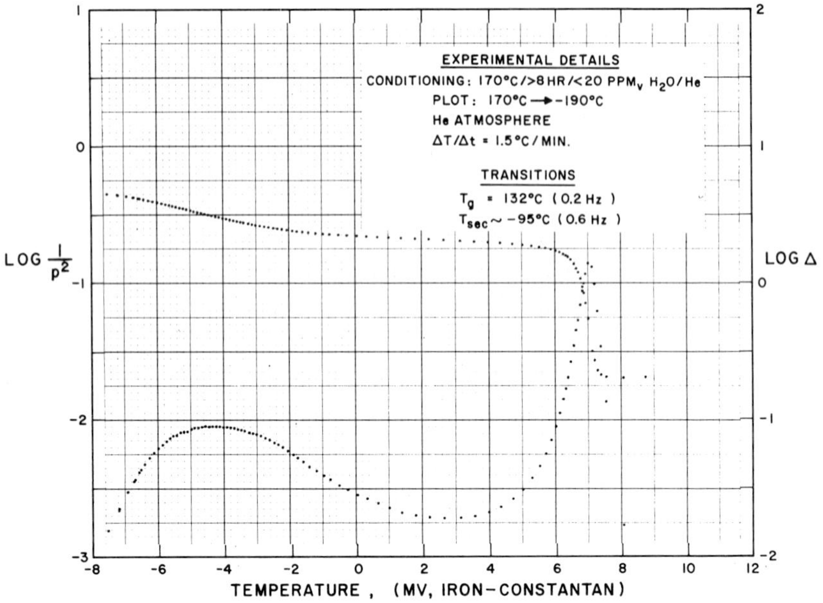

Fig. 20. Plot of epoxy system dried after conditioning in humid atmospheres.

The results for these experiments are preliminary in the sense that although a reversible water-induced transition has been located, complications may have been introduced by the experimental procedure of using the water-laden conditioning atmosphere in the subsequent testing. Studies of the kinetics of the effects of exposure to water vapor do support the experimental procedure at temperatures below 0°C (7). The location of the water, presumably either homogeneously distributed at limited molecular sites or deposited on the limited macroscopic surface of the specimen, has not been established. The apparent coupling of the intensities of the T_{H_2O} and the T_{sec} transitions, the apparent change in intensity of the T_{H_2O} transition with temperature of conditioning, the reversibility of the data (e.g. as in Fig. 17, $T < 0°C$), and the lowering of the glass transition temperature (below) by water vapor, all support homogeneous absorption.

2. *The T_g Transition and H_2O*

Whether or not the glass transition of epoxy systems is affected by water is a subject of controversy.

Thermomechanical data for specimens with high values of T_g (> 100°C) displayed glass transitions which did not appear to be affected by the presence of water vapor (e.g., cf. Fig. 16 and Fig. 20 with Fig. 17). This may have been a consequence of the low relative humidity at higher temperatures. The influence of water vapor on the glass transition was therefore investigated using an epoxy system with a low value of T_g.

A rubber-modified epoxy system was cured at 170°C for 1 hour in the TBA apparatus using a glass braid as a substrate; all subsequent conditioning was at 100°C and lower. The thermomechanical behavior of the cured and dried material (Fig. 21) revealed the T_g of the epoxy at 37°C, and a rubber glass transition and epoxy glassy state transition at lower temperatures. After conditioning at 15°C at 2800 ppm H_2O, the thermomechanical spectrum (Fig. 22) displayed a T_{H_2O} transition and a reduced value of 25°C for the glass transition of the epoxy. After drying, the spectrum of the original material (Fig. 21) was obtained, demonstrating the reversibility of the effect of water on both the T_{H_2O} and T_g transitions.

3. *The T_g Transition and Organic Liquid*

The following experiments were performed.

A rectangular specimen was cut from a cured, flexible epoxy/single ply glass cloth composite (Figs. 23 and 24,

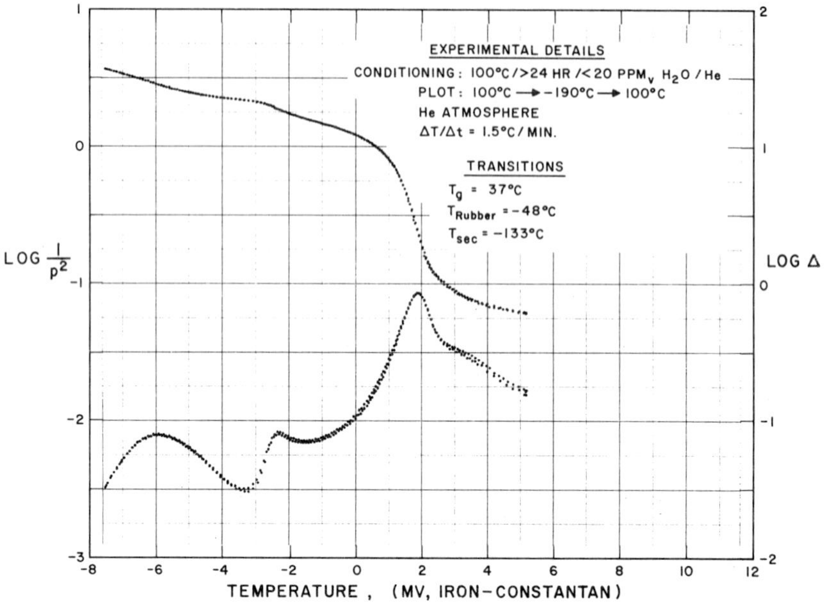

Fig. 21. Plot of dry cured epoxy/rubber system.

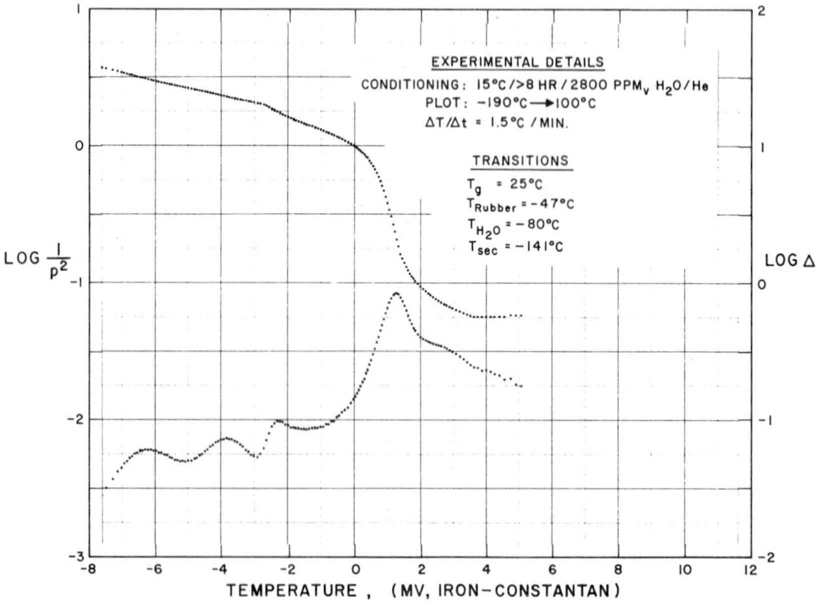

Fig. 22. Plot of epoxy/rubber system after conditioning in a humid atmosphere.

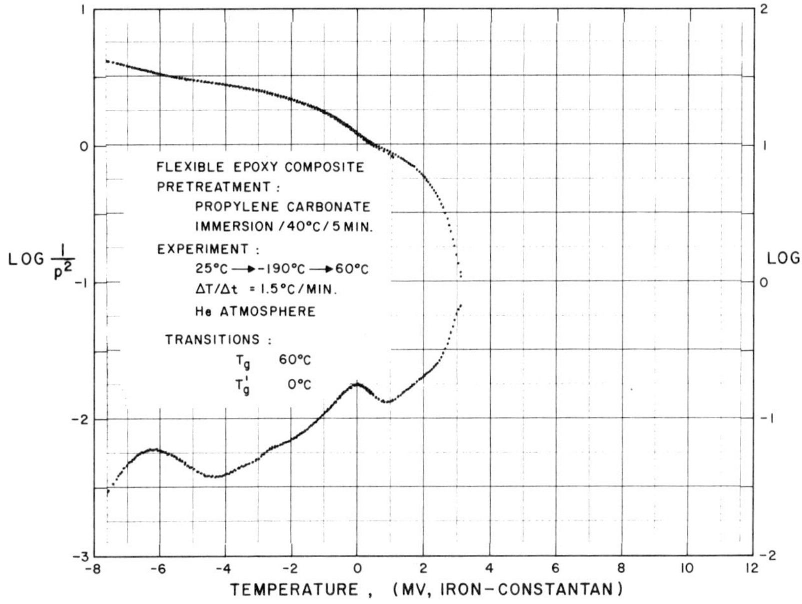

Fig. 23. Plot of flexible epoxy/glass cloth composite after immersion in propylenecarbonate.

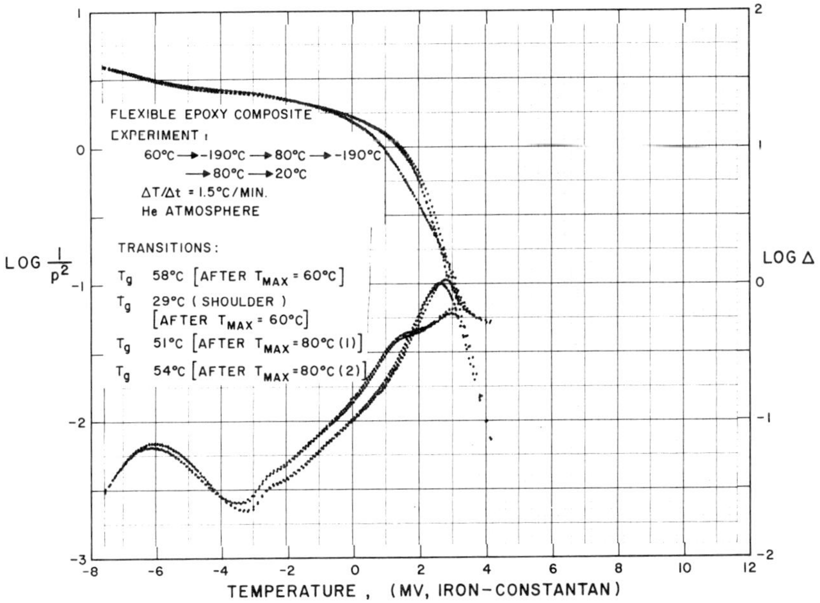

Fig. 24. Plot showing effect of temperature on plasticized flexible epoxy/glass cloth composite.

"Flexible epoxy composite"). After immersion in propylene carbonate at 40°C for 5 minutes, excess liquid was wiped off and the specimen was mounted in the TBA apparatus. The sequence of temperature change, 25°C → -190°C → 60°C (Fig. 23), was followed by the sequence, 60°C → -190°C → 80°C → -190°C → 80°C → 20°C (Fig. 24) in order to monitor the effect of heating to successively higher temperatures on the transitions. Experimental details and a summary of the transitions appear in Figs. 23 and 24. An interpretation follows.

A limited amount of liquid was absorbed on immersion at 40°C and formed a homogeneously plasticized phase around unplasticized polymer. Subsequent heating to 60°C resulted in migration of the plasticizer and a dilution of the concentration of plasticizer in the plasticized phase. The epoxy glass transition temperature of the plasticized phase correspondingly increased from 0°C (Fig. 23, T_g') to 29°C (Fig. 24, T_g'). The epoxy glass transition temperature of the unplasticized phase was essentially unchanged during this sequence [ca. 60°C, Fig. 23; 58°C, Fig. 24]. Heating to 80°C produced complete homogenization of the epoxy and an epoxy glass transition (51°C, Fig. 24) between those of the two precursor phases. The further shift upwards of the single epoxy glass transition temperature on heating to 80°C (for the second time) is attributed to loss of plasticizer to the environment.

It is apparent that the approach suggested by the above experiments represents a convenient and novel way of investigating interactions between liquids and polymeric materials.

V. ACKNOWLEDGEMENTS

Partial support of the Chemistry Branch of the Office of Naval Research is acknowledged.

VI. REFERENCES

1. J. K. Gillham, A.I.Ch.E. J., 20, 6, 1066 (1974).
2. P. G. Babayevsky and J. K. Gillham, J. Appl. Polym. Sci. 17, 2067 (1973).
3. J. K. Gillham, J. A. Benci and A. Noshay, J. Polym. Sci., Symp. No. 46, 279 (1974).
4. C. A. Glandt and J. K. Gillham, Polymer Preprints, Amer. Chem. Soc., 16(1), 694 (1975).
5. J. K. Gillham, Polym. Eng. Sci., 16, 353 (1976).
6. C. A. Glandt, Ph.D. Thesis, Princeton University, Princeton, N. J., Oct. 1976.
7. C. A. McPherson and J. K. Gillham, work in progress.
8. J. K. Gillham, National Technical Conference, High Performance Plastics, Cleveland, Ohio, Preprints, pp 14-18, Soc. Plastics Eng., Oct. 5-7, 1976.
9. Y. Ozari, R. H. Chow and J. K. Gillham, Polym. Preprints, Amer. Chem. Soc., 18(1) (1977).

DIFFERENTIAL SCANNING CALORIMETRY OF PHENOLIC RESINS

James A. Koutsky
Robert Ebewele
University of Wisconsin

Resole phenolic resins were polymerized and analyzed by differential scanning calorimetry. Glass spheres, 40 microns in diameter, and white pine wood fines were used as filler materials. The calorimetric studies were performed from -140°C to 350°C. Characteristic low temperature DSC shifts were observed from -50°C to -110°C for all the resins studied. The shifts decreased in magnitude but remained even in highly cured specimens. The DSC shifts were associated with dynamic mechanical peaks observed by torsion braid experiments. Absorption of water had slight effect on these low temperature DSC shifts. Increased filler concentrations appeared to diminish the shifts by lowering the mass fraction of the resin in the composite but did not greatly change the temperature of the observed shift from the resin. Effects of NaOH and $Ca(OH)_2$ catalyst concentrations were studied as well as the effects of initial water content. Results agree with previous authors with regard to approximate location of endo and exotherm peaks.

I. INTRODUCTION

Numerous investigators have observed the thermal behavior of phenolic resole resins (1-6). Thermal analysis studies have shown that broad endothermic activity is observed as a resole resin is heated from ambient temperatures to 100°C to 130°C. Chow has concluded that for base catalyzed resins containing large water contents, two basic endothermic peaks were seen from DTA studies. The peaks occurred in the regions of 122°C to 135°C and 145°C to 170°C depending on the heating rates. TGA studies revealed that the first DTA peak is probably split into two contributions of endothermic activity. The first, about 85°C, is due to a maximum rate of water evaporation and the second is another maximum rate of water evaporation from the polymerization as well as from the remaining solvent. The second DTA endothermic peak was associated with final curing which is often crucial to develop maximum durability properties of these resins.

Previous work has concentrated on the thermal behavior of these highly crosslinked phenolic resins above ambient conditions. There is evidence, however, of thermal activity below ambient conditions for many commercial glassy linear polymers such as atactic polyvinyls and polyesters. A complicating factor in phenolic resins,as with many other polymers in interpreting low temperature behavior,is the affinity of these resins for water absorption. Since resole resins are particularly receptive to water absorption care must be made to distinguish thermal activity from molecular chain and polymer side group motion and the effects of water. However, little data has been published on thermal behavior of such resins below ambient conditions. Also, thermal activity observed at low temperatures could be directly related to degree of cure and could possibly be used to monitor subtle molecular motions in the glassy state.

II. EXPERIMENTAL

Phenolic resins were prepared using the procedures outlined by the Forest Products Laboratory, Madison, for a standard resole plywood adhesive. The list of ingredients for the resins are given in table 1. All chemicals were reagent grade. Resins were prepared in a 500 ml stirred glass reactor over nitrogen. The reaction vessel was heated externally to 100°C and the mixture was refluxed for 100 minutes until the viscosity began to increase. Three equal additions of the caustic were made during the run to reduce the viscosity. On the last addition the resins were held at 80°C until the viscosity reached 4 to 5 poise. The resins were then stored in a refrigerator under nitrogen at 5°C.

TABLE 1

The Preparation of Standard Resole Phenolic Resins

Ingredients	*15wt% NaOH wt%*	*7wt% NaOH wt%*	*1wt% $Ca(OH)_2$ wt%*
Phenol(100%)	*22.87*	*22.87*	*22.87*
Water(distilled)	*21.41*	*29.53*	*32.53*
Formaldehyde(37%)	*40.60*	*40.60*	*40.60*
NaOH	*15.12*	*7.00*	*0.00*
$Ca(OH)_2$	*0.00*	*0.00*	*1.00*
	100.00	*100.00*	*100.00*

Commercial resins were also obtained from the Plastics Engineering Company of Sheboygan, Wisconsin. These were Type 650, which is a high caustic, 7%, polymerized resole used for the manufacture of fiber board, and Type 923 which is a low caustic resole used for impregnation of paper tubes.

Specimens were prepared for the DSC by weighing approximately 10 mg into sample pans and quickly transferring the samples to the DSC chamber. A Dupont series 900 DSC thermal analyzer, equipped with a liquid nitrogen coolant source, was used for this investigation. The chamber was pre-vacuum pumped and a nitrogen gas purge was maintained for at least 15 minutes before cooling began to eliminate atmospheric oxygen within the sample chamber. Non-sealed sample pans were used in the tests. Some resin specimens were pre-cured in a vacuum oven at various times and temperatures and then placed in the DSC chamber.

Wood flour composites were made using wood fines of White Pine,(Wilner Wood Products, Type 2501) which had a mesh size less than 200 mesh. Solid glass beads, obtained from Potters Industries, New Jersey, having an approximate size range of 25 microns, were also used in making composites. The resins were mixed with the fillers at different weight percent loadings in a small mull. Approximately 10 to 15 mg of these composite samples were used in the DSC measurements.

Other resin specimens for torsional braid tests were made by coating the resin onto glass braids of 3 to 4 inches in length. The glass braids were kept at 200°C for two hours in an oven before the resins were applied. The coated braid specimens were cured both in the torsion pendulum oven and in a temperature controlled oven. Torsion pendulum data were obtained by a modified free oscillatory pendulum apparatus described by Gillham (7). Fig. 1 shows a schematic of the apparatus used. Temperature ranges from -150°C to 250°C were explored using this technique.

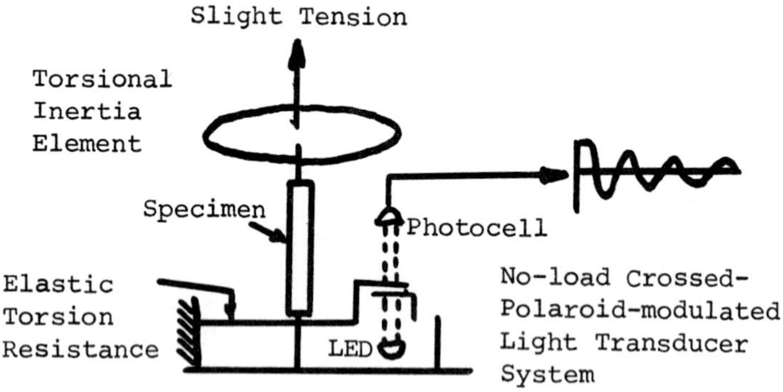

Fig. 1. Schematic of torsion pendulum used for torsional braid analysis.

III. RESULTS

The DSC data obtained for these resins is similar to that obtained from previous workers. Fig. 2 shows a thermogram of a precured resin (15 min. at 120°C, quenched to room temperature) revealing the two main endothermic peaks (60°C to 130°C) and (140°C to 180°C) which was also observed by Chow and co-workers. The exotherm observed by White and Rust does not appear to be evident in the 125°C to 150°C region. When such a resin is heated to 240°C in nitrogen and subsequently cooled quickly to liquid nitrogen temperatures the second scan shows little thermal activity above ambient conditions. What is interesting is the appearance of a discernible baseline shift occurring in the -100°C to -80°C

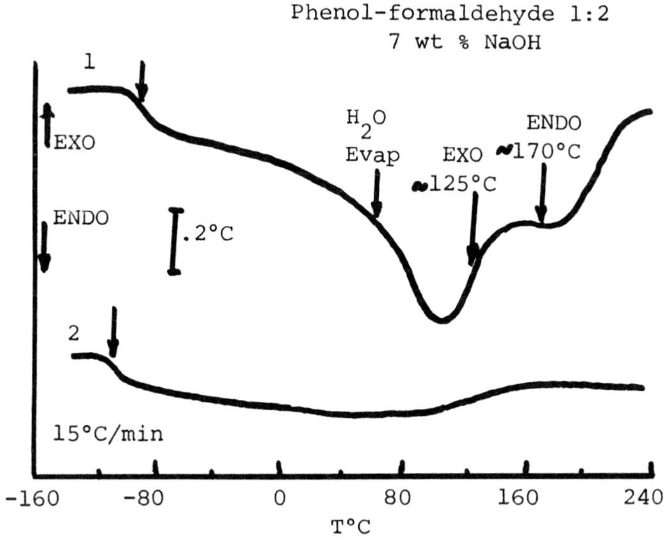

Fig. 2. DSC scans of a 7 wt% NaOH phenol-formaldehyde resin. Scan 1 corresponds to a precured resin, 11 mg, held for 15 minutes at 120°C in a oven and then transferred to the DSC cell and cooled in nitrogen to -140°C. Scan 2 is the repeated heating of the same sample from scan 1.

region. The magnitude of the shift appears to be slightly reduced on the second scan.

This low temperature shift was also observed with other resole resins. The $Ca(OH)_2$ catalyzed resin, Fig. 3, shows a large broad shift from -120°C to -60°C, scan 1, which decreases in magnitude in subsequent heating, scans 2 and 3. The sample was never removed from the DSC chamber.

Fig. 4 shows a comparison of the commercial 7 wt% NaOH Type 650 resin and the 7 and 15 wt% resoles made in our laboratories. Essentially no large difference in spectra occurred. Both of these samples were oven precured for 15 minutes at 120°C.

When the samples (1 gram sizes placed in petri dishes) are pre-dried in vacuo for 5 days at 40°C the spectra appears to be similar to that of White and Rust (5). Fig. 5 shows DSC scans for liquid and solid resins. The exotherm observed by White and Rust appears at 90°C to 135°C. The dotted line indicates the variability of the peak that was observed in four samples. Again note the low temperature shift which occurs at -110°C to -80°C.

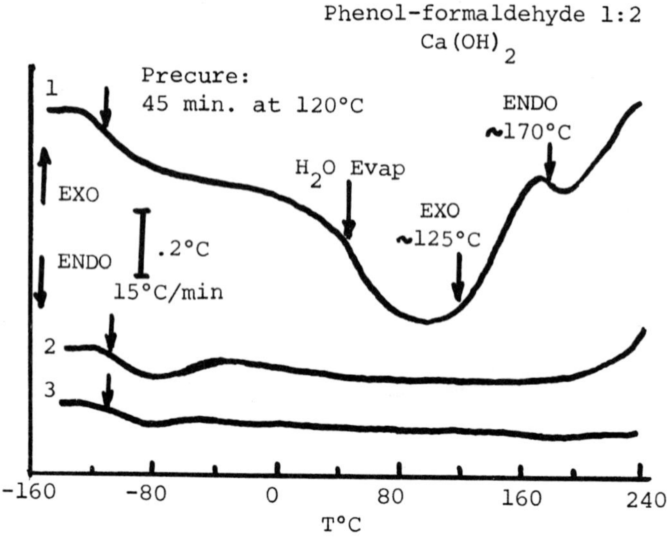

Fig. 3. DSC scans of a $Ca(OH)_2$ catalyzed resin. Scan 1 is a scan of a precured resin, 9.7 mg, held for 45 minutes at 120°C. Scan 2 is a repeated heating of the same sample from scan 1. Scan 3 is the third heating of the same sample from scan 1.

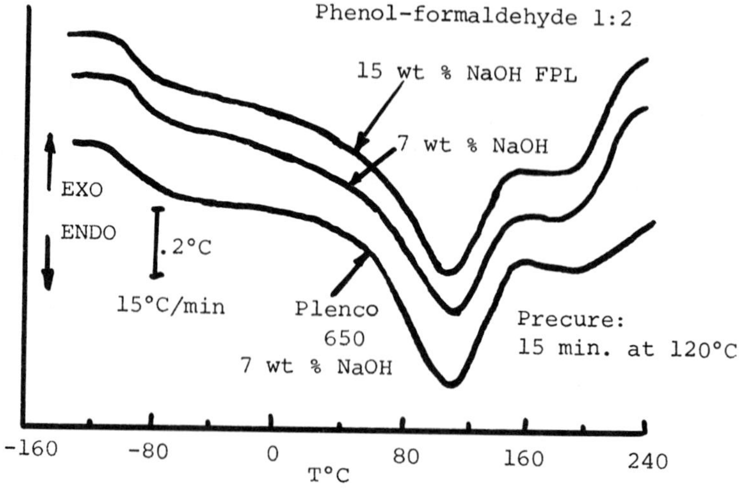

Fig. 4. DSC scans of various NaOH catalyzed resins precured for 15 minutes at 120°C. Note essential thermal activity is nearly the same for all the resins.

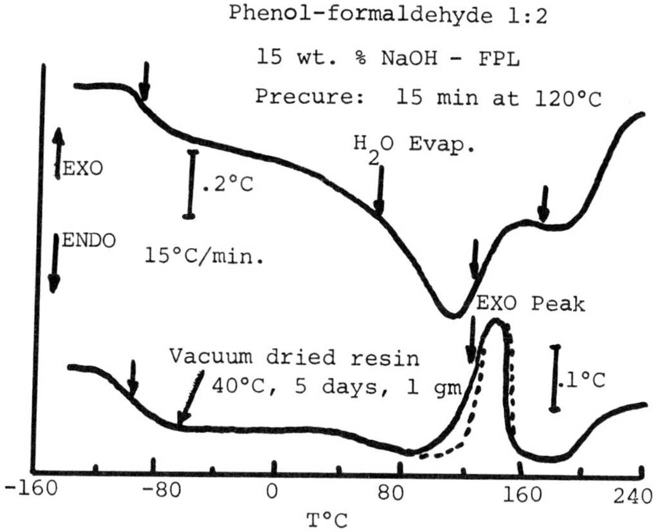

Fig. 5. A comparison of a 15wt% NaOH resin. The top scan is for a precured resin held for 15 min. at 120°C. The bottom scan, run at twice the sensitivity, is for a vacuum dried resin where most of the water has been removed. Note the exotherm which can be observed in the dried sample. The dotted line corresponds to the variability of the exotherm for different samples.

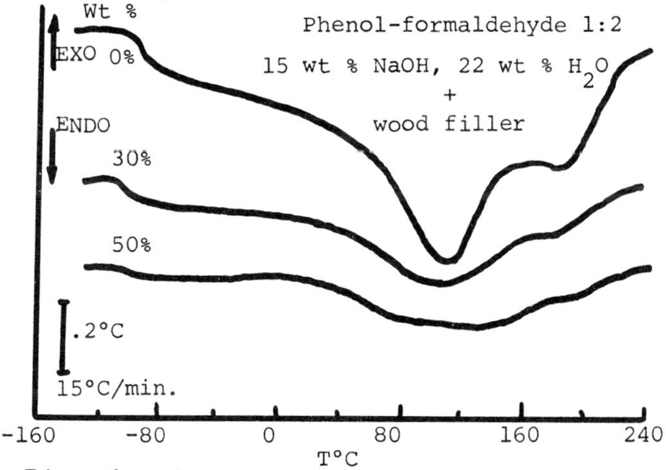

Fig. 6. DSC scans for various wt% of White Pine wood filler in 15 wt% NaOH resins which were precured for 15 min. at 120°C. As the wood content increases, the endotherm *peak at 110°C for 0% filler appears to shift to 120°C to 130°C for 50% filler. Repeated scans of these samples showed little thermal activity except the low temperature shift at -100°C.*

Fig. 6 shows the effect of White Pine wood filler on the DSC scan. Larger amounts of filler suppresses the endotherms as well as the low temperature shift. The endotherm of the 40°C to 130°C region appears not only to be reduced but also broadened to higher temperatures. The low temperature shift and the high temperature endotherm at about 70°C, do not appear to be greatly affected. This phenomena was observed with the other laboratory 7 wt%NaOH resin and with also the $Ca(OH)_2$ catalyzed resin. Compare scan 0, Fig. 7, with scan 1 which has 30% wood flour. Subsequent scans 2 and 3 in Fig. 7 show the decrease in thermal activity both at higher temperatures and at the low temperature shift which appears to be active about -70°C in scan 3. The low temperature shift of this resin system apparently is affected by the wood filler.

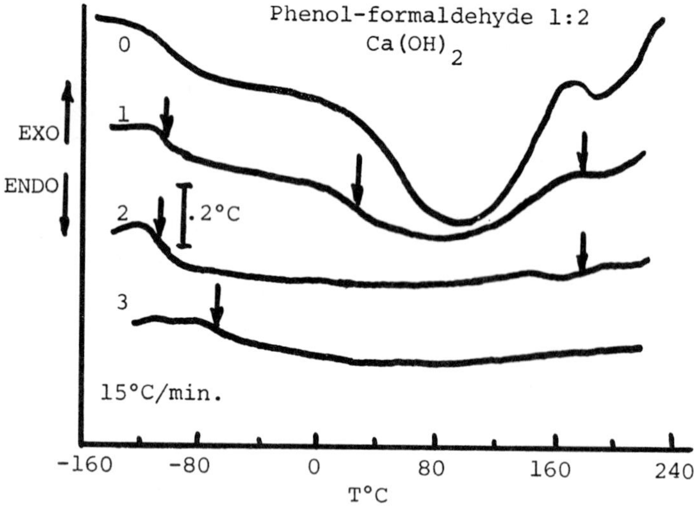

Fig. 7. Scan 0 corresponds to an unfilled $Ca(OH)_2$ catalyzed resin, 9.7 mg, precured for 45 minutes at 120°C. Scan 1 is for a 20% White Pine wood flour filled resin, 10 mg, precured for 20 minutes at 120°C. Scans 2 and 3 correspond to repeated heatings of the same sample in scan 1.

With composites of solid glass spheres the thermal activity is decreased according to the reduction of the mass fraction of the resin (see Fig. 8). However, the low temperature shift and higher temperature endotherms appear to be unaffected as to the temperature region of activity. This also appears to be the case for the other resins studied,

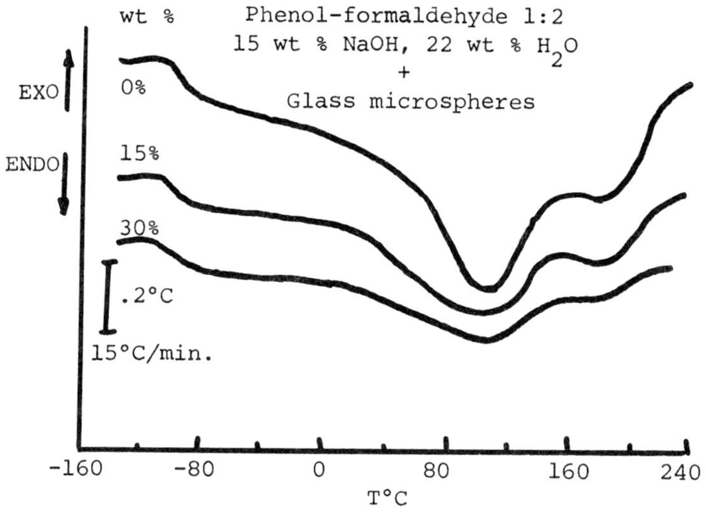

Fig. 8. DSC scans of various loadings of glass spheres in a 15 wt% NaOH resin. Precure for each sample was 15 minutes at 120°C. Sample sizes were approximately 11 to 12 mg.

Torsion braid analysis appeared to be more sensitive to the low temperature activity of these resins than the DSC. Fig. 9 shows a comparison of DSC data on the $Ca(OH)_2$ catalyzed resin and loss tangent data for a precured resin. The loss peaks from the torsional braid experiment are clearly revealed around -110°C to -40°C. There appears to be at least two peaks which can be observed with maximums at -62°C and -79°C with a possible third peak around -95°C. As the temperature is increased a large loss peak appears at 147°C which corresponds to the end of the first large endotherm.

The effects of cure on the low temperature peaks is shown in fig. 10. What is interesting is that only severe temperature treatments appear to reduce this low temperature activity. Heating the resin slowly (see insert, fig. 10) to 160°C and then quenching does not eliminate the low temperature activity. Only when the sample was heated to 200°C does the low temperature shift reduce substantially.

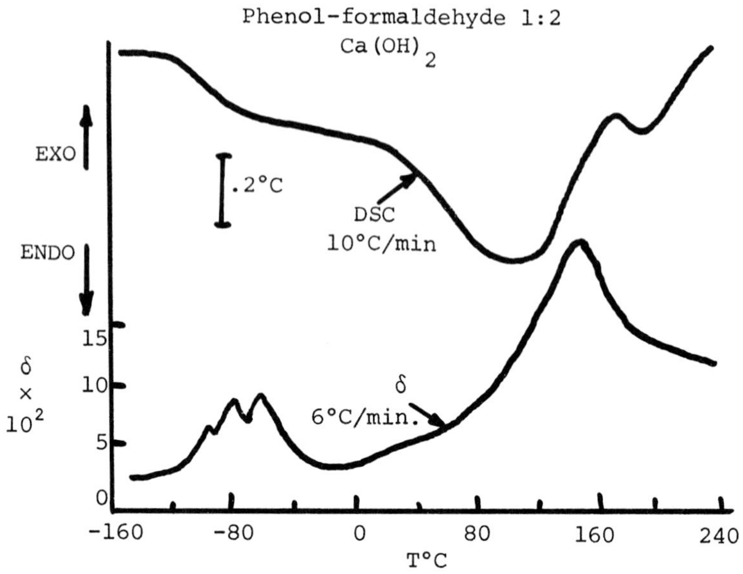

Fig. 9. Comparison of a DSC scan made at 10°C per min. with a dynamic mechanical loss scan made at 6°C per min. heating rate. Note the low temperature peaks of the dynamic mechanical loss(-110°C to -50°C) occur in the same region as the DSC shift. These samples were precured at 120°C for 1 hour. The DSC sample weighed 10 mg. The torsional braid sample was 4 inches in length and contained approximately 5 grams of resin.

DSC results on a precured 7 wt% NaOH resin system, shown in fig. 11, shows that water absorption can subtly affect the data. A sample precured for 15 min. at 120°C and then heated to 240°C and cooled gives the data in scan 1. A repeated scan of the sample, 2, shows very little thermal activity except near -100°C. The sample was then removed from the calorimeter and placed in 100% humidity for 1 week. Scan 3 shows evidence of some absorbed water particularly in the slight broadening of the low temperature shift and the evidence of a small endotherm whose maximum occurs around 110°C.

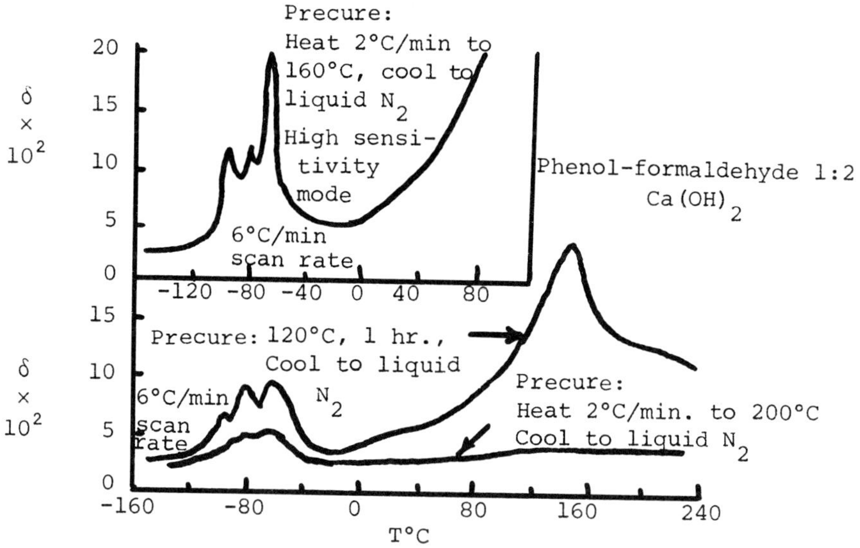

Fig. 10. The effect of cure on the dynamic mechanical loss peaks. Note for even high temperatures of cure (at rather slow heating rates) the low temperature peaks are still very evident. The sample must be heated to 200°C before a substantial drop in the loss peaks occurs. Note that in the high sensitivity mode(the elastic spring of the pendulum was removed) three peaks are apparent.

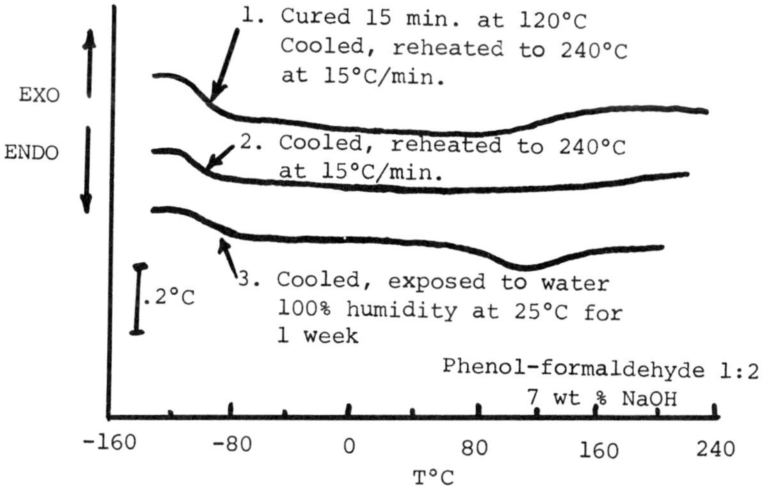

Fig. 11. The effect of water exposure for a highly cured 7 wt%NaOH resin. Note the endotherm at 70°C to 110°C and the broadened low temperature shift.

IV. DISCUSSION AND CONCLUSIONS

The DSC data obtained above ambient conditions essentially supports what has been previously observed in similar resin systems. What is of particular interest is the observation of the low temperature shift. Its magnitude is significant and it appears to be relatively unaffected by usual cure procedures, when the highest temperature is less than 160°C. Also what is of interest is that even in the most cured condition the shift can be observed and surprisingly two or three separate peaks can be ascertained from torsional braid analysis.

The question remains as to whether this low temperature peak is of water origin or not. If the resin is close to fully cured, these systems have mainly methylene bridges joining phenyl rings giving little chance for molecular mobility. However it has been previously noted that full cure of these resins is difficult and normal industrial cures for wood adhesives usually do not approach the long times and high temperatures used in this study. Therefore considerable molecular mobility must be occurring in these resin systems at ambient conditions.

Support for some polymer molecular mobility occurring in even highly cured systems is seen in data obtained from DSC measurements, fig. 3, for systems exposed to high temperatures, 240°C. Repeated scans do not appear to change the low temperature shift. The torsion pendulum data show peaks which are only reduced when temperatures above 160°C are maintained. The low temperature peak never appears to vanish completely. If water is the cause of such peaks, then it must be bound to a considerable extent to the resin. Since large amounts of caustic are involved in such resole systems then it would not be surprising that water could be maintained in the resin even at high temperatures.

In order to clarify whether this low temperature peak is due to molecular motion of the polymer network or of side groups it will be necessary to perform additional experiments with model compounds. It appears, however, that the low temperature shift, as well as torsional braid analysis, might be additional tools to sensitively monitor complete cure of phenolic resole resins and/or low levels of moisture content.

V. REFERENCES

1. S. Chow, Holzforschung 26,229 (1972).
2. M.Ezrin, and G.C. Claver, Appl. Polymer Symp. 8, 171 (1969).
3. Z. Katoviv, J. Appl. Polymer Sci. 11, 85(1967).
4. R. Burns, and E.W. Orrell, J. Mat. Sci. 2,72 (1967).
5. R.H. White, and T.F. Rust, J. Appl. Polymer Sci. 9,777 (1965).
6. Y. Nakamura, Kogyo Kagaku Zasshi 64, 392 (1961).
7. J.K. Gillham, AIChE J. 20,1066 (1974).

VI. ACKNOWLEDGMENTS

The authors gratefully thank the Forest Products Laboratory, Madison personnel, especially Drs. Robert Gillespie and George Myers for their stimulating discussions and help with this work. We would also like to thank Dr. Phillip Waitkus for providing the commercial resins used in this study.

PHOTOPOLYMERIZATION OF MULTIFUNCTIONAL ACRYLATES AND METHACRYLATES

James E. Moore
General Electric Research and Development Center

The recently described photocalorimetric technique has been extended to investigate isothermal photopolymerizations of a number of acrylate and methacrylate monomers in the differential scanning calorimeter. Relationships between monomer structure and extents and rates of polymerization have been examined.

Typically, acrylates show both high extents of conversion of monomer to polymer and high rates of polymerization while the corresponding methacrylates show both lower extents of conversion and much slower rates of polymerization. At 30°C, under the conditions employed, diacrylates of long chain glycols such as 1,6-hexanediol diacrylate and diethyleneglycol diacrylate are polymerized to fairly high extents (80 and 69%) and at high rates (14.8 and 19.8%/minute). The more highly functional, but more sterically hindered, trimethylolpropane triacrylate and pentaerythritol tetraacrylate polymerize to only 43 and 33% conversion at rates of 14.2 and 10.0%/minute.

The corresponding methacrylates hexanediol dimethacrylate and trimethylolpropane triacrylate polymerize to 65 and 39% conversion rates of 3.23 and 3.20%/minute.

Peroxides were used to initiate polymerizations which were thermally scanned from 30 to 250°C. As with the UV-initiated polymerizations conducted at lower temperatures, the thermally scanned polymerizations are restricted by monomer stereochemistry.

I. INTRODUCTION

Investigations of multifunctional acrylic polymerizations have been conducted for some time (1-5). Ethyleneglycol dimethacrylate (EGDMA) has been the monomer most often used in these studies. Loshaek and Fox (1) used dilatometric techniques to study thermal polymerizations of EGDMA, decamethyleneglycol dimethacrylate (DMGDMA), neopentylglycol dimethacrylate (NPGDMA), and 2-ethyl,2-butylpropanediol dimethacrylate (2-E,2-B PDMA). McGinnis and Holsworth (5) used a dilatometric method to study the photopolymerization of EGDMA. The same method was used by McGinnis and Ting (4) for their study of commercially available acrylates such as hexanediol diacrylate (HDDA), trimethylolpropane triacrylate (TMPTA), and pentaerythritol triacrylate (PET_3A). Horie et al (3) introduced calorimetric techniques to the study of thermally activated EGDMA polymerizations. Moore et al (7) have extended the calorimetric technique to the measurement of the extent of polymerization of HDDA, neopentylglycol diacrylate (NPGDA), and trimethylolpropane triacrylate (TMPTA) activated by both photochemical and thermal initiators. The calorimetric investigations described in this paper extend our earlier polymerization studies to include a comparison of a number of multifunctional acrylates and the corresponding methacrylates.

II. EXPERIMENTAL

A. Materials

Acrylic monomers were obtained from commercial sources and were used as received. The monomers used and the abbreviations used for them are listed in Table 1. The initiators, Trigonal 14 (Noury Chemical Corporation; a mixture of butyl benzoin ethers), benzoyl peroxide (Fisher Scientific) and t-butyl perbenzoate (Lucidol) were also used as received.

B. Apparatus

Polymerizations were conducted in both the modified Perkin-Elmer DSC-1B and DSC-2 described in References 6 and 7 (Figure 1). The UV light source was a 400 watt H3T7 medium pressure mercury arc lamp which gave an intensity of about 57.2 mW/cm^2 at the sample pan.

C. Procedure

Monomers used in the photopolymerization studies contained one part by weight of Trigonal 14 in 100 parts of monomer. The thermal polymerizations were initiated by one part of benzoyl peroxide and one part of t-butyl perbenzoate in

TABLE I

Abbreviations for Monomers Used in Text

Lauryl Acrylate	LA
2-Ethylhexyl Acrylate	EHA
2-Hydroxyethyl Acrylate	HEA
Ethyleneglycol Diacrylate	EGDA
1,3-Butanediol Diacrylate	BGDA
1,6-Hexanediol Diacrylate	HDDA
Decamethyleneglycol Diacrylate	DMGDA
Neopentylglycol Diacrylate	NPGDA
Diethyleneglycol Diacrylate	DEGDA
Tetraethyleneglycol Diacrylate	TEGDA
Trimethylolpropane Triacrylate	TMPTA
Pentaerythritol Tetraacrylate	PET_4A
Lauryl Methacrylate	LMA
2-Hydroxyethyl Methacrylate	HEMA
Ethyleneglycol Dimethacrylate	EGDMA
1,6-Hexanediol Dimethacrylate	HDDMA
Neopentylglycol Dimethacrylate	NPGDMA
Tetraethyleneglycol Dimethacrylate	TEGDMA
Trimethylolpropane Trimethacrylate	TMPTMA

100 parts of monomer.

Photopolymerizations were conducted isothermally at 30 and 50°C in the modified calorimeters using ordinary open aluminum DSC sample pans containing 0.5 to 10 milligrams of sample. Base lines for the polymerization curves were obtained by extrapolating from the final flat portions of the curves.

Thermally activated polymerizations were conducted in sealed volatile sample pans. These were thermally scanned at 20°C/min from 30 to 250°C. A base line for the thermal scan was obtained by a second thermal scan of the reacted material over the same temperature range. Curve area integrations were achieved by duplicating the curves, cutting, and weighing. A calibrated area was used as a reference standard for each curve.

III. RESULTS

A. Acrylates

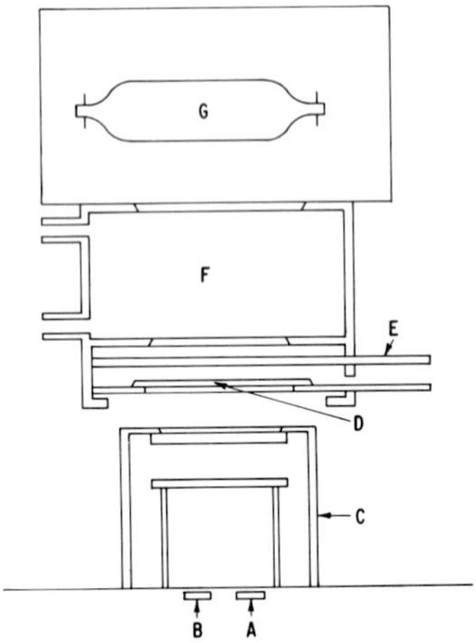

Fig. 1. Modified DSC Apparatus. (A) Sample Holder; (B) Reference Holder; (C) Sample Holder Cover; (D) Neutral Density Filter; (E) Shutter; (F) Heat Filter; (G) UV Lamp.

The heats of polymerization of a number of acrylate monomers are listed in Table 2. The values for percentage conversion of double bonds and average number of double bonds reacted are based on the value of 20.6 Kcal/mole determined for the thermal polymerization of lauryl acrylate in this study.

The maximum rates of polymerization of the various acrylates were calculated from the maximum heights of the exotherm curves and are listed in Table 3. This table also includes the times required for conversion of 50% of the monomer double bonds and the monomer order as determined from a log-log plot of polymerization rate versus monomer concentration (7) for polymerizations conducted at 50°C.

B. Methacrylates

The heats of polymerization of the methacrylate monomers are listed in Table 4. The values for percentage conversion of double bonds and average number of double bonds reacted are based on the 13.6 Kcal/mole determined for the thermal polymerization of lauryl methacrylate in this study. This value agrees well with the heat of polymerization of

TABLE 2

Heat of Polymerization of Acrylate Monomers

	Monomer	ΔHp Kcal/ C=C	% Reaction	Average No. of C=C· Bonds Reacted	Reference 7 % Reaction
Thermal Scans	LA	20.6	100	1.00	100
	HEA	19.5	94.7	0.947	-
	EGDA	17.7	85.9	1.72	-
	BGDA	16.7	81.1	1.62	-
	HDDA	18.9	91.7	1.83	91.7
	DMGDA	18.7	90.8	1.82	-
	NPGDA	17.3	84.0	1.68	87.0
	DEGDA	20.0	97.1	1.94	-
	TEGDA	20.5	99.5	1.99	-
	TMPTA	16.2	78.6	2.36	80.2
	PET_4A	14.0	68.0	2.72	-
Photopolymerizations at 30°C	LA	16.2	78.6	0.786	90.6
	EHA	18.8	91.3	0.913	-
	HEA	18.2	88.3	0.883	-
	EGDA	12.8	62.1	1.24	-
	BGDA	12.6	61.2	1.22	-
	HDDA	16.4	79.6	1.59	60.9
	DMGDA	-	-	-	-
	NPGDA	11.8	57.3	1.15	42.7
	DEGDA	14.3	69.4	1.39	-
	TEGDA	17.0	82.5	1.65	-
	TMPTA	8.8	42.7	1.28	47.4
	PET_4A	6.7	32.5	1.30	-
Photopolymerizations at 50°C	LA	17.6	85.4	0.854	-
	EHA	17.1	83.0	0.83	-
	HEA	18.7	90.8	0.908	-
	EGDA	14.2	68.9	1.38	-
	BGDA	13.7	66.5	1.33	-
	HDDA	16.4	79.6	1.59	86.5
	DMGDA	15.0	72.8	1.46	-
	NPGDA	12.5	60.6	1.21	50.5
	DEGDA	18.7	90.8	1.82	-
	TEGDA	16.9	82.0	1.64	-
	TMPTA	10.7	51.9	1.56	53.1
	PET_4A	8.0	38.8	1.55	-

TABLE 3

Acrylate Photopolymerization Rates

Monomer	*Polym. Temp(°C)*	*Polym. Rate (%/Sec)*	*Ref. 4 Relative Polym. Rates*	*Time for 50% React. (Sec)*	*Monomer Order*	*Ea (Kcal/mole)*
LA	30	2.51	-	-	-	
EHA	30	1.73	1.99			
HEA	30	13.9	3.52	-	-	
EGDA	30	12.5	-	-	-	
BGDA	30	11.7	-	-	-	
HDDA	30	14.8	1.04	-	-	
NPGDA	30	9.6	-	-	-	
DEGDA	30	19.8	1.40	-	-	
TEGDA	30	22.1	-	-	-	
TMPTA	30	14.2	1.00	-	-	
PET_4A	30	10.0	-	-	-	
LA	50	4.21		17.7	1.18	5.04
EHA	50	2.21				
HEA	50	25.7		6.5	1.54	5.98
EGDA	50	22.4		3.9	2.14	5.68
BGDA	50	25.2		4.3	2.95	7.47
HDDA	50	23.2		4.3	2.92	4.38
DGMDA	50	22.5		5.6	1.97	-
NPGDA	50	22.0		4.3	2.18	8.08
DEGDA	50	29.7		3.5	3.48	3.95
TEGDA	50	30.3		2.9	2.47	3.07
TMPTA	50	17.1		5.2	2.65	1.81
PET_4A	50	14.5		5.7	2.19	3.62

methyl methacrylate (13.1 Kcal/mole) determined calorimetrically by Horie et al (8) and at 13.2 Kcal/mole determined by Malavisic et al (9).

Table 5 contains the maximum polymerization rates calculated for the methacrylate polymerizations. It also gives examples of times required for 50% double bond conversion and of monomer order as determined from the final part of the log-log plots of polymerization rate versus monomer concentration.

IV. DISCUSSION

TABLE 4

Heats of Polymerization of Methacrylate Monomers

	Monomer	ΔHp Kcal/ C=C	% Reaction	Average No. of C=C Bonds Reacted	Reference 1 % Reaction
Thermal Scan	LMA	13.6	100	1.00	-
	HEMA	-	-	-	-
	EGDMA	12.4	91.2	1.82	64
	HDDMA	-	-	-	-
	NPGDMA	12.5	91.9	1.84	67
	TEGDMA	-	-	-	-
	TMPTMA	10.9	80.1	2.40	-
Photopolymerization at 30°C	LMA	Too slow to measure			
	HEMA	9.94	73.1	.731	
	EGDMA	7.16	52.6	1.05	82[5]
	HDDMA	8.79	64.6	1.29	
	NPGDMA	7.03	51.7	1.03	
	TEGDMA	10.1	74.3	1.49	
	TMPTMA	5.29	38.9	1.17	
Photopolymerization at 50°C	LMA	Too slow to measure			
	HEMA	10.4	76.5	.765	
	EGDMA	7.43	54.6	1.09	
	HDDMA	8.92	65.6	1.21	
	NPGDMA	7.02	51.6	1.03	
	TEGDMA	10.8	79.4	1.59	
	TMPTMA	5.54	40.7	1.22	

A. Acrylates

Typical exotherm plots of the fast acrylate polymerizations are illustrated in Figure 2. Most of the polyacrylate photopolymerizations are so fast that samples of less than one milligram had to be used in our apparatus in order to avoid overloading the cooling capacity of the calorimeter.

It is apparent from Table 2 that photopolymerizations of many of the polyfunctional acrylates fall far short of completion. The acrylates of long chain glycols (HDDA, DMGDA, DEGDA, and TEGDA) give the highest conversions, while acrylates of the more highly functional, but more sterically hindered, polyols (TMPTA and PET_4A) give the lowest conversions. The same trends are noted in the thermal

TABLE 5

Methacrylate Photopolymerization Rates

Monomer	*Polym. Temp (°C)*	*Polym. Rate (%/Sec)*	*Time for 50% React. (Sec)*	*Monomer Order*	*Ea (Kcal/ mole)*
LMA	30°	Too slow to measure			
HEMA	30°	4.25	-	-	
EGDMA	30°	2.11	-	-	
HDDMA	30°	3.23	-	-	
NPGDMA	30°	2.79	-	-	
TEGDMA	30°	6.64	25.6	1.97	
TMPTMA	30°	3.24	-	-	
LMA	50°	Too slow to measure			
HEMA	50°	6.41	85	2.31	4.00
EGDMA	50°	3.16	-	-	3.93
HDDMA	50°	4.52	-	-	3.27
NPGDMA	50°	3.81	-	-	3.03
TEGDMA	50°	11.1	20.6	1.91	5.00
TMPTMA	50°	4.19	-	-	2.50

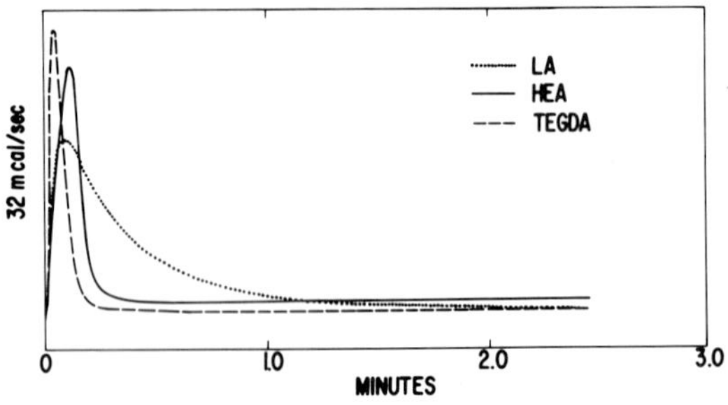

Fig. 2. Exotherm Plots of Acrylate Photopolymerizations at 50°C.

polymerizations.

The acrylate photopolymerization curves indicate a uniform fast conversion throughout the polymerization. If the polymerizations are going through a Tromsdorff acceleration, this effect has taken place before the system has come to equilibrium conditions. The maximum polymerization rates usually occurred within 5 seconds of opening the light shutter and at relatively low conversions. The acrylate polymerization rates (Table 3) show no obvious dependence on the monomer structure. The monofunctional LA shows a considerably lower rate than the polyfunctional acrylates, but the monofunctional HEA shows a rate similar to the polyfunctional acrylates. One point to note is that the diacrylates of the polyethylene glycols (DEGDA and TEGDA) consistently show the highest conversion rates. The relative polymerization rates obtained by McGinnis and Ting (4) are included in Table 3 for comparison. The rates determined by McGinnis and Ting are similar to those determined in this work. McGinnis and Ting polymerized relatively large samples in a polyolefin bag which was surrounded by water in a glass hypodermic syringe, while the results described in this paper are for small samples exposed to nitrogen. The differences in experimental procedures may account for any differences in results obtained by the two methods.

The monomer orders of 1.2 to 3.5 listed in Table 3 are higher than would be predicted by a simple kinetic scheme, but are in line with the values of 1.5 to 2.8 for acrylates cited by Scott and Senogles (10).

B. Methacrylates

Typical exotherm plots of methacrylate polymerizations are illustrated in Figure 3. The much slower rates of the

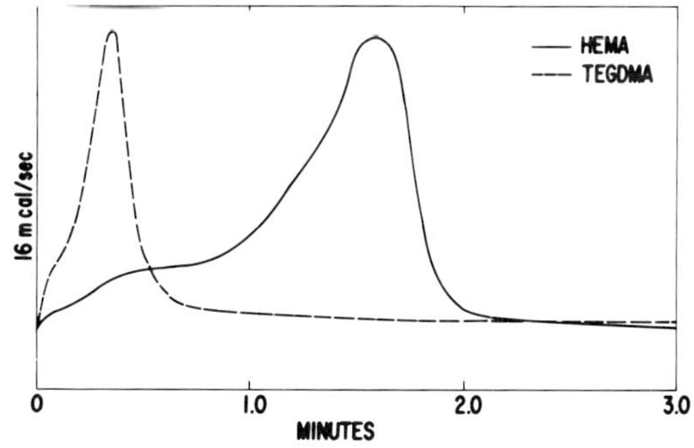

Fig. 3. Exotherm Plots of Methacrylate Photopolymerizations at 50°C.

methacrylate polymerizations make it possible to use larger samples than with the acrylates and also to use increased sensitivity ranges on the calorimeter. The complex shapes of the curves with a rate acceleration following the initial conversion rate indicate acceleration due to the Tromsdorff effect. It is apparent from Figure 3 that the Tromsdorff effect takes place at different degrees of conversion with different monomers.

The heats of polymerization of the various polyfunctional methacrylate monomers listed in Table 4 show again the difficulty of obtaining complete polymerization. As expected, the highest conversions are obtained from the dimethacrylates of the long chain flexible glycols (HDDMA and TEGDMA) and the lowest conversion is from the highly functional and highly sterically hindered TMPTMA.

The extent of polymerization of EGDMA has been determined by Losaek and Fox (1) to be 64%, and by McGinnis and Holsworth (5) to be 82%. Hoire et al (3) used the calorimetric technique and found the conversion to be 69% at 80°C. The results for the isothermal photopolymerizations described here agree well with the results of previous workers, but the results of the thermally scanned polymerization are higher than those described previously.

In comparing Tables 2 and 4, it is apparent that at a given temperature the methacrylates do not polymerize to as great an extent as the corresponding acrylates. The polyfunctional methacrylates would be expected to have higher glass temperatures (Tg) than the acrylates, thus polymerizations conducted below the Tg would reach limiting conversions in the methacrylates sooner than in the acrylates. (See Flory (11) pp. 127 and 128.)

Methacrylate photopolymerization rate measurements are complicated by the Tromsdorff effect. The rates listed in Table 5 are the maxima obtained after the Tromsdorff acceleration. These rates vary considerably among themselves with the polyethyleneglycol ester, TEGDMA, again showing the highest conversion rate. The acrylate photopolymerization rates are three to seven times faster than the corresponding methacrylates. The times required for 50% conversion and monomer orders were calculated for HEMA and TEGDMA and are also listed in Table 5. The acrylate polymerization rates are about 7 to 13 times faster than the methacrylate rates by these calculations also.

V. SUMMARY

The differential scanning calorimeter has been used to study both thermal and photopolymerizations of various mono, di, and polyfunctional acrylate and methacrylate monomers. Heats of photopolymerization of the acrylates vary from 10.7 to 18.7 Kcal/double bond at 50°C, while the heats of photopolymerization of the corresponding methacrylates vary from 5.54 to 10.8 Kcal/double bond. From these heats of polymerization, conversions of the various monomers have been calculated based on the thermal heats of polymerization of lauryl acrylate (20.6 Kcal/mole) and lauryl methacrylate (13.6 Kcal/mole).

The polymerization rates, times required for 50% monomer conversion, and monomer orders were calculated for the various monomers. Tetraethyleneglycol diacrylate and tetraethyleneglycol dimethacrylate gave the highest conversions and photopolymerization rates of the acrylates and methacrylates.

VI. ACKNOWLEDGMENTS

I wish to thank my colleagues S. H. Schroeter, A. R. Shultz, and L. D. Stang for many helpful discussions during the progress of this work. I also thank O. V. Orkin for obtaining infrared data which corroborated extents of conversion of the acrylate monomers.

VII. REFERENCES

1. S. Loshaek and T. G Fox, J. Am. Chem. Soc. 75, 3544 (1953).
2. V. D. McGinnis, R. M. Holsworth, and D. M. Dusek, ACS Coating and Plastics Preprints 34, (1) 669 (1974).
3. K. Horie, A. Otagawa, M. Muraoka, and I. Mita, J. Poly. Sci. Chem. 13, 445 (1975).
4. V. D. McGinnis and V. W. Ting, J. Rad. Curing, Jan. 1975, 14.
5. V. D. McGinnis and R. M. Holsworth, J. Appl. Poly. Sci. 19, 2243 (1975).
6. J. E. Moore, S. H. Schroeter, and A. R. Shultz, ACS Coating and Plastics Preprints 35, Vol 1, 239 (1975).
7. S. S. Labana, Ultraviolet Light Induced Reactions in Polymers, p. 90, Am. Chem. Soc. Symposium Series 25, Washington, D.C.
8. K. Horie, I. Mita, and H. Kambe, J. Poly. Sci. A-1 6, 2263 (1968).

9. T. Malavasic, I. Visovisek, S. Lapange, and A. Moze, Die Macromol. Chem. 175, 873 (1974).
10. G. E. Scott and E. Senogles, J. Macromol. Sci-Chem. A8 (4) 753 (1974).
11. P. J. Flory, "Principles of Polymer Chemistry", Cornell University, Ithaca, New York.

CHARACTERIZATION OF ANISOTROPIC MOTIONAL PHENOMENA IN POLYMERIC MATERIALS WITH MULTIPLE PULSE NMR

C. R. Dybowski and R. W. Vaughan
California Institute of Technology

The capabilities of the multiple pulse NMR techniques to characterize non-isotropic motion in a series of polymeric materials are demonstrated and discussed. The materials examined include: a natural gum sample of cis-polyisoprene and a carbon-filled, sulfur-vulcanized sample of the cis-polyisoprene, a cis-1,4-polybutadiene, and a model membrane material, dipalmitoyl lecithin.

I. INTRODUCTION

The use of nuclear magnetic resonance (NMR) to study the nature of molecular motions and interactions within polymeric materials has a long history (1-3). In particular, conventional measurements of line shapes, second moments and T_2's, and spin lattice relaxation rates, T_1 and $T_{1\rho}$'s, have been used to determine correlation times for molecular motion. However, both the line shapes and relaxation times observed in the presence of anisotropic or restricted motion can be complicated. The line shapes can be a function of several contributing Hamiltonians, and, in general, no means of sorting out and characterizing these various contributions to the line shapes has been developed. Consequently, much of the inherent information on the local physical and chemical environments within the polymeric material is not extractable from conventional NMR measurements. In this paper, it is demonstrated that the use of multiple pulse NMR techniques allows one to separately characterize various contributions to proton NMR spectra and thus extract more information on the local environment within the polymer (4).

The multiple pulse NMR techniques involve the repetitive application of periodic and cyclic pulse sequences to modify the time development of the spin system. Specific pulse cycles have been developed to reduce the effects of the static dipolar interaction (5-7). However, the presence of molecular motion interferes with the averaging effects of the pulse sequence, and, as the rate of molecular motion increases and approaches the time scale of the pulse sequence, the effectiveness of such a pulse cycle is expected to decrease and the line width begins to grow (8,9). In contrast, the effect of increasing molecular motion on the conventional NMR spectra of solids is to narrow the spectral lines as the time scale of the molecular motion approaches the inverse line width of the dipolar broadened spectra. If the molecular motion is isotropic, further increases in its frequency will effectively average the secular portion of the dipolar Hamiltonian to zero, and there is no need for a pulse sequence to remove static dipolar interactions. Consequently, most multiple pulse NMR studies to date have been of rigid solids and there has been no extensive use of the line-narrowing pulse cycles in cases involving molecular motion. However, if the molecular motion is not isotropic, very rapid motions may be present which do not average the secular portion of the dipolar Hamiltonian to zero and substantial benefit can accrue from the use of line-narrowing pulse sequences. The line shape observed in the case of restricted or anisotropic motion can be a complicated function of the effects of the molecular motion on the several contributing Hamiltonians; it will be demonstrated that, by performing several separate but related multiple pulse NMR measurements, it is possible to separate and determine the individual contributions to the line shape of protons in such a sample. This can be of considerable advantage in studies of molecular dynamics of motionally ordered systems such as polymers, liquid crystals, and ordered biological materials, as well as molecules moving on surfaces.

II. EXPERIMENTAL DETAILS

The measurements reported here were performed on a spectrometer operating at 56.4 MHz, which has been described in detail elsewhere (10). Measurements involved conventional transient free-induction decay and T_1 measurements and multiple pulse measurements using an eight-pulse cycle. A series of previous papers has described the eight-pulse sequence in detail (7,11,12), and the reader is referred particularly to reference (12) for a detailed analysis of the effects of this sequence. Three different eight-pulse sequence measurements were made, one in the conventional fashion and two in which the eight-pulse sequence was modified by introducing a phase error in the P_x pulse. This produced the additional zeroth order Hamiltonian (12)

$$\bar{H}_p^{(o)} = \frac{2}{t_c} (\phi_{-x} - \phi_x) I_y$$

which has the effect of removing the effects of chemical shift and magnetic field inhomogeneities from the spectra. Our previously published discussion (12) clearly demonstrates that this scheme should be appropriate for the small chemical shift anisotropies found in proton spectra. Two versions of this modified eight-pulse experiment were performed, one (P_x - M_y) involving the use of a P_x prepulse and observation of the y component of the precessing magnetization, M_y, and a second ($-M_x$) involving no prepulse and observation of the x component of the precessing magnetization, M_x. The rigorous analysis of the effect of these two modified eight-pulse sequences is being published elsewhere but can be summarized simply, if not completely precisely, by recognizing that the eight-pulse sequence has three major contributions: a second-order dipolar, a chemical shift, and a relaxation term. The effects of any field inhomogeneities are included in the chemical shift term and other small instrumental effects are being ignored here. In the ($-M_x$) version of the phase-altered eight-pulse sequence, the chemical shift term has been removed, while in the (P_x - M_y) version, both the chemical shift and the second-order dipolar terms do not contribute to the line shape. Thus, one has three experiments and three unknowns and, in principle, is able, from the results of the three measurements, to separately characterize each of the dipolar, chemical shift, and relaxation contributions. In addition, the free-induction decay line shape is available and contains additional information, basically the full dipolar interaction and the chemical shift term and thus, by combining that information with the multiple pulse results, additional information of the dipolar interaction can be extracted as well.

III. RESULTS AND DISCUSSION

The utility of these NMR techniques is demonstrated by a set of experiments on several simple polymers: samples of cis-polyisoprene, natural gum rubber, and a carbon-filled, sulfur-vulcanized sample of the cis-polyisoprene (4), cis-1,4-polybutadiene, and a model membrane material, dipalmitoyl lecithin.

Figure 1 illustrates the room temperature free-induction decay and eight-pulse spectrum for the natural gum sample of cis-polyisoprene. As can be seen, the free-induction decay

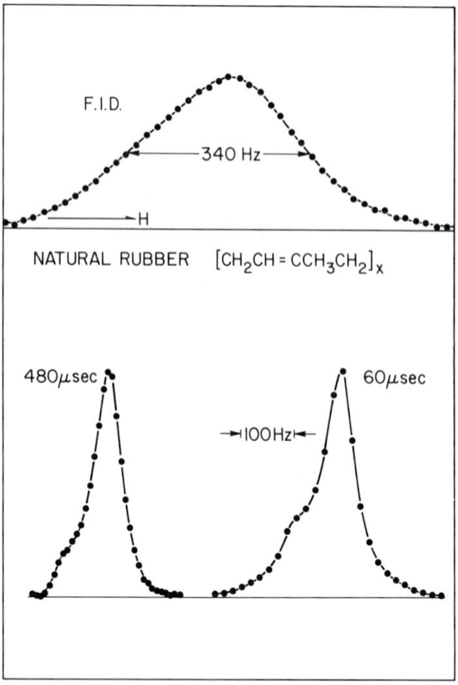

Fig. 1. Free-induction and eight-pulse spectra of natural rubber. The eight-pulse spectra were taken at two cycle times, 60 and 480 μsec. (From C. R. Dybowski and R. W. Vaughan, Macromolecules 8, 50 (1975), copyright by the American Chemical Society.)

spectrum is slightly asymmetric, hinting at the presence of fine structure on the line, and its width of 340 Hz indicates a substantial amount of molecular motion is present. A two-peaked spectrum is observed in the multiple pulse spectrum, and the small shoulder peak can be associated with the chemically shifted proton bonded to the vinyl carbon. In order to determine what portion of the eight-pulse line shape is due to chemical shift, the ($-M_x$) version of the phase-altered eight-pulse sequence was performed, and Figure 2 is a plot of the decay envelope obtained. The decay is exponential within experimental error with a time constant of 17 msec, and thus a combination of higher-order dipolar and relaxation terms would produce a line of only 20 Hz in width. This can be treated as a broadening function and can be deconvoluted from the normal eight-pulse spectrum and the remainder attributed to superposition of partially motionally averaged chemical shift powder patterns for the chemically inequivalent protons present in the sample. Although it will

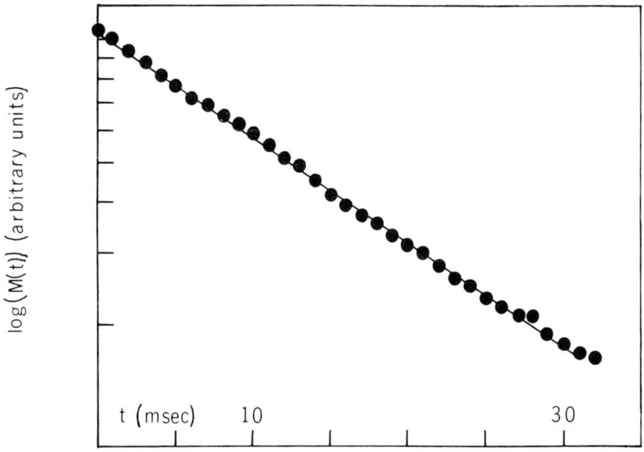

Fig. 2. Plot of decay envelope of the ($-M_X$) phase-altered eight-pulse spectrum in Fig. 1. (From C. R. Dybowski and R. W. Vaughan, Macromolecules 8, 50 (1975), copyright by the American Chemical Society.)

not be discussed in this paper, further detailed analysis of this spectrum furnishes information on the anisotropic nature of the motional processes present. It will only be noted here that by calculating the second moment of the deconvoluted eight-pulse spectrum, one obtains the chemical shift contribution to the second moment of the free-induction decay, 1.9 ppm^2 or 11,200 Hz^2. The second moment of the free-induction decay spectrum in Figure 1 is near 23,700 Hz^2 and, when corrected for the chemical shift contribution, one obtains a secular dipolar contribution of 12,500 Hz^2. Information on the anisotropic and restricted nature of the molecular motion present in the sample can be obtained from the size of the secular dipolar contribution and the fact that it can be removed by application of the eight-pulse cycle. For instance, ability to remove the dipolar contribution implies that over the time relevant to eight-pulse cycles used (see Figure 1), it is an effectively static quantity and is thus due to anisotropic or restricted motion. One can therefore, define an order parameter for this system as the square root of the ratio of the second moment of secular dipolar contribution to the rigid lattice second moment (3.26×10^8 Hz^2) (13) and obtain a value of 0.006 for natural rubber at room temperature. This order parameter is a measure of the freedom of the spins on the polymer to move in the hindering potential of the polymer network.

These same series of measurements were performed at room temperature on the carbon-filled, sulfur-vulcanized rubber and on a multiple-layer sample of dipalmitoyl lecithin.[1] Of particular interest are the results of the $(-M_X)$ phase-altered eight-pulse sequence. Figure 3 illustrates the $(-M_X)$ for the carbon-filled, sulfur-vulcanized rubber sample and demonstrates that it is possible to fit the observed decay with a sum of two exponentials.

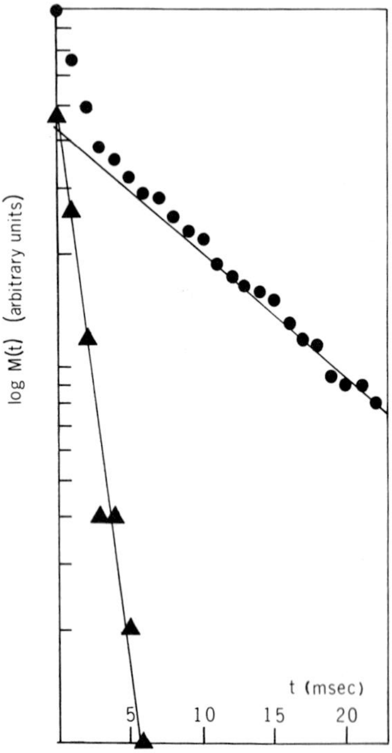

Fig. 3. Plot of decay envelope of the $(-M_X)$ phase-altered eight-pulse spectrum of the carbon-filled, sulfur-vulcanized rubber sample. The long triangles represent the difference between the line fitting the long-time behavior and the experimental points. (From C. R. Dybowski and R. W. Vaughan, Macromolecules 8, 50 (1975), copyright by the American Chemical Society.)

---

[1]The dipalmitoyl lecithin sample used in this work was furnished by G. W. Feigenson, C. H. Seiter, and S. I. Chan. For discussions of experimental and theoretical efforts to understand the non-isotropic motion in this material the reader is referred to: G. W. Feigenson and S. I. Chan, JACS 96, 1312 (1974); C. H. A. Seiter and S. I. Chan, ibid. 95, 7541 (1973); and to a review submitted to Biochem. by N. O. Peterson and S. I. Chan as well as references therein.

Similar results were obtained for the dipalmitoyl lecithin sample as illustrated in Figure 4, and the time constants for the ($-M_x$) decay envelopes are reported in Table I for all three samples. The relative intensities of the exponential

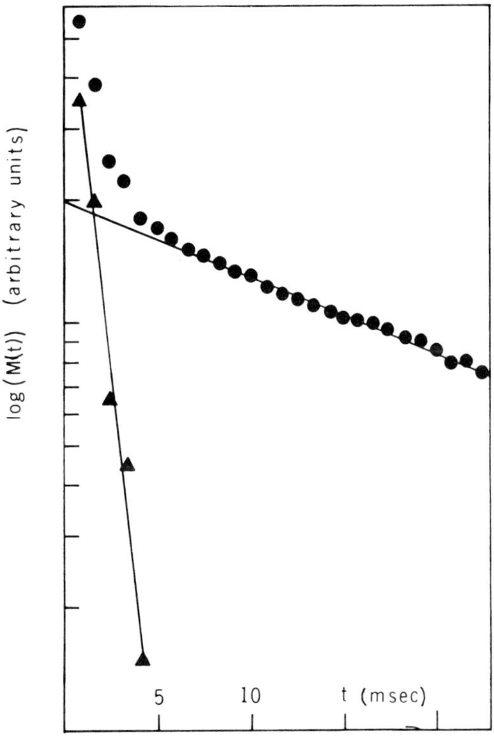

Fig. 6. Plot of decay envelope of the ($-M_x$) phase altered eight-pulse spectrum of a multilayer dipalmitoyl lecithin sample. The triangles represent the difference between the line fitting the long-time behavior and the experimental points at short times.

decays are also reported, indicating what fraction of protons could be responsible for each decay. Table I also shows what fraction of the protons in each sample are in terminal methyl groups and what fraction of the protons are directly attached to a backbone carbon. One notes a good correspondence of the relative intensity of the long decay and the fraction of

Table I

	Long decay constant (msec)	Short decay constant (msec)	% methyl	% long decay
Gum rubber	17 ± 2	---		
Carbon-filled rubber	14 ± 2	1.5	38	∿40
Dipalmitoyl lecithin	22 ± 4	1.0	23	∿20

methyl protons in the samples. While the simple correspondence of the relative intensities of the two decays to the ratio of methyl to backbone protons is not alone justification to associate the observed decay constants with these groups, there are other reasons to expect the methyl and backbone protons to behave in the observed fashion. The damping constant under the influence of the mlutiple pulse sequences is expected to be partially sensitive to motions near the cycle frequency, $2\pi/t_c$, and the cooperativity associated with cross linking is expected to enhance the power spectrum in this region. The methyl groups are attached to the molecular frame at only a single point and thus have substantially more freedom of motion than the backbone protons (which are on carbons which are an integral part of the molecular frame), and their frequency spectrum would be altered less by the cross-linking process. Thus one would expect a larger decrease in the decay constant for backbone protons than for the methyl protons under the influence of the multiple pulse sequence. The correspondence of the experimental fractions to the calculated fractions supports this argument.

Figures 5 and 6 illustrate partial results of applying these techniques to a cis-polybutadiene sample.[2] This sample gives evidence (14-16) of going through a chain-ordering transition near 0°C and has been studied recently in order to attempt to characterize the motional processes present (16-21), including recent efforts to characterize non-isotropic motion with sample spinning and solid echo NMR techniques (20,21). Figure 4 illustrates the effect of the

[2]The cis-1,4-polybutadiene sample used for this work was furnished by Rudolph Lenk, and we wish to acknowledge Dr. Lenk's collaboration on the work on this sample.

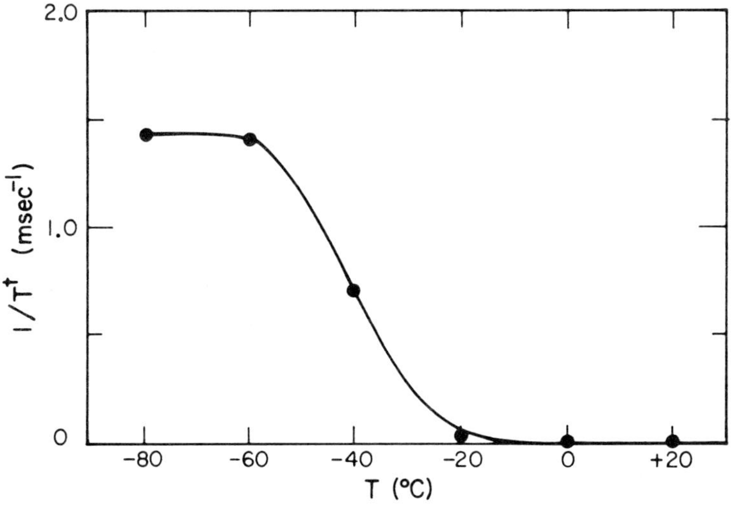

Fig. 5. The inverse of the time required for the decay from the ($-M_x$) phase-altered eight-pulse sequence to reach 1/e of its initial value on a sample of cis-polybutadiene as a function of temperature.

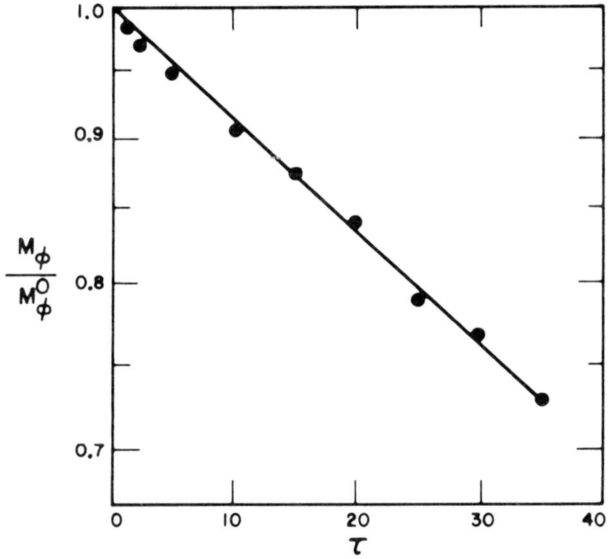

Fig. 6. Decay observed in cis-polybutadiene for the (P_x - M_y) phase-altered eight-pulse cycle performed at room temperature. The decay amplitude has been normalized to its initial value.

development of longer-range cooperative motions within the polymer on the ($-M_x$) phase-altered eight-pulse decay envelopes. The inverse of the time, T^+, for the ($-M_x$) signals to decay to 1/e of the initial values has been plotted as a function of temperature, and clearly a transition region appears just below 0° C. Of some considerable interest is the fact that the decays observed were not all exponential; the 0° C and 20° C decays (near the onset of the chain ordering) were convex on a plot of ln (amplitude) vs. time. The (P_x - M_y) sequence was performed on the sample at 20° C, and the results are illustrated in Figure 5. The (P_x - M_y) decay has a decay constant greater than 120 msec compared to about 30 msec for the ($-M_x$) decay, thus demonstrating that the ($-M_x$) decay was primarily due to the higher-order dipolar term and not to spin-lattice effects. One can explain such convex decays by the presence of "memory" or correlation persistence of cooperative fluctuations of the polymer chains at these temperatures (15-18), and a more quantitative explanation based on these ideas is presently being pursued.

IV. SUMMARY AND CONCLUSIONS

An attempt has been made through several different examples to demonstrate the potential utility of the multiple pulse NMR techniques for studies of molecular motion in polymeric materials. Only partial results of several studies are reported here. The results on the natural rubber presented here can be compared with previous results of proton NMR studies of natural rubber (13,22,23) where it was only possible to speculate on the presence of non-isotropic motional phenomena and with ^{13}C studies (24-26) where indication of non-isotropic motion was suggested. The work presented here has required a minimum of experimental results, and these results have been subjected to only a crude analysis at this point. By performing the multiple pulse NMR measurements as a function of various experimental parameters, particularly those which determine the time domain in which motional processes are studied, the cycle times, the radio frequency field levels, and the resonance frequency, as well as collection of data as a function of temperature, coupled with a more complete theoretical analysis, it will be possible to obtain a more complete characterization of the complex motion found in such systems as these.

V. ACKNOWLEDGMENT

This work was supported in part by the National Science Foundation and the donors of the Petroleum Research Fund, administrated by the American Chemical Society. In addition, support received from the Camille and Henry Dreyfus Foundation is gratefully acknowledged. S. I. Chan and G. W. Feigenson kindly furnished the dipalymitoyl lecithin sample, and we wish to acknowledge the collaboration of Rudolf Lenk on the cis-1,4-polybutadiene work.

VI. REFERENCES

1. D. W. McCall, in "Molecular Dynamics and Structure of Solids" (R. S. Carter and J. J. Rush, Eds.), pp. 475-537. National Bureau of Standards Special Publication #301, U. S. Government Printing Office, Washington, D.C., 1969.
2. W. P. Slichter, in "NMR Basic Principle and Progress" (P. Diehl, E. Fluck, and R. Kosfeld, Eds.), Vol. 4, pp. 209-232. Springer-Verlay, Berlin, 1971.
3. I. Y. Slonim and A. N. Lyubimov (trans. from the Russian by C. N. Turton and T. I. Turton), "The NMR of Polymers," Plenum Press, New York, 1970.
4. C. R. Dybowski and R. W. Vaughan, Macromolecules 8, 50 (1975).
5. J. S. Waugh, L. M. Huber, and U. Haeberlen, Phys. Rev. Lett. 20, 180 (1968); U. Haeberlen and J. S. Waugh, Phys. Rev. 175, 453 (1968).
6. P. Mansfield, J. Phys. C. 4, 1444 (1971).
7. W.-K. Rhim, D. D. Elleman, and R. W. Vaughan, J. Chem. Phys. 59, 3740 (1973).
8. U. Haeberlen and J. S. Waugh, Phys. Rev. 185, 420 (1969).
9. H. Schmiedel, D. Freude, and W. Grunder, Phys. Lett. A 34, 162 (1971); W. Grunder, H. Schmiedel, and D. Freude, Ann. Phys. (Leipzig) 27, 409 (1971).
10. R. W. Vaughan, D. D. Elleman, L. M. Stacey, W.-K. Rhim, and J. W. Lee, Rev. Sci. Instrum. 43, 1356 (1972).
11. W.-K. Rhim, D. D. Elleman, and R. W. Vaughan, J. Chem. Phys. 58, 1772 (1973).
12. W.-K. Rhim, D. D. Elleman, L. B. Schreiber, and R. W. Vaughan, J. Chem. Phys. 60, 4595 (1974).
13. H. S. Gutowsky, A. Saika, M. Takeda, and D. E. Woessner, J. Chem. Phys. 27, 534 (1957).
14. G. Natta and P. Corradini, Nuovo Cimento 15, suppl. 1, 31 (1960).
15. F. S. Dainton, D. M. Evans, F. E. Hoare, and T. P. Milia, Polymer 3, 297 (1962).
16. Y. Martin-Borret, J. P. Cohen-Addad, and J. P. Messa, J. Chem. Phys. 58, 1700 (1973).
17. R. Lenk, Physica 60, 159 (1972).
18. R. Lenk and J. P. Cohen-Addad, Solid State Comm. 8, 1869 (1970).

19. J. P. Cohen-Addad and M. Battezzati, J. Chem. Phys. 58, 3717 (1973).
20. J. P. Cohen-Addad, J. Chem. Phys. 63, 4880 (1975); ibid. 64, 3438 (1976).
21. J. P. Cohen-Addad and C. Rody, J. Chem. Phys. 63, 3095 (1975).
22. W. P. Slichter and D. D. Davis, J. Appl. Phys. 34, 998 (1963).
23. D. W. McCall and D. R. Falcone, Trans. Faraday Soc. 66, 262 (1970).
24. See, for example, (a) J. Schaefer, Macromolecules 6, 882 (1973); (b) F. A. Bovey, "High Resolution NMR of Macromolecules," Academic Press, New York, 1972.
25. J. Schaefer, S. H. Chin, and S. I. Weissman, Macromolecules 5, 798 (1972).
26. J. Schaefer, Macromolecules 5, 427 (1972).

VISCOELASTICITY OF SWOLLEN NETWORKS AS PROBED BY LIGHT INTENSITY FLUCTUATION SPECTROSCOPY

K. L. Wun
University of California

The intensity fluctuations in time of the scattered light as induced by the random thermal motions of the scattering entities provide information about the dynamics of the system. If one considers the network as composed of harmonically-bound particles, each oscillating independently about a mean position, the intensity autocorrelation function can be used for determining both the friction coefficients and the storage moduli of the swollen networks. Quantitative measurements were done on polyacrylamide from which the equilibrium storage moduli deduced from light scattering were compared with those determined by unilateral compression measurements. Some of the data on poly(2-hydroxyethylmethacrylate) and polyacrylamide were also analyzed according to a different theoretical model proposed by Tanaka et al. (1973) for comparison.

A. INTRODUCTION

With the advent of the laser as an intense and highly monochromatic light source, light scattering has become a very useful probe for the dynamics as well as the structure of a macromolecular system. The time-averaged scattered intensity at small angles (operationally defined as $1° < \Theta < 20°$) provides information on the submicroscopic structure of a crystalline polymer or an amorphous gel and wide-angle light scattering (operationally defined as $\Theta > 20°$) may be used to determine the size and shape of a macromolecule in solution (1, 2). On the other hand, measuring the thermally-induced intensity fluctuations in time of the scattered light by light beating spectroscopy provides information about the dynamics of the scattering system.

For a rubbery network, its relaxation spectrum is usually determined experimentally by imposing an external mechanical driving force over a wide range of frequencies. However, one can derive, in principle, similar informations from the intensity autocorrelation function in a light scattering experiment. Furthermore, since only a very small volume of the sample is being illuminated by the focused light beam (typically of the order of 10^{-5} cm^3), it is the local viscoelasticity that is being probed. Hence, measurements by aligning different portions of the sample with the light beam might also be used to probe at any microscopic inhomogeneity of the networks. In this paper, a theoretical model will be presented whereby the experimental autocorrelation function is derived in terms of the elastic and frictional parameters of a swollen network. Experiments on polyacrylamide will be reported of which the results from light scattering will be compared with those obtained by independent measurements.

B. THEORY

For a dilute solution of freely diffusing macromolecules, the normalized intensity autocorrelation function in an optical self-beating experiment may be written as (3):

$$g^{(2)}(\tau) = 1 + \left|g^{(1)}(\tau)\right|^2 = 1 + \alpha \exp(-2DK^2\tau) \quad (1)$$

where $g^{(1)}(\tau)$ is the optical field autocorrelation function; α is an instrumental constant to account for any spatial incoherence at the photodetector; D is the diffusional coefficient; K is the amplitude of the scattering wave vector given by $(4\pi\eta_o/\lambda_o)$ X sin $\Theta/2$ with η_o being the refractive index of the scattering medium, λ_o the wave length of the incident light in vacuum and Θ the scattering angle; and τ is the delay time. If one follows experimentally the intensity fluctuations by photon counting and determined $g^{(2)}(\tau)$ which in this simple case, is just a single-exponential in τ, the time constant at a given scattering angle will yield the diffusional coefficient, D.

In a swollen network or a macromolecular gel in general, however, the macromolecules are very much restricted in their mobility by the closely packed neighbors and the concept of free diffusion does not apply any more. In fact, if one calibrates the instrument with a monodispersed, freely diffusing system such as polystyrene lattices and determines α by properly normalizing the experimental autocorrelation functions with respect to its theoretical background which is just the statistical noise in the measurements (typically, α is about 0.7 to 0.8, depending on the optics of a given spectrometer), one would find the initial amplitude at $\tau = 0$, i.e., $g^{(2)}(0) - 1$, will decrease drastically from the 'sol' to the 'gel' state and becomes much less than α for the reversibly gelling systems studied so far (4, 5). The initial amplitude, therefore, seems to correlate directly with the mobility of the scattering entities. It is also reasonable to expect the gel particles, i.e., the macromolecular chains, to execute only limited motions about a stationary mean, with the constraint provided by its closely-packed neighbors. In the case of covalently crosslinked gels, the crosslinks themselves may also affect the motions of the chains. So, if one considers the gel to be a collection of identical, harmonically-bound particles, each executing Brownian motion independently about a mean position, the normalized intensity autocorrelation function may be derived by applying the Ornstein and Uhlenbeck distribution function (6). For the highly overdamped case, it has the form (4):

$$g^{(2)}(\tau) \equiv \langle I(t)I(t+\tau)\rangle/\bar{I}^2 = 1 - \exp(-2\Gamma_0) + \exp(-2\Gamma_0\tau_0) \quad (2)$$

where $I(t)$, $\bar{I}^2$ are the instantaneous and mean-square intensity of the scattered light respectively; $\Gamma_0 \equiv DK^2/\gamma$ with γ (sec^{-1}) being the ratio of the chain elastic instant k(dyn/cm), to the frictional constant f (dyn sec/cm); and $\tau_0 \equiv 1-\exp(-\gamma\tau)$. However, in deriving the above expression, uncorrelated Rayleigh scattering has been assumed which in effect has neglected the presence of a large component of static scattering by gels due to interparticulate interference (7) and microscopic inhomogeneities (8). This additional component may act as a local heterodyning source which in turn may contribute to the lowering of the initial amplitude in addition to that due to the constrained motions. Therefore, an additional term, I_x, which is time-independent, needs be added to the total scattered light intensity in order to account for the additional static scattering. It is also assumed to be practically constant at scattering angle larger than 30° (see Fig. 3). Hence, the average intensity may be expressed in terms of three components:

$$\bar{I} = I_x + I_o + I_s \qquad (3)$$

where I_o and I_s are the time independent and time dependent components from the constrained Brownian particles (4). Expressing the static component as a fraction of the total intensity, $\beta = I_x/I$, gives for the other two components:

$$I_o = (1-\beta)\,\bar{I}\,\exp(-\Gamma_o) \qquad (4)$$

$$I_s = (1-\beta)\bar{I}[1 - \exp(-\Gamma_o)] \qquad (5)$$

and the intensity autocorrelation function is:

$$\langle I(t)I(t+\tau)\rangle = \langle[I_x + I_o + I_s g^{(1)}(t)][I_x + I_o + I_s g^{(1)}(t+\tau)] \qquad (6)$$

where $g_s^{(1)}(\tau)$ has been shown to be (4):

$$g_s^{(1)}(\tau) = \frac{\exp(-\Gamma_o\tau_o) - \exp(-\Gamma_o)}{1 - \exp(-\Gamma_o)} \qquad (7)$$

The final expression for the normalized intensity autocorrelation function and its initial amplitude after applying Eqs. 4, 5, and 7 to 6 and performing the multiplications is:

$$g^{(2)}(\tau) - 1 = 2\beta(1-\beta)[\exp(-\Gamma_o\tau_o) - \exp(-\Gamma_o)] - (1-\beta)^2\exp(-2\Gamma_o) + (1-\beta)^2\exp(-2\Gamma_o\tau_o) \qquad (8)$$

$$g^{(2)}(0) - 1 = (1-\beta)^2 + 2\beta(1-\beta)[1-\exp(-\Gamma_o)] - (1-\beta)^2\exp(-2\Gamma_o) \qquad (9)$$

Of course, in the limit of ideal Rayleigh scatterers, $\beta \to o$, the above expressions simplify to those derived by Carlson and Fraser (4).
Hence, intensity autocorrelation measurements at different angles should yield the frictional factor, f (or equivalently the diffusional coefficient, D) as well as the chain elastic constant, k. One may then apply Gaussian chain statistics to derive the theoretical storage modulus from the two parameters

(see Results and Discussion).

A series of polyacrylamide gels copolymerized in water and ethylene glycol has been studied in order to test this model. For comparison, compression measurements were also performed on gels prepared from the same monomer mixtures to determine the moduli independently.
Tanaka et al (9) have proposed in 1973 a different model by considering the gel as an elastic continuum and derived an expression for the normalized intensity autocorrelation function of the form:

$$g^{(2)}(\tau) - 1 = \exp(-2\mu K^2\tau/f) \qquad (10)$$

where μ is the shear modulus, K is the amplitude of the scattering wave-vector defined earlier and f, the frictional constant. However, the effects of interparticulate interferences and microscopic inhomogeneities have not been considered in their derivation and according to Eq. (10), the initial amplitude, $g^{(2)}(o)-1$, will be 1 theoretically, being the same as the case of free diffusion. Some of our data on poly (2 - hydroxyethylmethacrylate) (PHEMA) and polyacrylamide (PAM) will be analyzed according to the continuum model for comparison in the discussion section.

C. EXPERIMENTAL SECTION

PHEMA gels were prepared by copolymerization of the monomer, 2 - hydroxyethylmethacrylate (HEMA), with ethylene glycol dimethacrylate (EGDM) in ethylene glycol. PAM gels were prepared by copolymerization of acrylamide and N,N^1 - methylenebisacrylamide (MBAC) in water and in ethylene glycol. Details of sample preparation have been described before (8,10). Special cares were taken to eliminate dust in the samples and in their containers for light scattering experiments. As a control for free diffusion measurements, a 5% acrylamide aqueous solution with no crosslinking agent was allowed to polymerize at 45°C using the ammonium persulfate - sodium bisulfite couple as initiator, resulting in a very viscous liquid (sample 500). In light intensity fluctuation spectroscopy, one follows the fluctuations by optical beating and the output can be analyzed either by a spectrum analyzer or a digital

autocorrelator. Our instrument employs a He-Ne laser (λ_o = 632.8 nm) as light source, a hard-wired autocorrelator to perform the photoelectron autocorrelation and an on-line mini-computer to process the data directly (11). Basic theoretical and technical informations for this technique have been reported by Foord, et al, (12) and Jakeman, Oliver and Pike (13).
Moduli of PAM gels were also determined by unilateral compression measurements. The procedures were same as those described previously by Wun and Prins (8). The modulus G of each sample was determined by a least - squares fit to the equation:

$$\sigma_t = G[(L/L_o)^2 - (L_o/L)] \qquad (11)$$

in which L_o and L are the initial and compressed thickness of the sample respectively and σ_t is the true stress, i.e., force per unit area of strained cross section: $A=A_o(L_o/L)$. The modulus is given by (14):

$$G = \nu q_o^{-2/3} q^{2/3} k_b T \qquad (12)$$

where ν is the number of chains per cubic centimeter of gel; $q_o^{-2/3}$ is the ratio of the average chain dimension at the dry state to that of the unperturbed, swollen state, i.e.,
and is equivalent to the so-called isotropic dilation factor; q is the volume degree of swelling; k_b is the Boltzman constant; and T is the temperature in degrees Kelvin.

D. RESULTS AND DISCUSSION

Figure 1 illustrates the $g^{(2)}(\tau)$ of 5% polyacrylamide (sample 500) in aqueous solution which serves as a control for free diffusion and the measured $g^{(2)}(\tau)$ for a gel containing the same amount of monomer (5% acrylamide) and 6% (relative to monomer) of crosslinker (sample 506). The initial amplitude is only about 1/3 that of the control at $\Theta = 68°$ and decreases to 1/6 at $\Theta = 28°$. In general, the measured $g^{(2)}(0)-1$ values of all the gel samples are found to decrease monotonically with decreasing scattering angles and approaching zero for angles below 20°. This very strong angular dependence of the initial amplitude between 20° and

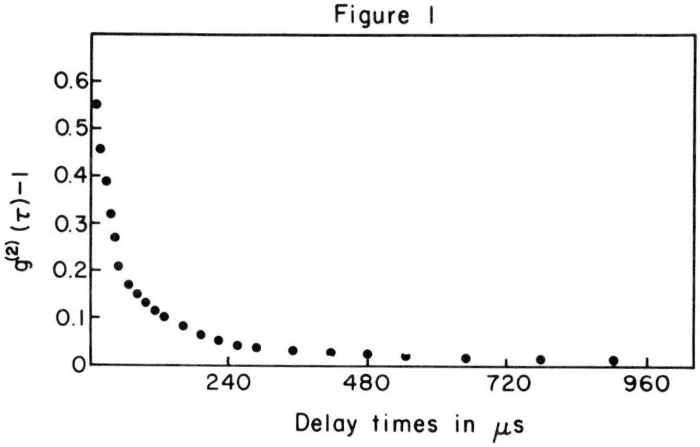

Figure 1. Sample intensity autocorrelation function of 5% polyacrylamide in aqueous solution (sample 500) measured at $\Theta = 83°$ with the ordinate being normalized to the theoretical background. All experiments were regulated at $25 \pm 0.2°$. The apparent diffusion coefficient is 3.3×10^{-7} cm^2/sec.

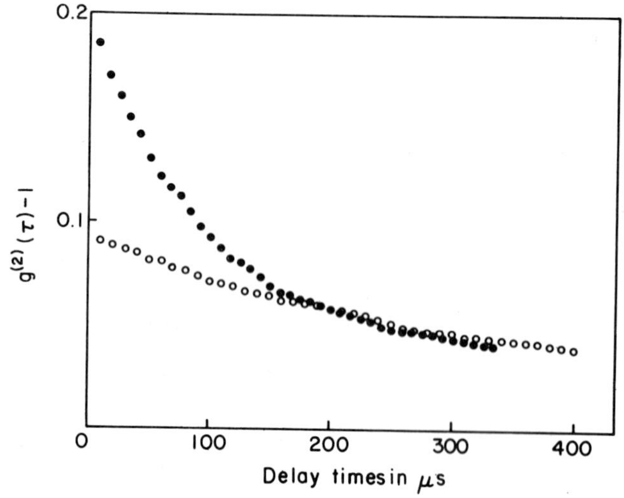

Figure 2. Sample intensity autocorrelation functions of 5% polyacrylamide gel (sample 506) at different scattering angles: (o) θ = 68°; (O) θ = 29°.

110° (see Table I) seems to exclude heterodyning with local static scattering elements as the sole explanation for the observed drop in initial amplitudes, since in general the scattered intensities at large angles (θ =2 to 22° for sample 1506E (see footnotes of Table I for sample composition). The strong angular dependence at small angles (2°-10°) commonly observed in gels (8, 15, 16), indicates the presence of significant interparticulate and microscopic inhomogeneity effects as mentioned earlier.

Figure 3

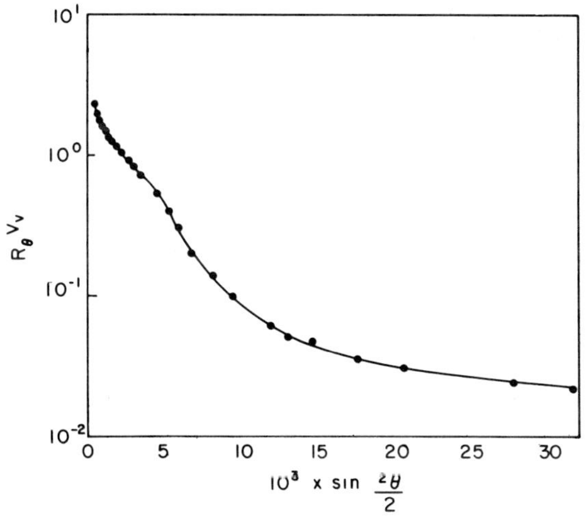

Figure 3. The logarithm of the Rayleigh ratios (measured with vertical polarizer and vertical analyzer) as a function of scattering angles. The range is 2-22°. The sample is 1506E. Note the strong angular dependence at small angles and its leveling off at higher angles.

β and D/γ can be evaluated by measuring $g^{(2)}(0)-1$ at two different scattering angles normalizing with respect to the instrument constant, α, which is 0.67 for our present experimental conditions. The chain elastic constant, k, can be estimated from a given D/γ value if one ignores any small differences between bulk and local viscosities within the macromolecular network, i.e., $k=k_b T/(D/\gamma)$. The values of β and k reported in Table 1 were obtained by taking several pairs of measurements of $g^{(2)}(0)-1$ at various angles for the same sample and iterated to a consistent set of values for β and D/γ for each sample (they agreed to within 5%). To determine f (or equivalently, D), the data were iterated for a given ratio of D/γ with Eq. 8 until the differences between the experimental and theoretical data reached a minimum. The average deviation was between 5 and 10%. The initial value of D was determined by force-fitting the data to single exponentials even though the cumulant analysis (17) as well as the variance ratio test (18) indicated that all the autocorrelation functions for the gel samples we measured were not single exponentials. To obtain an estimate of the storage modulus, G_s, from k, the network is assumed to be a collection of identical Gaussian free chains (19) each with a mean-square end-to-end distance given by a random coil in the absence of any excluded voume effect (20), consequently:

$$G_s = k\nu f^2 / 78.3\,\eta_o^2 \qquad (13)$$

where ν is the chain density, η_o is the viscosity of the medium. With recourse to Eq. 12, if one assumes that:

$$q_o^{-2/3} = \langle r^2\rangle_d / \langle r^2\rangle_{o,s} \sim (V_d/V_s)^{2/3} = q^{2/3} \qquad (14)$$

where V_d and V_s are the volume of thd dry and swollen network respectively, the modulus G from unilateral compression measurements also approaches to the approximation by $\nu k_b T$, which then becomes equivalent to G_S. For deriving any molecular parameter from equilibrium compression and swelling measurements on swollen networks, it is usually necessary to make some assumptions regarding $q_0^{-2/3}$. Table I summarizes the results.

In comparing G_S (from light scatterings) and G (from compression measurements) in Table I, it is important to note that the chain density, ν, used in calculating G_S, was estimated from stoichiometry of the monomeric compositions assuming 100% conversion. In practice, of course, the conversion is seldom complete and the true chain density with the network is usually lower. In fact, the much larger value of G_S compared to G for sample 1506E may indicate that the copolymerization is much less efficient in ethylene glycol than in water as indeed the hydroxyl groups are known to be chain transfer agents for acrylamide polymerization (21). Also, much short chains would be formed in that case which explains why the modulus is higher than that in water. It is interesting to note that the fraction of static scattering, β, is lower the higher the concentration of monomers before crosslinking for a given diluent. This is consistent with the observation of Wun and Prins (8) that for highly swollen networks, non-random crosslinking giving rise to large local fluctuations in refractive indices becomes the dominant contribution to light scattering. It has been found that higher concentration of monomers or crosslinkers present during the crosslinking process leads to less non-random crosslinking locally (22). While the usual concentrationenhancement for Rayleigh scatterers is included in I_0 of Eq. 3, β, which is $I_x/\bar{I}$, seems to reflect other contributions due to the spatial structuring of the scattering elements.

Table II compares our measured frictional constants to those of White (23) obtained from permeability measurements.

TABLE I
SUMMARY OF RESULTS

Sample[a]	Chains/cm^3 [b]	θ,deg	$g^{(2)}(0)/0.67 - 1$	β	k X 10^3 dyn/cm	f X 10^8 (dyn sec)/cm	G_s X 10^{-5} dyn/cm^2	G X 10^{-5} dyn/cm^2 [c]
256	1.17 X 10^{19}	104.8	0.97	0.52	0.248	11.1	0.058	
		90.0	0.94					
		28.7	0.51					
		25.4	0.40					
		21.9	0.39					
		14.8	0.31					
506	2.34 X 10^{19}	68.1	0.27	0.51	2.34	9.36	0.78	0.265 ± 0.013
		28.7	0.14					
		21.9	0.054					
1506	7.02 X 10^{19}	104.8	0.23	0.35	14.0	4.84	3.6	(1.36 ± 0.07)
		90.0	0.13					
		82.6	0.099					
1506E	7.02 X 10^{19}	103.8	0.88	0.51	4.34	5.74	4 4	(8.17 ± 0.40)
		90.0	0.66					
		83.0	0.27					

Footnotes for Table I:

[a]Samples 256,506, and 1506 represent gels prepared by copolymerizing 2.5, 5.0, and 15 wt % acrylamide, respectively, in water, all having the same weight ratio of MBAC to AC in the mixture: 6 to 100. Sample 1506E has the same monomer and cross-linker composition as that of 1506 but the solvent is ethylene glycol instead.

[b]The chain densities were estimated from the monomeric compositions assuming 100% conversion.

[c]Sample 256 could not be obtained in a reasonably sturdy form for conventional compression measurement. For the other samples, the force was measured to within ± 1g and the length to ± 0.01 mm.

TABLE II

Sample	f(this study)	f(M.L. White)
256	1.1×10^{-7}	1.3×10^{-7}
506	9.4×10^{-8}	5.7×10^{-8}
1506	4.8×10^{-8}	4.6×10^{-8}

The frictional constant within the same medium is higher for networks with lower concentration of crosslinks because the effective dimension of the chain is larger.

According to the continuum theory proposed by Tanka et al (9), the normalized intensity autocorrelation function for a gel is predicted to be a single exponential with the theoretical initial amplitude being 1 (see Eq. 10). While we have been able to force-fit some of our data on PAC and PHEMA gels (mostly the more swollen gels) to single exponentials to within experimental precision as illustrated in Fig. 4, but all our autocorrelation functions measured so far were found to be not single-exponentials according to the cumulant analysis and variance ratio test and the initial amplitudes measured were smaller than 1 (see Table I). However, one possibility is that the presence of a large portion of static scattering not accounted for in their derivation may act as a local heterodyning source leading to lower initial amplitudes and deviation from single-exponentials. This would seem rather unlikely since we have observed a pronounced angular dependence of the initial amplitude between 20° and 110° (see Table I) while the time-averaged intensity levels off to an almost constant value at angles beyond 20° (see Fig. 3). Nevertheless, for better insights, a sample of our normalized date (sample 506) was fitted with the following equation:

$$g^{(2)}(\tau) - 1/\alpha = 2B(1-B)\exp(-DK^2\tau) + (1-B)^2\exp(-2DK^2\tau) \quad (15)$$

which conforms with the continuum theory but with an added static fraction, B (analogons to β in Eq. 8 and 9) to account for the observed low initial amplitudes resulting a double-exponential expression

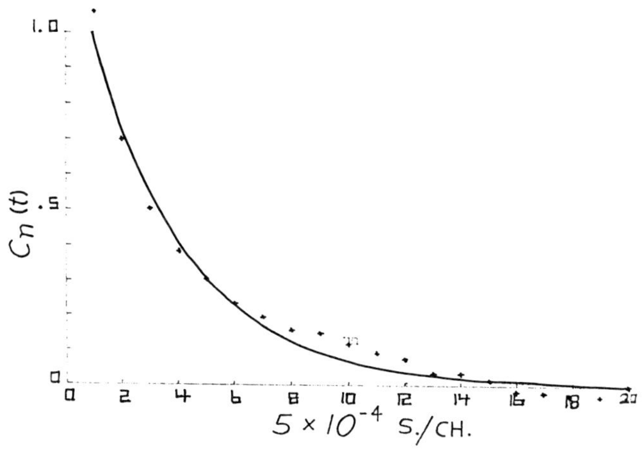

Figure 4. Intensity autocoreelationfunction of PHEMA (+). The solid line represents the theoretical fit to a single-exponential.

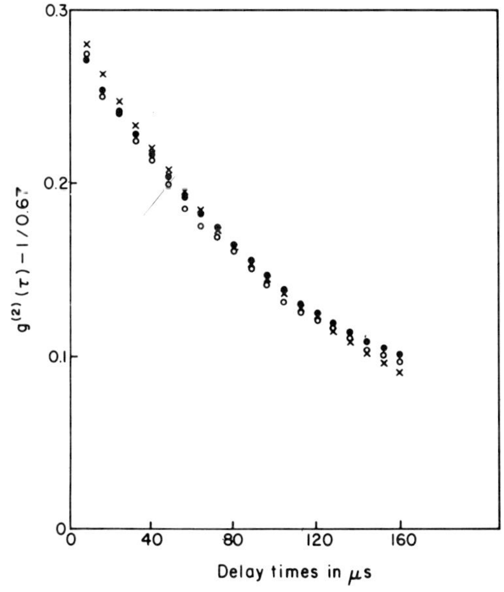

Figure 5. Comparison of the theoretical fits using Eq. 8 (0) and Eq. 15(X) to the experimental data (0) for sample 506 at θ=68°.

for the intensity autocorrelation function. B was first determined by solving Eq. 15 at $\tau=0$ with the corresponding value for $g^{(2)}(0)-1/\alpha$ measured experimentally. Then D was iterated with Eq. 15 until the average derviation from the experimental data (open circles) for using Eq. 8 (solid circles) and using Eq. 15 (crosses) is about the same (5% and 7%, respectively), but the shapes of the two functions are noticeably different.

Hence, it has been shown here how the viscoelastic parameters of a swollen network may be deduced from the relatively simple light scattering experiments. Of course, how well a microscopic parameter like the modulus can be deduced from the molecular parameter, k, depends on the adequacy of the network theory that one applies as well as the adequacy of the theoretical model for the light scattering of gels. It is implicitly assumed in this derivation that the whole network may be replaced by identical Gaussian chains of the same average length while in general most networks are formed with broad distribution of chain-lengths. Perhaps, stipulating a Gaussian or other appropriate distribution function into the calculation as well as including the coupled motions of those harmonically bound particles might provide some further improvements.

REFERENCES

(1) M. Kerker, "The Scattering of Light and Other Electromagnetic Radiation", Academic Press, New York, 1969.

(2) R.S. Stein, "Electromagnetic Scattering", in Proceedings of the Second Interdisciplinary Conference on Electromagnetic Scattering, R.L. Rowell and R.S. Stein, eds., Gordon and Breach Publ., N.Y., 1967.

(3) H. Swinney and H.F. Cummins, Prog. in optics, 8, 135 (1970).

(4) F.D. Carlson and A.B. Fraser, J. Mol. Biology, 89, 273 (174).

(5) K.L. Wun, G.T. Feke and W. Prins, Faraday Discussions, No. 57, 1974.

(6) G.E. Uhlenbeck and L.S. Ornstein, "On the Theory of the Brownian Motion", selected papers on "Noise and Stochastic Processes", N. Wax, Ed., Dover Publications, N.Y., 1954.

(7) R.S. Stein and P.R. Wilson, J. Appl. Phys., 33, 1914 (1962).

(8) K.L. Wun and W. Prins, J. Plym. Sci., Polym. Phys. Ed., 12, 533 (1974).

(9) T. Tanaka, L. Hocker and G. Benedek, J. Chem. Phys., 59, 5151 (1973).

(10) K.L. Wun and F.D. Carlson, Macromolecules, 8, 190 (1975).

(11) A. Fraser, Rev. Sci. Inst., 539, 1539 (1971).

(12) R. Foord, et al, Nature (London), 227, 243 1972).

(13) E. Jakeman, C.J. Oliver and R. Pike, Proc. Physc. Soc., London, 4, 827 (1971).

(14) M. Ilavsky and W. Prins, Macromolecules, 3, 415 (1970).

REFERENCES (Cont'd)

(15) T.C. Warren and W. Prins, Macromolecules, 5, 506 (1972).

(16) E. Pines and W. Prins, Macromolecules, 6, 888 (1973).

(17) D.E. Koppel, J. Chem, Phys., 57, 4814 (1972).

(18) C.E. Weatherburn, "A First Course in Mathematical Statistics", Cambridge University Press, London, 1968.

(19) F. Bueche, "Physical Properties of Polymers", Interscience, 1962.

(20) J.K. Ball et al, Biochem. Biophys. Acta, 103, 275 (1965).

(21) W.M. Thomas, "Acrylamide Polymers" in Encyclopedia of Polymer Science and Technology, Vol. I, H.F. Mark, N.G. Gaylor and N.M. Bikales, eds., Interscience, New York, N.Y., 1964.

(22) K. Dusek and W. Prins, Adv. Polymer Sci., 6, 1 (1969).

Subject Index

P

Q

R

S

T

U

V

A
B 7
C 8
D 9
E 0
F 1
G 2
H 3
I 4
J 5